HUMAN DEVELOPMENT 83/84

Hiram E. Fitzgerald, *Editor*
Michigan State University

Thomas H. Carr, *Editor*
Michigan State University

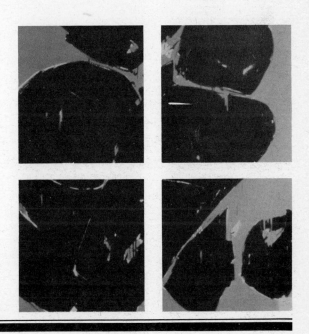

Cover Credit: Karemitsu, "Border Shift"; Courtesy, The Corcoran Gallery of Art.

ANNUAL EDITIONS

The Dushkin Publishing Group, Inc. Sluice Dock, Guilford, Ct. 06437

Volumes in the Annual Editions Series

Abnormal Psychology
- Aging
- American Government
- American History, Pre-Civil War
- American History, Post-Civil War
- Anthropology
Astronomy
- Biology
- Business
- Comparative Politics
- Criminal Justice
Death and Dying
- Deviance
- Early Childhood Education
Earth Science
- Economics
- Educating Exceptional Children
- Education
- Educational Psychology
Energy
- Environment
Ethnic Studies
Foreign Policy
Geography

Geology
- Health
- Human Development
- Human Sexuality
- Macroeconomics
- Management
- Marketing
- Marriage and Family
- Microeconomics
- Personal Growth and Behavior
Philosophy
Political Science
- Psychology
Religion
- Social Problems
- Social Psychology
- Sociology
Twentieth Century American History
- Urban Society
- Western Civilization, Pre-Reformation
- Western Civilization, Post-Reformation
Women's Studies
World History
- World Politics

● Indicates currently available

©1983 by the Dushkin Publishing Group, Inc. Annual Editions is a Trade Mark of the Dushkin Publishing Group, Inc.

Copyright ©1983 by the Dushkin Publishing Group, Inc., Guilford, Connecticut 06437

Eleventh Edition

Manufactured by George Banta Company, Menasha, Wisconsin, 54952

Library of Congress Cataloging in Publication Data
Main entry under title:
Annual editions: Human Development.
    1. Child study—Addresses, essays, lectures. 2. Socialization—Addresses, essays, lectures. 3. Old age—Addresses. essays, lectures. I. Human Development
HQ768.A55   155   72-91973
ISBN 0-87967-446-6

CONTENTS

1

Perspectives

2

Development During the Prenatal Period

3

Development During Infancy

4

Development During Childhood

5

Child Rearing and Child Development

6

Development During Adolescence and Early Adulthood

7
Development During Middle and Late Adulthood

TOPIC GUIDE

This guide can be used to correlate each of the readings in *Human Development* 83/84 with one or more of the topics usually covered in human development books. Each article corresponds to a given topic area according to whether it deals with the topic in a primary or secondary fashion. These correlations are intended for use as a general guide and do not necessarily define total coverage of any given article.

TOPIC AREA	TREATED AS A PRIMARY ISSUE IN:	TREATED AS A SECONDARY ISSUE IN:
Aggression	39. What Is TV Doing to America?	37. Suffer the Children 40. How I Stopped Nagging
Anthropological/ Cross-Cultural Perspectives	16. Ethnic Differences in Babies 19. How Children Influence Children 37. Suffer the Children 48. The Japanese Brain	
Attachment	14. Biology Is One Key to the Bonding 36. When Mommy Goes to Work…	8. Pregnancy 15. Newborn Knowledge 16. Ethnic Differences in Babies 18. Infant Day Care 35. A New Look at Life with Father
Behavior Disorders	20. If Your Child Doesn't Get Along with Other Kids 38. The Children of Divorce	22. The Myth of the Vulnerable Child 29. Islands of Genius 31. Diet and Schoolchildren 40. How I Stopped Nagging 46. Single Parent Fathers
Behavior Modification	40. How I Stopped Nagging	
Biological/Genetic Factors	1. Sociobiology 2. Twins 3. Searching for Depression Genes 7. Heredity, Constitution, and Individual Life 8. Pregnancy 25. The Instinct to Learn 49. She & He 53. The Aging Body 55. Living Longer	9. Hi-Tech Babies 12. Before Their Time 13. The Importance of Mother's Milk 14. Biology Is One Key to the Bonding 16. Ethnic Differences in Babies 50. Late Motherhood
Brain Development	24. The Violent Brain 48. The Japanese Brain	31. Diet and Schoolchildren 49. She & He
Child Abuse	37. Suffer the Children	
Child Rearing	16. Ethnic Differences in Babies 20. If Your Child Doesn't Get Along with Other Kids 22. The Myth of the Vulnerable Child 34. Parent and Child Development 35. A New Look at Life with Father 40. How I Stopped Nagging	10. A Perfect Baby 12. Before Their Time 13. The Importance of Mother's Milk 18. Infant Day Care 36. When Mommy Goes to Work… 39. What Is TV Doing to America?

TOPIC AREA	TREATED AS A PRIMARY ISSUE IN:	TREATED AS A SECONDARY ISSUE IN:
Child Rearing (cont.)	42. What Do We Know About Teenagers 46. Single Parent Fathers	
Cognitive Development: Adulthood/Aging	4. Piaget 28. Who's Intelligent?	53. The Aging Body
Cognitive Development: Childhood/Adolescence	4. Piaget 23. Mood and Memory 26. Learning About Learning 29. Islands of Genius 33. The Mind of the Puzzler	22. The Myth of the Vulnerable Child 30. Rites of Passage 39. What Is TV Doing to America?
Cognitive Development: Infancy/ Early Childhood	4. Piaget 15. Newborn Knowledge 18. Infant Day Care 26. Learning about Learning 27. Are Young Children Really Egocentric?	11. Premature Birth 12. Before Their Time 23. Mood and Memory
Conception	8. Pregnancy 9. Hi-Tech Babies 10. A Perfect Baby	7. Heredity, Constitution, and Individual Life
Divorce	38. The Children of Divorce 46. Single Parent Fathers	
Emotional Development	5. Erik Erikson's Eight Ages of Man 14. Biology Is One Key to the Bonding 17. Your Child's Self-Esteem 23. Mood and Memory 24. The Violent Brain 38. The Children of Divorce 43. The Sibling Bond 44. Too Weary to Go On 51. Stress Can Be Good for You 52. Coping with the Seasons of Life 56. Coping with Death in the Family	3. Searching for Depression Genes 18. Infant Day Care 38. Suffer the Children 39. What Is TV Doing to America? 41. Adolescents and Sex 42. What Do We Know About Teenagers 45. The Many Me's of the Self-Monitor 46. Single Parent Fathers
Family Relations	6. American Research on the Family 34. Parent and Child Development 35. A New Look at Life with Father 36. When Mommy Goes to Work… 38. The Children of Divorce 40. How I Stopped Nagging 46. Single Parent Fathers	17. Your Child's Self-Esteem 22. The Myth of the Vulnerable Child 37. Suffer the Children 42. What Do We Know About Teenagers 44. Too Weary to Go On 50. Late Motherhood

TOPIC AREA	TREATED AS A PRIMARY ISSUE IN:	TREATED AS A SECONDARY ISSUE IN:
Fathers	35. A New Look at Life with Father 40. How I Stopped Nagging 46. Single Parent Fathers	22. The Myth of the Vulnerable Child
Intelligence	4. Piaget 28. Who's Intelligent? 32. The Mismatch Between School and Children's Minds 33. The Mind of the Puzzler	31. Diet and Schoolchildren
Language		18. Infant Day Care 32. The Mismatch Between School and Children's Minds 48. The Japanese Brain
Learning	23. Mood and Memory 25. The Instinct to Learn 26. Learning About Learning	12. Before Their Time 28. Who's Intelligent? 29. Islands of Genius 33. The Mind of the Puzzler 39. What Is TV Doing to America?
Learning Disability	29. Islands of Genius 31. Diet and Schoolchildren	12. Before Their Time
Mothers	13. The Importance of Mother's Milk 14. Biology Is One Key to the Bonding 36. When Mommy Goes to Work.... 42. What Do We Know About Teenagers 50. Late Motherhood	11. Premature Birth 15. Newborn Knowledge 22. The Myth of the Vulnerable Child
Nutrition	8. Pregnancy 13. The Importance of Mother's Milk 31. Diet and Schoolchildren	44. Too Weary to Go On
Peers	19. How Children Influence Children 20. If Your Child Doesn't Get Along with Other Kids	
Perceptual Development	15. Newborn Knowledge 18. Infant Day Care	23. Mood and Memory
Personality Development	5. Erik Erikson's Eight Ages of Man 22. The Myth of the Vulnerable Child 45. The Many Me's of the Self-Monitor 47. Does Personality Really Change After 20? 51. Stress Can Be Good for You 52. Coping with the Seasons of Life 56. Coping with Death in the Family	11. Premature Birth 17. Your Child's Self-Esteem 18. Infant Day Care 20. If Your Child Doesn't Get Along with Other Kids 24. The Violent Brain 37. Suffer the Children 38. The Children of Divorce 43. The Sibling Bond

TOPIC AREA	TREATED AS A PRIMARY ISSUE IN:	TREATED AS A SECONDARY ISSUE IN:
Prematurity	11. Premature Birth 12. Before Their Time	10. A Perfect Baby 15. Newborn Knowledge
Prenatal Influences	8. Pregnancy 9. Hi-Tech Babies 10. A Perfect Baby 11. Premature Birth	
School Influences	18. Infant Day Care 30. Rites of Passage 31. Diet and Schoolchildren 32. The Mismatch Between School and Children's Minds	
Self-Concept	17. Your Child's Self-Esteem 45. The Many Me's of the Self-Monitor 52. Coping with the Seasons of Life	49. She & He
Sex Differences/Sexuality/Sexual Identity	41. Adolescents and Sex 42. What Do We Know About Teenagers 46. Single Parent Fathers 49. She & He	9. Hi-Tech Babies 24. The Violent Brain 29. Islands of Genius
Sibling Relations	43. The Sibling Bond	
Social Behavior/Development	5. Erik Erikson's Eight Ages of Man 6. American Research on the Family 20. If Your Child Doesn't Get Along with Other Kids 34. Parent and Child Development 50. Late Motherhood 56. Coping with Death	4. Piaget 11. Premature Birth 18. Infant Day Care 19. How Children Influence Children 30. Rites of Passage 41. Adolescents and Sex 42. What Do We Know About Teenagers
Sociobiology/Psychobiology	1. Sociobiology 7. Heredity, Constitution, and Individual Life 16. Ethnic Differences in Babies 25. The Instinct to Learn	2. Twins 14. Biology Is One Key to the Bonding 24. The Violent Brain
Twins	2. Twins	

PREFACE

During the past two decades the study of human development has expanded to include the full span of life, from conception to death. In the past, intensive concern about developmental issues in infancy and early childhood lead to neglect of adulthood and aging despite the fact that the years of adulthood comprise nearly three-fourths of the life span. The emphasis on early development was a reflection of the view that events of infancy and early childhood determined later developmental outcome. This "behavioral continuity" view has been challenged because it has proven difficult to find clear, concise predictors of behavior from one developmental period to another. The antithesis of behavioral continuity is "behavioral discontinuity." As extreme ends of a continuum it is likely that neither continuity nor discontinuity explains developmental process. Thus, the developmentalist must try to understand which characteristics of the individual change and which remain stable through the life span. It is clear, however, that developmentalists have rejected the static "machine" view of behavioral organization, in favor of a view that emphasizes the dynamic and active nature of the living organism and the environments to which the organism adapts. Thus, developmentalists try to understand how various factors blend together to affect the mutual interaction of organism and environment.

Just as students of human development emphasize interactional influences, they also recognize that no single discipline can provide all of the information that is required in order to comprehend the complexity of the organism. Regardless of one's specialized area of training, understanding human development requires some degree of familiarity with psychology, anthropology, sociology, genetics, physiology, anatomy, and all other basic disciplines that comprise the biomedical and behavioral sciences and professions. Moreover, the contemporary developmentalist must be trained as rigorously in field research techniques as in those associated with laboratory research inasmuch as more and more developmental research is being conducted in "natural" settings such as homes, hospitals, and schools. Information about human development in different cultures helps the developmentalist to understand which behavior patterns are culture-specific and which are species-characteristic. Cross-cultural research provides one way to gain important information about the range of variation in human development.

Finally, many developmentalists view the organization of behavior as occurring in various stages, such as those that have been proposed for cognitive, social, moral, emotional, psychosocial, and psychosexual development. Implicit in the stage approach is the idea that each successive stage brings about qualitative changes that are not fully predictable from events of preceding stages. Other developmentalists place less emphasis on stage theories.

The study of human development is exciting. New findings and new theories challenge or support the cumulative body of knowledge, with new problems emerging almost daily. It is our hope that much of this excitement will come through to you as you sample the articles in this eleventh edition of *Human Development*. The articles for *Annual Editions: Human Development 83/84* were selected, in part, with the advice of the readers and with that of members of the Annual Editions advisory board. Collectively, the articles provide a sample of the issues and topics of historical and contemporary interest in the field of human development.

We thank the authors and publishers who have made this reader possible by permitting the reprinting of their works. Each reader has the opportunity to express an opinion about the articles included in this volume by completing and mailing the article rating form located on the last page of the book. Which articles were most informative and/or interesting? Which topics are not covered and which are over-emphasized? Share your opinions with us; we will consider them carefully prior to the next revision of *Human Development*.

Hiram E. Fitzgerald,
Thomas H. Carr,
Editors

Perspectives

The multidisciplinary field of human development is concerned with stability and change throughout the life span. At present, no single theory gives comprehensive direction to the study of human development. Instead, developmentalists typically are guided by one of four theoretical perspectives: biological-evolutionary, environmental-behaviorist, psychoanalytic, or cognitive-developmental. The biological-evolutionary approach emphasizes genetic aspects of behavior. A contemporary variation of the biological-evolutionary theme, *sociobiology* has created much controversy as a result of the extent to which it attributes behavior to genetic inheritance. Part A of *Perspectives* draws attention to sociobiology as well as the broader biological-evolutionary theoretical tradition. The environmental-behaviorist position emphasizes learned aspects of behavior, giving little attention to genetic or cognitive explanations. Psychoanalytic theorists emphasize the importance of the early years for the formation of the ego, and conceptualize personality as being organized in a series of stages. Cognitive developmentalists propose a series of sequential stages that describe the various levels we achieve in our understanding of the events in the external, physical world. Part B of *Perspectives* includes articles that describe two prominent stage-theory approaches in human development, namely, those of Piaget and Erikson.

Each of these traditions has its strengths, but the inherent limitations of each prevents any from achieving the status of a general theory of human behavior and development. As a result, many developmentalists have turned to general systems theory in the hope that it can provide unity for the psychological, biological, social, and physical sciences.

The systems approach emphasizes the dynamic, active, transformational, interdependent, probabilistic, and informational aspects of natural phenomena. For example, the family is a system composed of a number of individuals, but it is not the simple additive sum of these individuals. A family generates characteristics of its own which are different from the characteristics of its individual members. The interrelationships of family members change during development and in so doing may transform the structure or organization of the family itself. Thus, whereas the form of the family may remain stable over time, transformations brought about by information exchange among family members will produce qualitative changes in its systemic character. In other instances the actual form of the family undergoes change which in turn influences its function. The matter is even more complex when one begins to take into account social and cultural influences on the family system. Part B of *Perspectives* includes an article in which a sociologist examines various approaches that have been taken to study the role of the family in socialization of children.

As you read each article in this unit of *Human Development 83/84*, try to determine how each of the major theoretical perspectives would counter sociobiological explanations of behavior or how each would interpret the role of the family in socialization of children.

Looking Ahead: Challenge Questions

Why is a comprehensive theory of human development necessary and how does one determine whether a theory adequately accounts for the phenomena of development?

How can studies be designed to tease out the relative contributions of genetics and environment for sex differences in behavior? Or, can these two influences be separated?

What is the role of the environment within the context of sociobiological theory?

How can the study of development in non-Western cultures contribute to our understanding of the role of the family in the socialization of children?

Sociobiology
A New View of Human Nature

Richard Nalley

Richard Nalley is editor of this section. He studied sociobiology at Harvard University. Rachel Wilder, contributor for this section, writes Science Digest's Challenge *column. Mary Batten, author of* The Tropical Forest, *has written more than 50 nature-science films. Lygeri Koromvokis, on staff at Cable News Network, visited several depression centers. Robert L. Trivers and Huey P. Newton are collaborating on a book about deceit and self-deception.*

Sociobiology: Rethinking Human Nature

When the news of Charles Darwin's "terrible theories" reached the Bishop of Worcester's wife, she is said to have exclaimed, "Descended from monkeys? My dear, let us hope it isn't true! But if it is true, let us hope that it doesn't become widely known!" Contemporary reactions to the young science of sociobiology mirror in many ways the earlier outcry over Darwin.

Pioneer sociobiologist Edward O. Wilson and colleagues have managed to fuel the flames of an old controversy by extending Darwin's argument to many areas of human social behavior. Man is not only descended from the apes, they say, his behavior, like that of all animals, is genetically influenced. It is not that man necessarily behaves *like* an orangutan but that the same mechanism, heredity encoded in genes, operates on both. In Wilson's succinct assessment, "Biology is the key to human nature."

Many sociobiological theories about how genes influence animal behavior have been readily accepted by the scientific community. But the inclusion of man in the theoretical framework continues to stick in the craw of critics. All too often such theories have been made to serve the ends of racist and other repressive social and political doctrines that essentially assert that some people are genetically inferior. Although denounced as "so-so biology" and "science with transparent political messages," sociobiology, proponents believe, puts forward an argument that binds human beings and animals together under consistent principles of natural law.

Until sociobiology came along, modern post-Darwinian evolutionary theorists like Nobel-laureate ethologist Konrad Lorenz believed that natural selection operated at the level of the group or species. According to this theory, altruism and aggression are favored by evolution because they benefit the group, even though the individual involved may perish. The action of a bee that dies stinging an intruder, for example, could be seen as adaptive in the Darwinian sense because other members of the hive benefit from it, especially the mother queen.

Sociobiologists contend, however, that this "species advantage" argument contradicts both Darwin's theory and common sense. They reason that if even a single fertile bee were genetically programmed to hold back from the fray, this bee's genes would swiftly spread through the hive population, since their carrier would live to reproduce, while the suicidal bee would not. Sociobiology shifts the examination of behavior from species to individual and even goes a step further. In the sociobiological view, the gene is the basic mechanism of natural selection.

GIVE UP YOUR LIFE

The biologist J.B.S. Haldane was once asked whether he would give up his life for his brother. No, Haldane replied, tongue firmly planted in cheek, he would not, but he would give up his life for *three* brothers or nine cousins. Haldane might be gone, but his genes would be well represented in the next generation, and so his action would prove adaptive from the standpoint of natural selection. The key concept here is that you, the individual, are not the only one who can reproduce your genes. Your brother and sister, for example, share an average of one-half of your gene pool, your cousin one-eighth, and so on. Your "inclusive fitness," therefore, would take into account not only your own fitness (your children) but also the proportional influence of your genes shared with relatives.

The act of the kamikaze bee is, in fact, not altruism at all, since it operates to the "selfish" advantage of the gene. Zoologist David Barash proposes what he calls the Central Theorem of sociobiology: when any behavior under study is genetically based, animals will behave in a way that will maximize their inclusive fitness.

Conflicts are inevitable. Among the langur monkeys of India, for example, a male who has just won out in a struggle for dominance of a troop makes it his first order of business to kill all the suckling infants sired by his predecessor. This benefits him, since it will cause the female to return to heat more quickly, and he can set about increasing his own reproductive fitness. The female langur, of course, looks at the question entirely differently: she wants to protect the 50 percent of her genes invested in her young. Pregnant female langurs have a strategy to do just that, a capability for manifesting a "false estrus," showing all the outward signs of being in heat though already pregnant. A female mates with the male, tricking him into thinking that her already conceived child is his.

YOU AND THE ZULU

What can sociobiology tell us about ourselves? When presented with the widely differing attitudes of a Zulu warrior and a Wall Street banker, we may conclude that, in fact, there is no such thing as a "human nature." Sociobiologists, however, believe that the similarities between the two are profound.

Evidence of a human nature can be found in the long list of behavioral traits common to every culture in recorded history; the list includes incest taboos, male dominance, kin groups, lawmaking, age-grading and many others. Sociobiologists conclude that the universal prevalence of these traits can only be accounted for by genetic influence, and that, this being the case, the traits must in some way be selected for by evolution.

Genes do not have the last word in the matter; human beings are not windup toys made to march in an unalterable cadence. Humans are a combination of genetic and cultural influences—genes prescribe only the capacity to develop certain traits, but culture molds the individual personality and can mitigate the genes' influence. There seems to be no gene favoring the wearing of top hats, for instance, but every human society has developed certain characteristic body adornments.

As early human beings banded together in social groups, perhaps for the purpose of cooperative hunting, selection pressures began to build for those traits that allowed them to adapt to community life. Genes promoting flexibility and conformity, for example, were probably passed on. Aggression had to be harnessed, social structure improvised and forms of communication developed. This acted as a kind of positive feedback loop: better communications led to reduced aggression, and vice versa.

The group, led by a dominant male, benefited each individual and his self-interested genes by providing protection, a ready supply of eligible mates and the ability to surround and bring down larger animals. From these cooperative dealings, sociobiologists say, culture arose: art, ethics, courtship rituals and the rest. Humans came to reflect a mosaic of traits, each adaptive and not necessarily inherent in their old primate nature.

In the following pages, the legacy of the hominids—a host of human behaviors, from the double standard to depression, from rape to sibling rivalry, from violent to artistic impulses—is examined in the newly kindled light of sociobiology.

ARTISAN APES

Artistic impulses are by no means limited to man. In 1962, when Desmond Morris reviewed the subject in *The Biology of Art,* 32 individual nonhuman primates had produced drawings and paintings in captivity. None received special training or anything more than access to the necessary equipment. Both young and old animals became so engrossed with the activity that they preferred it to being fed and sometimes threw temper tantrums when stopped. Two chimpanzees studied extensively were highly productive. Alpha produced over 200 pictures, while Congo, who deserves to be called the Picasso of the great apes, was responsible for nearly 400. The patterns were far from random. Congo's patterns progressed along approximately the same developmental path as those of very young human children, yielding fan-shaped diagrams and even complete circles.

The artistic activity of chimpanzees may well be a special manifestation of their tool-using behavior. The chimpanzees have a considerable facility for inventing new techniques, such as the use of sticks to pull objects through cage bars and to pry open boxes. Thus the tendency to manipulate objects and to explore their uses appears to have an adaptive advantage for them.

The same reasoning applies even more forcefully to the origin of art in man. As the anthropologist Sherwood Washburn pointed out, human beings have been hunter-gatherers for over 99 percent of their history, during which time each man made his own tools. The appraisal of form and skill in execution were necessary for survival, and they probably brought social approval as well. Both forms of success paid off in greater genetic fitness. If the chimpanzee Congo could reach the stage of elementary diagrams, it is not too hard to imagine primitive man progressing to representational figures. Once that stage was reached, the transition to the use of art in sympathetic magic and ritual must have followed quickly. Art might then have played a reciprocally reinforcing role in the development of culture and mental capacity.
—*Edward O. Wilson*

ists are of low socioeconomic status and unable to climb the social ladder."

Although rape may ultimately increase biological fitness, men in complex technological societies don't rape to produce offspring. Fitness is easier to come by through legitimate courtship. In examining the motivation for rape, evolutionary biologist William Shields, of the State University of New York, and his collaborator Lea Shields agree with feminists that rape is most immediately an act of violence rather than a sexual act.

If rape is biologically programmed into male behavior, how can society control it? The Shieldses point out that human beings are programmed by natural selection to make learned assessments about risks associated with certain types of behavior. If the cost is greater than any potential benefit, the behavior is unlikely to persist. "Hanging is one alternative. Castration is another," says William Shields. "Both result in genetic death and are therefore the ultimate deterrent." Since such extremes may not be acceptable, enforcement of whatever punishment is prescribed is paramount if rape is to be controlled.

–Mary Batten

THE POLYGAMOUS MAJORITY

As a species, human beings are not as monogamous as you might think. One study of 853 societies found that having just one mate was the norm in only 16 percent of them. The majority, 83.5 percent, were polygynous: men were allowed to have more than one wife. A tiny minority, about 0.5 percent, practiced polyandry, in which women have more than one husband. Such statistics might shock the bird kingdom, an estimated 91 percent of whose species are monogamous at least during the breeding season. But in the rest of the animal world, polygyny is the rule.

The degree of polygyny varies across cultures. "Moslems may have only four wives under Koranic law," anthropologist Weston LaBarre writes, "while the King of Ashanti in West Africa was strictly limited to 3,333 wives." Most men in polygynous societies, however, have just one wife; only the wealthiest can afford more.

What does the prevalence of polygyny tell us about human nature? According to sociobiologist Robert Trivers, of the University of California, Santa Cruz, the type of sexual selection occurring in a species is linked to parental investment—the amount of time and energy a parent must devote to caring for offspring.

If the mother alone can provide enough resources for the young to survive, the father is then free to find and inseminate other females. In this case, a polygynous strategy will enable him to pass on more of his genes. But if his offspring need his care in order to survive, the male profits more from tending to a limited number than from fathering many offspring that may not survive to pass on his genes.

Among mammals, the female's initial investment in a sexual encounter is greater; the egg she contributes is larger (in humans, 85,000 times the size of a sperm), richer in nutrients and more precious, since she will produce only a limited number in her lifetime. Then, if she becomes pregnant, she will not only carry the child until birth but also nourish and care for it at least through infancy. This is a huge investment compared to the male's contribution; one tiny sperm among the billions he will produce in a lifetime.

For this reason, "monogamy is rare in mammals, almost unheard of in primates . . . and it appears to be a relatively recent invention of certain human cultures," according to zoologist David Barash of the University of Washington.

"Fidelity is a special condition," says Harvard entomologist Edward O. Wilson. It evolves only when the advantage of cooperation in rearing offspring outweighs the advantage of seeking extra mates. For example, the hoary marmot, a large ground squirrel, normally lives in family groups consisting of one male, his females and their offspring. Females care for the young, and males divide their time between guarding their own females and attempting to copulate with females in other families of the colony. When resources are scarce, however, and the marmot population is depleted, the marmots live monogamously in isolated families of one male, one female and their young.

Polyandry occurs very rarely in nature. Tasmanian native hens are among the few species that regularly practice polyandry. They form triangles that consist of two males and a female; the males are almost invariably brothers. This means that neither brother will entirely waste his parental investment.

In human societies, polyandry is practiced only under adverse conditions—when resources are so limited that it takes two men to support one woman or when women are unusually scarce. A woman with more than one husband is usually married to brothers. In southern India, polygyny occurs among the upper classes, while polyandry is practiced among the lower classes; the tradition of women marrying "up" creates a scarcity of women at the bottom and a glut at the top.

–Rachel Wilder

Sociobiology: Sex and Survival

THE LITTLEST BLACKMAILER

Darwinism moved from the jungle to the playroom when sociobiologist Robert Trivers created his theory of parent-offspring conflict.

Trivers observed that while every child is 100 percent genetically related to himself, he is only 50 percent related to either parent or to any sibling. This 50 percent difference in relatedness represents an area of potential conflict, since each individual has his own best interests at heart and shares only part of this interest, genetically speaking, with even his closest relatives. The resentment shown by an older child toward a new sibling is a familiar example of this conflict. The parents, equally related to both children, find it in their best interest to withdraw some investment from the older child. So where once the older child had a monopoly on the parents' investment of time and resources, he now receives only a share. The child, plainly, resists this.

The competition for parental attention is strikingly demonstrated in the crying behavior of many baby birds. Ideally, the hungriest bird should cry the loudest—and since the parents would tend to grease the squeaky wheel, each hungry bird would eventually get its worm. In practice, however, a bird that "knew" to cry, whether hungry or not, would receive a disproportionate amount of food, thereby increasing both its own fitness and the probability that the trait of deceitful caterwauling would be passed on to the next generation.

The noise level in the nest might increase indefinitely if it weren't limited by several factors. Constant chirping would attract predators, for example. But in the view of Israeli sociobiologist Amotz Zahavi, this danger may be precisely the point. He sees crying behavior as a kind of blackmail. The young are in effect saying, "Fox, fox, come and get me," forcing the parents to pay hush money in the form of food.

So selfish behavior is the order of the day when an individual is 100 percent related to himself and only 50 percent related to his parents and siblings. Sibling rivalry and the Oedipus complex, in which a male child competes with his father for his mother's affections, are only two of the possible outgrowths of this behavior. Even the universal and apparently unlearned sweet smile of an infant can be viewed as a continually reinforced behavior to attract parental investment.

–Richard Nalley

SELFISH GENES, UNSELFISH ACTS

A robin, spying a hawk high above, whistles a warning call, alerting others to the danger. Why doesn't the robin just fly away quietly rather than risk being spotted?

This seemingly altruistic act has an underlying survival advantage, sociobiologists point out. Many of the birds that share the robin's habitat—and benefit from the warning—are its relatives. By alerting them, the robin increases their likelihood of reproducing and, therefore, helps perpetuate shared genes.

This kin-selecting altruism will appear in any species if it is likely to increase the total number of genes transmitted to future generations by the altruist and his relatives. Even if the altruist dies as a result of his actions, his tendency will live on through the benefiting relatives.

Of course, one wouldn't do just anything for any relative. For altruism to be worthwhile, the genetic benefits must exceed the costs. To estimate who is most likely to help whom and at what cost, sociobiologists have developed a mathematical model based on the degree of relatedness (r)—the average fraction of genes shared by individuals with a common ancestor. Parents and children, sharing one-half their genes, have a relatedness index of r = one-half. So do siblings. For an aunt and a nephew, r = one-quarter.

We would not expect an individual (r = one) to offer his life for a sibling (r = one-half) or a nephew (r = one-quarter) or a cousin (r = one-eighth), but we would expect this sacrifice to be made for three siblings (r = three times one-half, or three-halves), five nephews (r = five times one-quarter, or five-quarters) or nine cousins (r = nine times one-eighth, or nine-eighths), because the number of shared genes saved would be greater than the individual set of genes lost.

But kin-selecting altruism does not account for the harmonious nonfamilial relationships upon which all civilizations are based. In such cases, sociobiologists explain, good deeds often result from reciprocal altruism.

Remember the fable? The slave Androcles takes pity on a lion and pulls a thorn from its paw. Later, in a Roman arena, the lion recognizes its benefactor and refuses to attack him. This scenario would probably have struck Charles Darwin as highly unlikely. He once stated that if a single characteristic of a living thing existed for the sole benefit of another species, it would annihilate his theory of natural selection. Sociobiologists go a step further, applying Darwin's statement even to members of the same species.

Thanks to sociobiologist Robert Trivers, we now have an explanation for Androcles' behavior that Darwin himself might have appreciated. Using probability theory to calculate the possible cost to the individual of an altruistic act versus its perceived benefit, Trivers reasoned that natural selection would favor altruistic behavior if the individual expected some form of return at a later date. This mechanism, called reciprocal altruism, is really selfishness in disguise, since it is based on the expectation of return.

Reciprocal altruism has been observed among animals in the mutual grooming behavior of chimpanzees, but it reaches its most complex form in the social life of man. For instance, parents give selflessly to their children when a child is young and helpless, partly in the expectation that they will receive care in the helplessness of old age. Genes promoting this type of mutually beneficial behavior would spread, particularly within closely knit tribes or groups in which the provider of a service would be in constant contact with the beneficiary. And we might expect Golden Rules and other types of institutionalized moral suasion to develop ensuring that an individual would carry out his end of the bargain.

Perhaps the most perverse example of reciprocity occurred in a ceremony of the Kwakiutl Indians of the Pacific Northwest. At events called potlatches, great chiefs competed to see who could give away the most to the guests. The more they gave away, the higher their status became. Rather than delighting in this windfall, however, the guests became increasingly dismayed, since they would have to return the favors in kind when their turn came around.

–Nancy Solomon and Richard Nalley

THE COOLIDGE EFFECT, OR CAL COUNTS HIS CHICKENS

Sociobiologists are still talking about a story told of the day that President and Mrs. Calvin Coolidge took separate tours of a government farm. Arriving at the chicken pens, Mrs. Coolidge, the story goes, asked whether the rooster there copulated more than once each day.

"Oh, dozens of times," her guide answered.

"Please tell that to the President," she requested.

When the President was later told, he asked, "Same hen every time?"

"No sir, a different one every time."

"Well," said the President, "tell *that* to Mrs. Coolidge."

The phenomenon of renewed male arousal at the introduction of new females has been dubbed the Coolidge effect in honor of Silent Cal's celebrated remark. It occurs in varying degrees among male mammals and is most extreme in species such as cattle and sheep in which males acquire and inseminate large harems.

When a ram is placed in a pen with a ewe in heat, studies show, he will copulate about five times with her, then lose interest. But when a new ewe is substituted, the ram will begin copulating again. He will do this every time another ewe is introduced, and his rate of ejaculation will be the same with the *twelfth* ewe as it was with the first. Scientists even tried disguising ewes by covering their heads and bodies with canvas sacks. But the ram was never fooled by the reintroduction of a masked ewe with which he had already mated.

Something like the Coolidge effect also occurs among humans. A Kgatla man of South Africa, speaking of his two wives, said, "I find them both equally desirable, but when I have slept with one for three days ... and when I go to the other, I have greater passion, she seems more attractive ... but it is not really so, for when I return to the former again there is the same renewed passion."

Being aroused by a change of partners is highly adaptive for males; each new copulation enables them to pass on more of their genes, while this is not so for females. Since the males who were aroused by variety left more offspring, the trait came to be favored by natural selection—and the tendency to find a change of face attractive is now characteristic of the males of many species.

–Rachel Wilder

Sociobiology: Exploring New Worlds

BLUE GENES: DOES IT PAY TO BE DEPRESSED?

Can an illness that debilitates millions be adaptive? That's what zoologist David Barash suggests may be true of depression.

How does depression enhance fitness? Barash, a University of Washington professor of psychology and zoology, hypothesizes that the purpose of depression is to attract attention. "All social animals," he writes, "have a repertoire of 'care-eliciting' behaviors." For example, depressed wives of the southern African !Kung San tribe who want a divorce may attempt suicide to call attention to their feelings and win support for their cause, according to Harvard ethnologist Marjorie Shostak. In Western culture, postpartum depression sparks offers of help at the time a new mother most needs them.

Depressed women outnumber depressed men at least two to one, and they make many more suicide attempts. But more men succeed in killing themselves. Barash claims these differences in behavior reflect differences in sex roles. Men are traditionally supposed to provide care (food, shelter, protection), women, to receive it. Fewer men are depressed, he says, because the behavior would be an evolutionary disadvantage: care-eliciting men are undesirable as mates. Women who need care, however, are acceptable as mates. Since making dramatic pleas for help won't increase the reproductive fitness of depressed men, they actually intend to follow through on suicide.

Dr. Jonathan Himmelhoch, professor of psychiatry at the University of Pittsburgh School of Medicine, believes depression is a misplaced but highly adaptive response to life-threatening situations. The most common type of depression, characterized by anxiety and insomnia, may be physiologically identical to the fight-or-flight response.

Genetic vulnerability to this type of depression should be more common among people who, during the course of evolution, would need to be on the lookout for trouble, Himmelhoch says. The majority of patients are women.

Himmelhoch believes that women are the quintessential providers, not receivers, of care. The major responsibility for protecting the species rests with women, not men. The apprehensiveness seen in depressive illness in women is part of the adaptive mechanism they use to help guard their children from danger.

–Lygeri Koromvokis

THE EVOLUTION OF DECEIT AND SELF-DECEPTION

Organisms evolve many intricate devices that fit them more exactly to the particular world they inhabit. Deception is one such device.

It is an expected feature of *all* relations between living organisms that are not identically related. Relations between such individuals are marked by a conflict of self-interests in which one individual can gain at the expense of another. Mechanisms of deception often make such selfish gains easier to obtain. The deceived individual usually suffers a cost from basing actions on misinformation.

Within species, deception has evolved in competitive and aggressive relations and in relations between members of a family, between friends and neighbors and between the sexes.

Males and females often misrepresent themselves, at least slightly. Sometimes sexual deception is more dramatic, as when males pretend they are females.

Male 10-spined stickleback fish build nests shaped like small pipes into which females swim to lay their eggs. A typical nest can hold the eggs of as many as seven females, and females prefer to deposit their eggs in nests that already contain eggs. A male defends a territory containing his nest and cares for the eggs entrusted to him (by aerating them, for example). He courts a female arriving at the edge of his territory by performing a zig-zag dance that invites her to inspect his nest and his parental fitness. If she accepts him, she deposits her eggs, and he swims into the nest and fertilizes them.

It sometimes happens that while one female is spawning in the male's nest, another appears at the edge of his territory. Intending (so to speak) to double his reproductive success, the male swims to the new female and invites her in. After courtship, she swims into his nest and deposits a second clutch of eggs. The male then swims in and fertilizes both clutches. Or so he supposes. For the second female was, in fact, a male. And far from laying a clutch of eggs, "she" actually fertilized the first clutch!

How is the deception achieved? In many fish, coloration can be controlled by the individual. The deceiver approaches in the drab coloration of an adult female, timing his arrival to coincide with another courtship. His behavior mimics that of a female. Even when fertilizing the eggs, this male holds himself in the posture of a female depositing her eggs. When this deception is successful, the result is a large gain in the number of surviving offspring for the deceiver and a corresponding loss for his victim.

Not surprisingly, selection for deception has generated selection to spot deception. As spotting mechanisms become more subtle, organisms are selected to render some facts and motives unconscious, in order not to betray, by signs of self-knowledge, the deception being practiced.

With the advent of human language, the possibilities for deception and self-deception were greatly enlarged. If language permits the communication of much more detailed and extensive information, then it both permits and encourages the communication of much more detailed and extensive misinformation. A portion of the brain devoted to verbal functions must become specialized for the manufacture and maintenance of falsehoods. This will require biased perceptions, memory and logic, processes ideally kept partly unconscious.

An individual's perception of its own motivation may often be biased in order to conceal the true motivation from others. Consciously, a series of reasons may unfold internally to accompany action, so that when actions are challenged by others a convincing alternative explanation is at once available, complete with an internal scenario ("But I wasn't thinking that at all, I was thinking . . .") Of course, it must be advantageous for the truth to be registered somewhere, so mechanisms of self-deception must reside side by side with mechanisms for the apprehension of reality. The mind must be a complex structure, repeatedly split into public and private portions, with complicated interactions between the subsections.

Huey P. Newton
and Robert T. Trivers

ARE SEXUAL STANDARDS INHERITED?

For generations, defense of male honor was considered a legitimate motive for murder in Brazil; men who killed their adulterous wives were allowed to go free or given light sentences. Female honor was not similarly protected.

A 1976 study of 116 different societies found that roughly 65 percent were more permissive of extramarital intercourse for men than for women; 11 percent were equally tolerant of marital infidelity for both sexes; and 23 percent disapproved of it equally for men and women. No society, however, was more tolerant of female extramarital sex.

Sociobiologists believe this double standard arises from basic biological differences between men and women. Theoretically, a man could father thousands of children by copulating with enough different women. For him, the payoff for having sex with a variety of partners is high—he passes on more of his genes—and he has nothing to lose from each copulation but a few milliliters of sperm.

But a woman has a greater stake in any one reproductive act. For her, it could result in a major investment of resources: a nine-month pregnancy, childbirth, then years of feeding and caring for a dependent child. It is therefore in her interest to be more discriminating in her choice of partners and, once she has selected the most fit male available, to try to get as much help from him as she can in raising the offspring. If the male provides resources for his children, they will have a better chance of surviving and eventually reproducing. This strategy will further the male's genetic interest—but only if he is absolutely sure the children are his.

A woman has the advantage of always knowing who her children are, while a man can never be sure whether a child belongs to him or to some other male. This element of doubt—called uncertainty of paternity—encourages men to seek sex with other partners, sociobiologists contend. It's a way of hedging their bets.

Since a woman can bear only a limited number of children in her lifetime—rarely more than 20—seeking a variety of sexual partners gives her no reproductive advantage. Instead, she employs her own strategy: establish a stable relationship with one reliable mate who will stay with her and provide a steady supply of resources for her offspring. But as the anthropologist Pierre van den Berghe points out, the pair-bonding between a man and a woman is "asymmetrically binding." It *is* to a man's advantage to be a family man and provide for his offspring, but it is also adaptive for him to retain his roving eye, since it enables him to multiply his reproductive success.

—Rachel Wilder

TWINS
R·E·U·N·I·T·E·D

Constance Holden

Anyone who knows identical twins has undoubtedly experienced profound paradoxical reactions: astonishment at their similarities and amazement at their differences. Twins have always been regarded as special; in some aboriginal societies they are venerated, in some they are slain. Identical twins also have figured as protagonists in one of the oldest and bitterest disputes among scientists—the nature/nurture controversy.

It has been almost a century since Sir Francis Galton, the founder of the science of eugenics, first proposed studying identical twins to determine the relative influences of heredity and environment on human development. Now a group of researchers at the University of Minnesota are involved in the most comprehensive investigation ever undertaken of twins raised apart. Initiated by psychologist Thomas Bouchard, the study consists of exhaustive physical, psychological, and biographical inventories of every twin. So far, 15 pairs, each of whom spent a week at the university, have been tested. Bouchard has located 18 additional pairs with the help of the publicity the project is getting.

It will take at least five or six years to analyze definitively the masses of data accumulated so far. But after a year and a half of examining twin pairs, the 17 members of the research team, which includes six psychologists, two psychiatrists, and nine other medical experts, have been overwhelmed with the similarities of the participating pairs. Some similarities, of course, are clearly coincidental, such as the twins who are both named Jim. Others may only seem to be: Twin sisters who had never met before each wore seven rings on their fingers. They may not have inherited their fondness for rings; perhaps only the same pretty hands prompted the fondness. And still other similarities, like phobias, which were long thought to be learned, may turn out after all to be hereditary.

"I frankly expected far more differences than we have found so far," says Bouchard. "I'm a psychologist, not a geneticist. I want to find out how the environment works to shape psychological traits." Bouchard has encountered some hostility on the Minneapolis campus because he remains aloof from the ideological fashion, which holds that behavior is largely shaped by environmental influences. Student hostility is ironic in view of Bouchard's political activism at the University of California in the radical 1960s.

Actually Bouchard's quest is considerably more sophisticated than critics perceive. To discover how the environment shapes behavior, one first must have an idea of how innate tendencies work to select a particular environment. The same surroundings can be interpreted very differently by two individuals. One person may find a library a good place to read, for example, while another may regard it as an excellent hunting ground for members of the opposite sex.

In the hope of making some of these distinctions, Bouchard has drawn upon his extensive experience in personality testing to develop the battery of tests for each twin pair. In addition, the scientists take detailed medical histories that include diet, smoking and exercise habits, electrocardiograms, chest X rays, heart stress tests, and pulmonary exams. They inject the twins with a variety of substances to determine allergies. They wire them to EEG machines to measure their brain wave responses to various stimuli.

During the six days they devote to each twin pair, the team intersperses the physiological probes with several dozen written tests, which ask some 15,000 questions. These cover family and childhood environment, fears and phobias, personal interests, vocational aptitudes, values, reading and television viewing habits, musical tastes, and aesthetic judgments. Each pair of twins undergoes three comprehensive psychological inventories. In addition each takes ability tests: the Wechsler Adult Intelligence Scale, the main adult IQ test, and numerous others that reveal skills in information processing, vocabulary, spatial abilities, numerical processing, mechanical ability, and memory. Throughout the week there is a good deal of overlap in an attempt to "measure the same underlying factor at different times," says Bouchard.

No scientific conclusions can yet be drawn from the masses of data collected, but the team has made a number of provocative observations.

The "Jim twins," as they have come to be known, have histories that are riddled with bizarre coincidences. Jim Springer and Jim Lewis were adopted as four-week-old infants into working-class Ohio families. They never met each other until they were 39 years old. Both had law enforcement training and worked part time as deputy sheriffs. Both vacationed in Florida; both drove Chevrolets. Much has been made of the fact that their lives are marked by a trail of similar names. Both had dogs named Toy. They married and divorced women named Linda and remarried women named Betty. They named their sons James Allan and James Alan. While the laws of chance dictate against such an unlikely string of coincidences, Bouchard has noted that twins seem to be highly subject to such strange similarities.

Other similarities, however, are probably more than coincidental. In school both twins liked math but not spelling. They currently enjoy mechanical drawing and carpentry. They have almost identical drinking and smoking patterns, and they chew their fingernails down to the nubs. Investigators thought their similar medical histories were astounding. In addition to having hemorrhoids and identical pulse, blood pressure, and sleep patterns, both had inexplicably put on ten pounds at the same time in life. Each suffers from "mixed headache syndrome," a combination tension and migraine headache. Both first suffered headaches at the age of 18. They have these late-afternoon headaches with the same frequency and same degree of disability, and the two used the same terms to describe the pain they experienced.

The twins also have their differences. One wears his hair over his forehead; the other has it slicked back with sideburns. One expresses himself better orally, the others in writing. Even though the emotional environments in which they were brought up were different, still the profiles on their psychological inventories were much alike.

Another much publicized pair is 47-year-old Oskar Stöhr and Jack Yufe. These two have the most dramatically different backgrounds of all the twins studied. Born in Trinidad of a Jewish father and a German mother, they were separated shortly after birth. The mother took Oskar back to Germany where he was raised as a Catholic and a Nazi by his grandmother. Jack was raised in the Caribbean as a Jew by his father and spent part of his youth on an Israeli kibbutz. As might be expected, the men now lead markedly different lives: Oskar, an industrial supervisor in Germany, is married, a devoted union man, and a skier. Jack runs a retail clothing store in San Diego, is separated from his wife, describes himself as a workaholic, and enjoys sailing as a hobby.

Their families had never corresponded, yet similarities were evident when they first met at the airport. Both sported mustaches and two-pocket shirts with epaulets. Each had his wire-rimmed glasses with him. They share abundant idiosyncrasies: The twins like spicy foods and sweet liqueurs, are absentminded, fall asleep in front of the television, think it is funny to sneeze in a crowd of strangers, flush the toilet before using it, store rubber bands on their wrists, read magazines from back to front, dip buttered toast in their coffee. Oskar did not take all the tests because he speaks only German, but the two had similar profiles on the Minnesota Multiphasic Personality Inventory. Oskar yells at his wife, which Jack did before he was separated. Although the two were raised in different cultures, investigator Bouchard professed himself impressed by the similarities in their mannerisms, the questions they asked, their "temperament, tempo, the way they do things." He also thinks the pair supply "devastating" evidence against the feminist contention that children's personalities are shaped differently according to the sex of those who rear them, since Oskar was raised by women and Jack by men.

The Bouchard team has enjoyed a run on female British twins in their late 30s, all separated during World War II, and all raised by people who did not know each other. Although Bridget and Dorothy, the housewives sporting the seven rings each, were reared in different socioeconomic settings, the class difference was evident only in that the twin raised in modest circumstances had bad teeth. Otherwise, the investiga-

Though Barbara and Daphne were raised separately, their handwriting is remarkably similar.

The Coffman Gallery area of the Coffman Union Program Council is responsible for the visual arts Programs and exhibitions which are presented in its three formal gallery spaces and other facilities

The Coffman Gallery area of the Coffman Union Program Council is responsible for the visual arts programs and exhibitions which are presented in its three formal gallery spaces and other facilities.

tors conclude, the twins share "striking similarities in all areas."

Another pair, Daphne and Barbara, are fondly remembered as the "giggle sisters," because they were always setting each other off. There are evidently no gigglers in their adoptive families. The sisters both handle stress by ignoring it. Both avoid conflict and controversy; neither has any interest in politics. This similarity is particularly provocative since avoidance of conflict is "classically regarded as learned behavior," says Bouchard.

Irene and Jeanette, 35, who were brought up respectively in England and Scotland, turn out to have the same phobias. Both are claustrophobic, and balked when invited to go into a cubicle for their electroencephalograms. They independently agreed to enter the cubicle if the door were left open. Both are timid about ocean bathing; they resolve the problem by backing in slowly. Neither likes escalators. Both are compulsive counters, of everything they see, such as the wheels of trucks. Both count themselves to sleep.

Other similarities turned up in a number of twin pairs. Tests of vision, for example, showed that even in cases in which one twin wears glasses and the other does not, both require the same type of correction.

Bouchard says it is commonplace for identical twins to engage in coincidental behavior: Both will buy the same gift for their mother, or even select the same birthday card. But he is finding that such coincidences often crop up with twins raised apart. A favorite episode involves two middle-aged women in his study. Once, as children, they were brought together briefly to meet each other. Both turned up wearing the same dress.

As for IQ, a hotly controversial area of psychological testing, the Minnesota study confirms what other researchers repeatedly have shown: that of all psychological traits measured in identical twins, this one shows the highest degree of similarity. Bouchard, mindful of charges of investigator bias that are often leveled at IQ testers, arranges for outside contractors to come in to administer and score the Wechsler intelligence test. He wants to avoid imputations of fraud such as those leveled recently at the eminent British educational psychologist, the late Sir Cyril Burt, who some accuse of "cooking" his IQ data in order to buttress his belief in the heritability of intelligence. In the case of the Minnesota study, most of the scores do not differ any more than those of two tests taken by the same person at different times. In the few that vary considerably, the variance appears to reflect large differences in education.

Psychological histories also correspond well to studies of twins reared together. Psychiatrist Leonard Heston, the father of identical twin girls, is particularly well suited to studying these histories. Scientists have known for some time that there is a genetic component, often involving chemical imbalance, in many mental illnesses. For example, if one twin suffers from depression or schizophrenia the other stands a 45 percent chance of succumbing as well. Heston was surprised by the extent to which twins raised separately tend to share emotional problems—"things such as mild depressions and phobias that I would never have thought of as being particularly genetically mediated," Heston remarks. "Now at least, there are grounds for a very live hypothesis."

Psychologist David Lykken finds that the brain waves of the twin pairs in the Minnesota study resemble each other in the same way as those of twins who have been raised together. Moreover, Lykken finds that tracings from each twin of a pair differ no more than tracings from the same person taken at different times.

To be sure, identical twins differ in myriad ways. One of the most common is in tendencies toward introversion and extroversion. Another common difference, according to the English researcher James Shields, is dominance and submissiveness. Bouchard and his colleagues note that one twin is likely to be more aggressive, outgoing, and confident.

But they find twins reared together usually differ the most in that respect. In other words, dominance and submission seem to be traits that twins use to assert their individuality. Because twins brought up together often feel compelled to exaggerate their differences, David Lykken thinks it is possible that twins reared separately may actually have more in common with each other than those raised together.

Because of the comparatively small numbers of twins they have studied, the investigators face difficulties in proving that their results are more than a random collection of case histories. What they would like to do, according to Tellegen, is "invent methods for analyzing traits in an objective manner, so we can get statistically cogent conclusions from a single case." This will require first establishing what is to be expected on the basis of chance alone. For example, how likely are two randomly selected IQ scores to be as similar as those of two identicial twins? This method of analysis will be crucial in weeding out similarities between twins that may be no more common than coincidences that occur between randomly paired people.

Of all the members of the Bouchard team, Lykken is the most willing to entertain ideas that so far are only supported by subjective impressions. He says, "Looking at these 15 pairs of identical twins, I have an enhanced sense of the importance of the genes in determining all aspects of behavior." But he acknowledges the importance of the environment as well. "What is emerging in my mind," Lykken concludes, "is that the most important thing to come out of this study is a strong sense that vastly more of human behavior is genetically determined or influenced than we ever supposed."

Searching for Depression Genes

LOIS WINGERSON

For years, psychiatrist Larry Pardue thought he had a character flaw. When he lost interest in life during college and his grades fell, he wrote himself off as "just a morning-glory," doomed to fail. He made it through college, but later, during his psychiatry training, he was plagued by insomnia, thoughts of suicide, and a sense of inadequacy. The very doctors who were training him to recognize clinical depression never saw that Larry Pardue had it himself.

Other members of his family also suffered from depression—although Larry Pardue did not know it then. His father had been so severely affected by something called "melancholia" that in 1952 he underwent a prefrontal lobotomy, a brain operation that left him incapable of ever again holding a job. When his niece began showing symptoms of depression in 1973, Pardue began to wonder. Then, when his great-uncle recalled that *his* uncle had killed himself, Pardue began to suspect that more than coincidence was involved. He decided to search his family tree for the "character flaw." What he now regards as the illness of depression turned up with depressing regularity: at least 19 Pardues had clear signs of it.

Pardue published his startling discovery (concealing the identity of his family) in 1975 in the *American Journal of Psychiatry*. His report became the starting point for a new research effort to determine if depression—or the tendency toward depression—can be inherited as well as caused by environmental influences. That notion, which not long ago would have been considered heretical by most psychiatrists,

was strengthened in November by a report in the *New England Journal of Medicine* that a gene apparently linked to depression had been located in human chromosomes.

The discovery, quickly challenged by some experts, was made by Lowell Weitkamp, a geneticist at the University of Rochester, in New York. Studying the anonymous family tree in Pardue's report, Weitkamp noticed that it seemed to fit a genetic pattern. He telephoned Pardue, now on the staff of Tulane University in New Orleans, and asked for blood samples from "his patient's family." Pardue eagerly agreed.

Weitkamp's analyses of the blood samples did reveal a genetic pattern, but not the one he had expected to find. This encouraged him to undertake a broader study; he began looking for that particular unexpected pattern in 20 different families with histories of depression, found it, and eventually zeroed in on the depression gene.

The Weitkamp study is one of the latest developments in a promising new approach to depression research. While Freud and his followers regarded depression as a result of anger turned inward, there is growing evidence that the illness may stem as much from body chemistry (controlled by genes) as it does from psychological pressures. The facts are not all in, but researchers like Weitkamp believe that important discoveries lie just beyond the horizon.

In the spirit of this fresh assault on an ancient human misery, Larry Pardue decided, after Weitkamp's November report, to reveal that the family referred to as "kindred M001" is actually his own—something that even Weitkamp was unaware of until a few months ago. "It is time to de-stigmatize depression, now that we're picking up its biological framework," says Pardue. "We're not

alone. Many, many studies indicate there are other families like us."

Characteristics and conditions other than depression seem to run in families—poverty, religion, even cake recipes. That does not necessarily mean they are inherited. But recent studies of depression in twins and in adopted children strongly suggest that susceptibility to depression *is* passed on in the genes. But how? One reason the answer has proved so elusive is that a baffling variety of emotional troubles go by the name of depression.

"The word depression represents everything from normal sadness to a full-blown mental and physical illness," Dr. Frederick Goodwin, chief of clinical psychobiology at the National Institute of Mental Health, told DISCOVER's Sana Siwolop. By "clinical depression," psychiatrists do not mean the unhappy phases that give rhythm and depth to life. What they do mean by it is harder to define, but it is much more serious, affecting about 2 per cent of the U.S. population. At its worst, depression leads to suicide, which claims about 75,000 American lives each year.

In describing the spectrum of depression, Goodwin draws a horizontal line; at one end is a normal (and transient) bad mood, at the other the emotional roller-coaster of alternating despair and euphoria known as manic, or bipolar, depression. Goodwin thinks the daily pressures of normal life can account for the milder forms of depression; but at the other extreme, while daily experience may still play a role, genes and chemistry may be the main culprits.

Between the mildest and the most severe forms of depression is an ill defined problem called unipolar depression, which probably results from a mixture of causes. People who have it report "low" episodes that last for weeks or months, loss of interest in food and sex, insomnia, and suicidal thoughts. There seem to be many varieties of unipolar depression; some doctors believe alcoholism is one of them.

Most studies show that the inheritance of depression is much too complex to be explained by a single, isolated gene. That was the intriguing thing about the Pardue family tree: it did seem to fit a one-gene pattern.

The best way to find a gene is to show that it is near another gene already known to cause a certain trait, and to demonstrate that the two traits are passed along together. But until now, every suggested link between depression and another trait had been disproved by later studies. The Pardues provided a chance to try again. Weitkamp tested them for 35 such traits—and failed. Once again, no single gene could be linked to depression.

But Weitkamp did find a pattern in the Pardues, one he later discovered for juvenile diabetes. The pattern was in a class of substances called human leukocyte antigens (HLA), which are essential to the immune system. The production of these proteins by the body's cells is controlled by a specific group of genes on chromosome six in the human genome (all the chromosomes in a cell). Some fifty diseases have been linked with particular HLA types.

Weitkamp found that not everyone with depression in the Pardue family had the same HLA type, but that close relatives often did. The pattern seemed suggestive enough for Weitkamp to test for it in 20 other families that had been diagnosed by psychiatrist Harvey Stancer of the University of Toronto as having many depressed members.

The resulting paper by Weitkamp and Stancer (the one that caused all the fuss) conceded that, in general, the depression patients they had studied did not share HLA types more often than expected. Nevertheless, Weitkamp claimed that his statistical interpretation of the results (in which families with one or two depressed children were considered separately from families with three or more) did point to a genetic pattern. Only if they had *all* had the same HLA type would the results support a single-gene theory, but Weitkamp claimed that the pattern he found would be consistent with a secondary gene, near the HLA genes, contributing to depression—working with a yet-undiscovered primary gene somewhere else. The *New England Journal of Medicine* evidently agreed. Its editorial said the report represented "major progress in understanding the genetics of depressive disorders."

Other geneticists are skeptical. One of them, Dr. Elliot Gershon, chief of the psychogenetics section at the National Institute of Mental Health, says Weitkamp's method "doesn't make sense." Gershon says that his own studies have failed—even when he analyzed his own data by Weitkamp's methods—to show a link between depression and 24 selected genetic traits, including HLA. Weitkamp is not persuaded: he thinks Gershon's data do support his theory. "Weitkamp and I are both gentlemen and scholars," says Gershon, "but we don't agree about depression."

Robert Cloninger, of the Washington University School of Medicine in St. Louis, who is studying the genetics of alcoholism, thinks Weitkamp's sample may have been too small, and suggests that a new study, using larger families, might produce different results.

The answer only awaits the next spring thaw in Pennsylvania. When the snows melt and travel is easier, Janice Egeland, a University of Miami medical sociologist, will begin collecting blood samples for HLA typing from depressed people among the Amish, a religious sect who, among other things, travel by horse and buggy and refuse to use machines or electricity—and who have huge families. After decades of study, Egeland knows everyone with clinical depression among the 12,500 Amish people living near Lancaster. Although the depression rate among the Amish is only about half the national average, they are good subjects for medical studies, and not only because of their family size (each depressed person in Egeland's sample has about 13 immediate family members). They are also inbred and have lived in the same area for generations (Egeland has traced their family trees carefully). Alcoholism and drug addiction are almost nonexistent among them, so depression seldom masquerades as something else.

Weitkamp also plans to do genetic studies of larger families, and he hopes that, in addition to supporting his earlier findings, the results will stimulate new kinds of brain research. One question he would like to see answered is why the brains of people who commit suicide often contain an abnormal protein also found in the brains of people with multiple sclerosis. When David Comings, a geneticist at the City of Hope Medical Center in Duarte, California, discovered the protein in suicide victims, multiple sclerosis had already been linked with particular HLA types. Comings speculated that the "depression protein" might also be controlled by a gene in the HLA region.

Could this be Weitkamp's depression gene? Weitkamp and Comings suspect, in fact, that they may be studying different manifestations of the same chemical abnormality, and that further research may establish the connection.

The chemical secrets behind depression lie hidden deep within the brain, in a primitive region called the limbic system, which controls such emotions as fear, hunger, and rage. The limbic system lies at a crossroad, receiving signals from both the cortex, where decisions are made and memory is stored, and the thalamus, the receiving center for sensory messages. The central location of the limbic system may explain how any chemical variation there could bring on the many mental and physical symptoms of depression. Such chemical cross-linking turns up in unexpected ways. For instance, a chemical test used since the 1960s to diagnose a hormonal disorder called Cushing's syndrome turns out to be useful in identifying certain depressed people who can be helped by drugs.

Scientists have barely begun to explore the role of chemistry in moods and feelings, but some general principles are becoming evident. Messages travel along the brain's billions of nerve cells electrically, but to get from one cell to the next across the synapse, or gap, between, the electrical impulses must be translated into chemical reactions. Messages are passed across the gaps by some twenty chemicals called neurotransmitters, three of which, norepinephrine, dopamine, and serotonin, seem to be implicated in moods. Knowledge of this fact has already opened avenues for exploring and treating psychiatric illnesses.

Harvard psychiatrist Joseph Schildkraut and others discovered two decades ago that the supply of certain neurotransmitters in the brain, especially norepinephrine, is associated with mood swings in manic-depressives. They found deficiencies of such chemicals during periods of depression and overabundances of them during euphoria. Demonstrating this variation in supply was no easy task; neurotransmitters never leave the brain, and therefore cannot be measured directly in living people. But when norepinephrine breaks down, one of the resulting products, called MHPG, does escape into the blood stream, and can be measured.

Unfortunately, the relationship between the supply of neurotransmitters and mood is not so simple in people with the unipolar form of depression. For this reason, Schildkraut

3. Searching for Depression Genes

believes that unipolar depression may actually be a catch-all term for several different diseases with similar symptoms but different chemical causes. There is support for this idea in the wide variety of responses to antidepressant drugs. For example, everyone with depression in the Pardue family has been treated successfully with the same class of antidepressant drugs (tricyclics), which work by preventing nerve cells from reabsorbing neurotransmitters after they are released. But these drugs do not work for everyone. Some people respond to monoamine oxidase inhibitors, for example, which prevent a brain enzyme from destroying neurotransmitters like norepinephrine.

Antidepressant drugs might be expected to relieve the depressive phase of manic-depression, but for some unknown reason they do not. Manic-depressives have been greatly helped, however, by a drug called lithium carbonate.

None of these drugs is ideal. They can have side effects that range from dryness of the mouth to heart trouble. Furthermore, overdoses can be lethal, and some depression victims have used their medicine to commit suicide. For these reasons, drug companies are seeking antidepressants that are both safer and more specific.

In the latest efforts to understand and treat depression, Schildkraut sees parallels with the early clinical battles against pneumonia. Pneumonia was once diagnosed purely on the basis of symptoms, but today a doctor can tell from laboratory tests the specific type of pneumonia he is confronting and which drugs will be most effective against it. Ten years hence, Schildkraut says, present methods of treating depression will seem as crude as former pneumonia treatments seem now.

Geneticists will need more time to make sense of the causes of depression. But many believe that within the next 20 years, using new genetic engineering techniques, they will have mapped the locations on the chromosomes of most of the human genes. By then, any genes that contribute to depression should be much easier to spot than they are today.

Egeland, the scientist studying Amish families, is looking far into the future. She plans to freeze some samples of Amish blood so that they can be analyzed years from now to test new genetic theories. "We're closing in," she says, "and that's the exciting thing for everyone."

PIAGET

"He is advocating a revolutionary doctrine about human knowing that undermines the assumptions of much of contemporary social science."

DAVID ELKIND

David Elkind, Ph.D., is professor of psychology, psychiatry and education at the University of Rochester and the director of graduate training in developmental psychology.

It is probably fair to say that the single most influential psychologist writing today is famed Swiss developmentalist Jean Piaget.* His work is cited in every major textbook on psychology, education, linguistics, sociology, psychiatry and other disciplines as well. There is now a Jean Piaget Society that each year draws thousands of members to its meetings. And there are many smaller conferences, both here and abroad, that focus upon one or another aspect of Piaget's work. It is simply a fact that no psychologist, psychiatrist or educator today can claim to be fully educated without some exposure to Piaget's work.

The man who has made this tremendous impact upon social science is now in his 79th year and shows no signs of letting up his prodigious pace of research, writing and lecturing. In the last few years, he has published more than a half-dozen books, has traveled and lectured extensively (he received an honorary degree from the University of Chicago last fall) and continues to

*A/E Editor's note: Jean Piaget died in September of 1980 at the age of 84.

lead a year-long seminar attended by interdisciplinary scholars from around the world. The seminar is held in Geneva at Piaget's Center for Genetic Epistemology, which he founded more than 15 years ago. Each year Piaget invites scholars from all over the world to attend the Center for a year.

My first extensive exposure to Piaget occurred when I spent the 1964–65 year at the Center and learned something of Piagetian psychology firsthand. Although I have never been among the small intimate group of colleagues and students who surround Piaget, we have remained good friends over the years. I last visited with him about two years ago in New York when he came to America to receive the first International Kittay Award (of $25,000) for scientific achievement. The ceremony was held at the Harvard Club and was attended by a small group of invited guests, many of whom, like myself, had worked with or been associated with Piaget in some way. He presented a paper in the afternoon and a brief acceptance speech at the formal dinner that evening.

When Piaget arrived, he wore his familiar dark suit and vest with the remarkably illusionary sweater that somehow seems to keep appearing and disappearing as you watch him. He is of average height, solid in build and looks a little like Albert Einstein, a resemblance that is heightened by the fringe of long white hair that surrounds his head and by the scorched meerschaum that is inevitably in his hand or in his mouth. Up close, his most striking feature is his eyes, which somehow give the impression that they possess great depth and insight. My fantasy has always been

that Freud's eyes must have looked something like that. (Piaget's eyes are remarkably keen as well, despite his glasses. A year before the Kittay ceremony, I visited him in Geneva and we took a walk together. As we climbed the small mountain in the back of his home, he pointed out wild pigeons and flora and fauna towards the top that I could not see at all!)

conscious-awareness

That afternoon, Piaget talked about his research on conscious-awareness. As one has come to expect from him and his co-workers, the studies were most original. In one investigation, he asked children to walk upon all fours and then describe the actions they had taken. "I put my left foot out, then my right hand" and so on. What he found was that young children have great difficulty in describing their actions and that it is not until middle childhood that they can describe their actions with any exactness. Piaget also said (but was most probably joking) that he also asked some psychologists and logicians to perform the same task. The psychologists did very well but the logicians, at least according to Piaget, constructed beautiful models of crawling that had nothing to do with the real patterning of their actions.

At the dinner meeting that evening, Piaget accepted the award. In his talk, he related his fantasy of the committee meeting at which it was decided that the award should go to him. He imagined, he said, that the physicians on the committee were reluctant to give the award to a neurologist or physiologist who in turn were reluctant to see it go to a neurochemist or molecular biologist. Piaget appeared as the compromise candidate because he belonged to no particular discipline (except to the one he himself created, although he did not say this) and was, therefore, the only candidate upon whom everyone could agree. The speaker who gave Piaget the award assured him that while his fantasy was most amusing, it had no basis in fact, and that Piaget was the first person nominated and unanimously chosen by the selection committee.

There was not much chance to talk to Piaget after the dinner, but it was probably just as well. He does not really like to engage in "small talk," and at close quarters it is often difficult to find things to say to him other than discussion of research, which seems rather inappropriate at dinner parties. Yet his difficulty with small talk does not seem to extend to women, and with them he can be most charming in any setting. He is even not above clowning a bit. It should be said, too, that on formal social occasions, when he is officiating or performing some titular function, he is most gracious and appropriate. It is the small interpersonal encounters, such as occur at the dinner table, that seem most awkward for him. Perhaps his total commitment to his work has produced this social hiatus. It is certainly a small price to pay for all that he has accomplished.

Despite the enormity of his collected works, the extent of Piaget's influence is surprising for several reasons. For one thing, it has been phenomenally rapid and recent. Although Piaget began writing in the early decades of this century, his work did not become widely known in this country until the early 1960s. It is only in the past 10 years that Piaget's influence has grown in geometric progression from his previous recognition. Piaget's influence is also surprising because he writes and speaks only in French; so all of his works have had to be translated. Moreover, his naturalistic research methodology and avoidance of statistics are such that many of his studies would not be acceptable for publication in American journals of psychology. But most surprising of all is the fact that Piaget is advocating a revolutionary doctrine regarding the nature of human knowing that, if fully appreciated, effectively undermines the assumptions of much of contemporary social science.

What then is it about Piaget's work and theory that has made him so influential despite his controversial ideas and his somewhat unacceptable (at least to a goodly portion of the academic community) research methodology? The fact is that, theory and method aside, his descriptions of how children come to know and think about the world ring true to everyone's ear. When Piaget says that children believe that the moon follows them when they go for a walk at night, that the name of the sun is in the sun and that dreams come in through the window at night, it sounds strange and is yet somehow in accord with our intuitions. In fact, it was in trying to account for these strange ideas (which are neither innate, because they are given up as children grow older, nor acquired, because they are not taught by adults) that Piaget arrived at his revolutionary theory of knowing.

In the past, two kinds of theories have been proposed to account for the acquisition of knowledge. One theory, which might be called camera theory, suggests that the mind operates in much the same way as a camera does when it takes a picture. This theory assumes that there is a reality that exists outside of our heads and that is completely independent of our knowing processes. As does a camera, the child's mind takes pictures of this external reality, which it then stores up in memory. Differences between the world of adults and the world of children can thus be explained by the fact that adults have more pictures stored up than do the children. Individual differences in intelligence can also be explained in terms of the quality of the camera, speed of the film and so on. On this analogy, dull children would have less precise cameras and less sensitive film than brighter children.

A second, less popular theory of knowing asserts that the mind operates not as a camera but rather as a projector. According to this view, infants come into the world with a built-in film library that is part of some natural endowment. Learning about the world amounts to running these films through a projector (the mind), which displays the film on a blank screen—the world. This theory asserts then that we never learn anything new, that nothing really exists outside of our heads and that the whole world is a product of our own mental processes. Differences be-

tween the world of adults and the world of children can be explained by arguing that adults have projected a great many more films than have children. And individual differences can be explained in terms of the quality of the projection equipment or the nature and content of the films.

The projector theory of knowing has never been very popular because it seems to defy common sense. Bishop Berkeley, an advocate of this position, was once told that he would be convinced that the world was not all in his head if, when walking about the streets of London, the contents of a slop bucket chanced to hit him on the head. The value of the projector, sometimes called the idealistic or platonic theory of knowing, has been to challenge the copy theorists and to force them to take account of the part that the human imagination plays in constructing the reality that seems to exist so independently of the operations of the human mind.

In contrast to these ideas, Piaget has offered a nonmechanical, creative or constructionist conception of the process of human knowing. According to Piaget, children construct reality out of their experiences with the environment in much the same way that artists paint a picture from their immediate impressions. A painting is never a simple copy of the artist's impressions, and even a portrait is "larger" than life. The artist's construction involves his or her experience but only as it has been transformed by the imagination. Paintings are always unique combinations of what the artists have taken from their experience and what they have added to it from their own scheme of the world.

In the child's construction of reality, the same holds true. What children understand reality to be is never a copy of what was received by their sense impressions; it is always transformed by their own ways of knowing. For example, once I happened to observe a friend's child playing at what seemed to be "ice-cream wagon." He dutifully asked customers what flavor ice cream they desired and then scooped it into make-believe cones. When I suggested that he was the ice-cream man, however, he disagreed. And when I asked what he was doing, he replied, "I am going to college." It turned out his father had told him that he had worked his way through college by selling Good Hu-

"When he was 10, his observations on a sparrow were published in a science journal, initiating a publications career equalled by few."

In a few free moments, Piaget studies his own garden handiwork.

mor ice cream from a wagon. The child has recreated his own reality from material offered by the environment. From Piaget's standpoint, we can never really know the environment but only our reconstructions of it. Reality, he believes, is always a reconstruction of the environment and never a copy of it.

Looked at from this standpoint, the discrepancies between child and adult thought appear in a much different light than they do for the camera and projector theories. Those theories assume that there are only quantitative differences between the child and adult views of the world, that children are "miniature adults" in mind as well as in appearance. In fact, of course, children are not even miniature adults physically. And intellectually, the child's reality is qualitatively different from the adult's because the child's means for constructing reality out of environmental experiences are less adequate than those of the adult. For Piaget, the child progressively constructs and reconstructs reality until it approximates that of adults.

To be sure, Piaget recognizes the pragmatic value of the copy theory of knowing and does not insist that we go about asserting the role of our knowing processes in the construction of reality. He does contend that the constructionist theory of knowing has to be taken into account in education. Traditional education is based on a copy theory of knowing that assumes that if given the words, children will acquire the ideas they represent. A constructionist theory of knowing asserts just the reverse—that children must attain the concepts before the words have meaning. Thus Piaget stresses that children must be active in learning, that they have concrete experiences from which to construct reality and that only in consequence of their mental operations on the environment will they have the concepts that will give meaning to the words they hear and read. This approach to education is not new and has been advocated by such workers as Pestalozzi, Froebel, Montessori and Dewey. Piaget has, however, provided an extensive empirical and theoretical basis for an educational program in which children are allowed to construct reality through active engagements with the environment.

Piaget's concern with the educational implications of his work comes naturally because he has, for the whole of his career, been associated with the J. J. Rousseau Institute, which is essentially a training school for teachers. And Rousseau made explicit a theme that has permeated Piaget's work, namely, that child psychology is the science of education. The union of child development and educational practice is thus quite natural in Switzerland, particularly in Geneva where Rousseau once lived and worked. Indeed, Piaget's Swiss heritage, while it does not explain his genius, was certainly an important factor in determining the directions towards which his genius turned.

Besides its beauty, perhaps the most extraordinary thing about Switzerland is the number of outstanding psychologists and psychiatrists it has produced in relation to the modest size of its population (two million people). One thinks of Claparède who preceded Piaget at the Institut de Rousseau in Geneva; of Carl Gustav Jung, the great analytic psychologist; of Herman Rorschach, who created the famed Rorschach inkblot test; and of Frederich Binswanger, the existential psychiatrist. And then, of course, there is Jean Piaget. But it is important to recognize that there appears to be something in the Swiss milieu and gene pool that is conducive to producing more than its share of exceptional social scientists.

Piaget himself was born in a small village outside Lausanne. His father, a professor of history at the University of Lausanne, was particularly well-known for his gracious literary style. Piaget's mother was an ardently religious woman who was often at odds with her husband's free thinking and lack of piety. Growing up in this rather conflictual environment, Piaget turned to intellectual pursuits, in part because of his natural genius, but perhaps also as an escape from a difficult and uncomfortable life situation.

As often happens in the case of true genius, Piaget showed his promise early. When he was 10, he observed an albino sparrow and wrote a note about it that was published in a scientific journal. Thus was launched a career of publications that has had few equals in any science. When Piaget was a young adolescent, he spent a great deal of time in a local museum helping the curator, who had a fine collection of mollusks. This work stimulated Piaget to undertake his own collection and to make systematic observations of mollusks on the shores of lakes and ponds. He began reporting his observations in a series of articles that were published in Swiss journals of biology. As a result, he won an international reputation as a mollusciologist, and, on the basis of his work, he was offered, sight unseen, the curatorship of a museum in Geneva. He had to turn the offer down because he was only 16 and had not yet completed high school.

Although Piaget had a natural bent for biological observation, he was not inclined toward experimental biology. The reason, according to Piaget, was that he was "maladroit" or not well coordinated enough to perform the delicate manipulations required in the laboratory. But Piaget had other intellectual pursuits. He was very interested in philosophy, particularly in Aristotle and Bergson, who speculated about biological and natural science. Piaget was initially much impressed by the Bergsonian dualism between life forces (*élan vital*) and physical forces, but he eventually found this dualism unacceptable. More to his liking was the Aristotelian position that saw logic and reason as the unifying force in both animate and inanimate nature. What living and nonliving things have in common is that they obey rational laws. Not surprisingly, Piaget came to regard human intelligence, man's rational function, as providing the unifying principle of all the sciences—including the social, biological and natural disciplines. It was a point of view that was to guide him during his entire career.

In 1914, Piaget had intended to go to England for a year to learn English as many young Europeans did, but the war intervened. Consequently, despite rumors to the contrary, Piaget does not speak or understand spoken English very well, although he has a fair command of written English.

At the University of Lausanne, Piaget majored in biology and, not surprisingly, conducted his dissertation on mollusks. Early in his college career, Piaget took what Erik Erikson might call a "moratorium"—a period away from his studies and his family. Piaget's moratorium was spent in a Swiss mountain spa. There, he wrote a novel that described the plan of research he intended to pursue during his entire professional career. To a remarkable degree, he has followed the plan he outlined in that book.

After obtaining his doctorate, Piaget explored a number of traditional disciplines seeking one that would allow him to combine his philosophical interest in epistemology (the branch of philosophy concerned with how we know reality) and his interest in biology and natural science. He spent a brief period of time at the Burgholzli in the psychiatric clinic in Zurich where Carl Gustav Jung had once worked. In those years, he was much impressed by Freudian theory and even gave a paper on children's dreams in which Freud showed some interest. But he never had any desire to be a clinician and left the Burgholzli after less than a year.

From Zurich, Piaget traveled to Paris where he worked in the school that had once been used as an experimental laboratory by Alfred Binet. Piaget was given the chore of standardizing some of Sir Cyril Burt's reasoning tests on French children. Although the test administration was

At the age of 79, the eminent psychologist carries a challenging research load.

boring for the most part, one aspect of the work did capture his interest: often when children responded to an item, they came up with unusual or unexpected replies. Although these replies were "wrong" or "errors" for test purposes, they fascinated him. In addition, when children came up with the wrong answer to questions such as "Helen is darker than Rose and Rose is darker than Joyce, who is the fairest of the three?" Piaget was curious about the processes by which the wrong response was arrived at. It seemed to him that the contents of the children's errors and the means by which they arrived at wrong solutions were not fortuitous but systematic and indicative of the underlying mental structures that generated them.

These observations suggested to Piaget that the study of children's thinking might provide some of the answers he sought on the philosophical plane. He planned to investigate them, then move on to other problems. Instead, the study of children's thinking became his lifelong preoccupation. After Paris, Piaget moved permanently to Geneva and began his investigations of children's thinking at the J. J. Rousseau Institute. The publication of his first studies in the field, *The Language and Thought of the Child,* and later, *Judgment and Reasoning in the Child, The Child's Conception of the World* and *The Moral Judgment of the Child,* gained worldwide recognition and made Piaget a world-renowned psychologist before he was 30. Unfortunately, these books, which Piaget regarded as

preliminary investigations, were often debated as finished and final works.

When Claparède retired from his post as director of the Institute of Educational Science at the University of Geneva, Piaget was the unanimous choice to succeed him. Piaget retained this post, as well as his professorship at that university, until his recent retirement. As Piaget's work became more well-known, many students came to work with him and collaborate in his research efforts. One of these students was Valentine Châtenay, whom Piaget proceeded to court and to wed. In due course they had three children, Jacqueline, Laurent and Monique. These children, all grown now, have been immortalized by Piaget in three books that are now classics in the child-development literature, *The Origins of Intelligence in the Child, The Construction of Reality in the Child* and *Play, Dreams and Imitation in Childhood.*

The books came about in this way. After Piaget's initial studies of children's conceptions of the world, he turned to the question of how these notions came to be given up and how children arrive at veridical notions about the world. What he was groping for was a general theory of mental development that would allow him to explain both the "erroneous" ideas he had discovered in his early works and the obviously valid notions arrived at by older children and adults. It seemed clear to Piaget that the mental abilities by which children reconstruct reality have to be sought in the earliest moments of psychic exis-

"Piaget took a novel tack: he didn't posit an outer reality for the infant; he saw construction of reality as the infant's basic task."

tence; hence, the study of infants.

In his study of infants, Piaget, as had other investigators such as Milicent Shinn and Bronson Alcott, used his own children as subjects. However, Piaget's infant studies were unusual in several respects. Perhaps the most novel aspect had to do with his own perspective. He did not assume that there was an external reality for the infant to simply copy and become acquainted with. Rather, he saw the construction of reality as being the basic task of the infant. This way of looking at infant behavior allowed him to observe and study aspects of the infants' reactions that had previously been ignored or the significance of which had not been fully appreciated. Piaget noted, for example, that infants do not search after desired objects that disappear from view until about the end of the first year of life. To him, this meant that young infants had not yet constructed a notion of objects that continue to exist when they are no longer present to their senses.

Traditional psychology has been very harsh towards any hint, in psychological writings, of anthropomorphism, the readings of feelings and thoughts into others without full justification. Piaget wanted to conjecture as to what the infants' experience of the world was, but he also wanted to do this in a scientifically acceptable and testable way. His solution to this difficult problem is another testament to his genius.

In *The Origins of Intelligence in Children*, Piaget describes the evolution of children's mental operations from the outside, as it were. In this book, he introduced some of the basic concepts of his theory of intelligence, including *accommodation* (changing the action to fit the environment) and *assimilation* (changing the environment to fit the action). Piaget could demonstrate these concepts by detailed accounts of infant behavior. When infants changed the conformation of their lips to fit a nipple, this provided one of many examples of accommodation. And when infants tried to suck upon every object that brushed their lips, this was but one of many examples of assimilation.

Other important theoretical concepts were also introduced. One of these was the *schema*.

A schema is essentially a structurized system of assimilations and accommodations—a behavior pattern. Sucking, for example, as it becomes elaborated, involves both assimilation and accommodation and the pattern gets extended and generalized as well as coordinated with other action patterns. When infants begin to look at what they suck and to suck at what they see, there is a coordination of the looking and the sucking schemata. Objects are constructed by the laborious coordination of many different schemata.

In *Origins*, Piaget thus emphasized description and concepts that, at every point, could be tied to behavioral observations. They are extremely careful and detailed and reflect Piaget's early biological training. I once had the opportunity to see his notebooks, and they were filled, page after page, with very neat notations written in a very small hand. Here is an example of one of Piaget's observations:

> Laurent lifts a cushion in order to look for a cigar case. When the object is entirely hidden the child lifts the screen with hesitation, but when one end of the case appears Laurent removes the cushion with one hand and with the other tries to extricate the objective. The act of lifting the screen is, therefore, entirely separate from that of grasping the desired object and constitutes an autonomous "means" no doubt derived from earlier and analogous acts.

In *The Construction of Reality in the Child*, Piaget concerned himself more with the content of infants' thought than with the mental processes. He employed many of the same observations but from the perspective of the child's-eye view of the world. These inferences were, however, always tied to concrete observations and were checked in a variety of different ways. In this book, Piaget talked about infants' sense of space, of time and of causality, but at each point buttressed the discussion with many illustrative examples and little experiments such as the following:

> At 0:3 (13) Laurent, already accustomed for several hours to shake a hanging rattle by pulling

the chain attached to it . . . is attracted by the sound of the rattle (which I have just shaken) and looks simultaneously at the rattle and at the hanging chain. Then while staring at the rattle (R) he drops from his right hand a sheet he was sucking, in order to reach with the same hand for the lower end of the hanging chain (C). As soon as he touches the chain, he grasps it and pulls it, thus reconstructing the series C-R.

Piaget used this example to demonstrate the infant's construction of a notion of practical time.

One of Piaget's important conclusions from the work presented in *Reality* is that for young infants (less than three months), objects are not regarded as permanent, as existing outside the infants' immediate experience. If, for example, one is playing with a young infant who is smiling and laughing up at the friendly adult, the child will not cease to laugh if the adult moves swiftly out of sight. To the young infant, out of sight is quite literally out of mind. By the end of the first year, however, infants cry under the same circumstances. One-year-olds have constructed, via the coordination of looking and touching, schemata, a world of objects that they regard as existing outside their immediate experience and that they can respond to in their absence.

Piaget's *Play, Dreams and Imitation in Childhood* is the third work in the infant trilogy and argues that the symbols with which we represent reality are as much constructions as the reality itself. Piaget found that symbols derive from both imitation (a child opens its mouth in imitation of a match box opening) and play (a child holds up a potato chip and says, "Look, a butterfly.") In Piaget's view, therefore, symbolic activities derive from the same developmental processes that underlie the rest of mental growth and are not separate from, but are part of, intellectual development. Piaget also found that the development of symbolic processes does not usually appear before the age of two. This coincides with the everyday observation that children do not usually report dreams of "night terrors" until after the second year. It is not until that age that most children have the mental ability necessary to create dream symbols.

Piaget's studies on infants were conducted during the 1930s, at which time he was also teaching, following new lines of research and writing theoretical articles on logic and epistemology. His fame attracted many gifted students to Geneva. One of these was Gertrude Szeminska, a Polish mathematician who did some fine work on mathematics and geometry. *The Child's Conception of Number* was one fruit of their collaboration. Another gifted graduate student was Bärbel Inhelder, whose thesis on the conservation and the intellectual assessment of retarded children was a landmark in the extension of Piagetian conceptions to practical problems of assessment and evaluation. Bärbel Inhelder became Piaget's permanent collaborator, and when Piaget retired, his university chair was given to Inhelder—a significant fact in a country where women still do not have the right to vote.

During the '30s, Piaget's lifelong academic affiliations and work patterns became fully established and solidified. Although he had a university appointment from the start of his career, the J. J. Rousseau Institute did not become an official part of the university until the 1940s. Piaget worked hard to insure that it was an interdisciplinary institute so that it would not be saddled with the stigma usually associated with schools of education at universities.

Largely because of Piaget's influence, teacher training is heavily weighted in the direction of child-development theory and research. In addition to the courses on child development offered by Piaget and his staff, students must participate in child-development research. With the aid of his student population, it was possible for Piaget and his graduate students to examine large numbers of children of all ages when they were conducting a particular research investigation. The assertion, which is sometimes made, that Piaget's studies were based on very few subjects, is true only for his infancy investigations. In all of his other explorations, Piaget employed hundreds of subjects.

Piaget's general mode of working is to set up a problem for a year or for several years and then to pursue it intensely and without distraction. Indeed, when Piaget is working, say on "causality," he does not want to talk about or deal with other research problems from the past. Once he has completed a body of work, he loses interest in it and all of his energies are devoted to the task at hand. Generally, Piaget meets with his colleagues and graduate students once a week, at which time the possible ways of exploring the problem are discussed and data from ongoing studies are presented. These are lively, exciting sessions in which new insights and ideas constantly emerge and serve as stimuli for still further innovation.

I have a rather vivid memory of one particular seminar meeting. It is usually the visiting scholars who are the most vocal while the Genevan graduate students tend to be rather quiet, although they are quite animated in their own meetings. In any case, Piaget had been talking about some of the research and I interjected, saying that I was playing devil's advocate, but why did he insist upon using the words *assimilation* and *accommodation*? After all, would not the American terms *stimulus* and *response* serve equally well? The question brought instant silence from the group, most of whom were aghast and waiting for lightning to strike me where I sat. Piaget, however, was most amused and a lively twinkle came into his eye. "Well, Elkeend," he said, "you can use *stimulus* and *response* if you choose, but if you want to understand anything, I suggest that you use *assimilation* and *accommodation*."

At the end of the year, Piaget gathers up all the data that has been collected and moves to a secret hideaway in the mountains. There he takes long walks, cooks loose omelets, thinks about the work that has been done and integrates it into one or several books that he writes in longhand on square pieces of paper. Piaget has a habit of writing at least four publishable pages every day, usually very early in the morning. The remainder of his mornings are spent teaching, meeting with students and staff or with a continuation of his early morning writing. In the afternoons, Piaget routinely takes a walk. It is then that he sorts out the ideas he is working on and thus prepares for the next day's writing. To this day, Piaget keeps to this routine as his health permits. It has been estimated that he has written the equivalent of more than 50, 500-page books.

Perhaps the major achievement of the 1930s and 1940s was the elaboration of Piaget's theory of intelligence into the four stages as we know them. This theory was articulated in close connection with his conservation experiments that provided the data base. The experiments, which resembled those on the permanence of objects in infants, enabled Piaget to compare children's performance on somewhat comparable tasks at many different age levels.

As a result of numerous investigations of children's conceptions of space, time, number, quantity, speed, causality, geometry and so on, Piaget arrived at a general conception of intellectual growth. He argues that intelligence, adaptive thinking and action develop in a series of stages that are related to age. Although there is considerable variability among individual children as to when these stages appear, Piaget does argue that the sequence in which the stages appear is a necessary one. This is true because each succeeding stage grows out of and builds upon the work of the preceding stage. At each level of development, children are again confronted with constructing or reconstructing reality out of their experiences with the world constructed during the previous stage. In addition, they must not only construct new notions of space, time, number and so on, they must also either discard or integrate their previous concepts with the new ones. From a Piagetian standpoint, constructing reality never starts entirely from scratch and always involves dealing with old ideas as well as with acquiring new ones.

In the last few decades, Piaget has extended his researches into new areas, such as memory, imagery, consciousness and causality. He has refined and consolidated his theoretical conceptions and has related them to different disciplines. While it is not really possible to review all of this work here, some aspects of it are significant for education.

One of the major research contributions during this period was the study of memory from the standpoint of Piaget's developmental stages. The research was published in a book under the joint authorship of Piaget and Inhelder.

As did Frederic C. Bartlett's book *Remembering*, this 1972 work by Piaget and Inhelder, *Memory and In-*

"What he has provided is much more valuable than tightly controlled experiments: challenging ideas that open whole new research areas."

telligence, has a good chance of becoming a classic in its field. As in the case of Bartlett's book, the Piaget and Inhelder work presents new data, new conceptualizations and fresh and innovative research approaches. While *Memory and Intelligence* provides no final answers to questions about memory, it offers a richness of hypotheses, and of experimental techniques, that will stimulate other researchers for years to come. Considering that this truly innovative book was written during Piaget's 70th year, one can only marvel at his unabated creativity and productivity.

The argument of the book is straightforward enough. What is the nature of memory? Is it passive storage and retrieval or does it involve intelligence at the outset and all along the way? Piaget's answer is that memory, in the broadest sense, is a way of knowing which is concerned with discovering the past. Although symbols and images are involved in memory, they do not constitute its essence. Rather, intelligence has to be brought to bear to retrieve the past. Hence, all "memories" bear the imprint of the intellectual schemata used to reconstruct them. Intelligence leaves its mark not only on the memory itself, but even upon the original registration that can only be coded within the limits of children's existing schemata.

All of this is not particularly new and could be derived from the work of Bartlett and other writers. What is new and what gives this book its special promise of becoming a classic is the repeated demonstration that children's memory of a given past experience changes with their level of intellectual development. A child, for example, who is shown a series of size-graded sticks before he or she can understand the relations involved, and who draws it poorly, may reproduce it correctly from memory six months later. The child's intel-

lectual understanding of the series modified the memory of it in ways that are predictable from cognitive developmental theory.

To be sure, there are many questions one can raise about the "experiments" themselves. Often the number of children involved is not very large and not all the children show the expected results. The procedures are not always clearly described and the results are presented in tables of percentage passing and without the imprimatur of significance tests. This is simply Piaget's style. There is no point in being annoyed by it or in demanding that he become more rigorous. What he has provided, in the end, is much more valuable than tightly controlled experiments: namely, ideas that challenge the mind and open up whole new areas for experimental research.

The work on memory is only one of a series of areas to which Piaget and his colleagues are applying this theory of intellectual development. In addition, work on imagery, learning, consciousness and causality have all been completed or are under way. Considering that much of this "creative" intellectual work has come during Piaget's eighth decade, one has to acknowledge that creative scientific work is not necessarily the province of the young.

Piaget has also published a number of books that serve to summarize and integrate much of the work that he has done over the past half-century. These books include a general text on child development that introduces the Piagetian work for a general audience. Then there is Piaget's book on biology and knowledge that relates the developmental findings regarding intelligence to more traditional biological conceptions and shows their underlying unity. A little gem of a book, *Structuralism*, outlines in a few brief chapters the central thrust of this movement, which unites many con-

temporary workers, including Piaget, Chomsky, Levi-Strauss' and Erving Goffman. Piaget makes clear that structuralism is a method of analysis and not a discipline or content area.

Of particular relevance to education is Piaget's *Science of Education and the Psychology of the Child*, which is essentially a critique of traditional education. The argument is that education is too concerned with the technology of teaching and too little concerned with understanding children. In Piaget's view, the overemphasis on the science of educating, rather than upon the science of the children being educated, leads to a sterile pedagogy wherein children learn by rote what adults have decided is valuable for them to learn. Basically, Piaget feels that teacher training and educational practice must have child development as their basic discipline. The psychology of the child should be the primary science of education.

These are but a few of the achievements of the last few decades of Piaget's work. And his energy and enthusiasm are unabated as he continues his work on physical and biological causality. Early this summer, he is participating in two conferences, an educational conference in New York and the annual Piaget conference in Philadelphia. At this writing, I am very much looking forward to seeing him again and hearing the latest ideas and research coming from Geneva. I have encouraged as many of my students who can attend to be present as well, since Piaget, to my mind, exemplifies more than genius. At least equally important is the example he presents of a man who, despite his early success, maintained an unwavering commitment to research, to intellectual independence and to the welfare of children all over the world.

Erik Erikson's Eight Ages Of Man
One man in his time plays many psychosocial parts

David Elkind

DAVID ELKIND *is professor of psychology and psychiatry at the University of Rochester.*

At a recent faculty reception I happened to join a small group in which a young mother was talking about her "identity crisis." She and her husband, she said, had decided not to have any more children and she was depressed at the thought of being past the child-bearing stage. It was as if, she continued, she had been robbed of some part of herself and now needed to find a new function to replace the old one.

When I remarked that her story sounded like a case history from a book by Erik Erikson, she replied, "Who's Erikson?" It is a reflection on the intellectual modesty and literary decorum of Erik H. Erikson, psychoanalyst and professor of developmental psychology at Harvard, that so few of the many people who today talk about the "identity crisis" know anthing of the man who pointed out its pervasiveness as a problem in contemporary society two decades ago.

Erikson has, however, contributed more to social science than his delineation of identity problems in modern man. His descriptions of the stages of the life cycle, for example, have advanced psychoanalytic theory to the point where it can now describe the development of the healthy personality on its own terms and not merely as the opposite of a sick one. Likewise, Erikson's emphasis upon the problems unique to adolescents and adults living in today's society has helped to rectify the one-sided emphasis on childhood as the beginning and end of personality development.

Finally, in his biographical studies, such as "Young Man Luther" and "Gandhi's Truth" (which has just won a National Book Award in philosophy and religion), Erikson emphasizes the inherent strengths of the human personality by showing how individuals can use their neurotic symptoms and conflicts for creative and constructive social purposes while healing themselves in the process.

It is important to emphasize that Erikson's contributions are genuine advances in psychoanalysis in the sense that Erikson accepts and builds upon many of the basic tenets of Freudian theory. In this regard, Erikson differs from Freud's early co-workers such as Jung and Adler who, when they broke with Freud, rejected his theories and substituted their own.

Likewise, Erikson also differs from the so-called neo-Freudians such as Horney, Kardiner and Sullivan who (mistakenly, as it turned out) assumed that Freudian theory had nothing to say about man's relation to reality and to his culture. While it is true that Freud emphasized, even mythologized, sexuality, he did so to counteract the rigid sexual taboos of his time, which, at that point in history, were frequently the cause of neuroses. In his later writings, however, Freud began to concern himself with the executive agency of the personality, namely the ego, which is also the repository of the individual's attitudes and concepts about himself and his world.

It is with the psychosocial development of the ego that Erikson's observations and theoretical constructions are primarily concerned. Erikson has thus been able to introduce innovations into psychoanalytic theory without either rejecting or ignoring Freud's monumental contribution.

The man who has accomplished this notable feat is a handsome Dane, whose white hair, mustache, resonant accent and gentle manner are reminiscent of actors like Jean Hersholt and Paul Muni. Although he is warm and outgoing with friends, Erikson is a rather shy man who is uncomfortable in the spotlight of public recognition. This trait, together with his ethical reservations about making public even disguised case material, may help to account for Erikson's reluctance to publish his observations and conceptions (his first book appeared in 1950, when he was 48).

In recent years this reluctance to publish has diminished and he has been appearing in print at an increasing pace. Since 1960 he has published three books, "Insight and Responsibility," "Identity: Youth and Crisis" and "Gandhi's Truth," as well as editing a fourth, "Youth: Change ·and Challenge." Despite the accolades and recognition these books have won for him, both in America and abroad, Erikson is still surprised at the popular interest they have generated and is a little troubled about the possibility of being misunderstood and misinterpreted. While he would prefer that his books spoke for themselves and that he was left out of the picture, he has had to accede to popular demand for more information about himself and his work.

The course of Erikson's professional career has been as diverse as it has been unconventional. He was born in Frankfurt, Germany, in 1902 of Danish parents. Not long after his birth his father died, and his mother later married the pediatrician who had cured her son of a childhood illness. Erikson's stepfather urged him to become a physician, but the boy declined and became an artist instead—an artist who did portraits of children. Erikson says of his post-adolescent years, "I was an artist then, which in Europe is a euphemism for a young man with some talent and nowhere to go." During this period he settled in Vienna and worked as a tutor in a family friendly with Freud's. He met Freud on informal occasions when the families went on outings together.

These encounters may have been the impetus to accept a teaching appointment at an American school in Vienna founded by Dorothy Burlingham and directed by Peter Blos (both now well known on the American psychiatric scene). During these years (the late nineteen-twenties) he also undertook and completed psychoanalytic training with Anna Freud and August Aichhorn. Even at the outset of his career, Erikson gave evidence of the breadth of his interests and activities by being trained and certified as a Montessori teacher. Not surprisingly, in view of that training, Erikson's first articles dealt with psychoanalysis and education.

It was while in Vienna that Erikson met and married Joan Mowat Serson, an American artist of Canadian descent. They came to America in 1933, when Erikson was invited to practice and teach in Boston. Erikson was, in fact, one of the first if not the first child-analyst in the Boston area. During the next two decades he held clinical and academic appointments at Harvard, Yale and Berkeley. In 1951 he joined a group of psychiatrists and psychologists who moved to Stockbridge, Mass., to start a new program at the Austen Riggs Center, a private residential treatment center for disturbed young people. Erikson remained at Riggs until 1961, when he was appointed professor of human development and lecturer on psychiatry at Harvard. Throughout his career he has always held two or three appointments simultaneously and has traveled extensively.

Perhaps because he had been an artist first, Erikson has never been a conventional psychoanalyst. When he was treating children, for example, he always insisted on visiting his young patients' homes and on having dinner with the families. Likewise in the nineteen-thirties, when anthropological investigation was described to him by his friends Scudder McKeel, Alfred Kroeber and Margaret Mead, he decided to do field work on an Indian reservation. "When I realized that Sioux is the name which we [in Europe] pronounced "See us" and which for us was *the* American Indian, I could not resist." Erikson thus antedated the anthropologists who swept over the Indian reservations in the post-Depression years. (So numerous were the field workers at that time that the stock joke was that an Indian family could be defined as a mother, a father, children and an anthropologist.)

Erikson did field work not only with the Oglala Sioux of Pine Ridge, S. D. (the tribe that slew Custer and was in turn slaughtered at the Battle of Wounded Knee), but also with the salmon-fishing Yurok of Northern California. His reports on these experiences revealed his special gift for sensing and entering into the world views and modes of thinking of cultures other than his own.

It was while he was working with the Indians that Erikson began to note syndromes which he could not explain within the confines of traditional psychoanalytic theory. Central to many an adult Indian's emotional problems seemed to be his sense of uprootedness and lack of continuity between his present life-style and that portrayed in tribal history. Not only did the Indian sense a break with the past, but he could not identify with a future requiring assimilation of the white culture's values. The problems faced by such men, Erikson recognized, had to do with the ego and with culture and only incidentally with sexual drives.

The impressions Erikson gained on the reservations

were reinforced during World War II when he worked at a veterans' rehabilitation center at Mount Zion Hospital in San Francisco. Many of the soldiers he and his colleagues saw seemed not to fit the traditional "shell shock" or "malingerer" cases of World War I. Rather, it seemed to Erikson that many of these men had lost the sense of who and what they were. They were having trouble reconciling their activities, attitudes and feelings as soldiers with the activities, attitudes and feelings they had known before the war. Accordingly, while these men may well have had difficulties with repressed or conflicted drives, their main problem seemed to be, as Erikson came to speak of it at the time, "identity confusion."

It was almost a decade before Erikson set forth the implications of his clinical observations in "Childhood and Society." In that book, the summation and integration of 15 years of research, he made three major contributions to the study of the human ego. He posited (1) that, side by side with the stages of psychosexual development described by Freud (the oral, anal, phallic, genital, Oedipal and pubertal), were psychosocial stages of ego development, in which the individual had to establish new basic orientations to himself and his social world; (2) that personality development continued throughout the whole life cycle; and (3) that each stage had a positive *as well* as a negative component.

Much about these contributions—and about Erikson's way of thinking—can be understood by looking at his scheme of life stages. Erikson identifies eight stages in the human life cycle, in each of which a new dimension of "social interaction" becomes possible—that is, a new dimension in a person's interaction with himself, and with his social environment.

TRUST vs. MISTRUST

The first stage corresponds to the oral stage in classical psychoanalytic theory and usually extends through the first year of life. In Erikson's view, the new dimension of social interaction that emerges during this period involves basic *trust* at the one extreme, and *mistrust* at the other. The degree to which the child comes to trust the world, other people and himself depends to a considerable extent upon the quality of the care that he receives. The infant whose needs are met when they arise, whose discomforts are quickly removed, who is cuddled, fondled, played with and talked to, develops a sense of the world as a safe place to be and of people as helpful and dependable. When, however, the care is inconsistent, inadequate and rejecting, it fosters a basic mistrust, an attitude of fear and suspicion on the part of the infant toward the world in general and people in particular that will carry through to later stages of development.

It should be said at this point that the problem of basic trust-versus-mistrust (as is true for all the later dimensions) is not resolved once and for all during the first year of life; it arises again at each successive stage of development. There is both hope and danger in this. The child who enters school with a sense of mistrust may come to trust a particular teacher who has taken the trouble to make herself trustworthy; with this second chance, he overcomes his early mistrust. On the other hand, the child who comes through infancy with a vital sense of trust can still have his sense of mistrust activated at a later stage if, say, his parents are divorced and separated under acrimonious circumstances.

This point was brought home to me in a very direct way by a 4-year-old patient I saw in a court clinic. He was being seen at the court clinic because his adoptive parents, who had had him for six months, now wanted to give him back to the agency. They claimed that he was cold and unloving, took things and could not be trusted. He was indeed a cold and apathetic boy, but with good reason. About a year after his illegitimate birth, he was taken away from his mother, who had a drinking problem, and was shunted back and forth among several foster homes. Initially he had tried to relate to the persons in the foster homes, but the relationships never had a chance to develop becuase he was moved at just the wrong times. In the end he gave up trying to reach out to others, because the inevitable separations hurt too much.

Like the burned child who dreads the flame, this emotionally burned child shunned the pain of emotional involvement. He had trusted his mother, but now he trusted no one. Only years of devoted care and patience could now undo the damage that had been done to this child's sense of trust.

AUTONOMY vs. DOUBT

Stage Two spans the second and third years of life, the period which Freudian theory calls the anal stage. Erikson sees here the emergence of *autonomy*. This autonomy dimension builds upon the child's new motor and mental abilities. At this stage the child can not only walk but also climb, open and close, drop, push and pull, hold and let go. The child takes pride in these new accomplishments and wants to do everything himself, whether it be pulling the wrapper off a piece of candy, selecting the vitamin out of the bottle or flushing the toilet. If parents recognize the young child's need to do what he is capable of doing at his own pace and in his own time, then he develops a sense that he is able to control his muscles, his impulses, himself and, not insignificantly, his environment—the sense of autonomy.

When, however, his caretakers are impatient and do for him what he is capable of doing himself, they reinforce a sense of shame and doubt. To be sure, every parent has rushed a child at times and children are hardy enough to endure such lapses. It is only when caretaking is consistently overprotective and criticism of "accidents" (whether these be wetting, soiling, spilling or breaking things) is harsh and unthinking that the child develops an excessive sense of shame with respect to other people and an excessive sense of doubt about own abilities to control his world and himself.

If the child leaves this stage with less autonomy than shame or doubt, he will be handicapped in his attempts to achieve autonomy in adolescence and adulthood. Contrariwise, the child who moves through this stage with his sense of autonomy buoyantly outbalancing his feelings of shame and doubt is well prepared to be autonomous at later phases in the life cycle. Again, however, the balance of autonomy to shame and doubt

set up during this period can be changed in either positive or negative directions by later events.

It might be well to note, in addition, that too much autonomy can be as harmful as too little. I have in mind a patient of 7 who had a heart condition. He had learned very quickly how terrified his parents were of any signs in him of cardiac difficulty. With the psychological acuity given to children, he soon ruled the household. The family could not go shopping, or for a drive, or on a holiday if he did not approve. On those rare occasions when the parents had had enough and defied him, he would get angry and his purple hue and gagging would frighten them into submission.

Actually, this boy was frightened of this power (as all children would be) and was really eager to give it up. When the parents and the boy came to realize this, and to recognize that a little shame and doubt were a healthy counterpoise to an inflated sense of autonomy, the three of them could once again assume their normal roles.

INITIATIVE vs. GUILT

In this stage (the genital stage of classical psychoanalysis) the child, age 4 to 5, is pretty much master of his body and can ride a tricycle, run, cut and hit. He can thus initiate motor activities of various sorts on his own and no longer merely responds to or imitates the actions of other children. The same holds true for his language and fantasy activities. Accordingly, Erikson argues that the social dimension that appears at this stage has *initiative* at one of its poles and *guilt* at the other.

Whether the child will leave this stage with his sense of initiative far outbalancing his sense of guilt depends to a considerable extent upon how parents respond to his self-initiated activities. Children who are given much freedom and opportunity to initiate motor play such as running, bike riding, sliding, skating, tussling and wrestling have their sense of initiative reinforced. Initiative is also reinforced when parents answer their children's questions (intellectual initiative) and do not deride or inhibit fantasy or play activity. On the other hand, if the child is made to feel that his motor activity is bad, that his questions are a nuisance and that his play is silly and stupid, then he may develop a sense of guilt over self-initiated activities in general that will persist through later life stages.

INDUSTRY vs. INFERIORITY

Stage Four is the age period from 6 to 11, the elementary school years (described by classical psychoanalysis as the *latency phase*). It is a time during which the child's love for the parent of the opposite sex and rivalry with the same sexed parent (elements in the so-called family romance) are quiescent. It is also a period during which the child becomes capable of deductive reasoning, and of playing and learning by rules. It is not until this period, for example, that children can really play marbles, checkers and other "take turn" games that require obedience to rules. Erikson argues that the psychosocial dimension that emerges during this period has a sense of *industry* at one extreme and a sense of *inferiority* at the other.

1. PERSPECTIVES

The term industry nicely captures a dominant theme of this period during which the concern with how things are made, how they work and what they do predominates. It is the Robinson Crusoe age in the sense that the enthusiasm and minute detail with which Crusoe describes his activities appeals to the child's own budding sense of industry. When children are encouraged in their efforts to make, do, or build practical things (whether it be to construct creepy crawlers, tree houses, or airplane models—or to cook, bake or sew), are allowed to finish their products, and are praised and rewarded for the results, then the sense of industry is enhanced. But parents who see their children's efforts at making and doing as "mischief," and as simply "making a mess," help to encourage in children a sense of inferiority.

During these elementary-school years, however, the child's world includes more than the home. Now social institutions other than the family come to play a central role in the developmental crisis of the individual. (Here Erikson introduced still another advance in psychoanalytic theory, which heretofore concerned itself only with the effects of the parents' behavior upon the child's development.)

A child's school experiences affect his industry-inferiority balance. The child, for example, with an I.Q. of 80 to 90 has a particularly traumatic school experience, even when his sense of industry is rewarded and encouraged at home. He is "too bright" to be in special classes, but "too slow" to compete with children of average ability. Consequently he experiences constant failures in his academic efforts that reinforces a sense of inferiority.

On the other hand, the child who had his sense of industry derogated at home can have it revitalized at school through the offices of a sensitive and committed teacher. Whether the child develops a sense of industry or inferiority, therefore, no longer depends solely on the caretaking efforts of the parents but on the actions and offices of other adults as well.

IDENTITY vs. ROLE CONFUSION

When the child moves into adolescence (Stage Five—roughly the ages 12-18), he encounters, according to traditional psychoanalytic theory, a reawakening of the family-romance problem of early childhood. His means of resolving the problem is to seek and find a romantic partner of his own generation. While Erikson does not deny this aspect of adolescence, he points out that there are other problems as well. The adolescent matures mentally as well as physiologically and, in addition to the new feelings, sensations and desires he experiences as a result of changes in his body, he develops a multitude of new ways of looking at and thinking about the world. Among other things, those in adolescence can now think about other people's thinking and wonder about what other people think of them. They can also conceive of ideal families, religions and societies which they then compare with the imperfect families, religions and societies of their own experience. Finally, adolescents become capable of constructing theories and philosophies designed to bring all the varied and conflicting aspects of society into a working, harmonious and peaceful whole. The adolescent, in a word, is an impatient idealist who believes that it is as easy to realize an ideal as it is to imagine it.

Erikson believes that the new interpersonal dimension which emerges during this period has to do with a sense of *ego identity* at the positive end and a sense of *role confusion* at the negative end. That is to say, given the adolescent's newfound integrative abilities, his task is to bring together all of the things he has learned about himself as a son, student, athlete, friend, Scout, newspaper boy, and so on, and integrate these different images of himself into a whole that makes sense and that shows continuity with the past while preparing for the future. To the extent that the young person succeeds in this endeavor, he arrives at a sense of psychosocial identity, a sense of who he is, where he has been and where he is going.

In contrast to the earlier stages, where parents play a more or less direct role in the determination of the result of the developmental crises, the influence of parents during this stage is much more indirect. If the young person reaches adolescence with, thanks to his parents, a vital sense of trust, autonomy, initiative and industry, then his chances of arriving at a meaningful sense of ego identity are much enhanced. The reverse, of course, holds true for the young person who enters adolescence with considerable mistrust, shame, doubt, guilt and inferiority. Preparation for a successful adolescence, and the attainment of an integrated psychosocial identity must, therefore, begin in the cradle.

Over and above what the individual brings with him from his childhood, the attainment of a sense of personal identity depends upon the social milieu in which he or she grows up. For example, in a society where women are to some extent second-class citizens, it may be harder for females to arrive at a sense of psychosocial identity. Likewise at times, such as the present, when rapid social and technological change breaks down many traditional values, it may be more difficult for young people to find continuity between what they learned and experienced as children and what they learn and experience as adolescents. At such times young people often seek causes that give their lives meaning and direction. The activism of the current generation of young people may well stem, in part at least, from this search.

When the young person cannot attain a sense of personal identity, either because of an unfortunate childhood or difficult social circumstances, he shows a certain amount of *role confusion*—a sense of not knowing what he is, where he belongs or whom he belongs to. Such confusion is a frequent symptom in delinquent young people. Promiscuous adolescent girls, for example, often seem to have a fragmented sense of ego identity. Some young people seek a "negative identity," an identity opposite to the one prescribed for them by their family and friends. Having an identity as a "delinquent," or as a "hippie," or even as an "acid head," may sometimes be preferable to having no identity at all.

In some cases young people do not seek a negative identity so much as they have it thrust upon them. I remember another court case in which the defendant was an attractive 16-year-old girl who had been found "tricking it" in a trailer located just outside the grounds of an Air Force base. From about the age of 12, her mother had encouraged her to dress seductively and to go out with boys. When she returned from dates, her sexually frustrated mother demanded a kiss-by-kiss, caress-by-caress description of the evening's activities. After the mother had vicariously satisfied her sexual needs, she proceeded to call her daughter a "whore" and a "dirty tramp."

As the girl told me, "Hell, I have the name, so I might as well play the role."

Failure to establish a clear sense of personal identity at adolescence does not guarantee perpetual failure. And the person who attains a working sense of ego identity in adolescence will of necessity encounter challenges and threats to that identity as he moves through life. Erikson, perhaps more than any other personality theorist, has emphasized that life is constant change and that confronting problems at one stage in life is not a guarantee against the reappearance of these problems at later stages, or against the finding of new solutions to them.

to share and care about another person.

INTIMACY vs. ISOLATION

Stage Six in the life cycle is young adulthood; roughly the period of courtship and early family life that extends from late adolescence till early middle age. For this stage, and the stages described hereafter, classical psychoanalysis has nothing new or major to say. For Erikson, however, the previous attainment of a sense of personal identity and the engagement in productive work that marks this period gives rise to a new interpersonal dimension of *intimacy* at the one extreme and *isolation* at the other.

When Erikson speaks of intimacy he means much more than love-making alone; he means the ability to share with and care about another person without fear of losing oneself in the process. In the case of intimacy, as in the case of identity, success or failure no longer depends directly upon the parents but only indirectly as they have contributed to the individual's success or failure at the earlier stages. Here, too, as in the case of identity, social conditions may help or hinder the establishment of a sense of intimacy. Likewise, intimacy need not involve sexuality; it includes the relationship between friends. Soldiers who have served together under the most dangerous circumstances often develop a sense of commitment to one another that exemplifies intimacy in its broadest sense. If a sense of intimacy is not established with friends or a marriage partner, the result, in Erikson's view, is a sense of isolation—of being alone without anyone to share with or care for.

Concern with other + society

GENERATIVITY vs. SELF-ABSORPTION

This stage—middle age—brings with it what Erikson speaks of as either *generativity or self-absorption,* and stagnation. What Erikson means by generativity is that the person begins to be concerned with others beyond his immediate family, with future generations and the nature of the society and world in which those generations will live. Generativity does not reside only in parents; it can be found in any individual who actively concerns himself with the welfare of young people and with making the world a better place for them to live and to work.

Those who fail to establish a sense of generativity fall into a state of self-absorption in which their personal needs and comforts are of predominant concern. A fictional case of self-absorption is Dickens's Scrooge in "A Christmas Carol." In his one-sided concern with money and in his disregard for the interests and welfare of his young employee, Bob Cratchit, Scrooge exemplifies the self-absorbed, embittered (the two often go together) old man. Dickens also illustrated, however, what Erikson points out: namely, that unhappy solutions to life's crises are not irreversible. Scrooge, at the end of the tale, manifested both a sense of generativity and of intimacy which he had not experienced before.

Previous life
to look back + his life. regrets satisfaction in his life.

INTEGRITY vs. DESPAIR

Stage Eight in the Eriksonian scheme corresponds roughly to the period when the individual's major efforts are nearing completion and when there is time for reflection—and for the enjoyment of grandchildren, if any. The psychosocial dimension that comes into prominence now has *integrity* on one hand and *despair* on the other.

The sense of integrity arises from the individual's ability to look back on his life with satisfaction. At the other extreme is the individual who looks back upon his life as a series of missed opportunities and missed directions; now in the twilight years he realizes that it is too late to start again. For such a person the inevitable result is a sense of despair at what might have been.

These, then, are the major stages in the life cycle as described by Erikson. Their presentation, for one thing, frees the clinician to treat adult emotional problems as failures (in part at least) to solve genuinely adult personality crises and not, as heretofore, as mere residuals of infantile frustrations and conflicts. This view of personality growth, moreover, takes some of the onus off parents and takes account of the role which society and the person himself play in the formation of an individual personality. Finally, Erikson has offered hope for us all by demonstrating that each phase of growth has its strengths as well as its weaknesses and that failures at one stage of development can be rectified by successes at later stages.

The reason that these ideas, which sound so agreeable to "common sense," are in fact so revolutionary has a lot to do with the state of psychoanalysis in America. As formulated by Freud, psychoanalysis encompassed a theory of personality development, a method of studying the human mind and, finally, procedures for treating troubled and unhappy people. Freud viewed this system as a scientific one, open to revision as new facts and observations accumulated.

The system was, however, so vehemently attacked that Freud's followers were constantly in the position of having to defend Freud's views. Perhaps because of this situation, Freud's system became, in the hands of some of his followers and defenders, a dogma upon which all theoretical innovation, clinical observation and therapeutic practice had to be grounded. That this attitude persists is evidenced in the recent remark by a psychoanalyst that he believed psychotic patients could not be treated by psychoanalysis because "Freud said so." Such attitudes, in which Freud's authority rather than observation and data is the basis of deciding what is true and what is false, has contributed to the disrepute in which psychoanalysis is widely held today.

Erik Erikson has broken out of this scholasticism and has had the courage to say that Freud's discoveries and practices were the start and not the end of the study and treatment of the human personality. In addition to advocating the modifications of psychoanalytic theory outlined above, Erikson has also suggested modifications in therapeutic practice, particularly in the treatment of young patients. "Young people in severe trouble are not fit for the couch," he writes. "They want to face you, and they want you to face them, not a facsimile of a parent, or wearing the mask of a professional helper, but as a kind of over-all individual a young person can live with or despair of."

Erikson has had the boldness to remark on some of the negative effects that distorted notions of psychoanalysis have had on society at large. Psychoanalysis, he says, has contributed to a widespread fatalism—"even as we were trying to devise, with scientific determinism, a therapy for the few, we were led to promote an ethical disease among the many."

Perhaps Erikson's innovations in psychoanalytic theory are best exemplified in his psycho-historical writings, in which he combines psychoanalytic insight with a true historical imagination. After the publication of "Childhood and Society," Erikson undertook the application of his scheme of the human life cycle to the study of historical persons. He wrote a series of brilliant essays on men as varied as Maxim Gorky, George Bernard Shaw and Freud himself. These studies were not narrow case histories but rather reflected Erikson's remarkable grasp of Europe's social and political history, as well as of its literature. (His mastery of American folklore, history and literature is equally remarkable.)

While Erikson's major biographical studies were yet to come, these early essays already revealed his unique psycho-history method. For one thing, Erikson always chose men whose lives fascinated him in one way or another, perhaps because of some conscious or unconscious affinity with them. Erikson thus had a sense of community with his subjects which he adroitly used (he calls it *disciplined subjectivity*) to take his subject's point of view and to experience the world as that person might.

Secondly, Erikson chose to elaborate a particular crisis or episode in the individual's life which seemed to crystallize a life-theme that united the activities of his past and gave direction to his activities for the future. Then, much as an artist might, Erikson proceeded to fill in the background of the episode and add social and historical perspective. In a very real sense Erikson's biographical sketches are like paintings which direct the viewer's gaze from a focal point of attention to background and back again, so that one's appreciation of the focal area is enriched by having pursued the picture in its entirety.

This method was given its first major test in Erikson's study of "Young Man Luther." Originally, Erikson planned only a brief study of Luther, but "Luther proved too bulky a man to be merely a chapter in a book." Erikson's involvement with Luther dated from his youth, when, as a wandering artist, he happened to hear the Lord's Prayer in Luther's German. "Never knowingly having heard it, I had the experience, as seldom before or after, of a wholeness captured in a few simple words, of poetry fusing the esthetic and the moral; those who have suddenly 'heard' the Gettysburg Address will know what I mean."

Erikson's interest in Luther may have had other roots as well. In some ways, Luther's unhappiness with the papal intermediaries of Christianity resembled on a grand scale Erikson's own dissatisfaction with the intermediaries of Freud's system. In both cases some of the intermediaries had so distorted the original teachings that what was being preached in the name of the master came close to being the opposite of what he had himself proclaimed. While it is not possible to describe Erikson's treatment of Luther here, one can get some feeling for Erikson's brand of historical analysis from his sketch of Luther:

"Luther was a very troubled and a very gifted young man who had to create his own cause on which to focus his fidelity in the Roman Catholic world as it was then. . . . He first became a monk and tried to solve his scruples by being an exceptionally good monk. But even his superiors thought that he tried much too hard. He felt himself to be such a sinner that he began to lose faith in the charity of God and his superiors told him, 'Look, God doesn't hate you, you hate God or else you would trust Him to accept your prayers.' But I would like to make it clear that someone like Luther becomes a historical person only because he also has an acute understanding of historical actuality and knows how to 'speak to the condition' of his times. Only then do inner struggles become representative of those of a large number of vigorous and sincere young people—and begin to interest some troublemakers and hangers-on."

After Erikson's study of "Young Man Luther" (1958), he turned his attention to "middle-aged" Gandhi. As did Luther, Gandhi evoked for Erikson childhood memories. Gandhi led his first nonviolent protest in India in 1918 on behalf of some mill workers, and Erikson, then a young man of 16, had read glowing accounts of the event. Almost a half a century later Erikson was invited to Ahmedabad, an industrial city in western India, to give a seminar on the human life cycle. Erikson discovered that Ahmedabad was the city in which Gandhi had led the demonstration about which Erikson had read as a youth. Indeed, Erikson's host was none other than Ambalal Sarabahai, the benevolent industrialist who had been Gandhi's host—as well as antagonist—in the 1918 wage dispute. Throughout his stay in Ahmedabad, Erikson continued to encounter people and places that were related to Gandhi's initial experiments with nonviolent techniques.

The more Erikson learned about the event at Ahmedabad, the more intrigued he became with its pivotal importance in Gandhi's career. It seemed to be the historical moment upon which all the earlier events of Gandhi's life converged and from which diverged all of his later endeavors. So captured was Erikson by the event at Ahmedabad, that he returned the following year to research a book on Gandhi in which the event would serve as a fulcrum.

At least part of Erikson's interest in Gandhi may have stemmed from certain parallels in their lives. The 1918 event marked Gandhi's emergence as a national political leader. He was 48 at the time, and had become involved reluctantly, not so much out of a need for power or fame as out of a genuine conviction that something had to be done about the disintegration of Indian culture. Coincidentally, Erikson's book "Childhood and Society," appeared in 1950 when Erikson was 48, and it is that book which brought him national prominence in the mental health field. Like Gandhi, too, Erikson reluctantly did what he felt he had to do (namely, publish his observations and conclusions) for the benefit of his

Erikson in a seminar at his Stockbridge, Mass., home.

"Young analysts are today proclaiming a 'new freedom' to see Freud in historical perspective, which reflects the Eriksonian view that one can recognize Freud's greatness without bowing to conceptual precedent."

ailing profession and for the patients treated by its practitioners. So while Erikson's affinity with Luther seemed to derive from comparable professional identity crises, his affinity for Gandhi appears to derive from a parallel crisis of generativity. A passage from "Gandhi's Truth" (from a chapter wherein Erikson addresses himself directly to his subject) helps to convey Erikson's feeling for his subject.

"So far, I have followed you through the loneliness of your childhood and through the experiments and the scruples of your youth. I have affirmed my belief in your ceaseless endeavor to perfect yourself as a man who came to feel that he was the only one available to reverse India's fate. You experimented with what to you were debilitating temptations and you did gain vigor and agility from your victories over yourself. Your identity could be no less than that of universal man, although you had to become an Indian—and one close to the masses—first."

The following passage speaks to Erikson's belief in the general significance of Gandhi's efforts:

"We have seen in Gandhi's development the strong attraction of one of those more inclusive identities: that of an enlightened citizen of the British Empire. In proving himself willing neither to abandon vital ties to his native tradition nor to sacrifice lightly a Western education which eventually contributed to his ability to help defeat British hegemony—in all of these seeming contradictions Gandhi showed himself on intimate terms with the actualities of his era. For in all parts of the world, the struggle now is for *the anticipatory development of more inclusive identities* ... I submit then, that Gandhi, in his immense intuition for historical actuality and his capacity to assume leadership in 'truth in action,' may have created a ritualization through which men, equipped with both realism and strength, can face each other with mutual confidence."

There is now more and more teaching of Erikson's concepts in psychiatry, psychology, education and social work in America and in other parts of the world. His description of the stages of the life cycle are summarized in major textbooks in all of these fields and clinicians are increasingly looking at their cases in Eriksonian terms.

Research investigators have, however, found Erikson's formulations somewhat difficult to test. This is not surprising, inasmuch as Erikson's conceptions, like Freud's, take into account the infinite complexity of the human personality. Current research methodologies are, by and large, still not able to deal with these complexities at their own level, and distortions are inevitable when such concepts as "identity" come to be defined in terms of responses to a questionnaire.

Likewise, although Erikson's life-stages have an intuitive "rightness" about them, not everyone agrees with his formulations. Douvan and Adelson in their book, "The Adolescent Experience," argue that while his identity theory may hold true for boys, it doesn't for girls. This argument is based on findings which suggest that girls postpone identity consolidation until after marriage (and intimacy) have been established. Such postponement occurs, says Douvan and Adelson, because a woman's identity is partially defined by the identity of the man whom she marries. This view does not really contradict Erikson's, since he recognizes that later events, such as marriage, can help to resolve both current and past developmental crises. For the woman, but not for the man, the problems of identity and intimacy may be solved concurrently.

Objections to Erikson's formulations have come from other directions as well. Robert W. White, Erikson's good friend and colleague at Harvard, has a long standing (and warm-hearted) debate with Erikson over his life-stages. White believes that his own theory of "competence motivation," a theory which has received wide recognition, can account for the phenomena of ego development much more economically than can Erikson's stages. Erikson has, however, little interest in debating the validity of the stages he has described. As an artist he recognizes that there are many different ways to view one and the same phenomenon and that a perspective that is congenial to one person will be repugnant to another. He offers his stage-wise description of the life cycle for those who find such perspectives congenial and not as a world view that everyone should adopt.

It is this lack of dogmatism and sensitivity to the diversity and complexity of the human personality which help to account for the growing recognition of Erikson's contribution within as well as without the helping professions. Indeed, his psycho-historical investigations have originated a whole new field of study which has caught the interest of historians and political scientists alike. (It has also intrigued his wife, Joan, who has published pieces on Eleanor Roosevelt and who has a book on Saint Francis in press.) A recent issue of Daedalus, the journal for the American Academy of Arts and Sciences, was entirely devoted to psycho-historical and psycho-political investigations of creative leaders by authors from diverse disciplines who have been stimulated by Erikson's work.

Now in his 68th year, Erikson maintains the pattern of multiple activities and appointments which has characterized his entire career. He spends the fall in Cambridge, Mass., where he teaches a large course on "the human life cycle" for Harvard seniors. The spring semester is spent at his home in Stockbridge, Mass., where he participates in case conferences and staff seminars at the Austen Riggs Center. His summers are spent on Cape Cod. Although Erikson's major commitment these days is to his psycho-historical investigation, he is embarking on a study of preschool children's play constructions in different settings and countries, a follow-up of some research he conducted with preadolescents more than a quarter-century ago. He is also planning to review other early observations in the light of contemporary change. In his approach to his work, Erikson appears neither drawn nor driven, but rather to be following an inner schedule as natural as the life cycle itself.

Although Erikson, during his decade of college teaching, has not seen any patients or taught at psychoanalytic institutes, he maintains his dedication to psychoanalysis and views his psycho-historical investigations as an applied branch of that discipline. While some older analysts continue to ignore Erikson's work, there is increasing evidence (including a recent poll of psychiatrists and psychoanalysts) that he is having a rejuvenating influence upon a discipline which many regard as dead or dying. Young analysts are today proclaiming a "new freedom" to see Freud in historical perspective—which reflects the Eriksonian view that one can recognize Freud's greatness without bowing to conceptual precedent.

Accordingly, the reports of the demise of psychoanalysis may have been somewhat premature. In the work of Erik Erikson, at any rate, psychoanalysis lives and continues to beget life.

Freud's "Ages of Man"

Erik Erikson's definition of the "eight ages of man" is a work of synthesis and insight by a psychoanalytically trained and worldly mind. Sigmund Freud's description of human phases stems from his epic psychological discoveries and centers almost exclusively on the early years of life. A brief summary of the phases posited by Freud:

Oral stage—roughly the first year of life, the period during which the mouth region provides the greatest sensual satisfaction. Some derivative behavioral traits which may be seen at this time are *incorporativeness* (first six months of life) and *aggressiveness* (second six months of life).

Anal stage—roughly the second and third years of life. During this period the site of greatest sensual pleasure shifts to the anal and urethral areas. Derivative behavioral traits are *retentiveness* and *expulsiveness*.

Phallic stage—roughly the third and fourth years of life. The site of greatest sensual pleasure during this stage is the genital region. Behavior traits derived from this period include *intrusiveness* (male) and *receptiveness* (female).

Oedipal stage—roughly the fourth and fifth years of life. At this stage the young person takes the parent of the opposite sex as the object or provider of sensual satisfaction and regards the same-sexed parent as a rival. (The "family romance.") Behavior traits originating in this period are *seductiveness* and *competitiveness*.

Latency stage—roughly the years from age 6 to 11. The child resolves the Oedipus conflict by identifying with the parent of the opposite sex and by so doing satisfies sensual needs vicariously. Behavior traits developed during this period include *conscience* (or the internalization of parental moral and ethical demands).

Puberty stage—roughly 11 to 14. During this period there is an integration and subordination of oral, anal and phallic sensuality to an overriding and unitary genital *sexuality.* The genital sexuality of puberty has another young person of the opposite sex as its object, and discharge (at least for boys) as its aim. Derivative behavior traits (associated with the control and regulation of genital sexuality) are *intellectualization* and *estheticism.*

—D.E.

American Research on the Family and Socialization

John A. Clausen

John A. Clausen, Ph.D., is chairman, Department of Sociology, University of California, Berkeley, and research sociologist at the university's Institute of Human Development. His article is based on an address delivered at the US-USSR Seminar on Preschool Education in Moscow, U.S.S.R.

The family is a basic unit of social organization in all societies. However, its composition, the functions that it serves, the division of labor within it and the allocation of its resources vary greatly from one society to another. Anthropologists, sociologists, psychologists, educators, psychiatrists, historians and political scientists have all been active in family research in the United States. They seek to answer many questions, but one focal point for almost all is how the family orients a child to the world and how it prepares him or her for full participation in society, what we commonly call *socialization*—the whole process of the child's becoming a competent member of society.

There are several approaches to studying the family as an instrument of socialization. The family is, first of all, a context or matrix for development, set in the larger social environments of the neighborhood, the culture of which it is part and the social structure, including the economic and political systems.

The family has been characterized as a unit of interacting personalities, though it has been peculiarly difficult to conceptualize that unity in operational terms. Studies of the effect of family context on child development tend therefore to focus on structural features—the size and composition of the family, the partial or total absence of a parent (usually the father, since families without mothers tend to be seen as non-families)—or they focus on salient experiences or conditions such as economic deprivation, conflict between parents or the effects of life crises. In such research the investigator may seek (1) to delineate the ways in which socialization practices are influenced by the family's structural features or conditions of life or (2) to show that outcomes in child behavior are directly responsive to these features or conditions.

Related to the study of general features of the family as they affect the development of the child are those studies that ask how placement of the family in the larger social structure or cultural milieu influences the childrearing orientations and behaviors of parents and other agents of socialization. Social class and religious and ethnic background have been most utilized as indices of placement but features of parents' occupational experiences have also been examined recently.

Another type of investigation examines the ways in which particular orientations toward childrearing and the actual practices of parents impinge upon a child. The majority of psychologists' studies of childrearing are of this type. They seek to learn how particular modes of parental control, techniques of reward and punishment, communication patterns and the like influence a child and his cognitive, emotional and social development and competence. For the most part, the technique of analysis is correlational, seeking to relate current parental practices to a child's current behaviors. In a few instances, longitudinal studies make it possible to trace relationships between early parental behaviors and later child outcomes.

Each student of the family is influenced by the perspective and preoccupations of his own discipline. I shall comment on a number of trends in American research that seem to me both interesting and significant; as a sociologist I shall stress studies of contextual and structural features more than studies seeking to delineate relationships between specific parental practices and child behavior.

Interest in the history of the family and of childrearing has increased enormously in the past decade, with younger historians playing a leading role. Although historical studies can tell us little about childrearing in the distant past, they have called into question earlier assumptions about the family. For example, they have demonstrated a distinct difference between the household and the family as social units in pre-industrial Europe and North America. They indicate also the greater prevalence of the nuclear family of parents and their unmarried offspring than had previously been suspected. Moreover, studies using materials available in local archives which reflect life in the past century or two do permit reconstruction of the family life course in ways that illuminate the developmental experiences of children.[1]

Another area of family research that has implications for child socialization, though not directly concerned with it, relates to the correlates and consequences of age at marriage (especially the consequences of early marriage and of pregnancies of teenagers) and to decisions about childbearing and the spacing of pregnancies. Early marriages tend to be less stable and a substantial body of research now attests to the undesirable consequences of teenage pregnancy for both mother and child.

1. PERSPECTIVES

Social Change

Social change has continued to impinge sharply on the American family. During the past decade we have witnessed an increase by one-third in the proportion of women who remain single to age 25, along with a marked decrease in the average number of children born in a family.[2] The number of working mothers has more than doubled since the end of World War II—and half of all mothers of school-aged children are now in the labor force.

Working mothers of preschool children turn where they can to a variety of child care arrangements, formal and informal. In 1974, for example, approximately 1.3 million children were in licensed or approved day care centers or in family day care, 1.7 million were in informal out-of-home care and nearly 5 million were in nursery school or pre-kindergarten programs (about three-quarters of them part-time).[3] The care received in full-time day care centers has varied greatly; research on the effects of substitute care in some of the better centers suggests few differences between children reared at home and those raised in group care settings, but many day care centers, especially proprietary centers conducted for profit, give care that can only be rated "fair" or "poor."[4]

As the rate of marriage has declined, the rate of divorce has increased at all class levels. The number of single-parent families (most often a mother and young children) has nearly doubled in a decade, as a consequence both of increasing divorce on the part of parents of young children and a rise in illegitimacy, largely accounted for by adolescent pregnancies. The very strong movement for increased rights and equal treatment for women, both in and out of the home, has undoubtedly played a part in these trends.

Household size has steadily decreased over recent decades, as more housing has become available. Alternate living arrangements as opposed to the traditional family household are on the increase. In the decade of the 1960s there was an eightfold increase in the number of household heads who live apart from relatives but share their living quarters with an adult partner of the opposite sex. Communal living arrangements of groups of adults and children have also increased. In such households children tend to be warmly loved and well cared for in the early years but not to be much supervised as they grow older.[5]

Research on the effects of these changes is still very limited. There have been a number of studies which examined the effects of the presence or absence of a parent on the child's development. Most frequently, of course, it is the father who is absent. A very careful review on the topic of "Children in Fatherless Families" concludes that there is little solid evidence that mere absence of the father produces serious distortion in the child's cognitive and emotional development or gender identity.[6] In general, the way in which a mother functions with her children is far more important than the number of adults in the household. At the same time, there can be no question but that a mother who must cope alone with problems of household and income maintenance faces a much more stressful situation than one who can count on a husband's help. Much depends on the kind of child care arrangements that can be made if the mother works, and on the mother's ability to arrange some time for relaxed enjoyment of her children. Perhaps the most consistent finding relating to the effect of father absence on children's cognitive development is that boys from such families tend to have higher verbal than mathematical skills, a reversal of normal expectation when both parents are present.

More important than his mere presence or absence is the actual role of the father in the socialization of a child. Although fathers were long neglected by students of child development, they are now being studied increasingly. Indeed, several recent books are devoted entirely to the father's role in childrearing, drawing on considerable research evidence.[7] The father is important not only as a role model for the child and a source of emotional support and childrearing partner to the mother but also as a source of orientation to that segment of the culture shared by males. The father also plays an important part in the establishment and maintenance of the set of standards and values that provides the moral climate of a family. This role may be filled by others, as can the emotional support role, but there is increasing evidence that both mothers and children benefit markedly from a father's active participation in child care.

Social Class and Socialization

It is 20 years since Urie Bronfenbrenner published his analysis of "Socialization and Social Class Through Time and Space," showing evidence that in some respects, at least, the social classes were moving closer together in their childrearing practices.[8] Social class has continued to be a major variable in examining not only parental practices but general orientations toward childrearing, contexts of development and transitions such as those to school and work. Two decades ago Daniel Miller and Guy Swanson examined differences among families classified not only on the basis of social class but also on the setting of the father's occupation, whether "entrepreneurial" or within a large bureaucratic organization.[9]

More recently, Melvin Kohn, building upon the insights of Marx and Weber, has attempted to analyze how the conditions of occupational life affect the psyche, values and childrearing orientations of American parents.[10] In his early work, Kohn demonstrated that middle-class parents are more likely than working-class parents to want their children to be considerate of others, intellectually curious, responsible and self-controlled, while working-class parents are more likely to want their children to have good manners, to do well in school and to be obedient. Thus the middle-class parent tends to put emphasis upon self-direction for the child, the working-class parent to place a higher value on conformity. But Kohn does not stop at social class. He is able to demonstrate that fathers whose jobs entail self-direction—who are not closely supervised, who work with ideas rather than things, and who face great complexity on the job—value self-direction in their children, while those whose work requires them to conform to close supervision and a highly structured work situation are more likely to want their children to be conforming.

Categorization by social class, as used in American research, rests largely on educational attainment and occupational status. So measured, social class indexes a whole host of differences in life experiences, among them the type of housing occupied and the neighborhood of residence, the role differentiation between the parents, the fluency of language usage in the family, tendencies toward concrete versus abstract verbal expression and thought and the breadth of social participation of the parents. Under these circumstances, to know that various aspects of child development are associated with social class is merely to reiterate that life style and life chances are markedly influenced by a family's place in the social structure. Many efforts are now being directed to delineating the specific mechanisms by which such effects are mediated, since childrearing practices are associated with, but by no means wholly determined by, class position.[11]

Much recent research focuses on the development of competence in the child. In general, the competent child is characterized as self-reliant, self-controlled and uninhibited in his relationships with others but not overly aggressive or demanding. Competence obviously entails the development of cognitive, physical and social skills as well as emotional control. Parental warmth and encouragement coupled with parental control seem to be essential ingredients in the production of competent children, but it appears that the combinations of parental acceptance and control appropriate for producing competent young children differ for boys and girls. For the induction of competence away from home in children of preschool age, recent research indicates that neither the affectionate and permissive parent nor the cold, authoritarian parent is as effective as the parent who combines affection with strict control and yet encourages joint discussion of family-related issues.[12]

Another topic which has received a great deal of attention in the past decade is the nature and explanation of sex differences in personality and performance. A recent assessment of available research evidence demonstrates that many of the widely held beliefs about sex differences are simply not substantiated. For example, the long-standing belief that girls are more "social," more "suggestible" and have lower achievement motivation than boys, or that girls are better at rote learning and simple repetitive tasks while boys are better at those that require a higher level of cognitive processing—all these have been disproven by systematic research.[13] A few sex differences seem more firmly established: that girls have greater verbal ability than boys, that boys excel in mathematical ability and in visual-spatial ability beyond age 12, and that males are more aggressive.

Differences in parental response to girls and boys seem to increase as children grow older and to be greater in the case of fathers than in that of mothers, but studies bearing directly on sex-differentiated responses of fathers or of either parent toward older children are relatively rare. Recent research on the interactions of

biological and social systems suggests that parenting behaviors are more influenced by biology than some celebrants of unisex would like to believe; in particular, hormonally related responsiveness of mothers to infants seems firmly established.[14]

The fact that boys and girls are responded to quite differently by their parents in all known societies cannot be unimportant in leading to typical patternings in the development of the sexes. Since parents are often unaware of the ways in which their behaviors differ, however, observational studies of the actual behaviors of the parents toward boys and girls are needed to supplement interview materials. Such research is now going on, and, indeed, a major development in recent socialization research has been the turn to painstaking observation in place of or as a supplement to interviewing.

Methodological advances include the systematic assessment of bias and unreliability when retrospective data are obtained on early family experiences and childrearing practices; the development of observational techniques and category systems for use in both naturalistic and laboratory settings; and the utilization of short-term longitudinal studies of over-lapping cohorts in order to differentiate cohort effects—that is, the effects of particular historical events or social changes—from the effects of age.[15]

Studies by anthropologists continue to increase our knowledge of the ways in which very different social structural arrangements and cultural themes influence childrearing. Especially influential here has been the work of Beatrice and John Whiting in their studies of six different cultures.[16] Their publications have focused successively on the cultures and their general patterns of childrearing, on mothers and their behaviors (with some examination of fathers' roles as well) and on the children themselves. It should be noted that attempts to delineate modal personality types in various cultures or nations has been largely abandoned. Efforts are rather concentrated on delineating the specific linkages between features of the basic maintenance systems of societies, household composition, parental practices and child behaviors.

The anthropological perspective leads naturally to a consideration of the family as a whole. The family is an organized unit, one that functions through ongoing transactions among members and between the family and the larger community. What attributes of that unit as a whole best index its effects on the development of children? Past research leaves much to be desired, but the following are surely among those important features of families that are associated with favorable child development in the United States: harmony rather than conflict between parents; equality of authority or at most modest differences in parental power and authority; clearly patterned, mutually acceptable procedures for dealing with important problems and decisions; involvement of the child in decisions affecting him or her, as appropriate to the child's age; and accurate labeling of feelings and intentions in communication within the family.

The study of communication processes in the family has been of particular interest to workers in the field of psychiatric disorders. Parents in families with a schizophrenic child, in particular, have been found to "mislabel" their emotions and actions, to have difficulty in achieving a shared focus of attention, to disqualify their own utterances, and to maintain shared fictions about the family as a unit.[17] There is much evidence to suggest a genetic component in schizophrenia, but since fewer than half of identical twins are concordant for schizophrenia, experiential features are probably involved as well.

We are now beginning to get much more systematic research on communication processes in normal families, usually involving the observation of the family in a laboratory situation but occasionally entailing videotaping in the home.[18] It is not yet clear what the major correlates and consequences of communication deviance are, but the field seems a promising one. For example, observational studies of parent-child interaction in the home suggest that very low levels of communication from mother to child are involved in instances of markedly retarded language development.[19]

The ways in which illness or psychopathology of a parent impinge upon the child in other respects, particularly as threatening behaviors or child neglect are entailed, are also under investigation in many places. Mental illness may go unnoted and untreated, often leading to conflict between parents and feelings of abandonment by the child.[20]

Long-term longitudinal studies continue to add to our knowledge of socialization in the family. Two major contributions have come from the Institute of Human Development at Berkeley, which has for more than 40 years followed several hundred study members born in the 1920s. Jack Block and Norma Haan have examined continuities and discontinuities in personality from the pre-adolescent years to the late thirties[21] Parental warmth, acceptance and stability tend to affect the child's development and performance at all age levels, but there is much personality change well beyond childhood. Some study members who had unhappy childhoods and showed serious problems in adolescence nevertheless arrived at age 40 competent and self-accepting. Others who gave early promise have had a more problematic time in middle age.

A recent book by Glen Elder traces the effects of economic deprivation during the depression of the 1930s upon the lives of the then pre-adolescent study members.[22] The boys, in particular, appear to have been challenged by the dismal experiences of their families and many rose to the challenge by taking on part-time jobs to help their parents. Girls, on the other hand, were more largely pushed into help with domestic chores. Not accidentally, the birth cohort to which these women belong has been the most home-oriented of any in recent decades.

In conclusion, the family mediates between the larger community and its demands and the developing child. It is responsive to the conditions of life in the society, to economic conditions, wars, and to natural catastrophes that from time to time afflict all societies. A major thrust in interdisciplinary studies now in process is to seek to trace the effects of such family adaptations upon the child.

[1]See, for example, the papers prepared for a workshop, "The Family Life Course in Historical Perspective," published in Volume I of the newly founded *Journal of Family History* (Winter 1977).
[2]See Arthur J. Norton and Paul C. Glick, "Changes in American Family Life," *CHILDREN TODAY*, May-June 1976 and Urie Bronfenbrenner, "The Challenge of Social Change to Public Policy and Developmental Research," paper presented at the President's Symposium, "Child Development and Public Policy," at the Annual Meeting of the Society for Research in Child Development, Denver, April 1975.
[3]See *Toward A National Policy for Children and Families,* Report of the Advisory Committee on Child Development, National Academy of Sciences, Washington, D.C., 1976.
[4]*Ibid,* Appendix: "Research on the Effects of Day Care on Child Development." See also Mary Keyserling, *Windows on Day Care,* National Council of Jewish Women, New York, 1972.

ACYF Family Research

In 1974 the Office of Child Development—now the Administration for Children, Youth and Families—began a 5-part research effort centering on the family as a focal point for research bearing on child development. During the first two phases of the effort, ACYF supported research projects which looked at child development within different types of families—among them, one-parent families, minority families, low-income families and families in which both parents work. Research projects also examined the interaction of families with community services, schools and other institutions. Television was studied both within the family system and as part of the institutional system.

Now, in the third phase, ACYF is supporting pilot studies to test the kinds of changes in services and interventions needed to enhance child development and improve interaction between families and institutions. Full-scale demonstrations of promising programs will be supported in the next phase.

Finally, the knowledge derived from these and other studies will be used to design new programs and policies to meet the needs of children and families and to provide guidance for existing ACYF programs.

ACYF is also funding a series of projects which will look at ways to communicate scientific knowledge about child development to different types of families, examine the kinds of information that families have and need on child development and its impact on childrearing and study ways to make information on supportive services more accessible.

In addition, the Children's Bureau, ACYF, supports demonstration projects that are attempting to prevent foster placement of children by providing comprehensive services to families under stress. The use of social service contracts between agencies and families to improve case planning is being tested in other projects.

Demonstration projects that provide comprehensive services to abused and neglected children and their families, and research projects that are exploring factors contributing to child abuse and neglect and promising prevention and treatment techniques are supported by the National Center on Child Abuse and Neglect in the Children's Bureau.

[5] See, for example, Bennett M. Berger and Bruce M. Hackett, "On the Decline of Age Grading in Rural Hippie Communes," *Journal of Social Issues,* Volume 30, No. 2, 1974; also J. Rothchild and S. B. Wolf, *Children of the Counterculture,* New York, Doubleday, 1976.

[6] Elizabeth Herzog and Cecelia E. Sudia, "Children in Fatherless Families," in *Review of Child Development Research,* Volume 3, edited by Bettye M. Caldwell and Henry N. Riccuti, Chicago, University of Chicago Press, 1973.

[7] For example, David B. Lynn, *The Father: His Role in Child Development,* Belmont, California, Wadsworth, 1974; Michael E. Lamb (ed.), *The Role of the Father in Child Development,* New York, Wiley, 1976.

[8] Urie Bronfenbrenner, "Socialization and Social Class Through Time and Space," in *Readings in Social Psychology,* E. E. Maccoby, T. M. Newcomb and E. L. Hartley (eds.), New York, Holt, Rinehart and Winston, 1958.

[9] Daniel R. Miller and Guy E. Swanson, *The Changing American Parent: A Study in the Detroit Area,* New York, Wiley, 1958.

[10] Melvin L. Kohn, *Class and Conformity: A Study in Values,* Second edition, Chicago, University of Chicago Press, 1977.

[11] The evidence is summarized in Alan C. Kerchkoff, *Socialization and Social Class,* Englewood Cliffs, New Jersey, Prentice Hall, 1972.

[12] See Diana Baumrind, "The Development of Instrumental Competence Through Socialization," *Minnesota Symposium on Child Psychology,* Anne Pick (ed.), Minneapolis, University of Minnesota Press, 1973.

[13] Eleanor E. Maccoby and Carol N. Jacklin, *The Psychology of Sex Differences,* Stanford, California, Stanford University Press, 1974. A critical evaluation of the shortcomings of existing evidence is provided by Jeanne Block in "Another Look at Sex Differentiation in the Socialization Behaviors of Mothers and Fathers," to be published in *Psychology of Women: Future Directions for Research,* New York, Psychological Dimensions, Inc., 1978.

[14] See Alice S. Rossi, "A Biosocial Perspective on Parenting," *Daedalus,* Spring 1977.

[15] Marian Radke Yarrow *et al.,* "Recollections of Childhood: A Study of the Retrospective Method," *Monographs of the Society for Research in Child Development,* Volume 35, No. 5, 1970. The work of Baumrind, referred to in note 12, is illustrative of developments in observational methods. Issues of cohort and longitudinal analysis are dealt with in John R. Nesselroade and H. W. Reese, *Life Span Developmental Psychology: Methodological Issues,* New York, Academic Press, 1973.

[16] See Beatrice Whiting (ed.), *Six Cultures: Studies of Child Rearing,* New York, Wiley, 1963; Leigh Minturn and W. W. Lambert, *Mothers of Six Cultures: Antecedents of Child Rearing,* New York, Wiley, 1964; and B. B. and J. M. Whiting, *Children of Six Cultures: A Psychocultural Analysis,* Cambridge, Mass., Harvard University Press, 1975.

[17] Some of the research relating to schizophrenia is reported in David Rosenthal and Seymour Kety (eds.), *The Transmission of Schizophrenia,* London, Pergammon Press, 1968. (See especially Part III, "Social, Cultural and Interpersonal Studies.")

[18] A more general review of studies of communication in the family is given by Theodore Jacob, "Family Interaction in Disturbed and Normal Families: A Methodological and Substantive Review," *Psychological Bulletin,* January 1975.

[19] Margaret Wulbert *et al.,* "Language Delay and Associated Mother-Child Interactions," *Developmental Psychology,* January 1975.

[20] Several studies examining such effects are contained in *The Child in His Family,* edited by E. James Anthony and C. Koupernik, New York, Wiley, 1970. See also J. Clausen and C. Huffine, "The Impact of Parental Mental Illness on the Children," in *Research on Community and Mental Health,* Roberta Simmons (ed.), Greenwich, Conn., JAI Press. (To be published in 1978.)

[21] Jack Block and Norma Haan, *Lives Through Time,* Berkeley, California, Bancroft Press, 1972.

[22] Glen H. Elder, Jr., *Children of the Great Depression,* Chicago, University of Chicago Press, 1974.

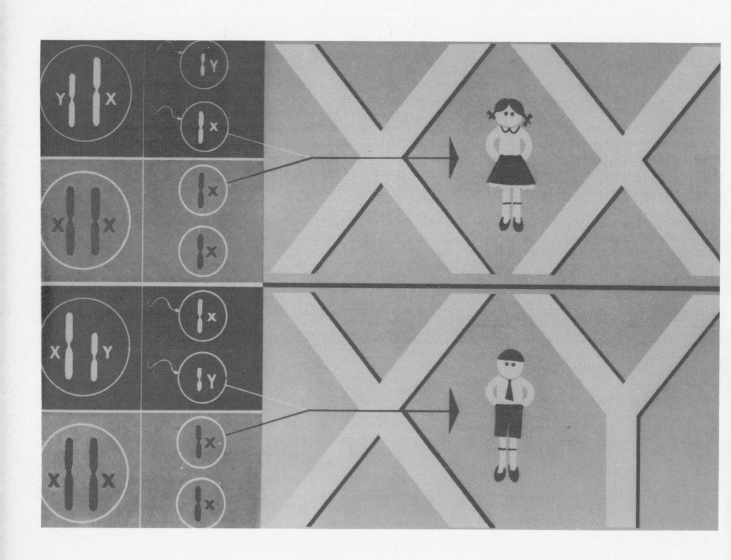

Development During the Prenatal Period

The months of prenatal development are subdivided into three major periods: zygote (conception to two weeks), embryo (two to eight weeks), and fetus (eight weeks to term). Major events of the period of the zygote include reduplication of cells and implantation of the zygote into the uterine lining. The period of the embryo is characterized by differentiation of the physical structures from three embryonic layers. For example, the nervous system differentiates from the ecotoderm, the circulatory system from the mesoderm, and the gastrointestinal tract from endoderm. During the period of the fetus the organism gains weight and undergoes rapid changes in brain growth and development.

During each of the periods of prenatal development the conceptus is vulnerable to a variety of environmental stresses. Factors such as infectious disease, malnutrition, blood incompatibility, drugs, radiation, parental age, maternal emotional state, and environmental toxins can compromise the intrauterine environment and interfere with normal pathways of development. In addition, a variety of hereditary and non-hereditary genetic factors can place the conceptus at risk for death or disability.

Recent technological advances have led to the development of a variety of techniques for assessing the developmental status of the prenatal organism. Whereas each of these techniques contributes to a more complete assessment of the structural and biological viability of the conceptus, each technique also raises ethical and moral problems concerning decisions to retain or abort the conceptus. If one knows by the second or third prenatal month that the conceptus is at risk for a handicapping condition, does one choose to terminate pregnancy or allow it to continue to term? For some individuals the question of abortion is easily resolved by appeal to some higher ethical or theological dictum. For many other individuals, however, the question has no easy solution. It is certain, though, that as biomedical technology continues to accelerate, still newer and more precise methods will be developed to evaluate the status of the conceptus. Certainly ethical issues are not restricted to the question of abortion. They also come up with respect to premature birth. Thirty years ago, prematurity generally referred to infants born no more than about 2-3 months prior to the expected date, and those infants less than 7 months gestational age had very little chance of surviving. Today, premature infants as small as 600 grams and just a few months gestational age are brought to term with the assistance of biomedical technology. Caregiving intervention, however, has not kept pace with biomedical technology, and as a result the caregiving that many prematurely born infants receive is not equal in quality to that offered by life-sustaining technology. Moreover, we have no knowledge of the possible long-term consequences of such birth. It is clear, however, that without modern biomedical technology infants weighing less than 2500 grams are at increased risk for death or disability and those below 1500 grams are at greatest risk.

The articles in this section introduce the reader to many of the discoveries that have been made regarding ways to evaluate the biological status of the preterm organism, as well as the consequences of preterm birth for the infant and for infant-caregiver interaction.

Looking Ahead: Challenge Questions

Who should have the final word on whether the fetus should be aborted or brought to term? Mother? Father? Priest? Legislator? Physician?

How might the delivery process itself impose risk factors on the newborn? When you sign papers in the hospital authorizing the use of obstetrical medications during delivery, do you really understand what you are signing?

What guidelines would you develop to assist decision making regarding the question of abortion? What are the legal implications of your guidelines?

What changes in the hospital management of the preterm infant would you recommend in order to prevent poor caregiver-infant relationships that often are associated with premature birth?

Hereditary Constitution and Individual Life

Clifford Grobstein

Clifford Grobstein is professor of biology and of biological science and public policy at the University of California, San Diego. He is the author of A Double Image of the Double Helix *and* From Chance to Purpose: An Appraisal of External Human Fertilization.

The "time of origin of human life" has become an issue in the United States as part of a continuing national and worldwide controversy over abortion. The same issue has been discussed in relation to the procedure for external (in vitro) human fertilization, a process that has now yielded more than half a dozen births (including a pair of twins) in England, India, Australia, and the United States. In connection with external human fertilization, the issue is one of a number raised by our increasing capability to intervene in reproductive processes, including both heredity and development, a capability that could have profound implications if widely applied to the human species.

The Supreme Court, in its landmark decision in *Roe v. Wade,* said the following: "We need not resolve the difficult question of when life begins. When those trained in the respective disciplines of medicine, philosophy and theology are unable to arrive at any consensus, the judiciary at this point in the development of man's knowledge is not in a position to speculate." The Court thus abstained on a central issue, while asserting the primacy of a woman's right of choice at least through the second trimester of pregnancy. In so doing it left open the status of a human embryo developing externally for several days or more.

Senate Bill 158, the subject of hearings in the Subcommittee on the Separation of Powers of the Senate Judiciary Committee, stipulates that "the Congress finds that present day scientific evidence indicates a significant likelihood that human life exists from conception." Commenting on the bill, a National Academy of Sciences resolution of April 28, 1981, asserts that this statement "cannot stand up to the scrutiny of science." It "purports to derive its conclusions from science, but it deals with a question to which *science can provide no answer.*" The Academy statement further asserts that "The proposal in S.158 that the term 'person' shall include 'all human life' has no basis within our scientific understanding. Defining the time at which the developing embryo becomes a 'person' must remain a matter of moral or religious values." The Academy, like the Court, thus abstains on the same central issue.

Given these patently conflicting and confusing statements on a profoundly important issue, it is essential to summarize what developmental science does and does not know about the onset of human life:

- No form of life begins in each generation; rather, life is continuous on the contemporary earth; it is all descended from pre-existing life. Life is transmitted, not initiated, as new generations arise.
- This is true of human life. The egg and sperm that unite in fertilization are themselves living, human cells, as were their precursors in the parental bodies. Their union does not initiate human life but continues it. The humanness and vitality of eggs and sperm are not readily apparent to casual observation, but they are readily demonstrable scientifically.
- This means that fertilization is not "when life begins"; it is a particularly significant stage in its continuity.
- What fertilization does initiate is a new generation. There are two aspects of this initiation. The first is that fertilization activates the egg to continue development, and it is in development that a new individual is generated. The second aspect is that as a result of fertilization the fusion-cell carries hereditary contributions from two members of the preceding generation, borne in the egg and sperm and combined when they fuse.
- The fusion-product is thus hereditarily new. It is not yet, however, a new individual in the developmental sense. Its genetic difference from either parent makes it a new generation, one with a unique set of properties derived in complex ways from those of its parents. However, it is not yet a new stable biological entity or individual, because depending upon circumstance it can yield less than a complete individual or more than one individual. For example, in mice, it yields less than one individual when embryos are fused at the 4-cell stage to yield a single

individual whose cells are descendant from both donor embryos. When the donor embryos have different hereditary constitutions—for example, coat color—both colors are represented in the mosaic product. On the other hand, a fusion-cell yields more than one individual in human identical twinning, when a single fertilized egg gives rise to two individuals with the same hereditary constitution.

■ The product of fertilization, up to at least the 8-cell stage, is a cluster of individual cells equivalent in developmental capacity. Deletion or addition of cells, or exchange among them even between embryos, does not disturb the later production of a single complete normal individual. Therefore, both the fusion-cell and its early products exist as individual cells and are not yet integrated parts of a multicellular organism. This non-integrated state persists for at least several days beyond fertilization. The cells then become more closely adherent and more difficult to separate. This process of compaction may begin the transition to a multicellular entity.

■ However, it is not until several days later that the first precursor of the actual embryo (inner cell mass) is distinguishable from the outer cells that give rise not to parts of the embryo but to the supportive and protective extra-embryonic membranes. At about two weeks after fertilization, when the developing embryo is embedded in the uterine wall, there is evidence that twinning can still occur through splitting of the inner cell mass. Full singleness of an individual, therefore, has not yet been stabilized even at this point.

Developmental Stages

The language of S.158 must be examined in the light of these six statements. The bill states that "present day scientific evidence indicates a significant likelihood that *actual* human life exists from conception." Human life does exist at conception, but it also exists before it. What the word *actual* is intended to convey is not obvious. If it is intended to mean that a new individual exists, it is correct only in the sense of a new hereditary constitution. But the particular hereditary constitution can later be expressed, as has been noted, in less than one individual or more than one. As it exists in a fertilized egg, however, the new hereditary program can only give rise to a new "actual" (recognizable) individual through the complex translations and transformations of development. It would be a return to the naive and rejected preformationism of more than a century ago to assume that hereditary constitution is itself equivalent to its expressed developmental product before development even begins.

The new generation in a hereditary sense is not yet stabilized as a single multicellular individual even two weeks after fertilization. We do not know exactly when

in the later course of human development this stabilization occurs. Information on animals implies that it probably is not many days beyond two weeks. But the development from the fertilized egg to this critical new multicellular individual state clearly is gradual and involves several transitions. No single moment or event appears to mark its initiation. Rather it emerges gradually in the post-fertilization process as an important new property that is *added* to those of life and humanness.

With that property, a living human multicellular individual in the biological sense has come into existence. This is not, however, a biologically mature individual and certainly not a socially mature one. It is, in fact, unrecognizable by the usual criteria by which we identify another member of our species. However, assuming a normal developmental course, an implanted individual of this early stage is now very likely to become a recognizable human being or person. It is this undefined quality of imminent human status about which the emotional abortion controversy rages.

Individuality, in the biological sense so far discussed, unquestionably is one of the essential characteristics of human beings or persons. The full expression of individuality in persons, however, includes many other important characteristics—including bodily and facial features, functional activities, particular behaviors, the sense of inner awareness of identity or self, and the capacity to evoke recognition and empathy in other selves. The first three categories, like biological oneness, can be traced scientifically and are found to arise gradually during the subsequent developmental course. For example, there is no recognizable body form at two weeks, but there clearly is at eight weeks.

Concerning the category of inner awareness or self, there is less certainty because there is limited scientific knowledge about the processes and mechanisms of inner awareness even at times when it is generally accepted as present. The general social and legal problem that is posed is whether to define some stage or minimal set of characteristcs that will confer full personhood in one step (e.g., fertilization, implantation, respiratory autonomy or birth) or to define successive stages or sets of characteristics that will provide steps in a gradual conferral of personhood. It is not the business or ability of science by itself to settle this question because the concept of a person is so intimately intertwined with individual and social values. Science can, however, lend support to the effort by clarifying characteristics that can be objectively identified, specified, and measured, and by clearly explaining what is known about their underlying nature and origins.

Important to the process of definition of such stages and steps is clear articulation of the intended uses of the definitions. The relevance of purpose to definition can be made more clear by a crude analogy. Airline schedules make definite statements about the departure times of flights. Flights rarely, if ever, leave before the scheduled time because passengers who arrive on time must not be left behind. For passenger purposes the departure time, therefore, is the scheduled time. However, flights sometimes are delayed. The passenger agent cannot leave his or her post so long as any additional passengers may be put on board. For the purposes of the passenger agent, the departure time is when the airplane door is finally closed, usually at least a little later than the scheduled time. However, in these days of air traffic congestion and expensive fuel, flights sometimes do not start engines even when the door is closed. Traffic control may hold a plane at the gate in order to avoid long waits on taxiways with engines running. For purposes of the flight engineer, who is responsible for fuel consumption, the departure time is best defined by engine start-up. However, for the pilot's purpose—centering on getting the airplane to the destination on time—departure does not occur until the airplane actually lifts off the ground. Finally, for the air traffic controller, the departure does not register until the pilot reports that the flight is air-borne and the controller confirms radar identification.

Suggested purposes for defining the time of origin of human life include: to accord social and legal rights, to preserve human dignity, to avoid cruelty, to protect human life potential, to provide criteria for acceptable medical practice, to adjudicate between maternal and fetal rights. It is not at all clear that all of these purposes can be equally satisfied by the same definition of the time of origin of human life. For example, the definition offered by S.158, whose purpose obviously is to protect life potential fully from the moment of fertilization, clearly places maternal and fetal rights in sharp conflict from that point on. Obstetrician-gynecologists argue that their task becomes impossibly difficult when they must care for two individuals whose lives are inextricably intertwined and may be unequally affected by a particular treatment. Similarly, the definition of S.158 appears to preclude the acceptability of external human fertilization, a procedure regarded as promising to relieve infertility. If definitions are to be equitable and sound for multiple purposes, it is necessary to balance what is gained with respect to one purpose against what may be lost in relation to others. This is essentially a political task, but it needs to be informed not only by the best scientific appraisal of relevant knowledge but by a careful assessment of consequences for the various values and interests involved. Instead the question has now become a battleground of political maneuver with powerful conflicting advocacy groups in confrontation. A more deliberative approach is called for.

It is not novel in the assignment of rights to take into account level of maturation in the developmental sense. For instance, newborn infants at term are accorded the right to life in our society. Certain other rights are accorded later, often with accompanying ceremony, as in confirmation. In the United States we changed the time of according the right to vote from twenty-one to eighteen years, in part to bring it into line with obli-

gations for military service. These precedents suggest that level of maturation can be fitted to clearly articulated purposes for according a particular right. It is not easy because the continuing progression of development necessarily requires some arbitrariness if a sharply defined stage is to be chosen to assign a particular right. However, scientific knowledge may be useful in showing that some stages are too early and others too late. The intermediate period then appropriately becomes one of transitional status for a particular right. In this way scientific knowledge, in many instances, may afford a rational and objectively demonstrable framework that limits the range of controversy.

As example, a particularly knotty issue is raised by the imperative purpose to avoid unwitting cruelty to a nascent human being. The issue focuses on the stage of development at which an embryo or fetus can be expected to become sentient, in the sense of capability to experience discomfort or pain. Our most direct knowledge of sentience comes from our own subjective experiences and the experiences we share with others through communication. In the absence of communication, we can only infer sentience from other behavior or from internal objective signs known to be correlated with discomfort or pain. In all instances the nervous system, particularly the brain, is the site of such reliably correlated signs. Objective indicators of nervous function are presence of characteristic nerve cells, electrical activity of these cells as they function, synaptic connections among them, and the demonstration of neurotransmitter substances and specific enzyme activities necessary for neural function.

The level of maturation of the nervous system therefore may afford clues to the earliest beginnings of sentience and the onset of capability for subjective experience. The rudiment of the nervous system is not recognizable in human embryos until about four weeks after fertilization. Even at this stage, however, the cells of the rudiment have not yet become recognizable nerve cells, there are no synaptic connections, no neurotransmitters and no characteristic electrical activity—i.e., there is no objective sign of the necessary cellular substrate for discomfort or pain.

With continued maturation these objectively diagnostic features gradually appear, but at different times at different sites within the nervous system. Unfortunately, current knowledge does not tell us with any precision exactly where to look in the nervous system for correlated changes associated with experiences of discomfort or pain. However, we do know that primitive and localized responsive movements have been recorded in therapeutically aborted embryos at about eight weeks after fertilization. This is much earlier than "quickening," the detection by the mother of larger and more general movements at about eighteen weeks. The beginning of movement is correlated with nerve cell maturation in the spinal cord. Generally speaking, cellular maturation in the nervous system proceeds from spinal cord to lower brain centers and then to higher brain centers. This corresponds with the kinds of movements and the sequence of appearance that have been described, indicating the dependency of organized movements on the maturation of the neural substrate. However, there is uncertainty about whether movement, in itself, implies subjective experience. Moreover, available observations on the level of cellular maturation of even the late fetal brain gives no assurance that subjective experience either is or is not possible. This currently is a terra incognita in which evidence is hard to come by, given the necessary limitation on observation and manipulation of human fetuses at these stages.

If, however, one accepts the impressive scientific evidence from many sources that subjective states depend upon some level of maturation and function of the brain—though not as yet specifiable in detail—it follows that such subjective states cannot exist prior to the appearance of functionally connected nerve cells in upper brain levels. By this minimal criterion, it would be at least several months after fertilization before a developing human embryo might experience discomfort and pain. More detailed scientific information and greater understanding of the essential requirements for discomfort and pain might further specify such a judgment, taking into account the moral imperative to maintain a margin of safety against invading the sensitivity of a nascent and sentient human being.

Returning to the characteristics that are fundamental to definition of persons, the final category earlier referred to—the evoking of recognition and empathy in other selves—deserves brief comment. Second-party recognition of self in nascent stages and the resulting generation of empathy toward the nascent being is a subject that appears not to have had major scientific attention. Yet the issue of such recognition clearly is a strong contributor to at least the emotional tone of the abortion controversy. Whether or not sentience is objectively demonstrable at a given stage, the perception and conviction that selfness *is* present, if widely shared, becomes a relevant social and political determinant. Moreover, it is not a trivial argument that callousness to *perceived* humanness can reduce sensitivities to human rights with unfortunate consequence in other contexts. For these reasons, if for no other, it seems important to focus scientifically on the nature and time of appearance of the cues that lead to second-party perception of self.

Definition and Purpose

It is not true, therefore, that science has no contri-bution to make to the definition of the origin of human life, providing particular purposes are specified. For example, with respect to the purpose of protecting sentient stages against discomfort or pain, there is a broad gap in our knowledge between relatively early stages almost certainly without sentience and developing infants almost certainly possessing it. Narrowing the gap will require additional knowledge. For other purposes, similar analyses are required. Should the multiple analyses not point to the same definition, some accommodation based on priorities among conflicting purposes will be necessary to achieve a socially viable definition. Throughout this process continuing scientific input will be essential. Moreover, the high significance the issue has achieved calls for heightened scientific effort on those matters that bear on the issue.

Although scientific knowledge cannot settle all issues, it can contribute to limitation of the area of controversy. No formulated policy with respect to the matter should either disregard or conflict with existing scientific knowledge. It is especially to be emphasized that with so complex and value-laden a phenomenon as human development, purposes must be carefully and fully specified since definitions may only be suitable if crafted for particular purposes. To impose an arbitrary and rigid definition to satisfy one purpose may do violence to other equally or more important purposes. A humane society cannot avoid finding this a troubling process. It is a price we pay for maintaining the right of self-decision on important personal matters that also have a large public impact.

Returning to the language of *Roe* v. *Wade* and S.158, it would be scientifically more accurate than both to say that "human life does not begin with fertilization (conception), but hereditary individuality does. Individuality in the sense of biological singleness and wholeness, however, cannot be said to be established until more than two weeks after fertilization. Individuality in the sense of a person, or socially recognizable entity, gradually emerges in still later stages. Precise designation of the time will always be difficult but will be aided by clearly articulated purposes. The time may very well differ depending upon the purpose."

Approaching the matter in these terms allows science to play a useful and appropriate role. The resulting injection of greater objectivity into the decision arena may lead to a public policy less directed toward satisfying one or the other polarized extreme and more sensitive to the need to accommodate diverse purposes that may be conflicting—even though each is individually directed to a humane and desirable end.

PREGNANCY: THE CLOSEST HUMAN RELATIONSHIP

Niles Newton and Charlotte Modahl

Niles Newton is professor of psychology at Northwestern University Medical School in Chicago. She has been studying childbirth and reproduction for many years. With Margaret Mead, she investigated the way different cultures treat reproduction. She conducted some of the first research in this country on human lactation. In one series of experiments she served as a subject, nursing her seven-month-old baby in a study that established oxytocin as the hormone responsible for the reflex that lets down milk in human beings. Newton also has studied the effects of stress during labor, and has surveyed women to discover their reactions to their hysterectomies. Her latest research explores the role of the hormone oxytocin in coitus, childbirth, and lactation. Newton is associate editor of Birth and Family Journal and a member of the executive board of the International Society of Psychosomatic Obstetrics and Gynecology.

Charlotte Modahl is a doctoral student in psychology at Northern Illinois University. She is collaborating with Newton on a study of hormonal similarities in coitus, childbirth, and lactation. Modahl is also working on a longitudinal study of sex-related legal cases, exploring sexual symbolism in psychic trauma. With Newton, she recently wrote an article on mood differences between mothers who nurse their babies and those who bottle-feed them.

During its life within the uterus, a baby develops from a single fertilized cell and becomes a human being who, though still immature and dependent, can survive in the outside world. In the course of those 38 weeks, the baby depends on its mother for all its physical needs. She, in turn, is aware that she carries within her a living being. As her baby grows, the mother undergoes profound physical and emotional changes. From conception to birth, the pair deeply affect each other, and their relationship may estab-lish attitudes and ways of interacting that persist for years.

Life begins when sperm and egg unite, and a woman's sexual enjoyment may make it more likely that the sperm will reach the egg. After a woman experiences orgasm, her cervix descends and enlarges, increasing the size of the passageway into the uterus and making it easier for the sperm to ascend and meet the egg. Orgasm also makes her vaginal secretion more alkaline, and according to obstetrician Landrum Shettles, sperm travel more easily in an alkaline environment than in the normally acid vaginal secretion.

At the same time, prostaglandins — substances that are found throughout the body but that are concentrated in the fluid that surrounds the sperm — enter the vaginal wall and are absorbed into the bloodstream. Oxytocin, a hormone, is produced by the woman's own body. In response to these substances the uterus contracts, then relaxes, and this sequence may help the sperm move into the uterus. By remaining relaxed and recumbent after intercourse a woman also helps the sperm make their way into the uterus.

The feeling of closeness that most couples have after intercourse may be the direct result of uterine responses to such substances as prostaglandins and oxytocin, which is released by the pituitary gland during sexual stimulation. Our own pilot studies, in which we measured the moods of both sexes immediately after intercourse, suggest that there is a postcoital decrease in anxiety and depression. The drop was sharper in men than in women. Learning by gradu-al conditioning also contributes to the closeness of a couple. Because the intense emotions involved in orgasm are extremely pleasurable, the experience of intercourse is reinforcing. Repeated intercourse tends to condition the two people to each other, binding them into a reproductive partnership and providing a foundation for family life and the nurture of the baby.

Of course, orgasm is not necessary for conception, nor is any affection for one's partner. However, there is a strong relationship between a woman's feelings toward her mate and the course of her pregnancy.

Frances K. Grossman and her colleagues at Boston University studied 98 pregnant women in an attempt to assess the effects of their emotions. They found that women with good marital relationships were less likely to be depressed and anxious during pregnancy than women with unhappy marriages.

Whether the good marital relationships led to low levels of anxiety and depression or whether women who are anxious and depressed generally have unhappy marriages cannot be determined. But Grossman did find that women who said, early in their pregnancies, that they had wanted to become pregnant were much less likely to have complications during labor and delivery than women who had not consciously wanted to become pregnant.

Conception does not occur for some time after intercourse and takes place without the awareness of the woman. Sperm travel at only 0.5 cm per minute, but with the aid of muscular contractions and natural chemical and hormonal

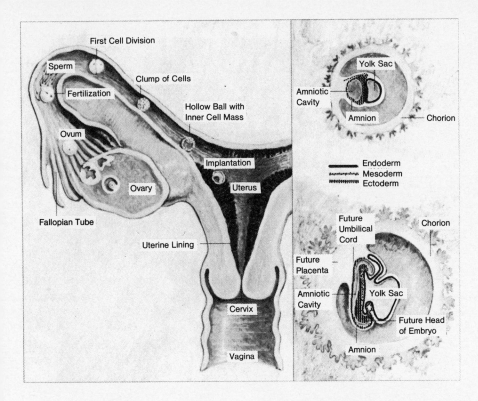

First Cell Division

Sperm

Clump of Cells

Fertilization

Hollow Ball with
Inner Cell Mass

Ovum

Implantation

Ovary

Uterus

Fallopian Tube

Uterine Lining

Cervix

Vagina

Yolk Sac

Amniotic
Cavity

Amnion

Chorion

Endoderm
Mesoderm
Ectoderm

Future
Umbilical
Cord

Chorion

Future
Placenta

Amniotic
Cavity

Yolk Sac

Future Head
of Embryo

Amnion

The fertilized egg divides many times on its way to the uterus. In the small drawings of the zygote on the left, cells in the black band will develop into the digestive system; those in the dotted band, into the heart, muscles, and skeleton; those in the lined band, into the skin and nervous system.

sloughing off its lining in a menstrual period as it normally does when an egg remains unfertilized, her uterus accepts the zygote in its thickened wall, and the dense network of blood vessels that has developed since ovulation begins to join the placenta.

The end of the baby's germinal phase coincides with the mother's expected menstrual period. At first she may think her period is only delayed, but soon her breasts begin to feel full, heavy, and tender, and she may start each day with nausea and vomiting.

Not all women become sick at the same time of day and many never feel nausea at all. Recently, Marilyn Theotokatos and Niles Newton collected information from over 500 women who were breast-feeding their babies. Sixty-eight percent of them reported experiencing nausea during their pregnancies, although only 16 percent said it had been severe. Among those who became nauseated, 40 percent also vomited.

By now the zygote has become an embryo, a term that describes the baby for the next six weeks. The placenta becomes more developed and from it the umbilical cord runs to the baby's navel. During this phase, the embryo develops its major organs.

At eight weeks, the baby is not much more than an inch long. It has a recognizable brain, a heart that pumps blood through tiny veins and arteries, a stomach that produces digestive juices, a liver that manufactures blood cells, kidneys that function, and an endocrine system. In the male embryo the testes produce androgens. The baby now has limbs and an enormous head with ears, nose, eyes, and mouth. Its eyelids have not yet developed and it has a definite tail, which will recede and become the tip of the spinal column. Nevertheless, it looks human.

Although the mother does not yet look

assistance, they may reach the Fallopian tubes within a few minutes after they are deposited in the vagina.

Although the egg may survive for approximately 72 hours after it is released from the ovary, it probably can be fertilized only during the first 24 hours. Some of the 400,000,000 sperm that are ejaculated by the man may survive within the woman for as long as seven days, although it is unlikely that they can penetrate and fertilize the egg after the first two days.

Planning the date of intercourse may help determine the baby's sex. About half the sperm released during intercourse carry an X chromosome; they will produce a girl. The other half carry a Y chromosome and they will produce a boy. The male-producing sperm are lighter and move faster, but they die sooner than the sperm that produce females. Because male-producing sperm tend to reach the fertilization site first, intercourse at the time the woman ovulates favors the conception of a boy. Because male-producing sperm die first, intercourse a day or two before ovulation increases the chances of the couple's conceiving a girl.

The first two weeks of a baby's life are called the germinal phase, and the fertilized egg is called a zygote. After the

sperm penetrates the egg, the zygote spends three or four days traveling down the length of the Fallopian tube and then another three to four days floating free in the uterus.

By the time the zygote is about nine days old, it has developed two sacs that surround it completely. The inner one is a fluid-filled sac that protects the zygote from injury, and the outer sac is the one from which the tendrils will grow that attach the zygote to the mother. Throughout this period, the cells of the zygote are dividing rapidly.

By the end of the second week, the zygote is firmly implanted in the uterine wall and has developed three layers of cells. The outer layer will produce the baby's skin, sense organs, and nervous system; the middle layer will develop into the baby's heart and blood vessels, muscles, and skeleton; the inner layer will become the digestive system and related organs such as the liver, the pancreas, and the thyroid gland.

The placenta, which transmits nourishment from mother to baby and takes away all waste products, is also developing at this stage.

Although the mother is unaware of the spectacular growth that is taking place within her, her body is responding to the implanted zygote. Instead of

2. THE PRENATAL PERIOD

pregnant, her baby has begun to react to its environment. It holds its hands close to its face; should they touch its mouth, the embryo turns its head and opens its mouth wide.

The behavior of the mother has also begun to change in response to changes in hormone production, to her bodily growth, and to her expectations that her way of life will soon be different. She may be unusually tired and sleep a good deal. As the growing embryo presses on her bladder, she may find herself urinating frequently.

Her eating habits are likely to change, perhaps in response to local custom. Many women have cravings for strange food at this time. S. M. Tobin asked 1,000 Canadian mothers "Did you have any peculiar food craving in pregnancy?" and 640 of them said "Yes." Sometimes these cravings may be intense but usually they involve milder yearnings. Craving for cornstarch or clay is common among poor groups in the United

States, whereas affluent women may crave ice cream or strawberries in winter. The reasons for these cravings are unknown, though they have been attributed to dietary deficiencies, anxiety, or conformity to cultural expectations.

With the appearance of bone cells at about the ninth week of development, the embryo is called a fetus, which will remain its technical name until birth. For the rest of its gestational period, the fetus is protected from the outside world by the amniotic fluid that fills the space between the inner and outer sacs that developed eight weeks earlier. The amniotic fluid provides a stable, buffered environment, and the fetus floats in a state of relative weightlessness. The fetus urinates directly into the fluid, and its waste products travel from the fluid through the placenta, from which they enter the mother's bloodstream. Exchange between the fetus and the amniotic fluid is slow, while exchange between the mother and the fluid is rapid. The fluid is completely replaced every two or three hours.

By the end of the third month, counting from the mother's last menstrual period, the fetus has grown to a length of three inches and weighs about half an ounce. It shows one of the signs of humanity—its thumb and forefinger are apposed so that, theoretically, it could grasp objects. It bends its finger when its palm is touched; it swallows. It has taste buds, sweat glands, and a prominent nose. By now it has eyelids, but they are sealed shut.

It is during the first trimester that the developing baby may be most sensitive to such influences as drugs, x-rays, disease, and the lack of essential nutrients. Mark Safra and Godfrey Oakley, Jr., of the Georgia Center for Disease Control found that women who take diazepam (a tranquilizer marketed as Valium) during the first trimester are four times as likely to have babies with cleft lips or cleft palate as mothers who do not take the tranquilizer.

During the 1960s, before the sedative was banned, mothers who took thalidomide during the first trimester sometimes gave birth to babies whose

The embryo pictured is eight weeks old. It is about an inch long and has a recognizable brain, heart, stomach, liver, kidneys, and endocrine system. Its tail will recede and become the tip of its spine. Although its head is enormous, it is obviously a developing human being.

arms and legs were nothing more than rudimentary flippers. Other drugs can cause abnormalities ranging from yellowed nails and teeth, which may follow the use of an antibiotic like tetracycline, to blindness, deafness, and gross malformations.

Only within the past six years has the existence of "fetal alcohol syndrome" been established. Kenneth L. Jones and his colleagues at the University of California at San Diego, have followed the pregnancies of alcoholic mothers and report that their babies are likely to be smaller and lighter than most babies, and that they are more likely to have slight facial, limb, and cardiovascular malformations. Some babies who are born to alcoholic mothers have conical heads and are mentally retarded. Animal research indicates that even the regular consumption of moderate doses of alcohol can affect the physical condition of offspring, but such a connection has not yet been established in human beings.

Heroin also affects the fetus. Babies whose mothers take heroin regularly will be born addicted to the drug and soon after birth must endure acute symptoms of heroin withdrawal.

Some minor illnesses may have profound effects. Some mothers who contract rubella (German measles) during the first trimester produce babies who are blind, deaf, mentally retarded, or have diseased hearts.

The fetus depends on its mother for all vitamins, minerals, and nutrients. In experiments with animals, severe protein shortages in early pregnancy have been associated with fetal brain damage. Stephen Zamenhof and his colleagues at the University of California School of Medicine, Los Angeles, found significantly fewer brain cells and cells with lower protein content in rats whose mothers had been placed on a protein-restricted diet before mating. They suggest that protein deprivation leads directly to mental retardation in children.

Research that severely restricts prenatal diets cannot be done on human beings, but records kept during the 1940s, when Germany occupied the Netherlands and Dutch diets were reduced below the minimum requirements for good health, showed an in-

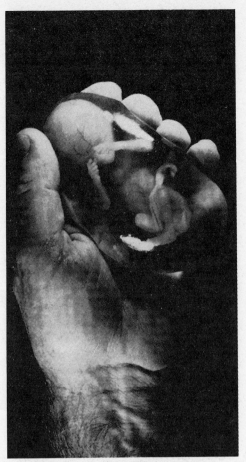

The features of the developing fetus show plainly in these photographs by radiologist Roberts Rugh. The three-month-old fetus can bend its finger and swallow.

crease in stillborn babies and premature births. As soon as diets returned to normal, the rates dropped. In depressed areas of the United States and in countries where the customary diet is deficient, infant mortality rates are high. In such places, dietary supplements have reduced mortality rates.

During the second trimester, the mother first feels her baby's movements. It is this quickening that makes many women acutely aware that they are carrying a living human being. Fetal movement patterns often give rise to maternal fantasies and expectations for the new baby. Women who reject the idea of motherhood when they first discover they have conceived generally come to accept the idea during this period of pregnancy.

The second trimester is generally a time of physical and emotional well-being. The mother no longer finds it necessary to sleep so much, her nausea has

gone, and her appetite has returned. She has lost the continual urge to urinate, and she often feels better than she did when not pregnant. Her condition is now apparent, and each time she looks at herself in the mirror, she has visible evidence of her baby's existence.

Her major worry at this stage may be in regard to her weight, for this is the period of most rapid weight gain. A few years ago, obstetricians urged their patients to restrict weight gain during pregnancy, and many mothers found themselves put on strict diets at a time when they both wanted and needed more nutrients.

Today it is realized that mothers who fail to gain adequately during pregnancy may have less healthy babies. According to the Committee on Maternal Nutrition of the National Research Council, the desirable weight gain during pregnancy is 24 pounds. The extra weight includes, in addition to the baby and the placenta, amniotic fluid, water that enlarges breast tissue, and extra blood needed for circulation. Some of the 24 pounds—on the average, about three and a half pounds—is stored as fat and protein to act as a buffer against the stresses of the postnatal period.

By the time the fetus is five months old, it appears in many ways to be a fully developed human being, but if it were taken from its mother, it could not survive. Only 10 inches long and weighing about half a pound, it has well-formed lungs that are not ready to function and a digestive system that cannot handle food.

This miniature being is often quite active within the uterus and seems to squirm or writhe slowly. Sometimes, by placing a hand on the mother's abdomen, it is possible to identify an elbow, a knee, or a tiny bottom. At this time, if one presses gently on the fetus, it is likely to respond with movements.

At the end of the second trimester, the six-month-old fetus wakes, sleeps, and has sluggish periods. It is likely to nap in a favorite position. It will open and close its eyes, look in all directions, and even hiccup. The grasp reflex is developed, and the fetus is capable of supporting its own weight with one hand. It is about 13 inches long and weighs about one and a

2. THE PRENATAL PERIOD

The 17-week-old fetus is so active within the uterus that its mother can now feel the separate life within her.

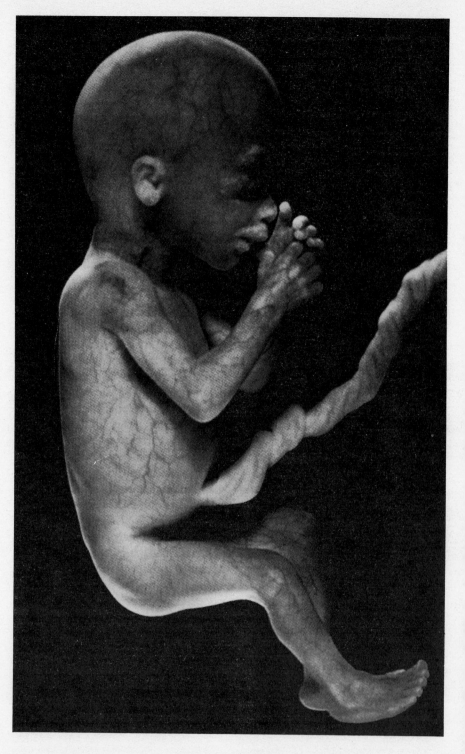

half pounds. With intensive care—regulated temperature, intravenous feeding, and oxygen supplementation—the fetus might now be able to survive outside its mother's body.

At Northwestern University, Marcia Jiminez studied 120 women who were pregnant for the first time, and examined their attitudes toward their jobs and their moods during the last three months of pregnancy. She found that women who expressed satisfaction with their work also felt less anxious, depressed, tired, and guilty and had less difficulty coping with their situation than did women who were dissatisfied.

Although it has been suggested that women who have strong career interests find it difficult to adapt to motherhood, Jiminez' work suggests that a woman's enjoyment of her occupation and her enjoyment of her pregnancy may both be part of a generally positive attitude toward life.

During the last trimester of pregnancy, the mother may respond with pride to the bulge of her enlarging uterus as a sign of fertility. In a society that advocates strict birth control measures, a woman's feelings about her pregnant body may be mixed. A mother who has seen few pregnant women in her life may feel that her body is uncomfortably different. The difference is accentuated if she wears shoes with high heels and stands in a poor posture. Her baby now may kick or punch sharply and sometimes uncomfortably, which can be an annoyance in the middle of the night.

The demand for nutrients is especially heavy at this time, and the baby will absorb 84 percent of all the calcium the mother eats, and 85 percent of the iron. The rapidly developing fetal brain also requires extra protein.

By the last trimester, the baby is aware of events outside its own body. The fetus lives in a noisy environment. Small microphones inserted through the cervix into the uterus of pregnant

women whose babies were due any day have detected a loud whooshing sound in rhythm with the mother's heartbeat. The sound is produced by blood pulsing through the uterus and is the constant companion of the fetus, which also hears the occasional rumbling of gas in its mother's intestines.

The unborn baby may also respond to outside sounds. Some mothers have complained that they cannot attend

symphony concerts because their babies respond to the music and applause with violent movement. Lester Sontag of the Fels Research Institute placed a small block of wood over the abdomens of women whose babies were due in about five weeks. When the board was struck with a doorbell clapper, about 90 percent of the fetuses immediately began kicking and moving violently. Their heart rates also increased. Besides responding to loud sounds, the fetus responds to the reaction of its mother's heart to such sounds.

Fetuses show individual differences in activity level and heart rate. Like people, some have heart rates that fluctuate greatly while others have hearts that tend to beat more regularly. Sontag has followed a dozen people from their fetal existence to adulthood and discovered that those whose heart rates showed wide variation within the uterus generally show the same wide variation as adults.

On the basis of three-hour interviews with a large group of children and adults, Sontag's colleagues have found that men with highly fluctuating heart rates tend to be reluctant to depend on people they love, to be in conflict over dependency, to be more compulsive, introspective, and indecisive than men with more stable heart rates. They have no explanation for this, but speculate whether they have discovered a genetic component of personality or an example of the influence of the uterine environment.

The relationship between a mother and her unborn baby is so close that the mother's emotions affect her baby's behavior, and the effect may persist after the baby is born. There is no way to ascertain when maternal emotions begin to influence a fetus, because there is no way to measure the effect in early pregnancy. But when a mother is emotionally upset, her body responds with physical changes.

Sontag has observed women in the last trimester of pregnancy who were suddenly faced with grief, fear, or anxiety. One young woman, whose fetus he was checking weekly for activity level and heart rate, came to him terrified after her husband suffered a psychotic breakdown and threatened to kill her. Her baby began kicking so violently that she was in pain, and recordings showed that its activity was 10 times greater than it had been in earlier recordings. The unborn baby of a woman whose husband was killed in an accident showed the same sharp rises in activity. Six other pregnant women who took part in Sontag's studies suffered similar emotional crises. In every case, their babies responded with violent activity. Sontag

followed these babies and found that, although they were physically and mentally normal, they were irritable and hyperactive, and three had severe feeding problems.

The link between mother and child has other postnatal effects. During the last three months of pregnancy, the mother confers on her baby immunity to a number of diseases that she may have contracted in the past. The antibodies manufactured by her immune system cross the placenta and circulate in the baby's bloodstream as well. If the mother has developed such immunities, the baby will have some resistance to measles, mumps, whooping cough, scarlet fever, colds, or influenza for the first few months of its life.

Other substances also cross the placental bridge. Women who smoke on a regular basis give birth to babies who are smaller and lighter than average. Recent studies by Gerhard Gennser and his colleagues showed that when such women smoke a single cigarette, the nicotine concentration in their blood quadruples and their heart rates increase. Within 30 minutes their unborn babies, all at eight months of development, showed a decrease in chest movements and short periods during which they did not "breathe" at all.

When the fetus has completed its 38 weeks in the uterus, the birth process begins. The exact sequence of the physiological changes that initiate labor is not clearly understood, but several substances — oxytocin, vasopressin, progesterone, and prostaglandins — are believed to be involved. Both the mother and the baby produce hormones, and some investigators believe that the fetus initiates the process, or at least gives the signal that tips the balance of factors that start labor.

The experience of childbirth varies from culture to culture. In societies that look upon birth as a fearful and secret experience, women often have long, difficult labors. In societies that are open about childbirth and expect it to be simple, women usually have short, uncomplicated labors. In normal deliveries, a relaxed, undisturbed environment, the presence of trusted helpers, and a minimum of medical interference

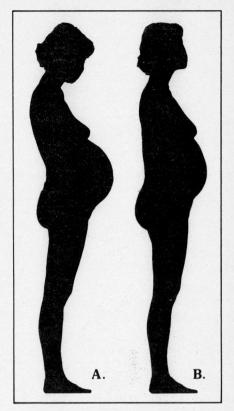

Women who stand improperly may be extremely uncomfortable during their pregnancies. The woman on the left, who is eight months pregnant, complained of pain in her abdomen and lower back. When shown how to stand correctly, she experienced immediate relief, and as the silhouette on the right shows, appeared less pregnant.

encourage the mother and infant to interact successfully.

Fear and disturbance may increase the mother's discomfort, and the excessive amounts of adrenaline that fear can place in a woman's bloodstream may counteract the work of hormones like oxytocin that help labor progress. Anxiety may cause the mother's muscles to become tense, converting simple contractions into painful cramps. Studies have shown that women who have a high level of anxiety during pregnancy are also likely to have complications during delivery.

In the first stage of labor, which may last from two to 16 hours or more, the uterus contracts at regular intervals while the cervix slowly dilates to allow the baby to pass into the birth canal. During this stage, the uterine contractions

Most obstetricians recommend that their patients gain about 24 pounds during pregnancy. Extra interstitial fluid, distributed throughout body tissues, contributes to weight gain. The weight that is not accounted for in the chart on the right is stored as fat and protein and helps the new mother withstand the stresses of the postnatal period.

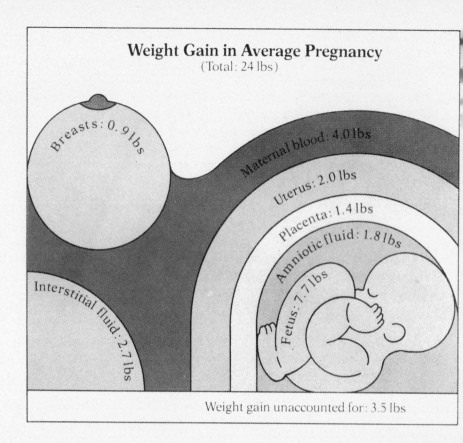

Weight Gain in Average Pregnancy
(Total: 24 lbs)

Breasts: 0.9 lbs

Maternal blood: 4.0 lbs

Uterus: 2.0 lbs

Placenta: 1.4 lbs

Amniotic fluid: 1.8 lbs

Fetus: 7.7 lbs

Interstitial fluid: 2.7 lbs

Weight gain unaccounted for: 3.5 lbs

are faint at first and gradually increase in strength. The mother may not realize that she is in labor until she notices the regular rhythm of the contractions.

In the second stage of labor, the baby usually passes headfirst down the vagina and into the world. This stage may last only a few minutes in women who have previously given birth. With first babies, it generally lasts more than an hour and varies greatly from woman to woman. This is the expulsive stage of labor, and the mother generally helps by bearing down during contractions. General or regional anesthesia may interfere with her efforts to push. The presence of the father in the labor and delivery room often helps the mother relax between contractions and enables the parents to be involved as a couple in the baby's arrival.

In the third stage of labor, the placenta is expelled. This stage can be described as a minilabor that ends with the delivery of the placenta. It usually lasts only a few minutes.

Drugs, even spinal injections, given to relieve a mother's pain or discomfort pass through the placenta to the baby and may interfere with the early bonding process. The baby may receive such a heavy dose that it spends its first few days in a drugged condition. Pediatrician T. Berry Brazelton of Harvard University found that drugged babies had trouble learning to suck and began to gain weight 24 hours later than a control group of unmedicated babies.

Heavily drugged babies may have slow heart and circulatory rates, bluish extremities, and an impaired ability to clear mucus from air passageways. The stimulation of the birth process may

wake them, but only for a short time. Brazelton reports that some drugged babies seem alert in the delivery room, only to lapse into a drugged state in the nursery.

Obviously, a drugged mother and a drugged baby have a hard time relating to each other during the first few days. When Ester Conway and Yvonne Brackbill followed a group of babies, they found that, a year after delivery, babies whose mothers had received medication during labor were still performing much more poorly on standard tests of behavior than babies of undrugged mothers.

And the more heavily drugged the mother had been, the worse the infant performed. Mothers who had required heavy medication differed from mothers requiring less medication, but Conway and Brackbill also discovered that the performance of the baby was related to the type of medication administered, and that the poorest performance levels followed the use of inhalant drugs. Whether the effects are permanent is still unknown.

In the United States, childbirth is often expected to be long and painful, even repellent. Our obstetrical pro-

cedures seem based on the premise that labor and birth are not natural experiences but a serious disease. Until recently, women have responded with deliveries that bore out the premise. Now research and practice have begun to dispel the image of suffering.

Women who have been prepared for childbirth, and who are allowed to go through the birth with a minimum of disturbance and with the support of their husbands, often describe their experience in terms that bear little resemblance to deliveries based on the pain and suffering model. Even women who report a good deal of pain also report feelings of joy, bliss, rapture, and ecstasy.

My own studies have noted a similarity between a woman's behavior during orgasm and at the birth of a baby. In both conditions there is fast, deep breathing in the early stages, the holding of breath at the climax, a tendency to make gasping noises, facial contortions, upper uterine contractions, contraction of abdominal muscles, the loss of sensory perception as delivery or orgasm approaches, and a sense of euphoria at the end.

A mother's emotional attachment to

her baby appears to intensify in the few hours after birth if she is awake and allowed to hold the baby. Breast-feeding is a powerful process that conditions both the mother and the child to a mutually pleasant and healthful interaction. When a baby sucks at the breast, sensory impulses go to the mother's pituitary gland, causing the release of oxytocin. Oxytocin causes the mother's uterus to contract, helping it return to normal size. The hormone also causes the grapelike alveoli in the breast, which hold milk, to contract, letting down milk for the baby.

Research on the nature of pregnancy is beginning to demonstrate what sensitive parents have long known. When pregnancy begins with a rich emotional and sexual relationship, mother and growing fetus continue the pattern. Many psychological and physiological patterns learned in the parents' relationship with each other are carried over to

create a bonding between parents and child.

The nutrients, heartbeat, and sleeping patterns that are shared by the mother and the fetus during pregnancy continue after the baby has been born. Hormones such as oxytocin that are present during intercourse, childbirth, and lactation provide a similar physiological basis for these processes, and the emotional reactions appear to be parallel in all. The result of these emotional patterns is the bonding of parents and baby into patterns of mutual pleasure and caring that promote the survival of the species.

For further information:

Brackbill, Yvonne. "Obstetrical Medication and Infant Behavior." *Handbook of Infant Development*, ed. J. D. Osofsky. John Wiley & Sons, 1978.

Gennser, Gerhard, Karel Marshal, and Bo Brantmark. "Maternal Smoking and Fetal Breathing Movements." *American Journal of Obstetrics and Gynecology*, Vol. 123, No. 8, 1975.

Jacobson, H. N. "Nutrition." *Scientific Foundations of Obstetrics and Gynecology*, ed. Elliot E. Philipp, Josephine Barnes, and Michael Newton. William Heineman Ltd., 1977.

Jones, Kenneth L., David W. Smith, Christy N. Ulleland, and Ann Pytkowicz Streissguth. "Pattern of Malformation in Offspring of Chronic Alcoholic Mothers." *The Lancet*, June 9, 1973, pp. 1267-1271.

Mead, Margaret, and Niles Newton. "Cultural Patterning of Perinatal Behavior." *Childbearing: Its Social and Psychological Aspects*, ed. S. A. Richardson and A. F. Guttmacher. The Williams & Wilkins Co., 1967.

Newton, Niles. "Emotions of Pregnancy." *Clinical Obstetrics and Gynecology*, Vol. 6, 1963, pp. 639-668.

Newton, Niles. "On Parenthood." *Handbook of Sexology*, ed. John Money and Herman Musaph. Elsevier/North Holland Biomedical Press, 1977.

Sontag, Lester W. "Implications of Fetal Behavior and Environment for Adult Personalities." *Annals New York Academy of Sciences*, Vol. 134, 1966, pp. 782-786.

Walker, David, James Grimwade, and Carl Wood. "Intrauterine Noise: A Component of the Fetal Environment." *American Journal of Obstetrics and Gynecology*, Vol. 109, No. 1, 1971.

HI-TECH BABIES

LANE LENARD

Lane Lenard, Ph.D., a psychobiologist, is Science Digest *articles editor and former managing editor of* Sexual Medicine Today.

"And the Lord visited Sarah as he had said, and the Lord did unto Sarah as he had spoken. For Sarah conceived, and bore Abraham a son. . . . And Sarah said, God hath made me to laugh, so that all that hear me will laugh with me." (Genesis 21:1–6)

Almost from the beginning, the inability to have children has caused couples great grief and sorrow. Abraham and Sarah were so desperate for a child that before God finally intervened on their behalf, Sarah suggested that Abraham sleep with her maid, a woman called Hagar. Abraham and Hagar were agreeable to this plan, and so Hagar became the world's first surrogate mother, giving birth to Ishmael and, legend would have it, the Arab race.

Not only Abraham but also his son by Sarah, Isaac, and Isaac's son Jacob each had a peculiar propensity for marrying barren women, and in each case, God had to intervene before they could have a child.

We do not know what physical abnormalities made Sarah and the other women infertile, nor do we know what medical miracles God performed to correct their problems. But it is ironic that today, when more and more couples want fewer and fewer children, medical science is learning to perform similar miracles, making it more likely that infertile couples who want children can have them.

Theologians can debate whether these medical efforts represent the twentieth-century version of divine intervention. In any case, thanks to an increased understanding of human reproductive biology, procedures such as in vitro (test-tube, literally, in glass) fertilization and artificial insemination now allow the conception and birth of human beings who would never have progressed beyond the twinkle in their parents' eyes just a few years ago.

While we all may know where babies come from, why baby does not come when it is supposed to is not always so clear. A man's ejaculation normally sends as many as 600 million sperm into the world. During her monthly menstrual cycle, a woman produces but a single ovum, or egg cell. Ultimately, at the moment of fertilization, a single sperm will have won the race to meet the ovum in the fallopian tube, or oviduct, and will penetrate it, beginning a new life.

Successful fertilization is dependent upon a delicate balance of hormonal, physiological and anatomic factors; a slight disruption of any of them can render a couple infertile. A change in a man's hormone balance can interfere with his sperm production, causing too few sperm or sperm of such poor quality that they cannot propel themselves through the female genital tract toward the ovum. A change in a woman's hormone balance can prevent ovulation, and even if millions of healthy sperm survive the journey, a mature ovum will not await them.

If a woman produces a normal ovum on schedule each month but healthy sperm are prevented from reaching it because her fallopian tubes are blocked, she will be sterile. This was the case with an Englishwoman named Lesley Brown when she was referred to the gynecologist Patrick Steptoe in early 1977.

When he was approached by Mrs. Brown, Dr. Steptoe's reputation for his work in fertility and sterility was already established worldwide. He had been collaborating with the Cambridge physiologist Robert Edwards for more than six years in an attempt to develop procedures that would help women like Mrs. Brown to become pregnant despite their blocked oviducts.

The basic procedure Steptoe and Edwards had worked out was quite simple. Since the oviducts (the tubes that connect each ovary to the uterus and the places in which fertilization normally takes place) were blocked, the two scientists wanted to bypass the blockage. They would remove the egg cell just as it was released from the ovary, mix it with sperm from the father-to-be in a special medium in a glass dish, culture the fertilized egg (that is, allow it to grow) for the time it would normally reside in the oviduct and then insert the now multicelled embryo into the mother's uterus.

Much of their procedure was already working well. At just the right time during the woman's menstrual cycle, Dr. Steptoe would insert a laparoscope through a tiny incision in her abdomen. This instrument illuminates and magnifies the inside of the abdomen. The laparoscope, which made possible routine tubal ligation, the operation that makes fertile women sterile, would now be used to make sterile women fertile.

The laparoscope enabled Dr. Steptoe to look inside the ovary, insert a needle into a follicle, which holds the egg cell as it matures, and suck the ovum out at close to the precise moment of ovulation. Plastic tubing connected the needle to a small vacuum-controlled aspirator bottle. Gentle suction drew the ovum through the tube and into the bottle. The whole recovery process took only 12 minutes.

Steptoe then sent the aspirator bottle to Edwards, who was in another room 15 yards away. They communicated by intercom. Edwards had to locate the ovum very quickly and transfer it to a special culture that closely approximated the interior of the mother's fallopian tubes. Even a slight variation in these conditions would preclude in vitro fertilization.

Edwards had prepared the husband's semen by separating out most of the sperm by centrifugation. He now checks the sperm for motility, the ability to move toward the ovum. If they are moving well, he adds the ovum to the solution. Millions of sperm instantly converge on the much larger ovum, though only one will penetrate its outer protective layer.

In a normal pregnancy, the fertilized ovum cleaves into two cells by the end of the first day. It divides into four cells after a day and a half and into eight cells after two and a half days. At the end of day five, it is a 16-cell embryo. If fertilization takes place in the fallopian tubes, the embryo passes into the uterus sometime between the 8- and 16-cell stages. There it implants itself into the uterine wall, begins to draw nourishment from the mother and to grow into a human infant.

Steptoe and Edwards had virtually perfected the tasks of ovum recovery and in vitro fertilization before Lesley Brown became their patient, but, in 105 attempts over more than six years, they had never been able to induce an externally fertilized ovum to implant in the womb and be carried successfully to term. Once in 1975 they had come close, but the tiny embryo had somehow made its way back into a fallopian tube and implanted itself there. The ectopic pregnancy had to be aborted to save the mother's life.

For the first few years, Steptoe and Edwards had attempted to facilitate ovum recovery by inducing ovulation with special drugs. These drugs, which can cause several ova to ripen at once, often result in multiple births in women whose infertility is caused by failure to ovulate. Now they were beginning to suspect that superovulation, as this technique is called, might be disrupting the internal reproductive environment.

They decided to abandon superovulation. Instead, they would seek out and recover the single ovum that naturally came to maturity each month—a much more difficult task.

To do so, they needed to know precisely when ovulation was going to occur. They knew that normal ovulation is preceded by a rapid rise in the level of luteinizing hormone (LH) released from the pituitary gland. They felt that by spotting this "LH surge," they would know that ovulation was imminent. Since there was no known method for spotting the LH surge, however, they had to develop one. They adapted a Japanese urine-assay technique for spotting the daily LH peak.

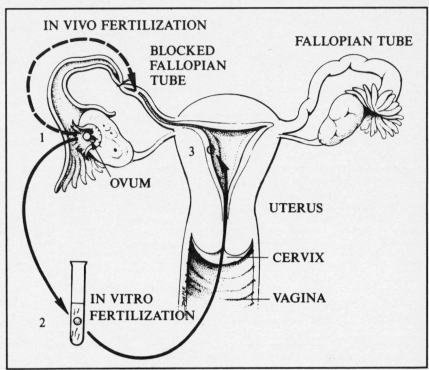

Test tube (in vitro) fertilization begins with 1) the surgical removal of an ovum. 2) Fertilization and division outside the body. 3) The eight-celled embryo implanted in uterine wall. An in vivo (inside the body) technique that would transfer the ovum to an unblocked portion of the oviduct for natural fertilization is under study.

TIDE OF LIFE

A striking new series of pictures taken through a scanning electron microscope (SEM) captures the remarkable sequence of events that brings sperm and egg together. Gynecologist Robert P. S. Jansen of the University of Texas Health Science Center photographed segments of the middle portion of the oviduct called the isthmus. His photos suggest that a tide of "tenacious mucus" rises each month from special cells that line the inside of the tube, which is only one millimeter in diameter.

The oviduct, or fallopian tube, which is blocked in women who require test-tube fertilization, serves as a conduit for both the sperm swimming up to the egg and for the egg moving down to the uterus from the ovary. Somewhere in the oviduct, sperm meets egg and life begins. Until now, though, just how the tube could permit the transport of sperm and egg in opposite directions has remained a mystery.

Jansen's photos show that for the first three to four days after ovulation, the mucus forms a block that holds the egg cell in place in the ampulla, the

portion of the oviduct closest to the ovary. At the same time, the mucus serves as a medium through which the sperm can transport themselves. It also protects the male gametes from the hairlike cilia that will later "beat" to sweep the egg toward the uterus.

When the mucous tide begins to ebb about 80 hours after ovulation, the constant sweeping motion of the now-exposed cilia moves the ovum or the embryo through the tube and into the uterus.

The whole sequence is apparently under the control of the hormone estrogen and perhaps progesterone, since oviductal mucous levels rise and fall with corresponding changes in the levels of these hormones.

The level of estrogen peaks just before ovulation, and photos taken at this time show the whole isthmus area blanketed with tenacious mucus. After ovulation, the estrogen level drops; the progesterone level increases.

At the start of menstruation, the mucosal surface is flat. By the end of the period, however, the cells that produce the tenacious mucus resume their secretory activity.

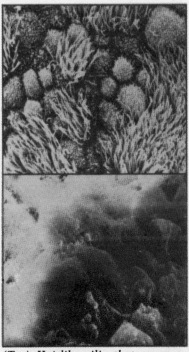

(Top) Hairlike cilia that sweep an egg down to the uterus are buried in mucus at ovulation (bottom) so sperm can swim up to meet the egg.

Instead of taking urine samples daily, though, they took them every three hours and found that they could spot the LH surge quite accurately in 86 percent of the patients they tested. "This is a seven-day-a-week job," Steptoe noted later. "We are entirely in the hands of the ladies."

Even so, success eluded them. Perhaps they were waiting too long before reimplanting the embryo into the uterus, Edwards thought. They had considered the 16-cell stage to be optimal but had consistently failed. With Lesley Brown, for the first time, they would try making the transfer at eight cells.

"So we went round to the hospital about six o'clock in the evening, expecting the possibility of doing the transfer there and then," Steptoe recalls. "But we found only six cells. So we went off and had our dinner. [It was Mrs. Steptoe's birthday.] We returned to the hospital at about ten o'clock and found it was only seven cells. And so we chatted and talked and, about midnight, an eighth cell appeared, and we transferred it."

The embryo was drawn up into a plastic tube, or cannula, that was then inserted through the cervix to the top of the uterus. Steptoe describes the extremely delicate procedure: "No instruments must touch the cervix. We must not cause the patient any discomfort; we use no anesthesia. Obviously, it is not a very easy business because you don't see the embryo with the naked eye. It has to be picked up from the vessel and carefully loaded into the end of the cannula under the microscope; then, we hope, not accidentally drawn out again; the amount of fluid is small [0.07 milliliter] so as not to provoke any contractions of the uterus."

And for the first time in history, a human egg cell, fertilized in vitro, attached itself to a uterine wall and began to grow normally.

DELIVERED AS PROMISED

Nearly nine months later, on July 25, 1978, Steptoe performed a cesarean section on Lesley Brown and, at 13 minutes to midnight, matter-of-factly announced to those present in the delivery room: "It's a girl . . . as was expected."

Six months after Louise Brown's birth, Alastair Montgomery was born in Scotland, the second of the Steptoe-Edwards "test-tube" babies. Last summer, an Australian woman gave birth to a baby girl conceived outside her body by a similar procedure, the world's third confirmed "test-tube" baby. Currently, in Australia, 12 other women have been successfully impregnated by similar procedures and are due to give birth this year.

Last year at Eastern Virginia Medical School in Norfolk a fertility clinic opened in the United States. The directors, Dr. Howard Jones and Dr. Georgeanna See-

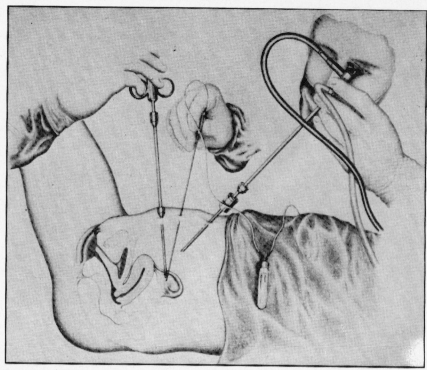

Before removing a woman's egg for test-tube fertilization, a doctor first searches her ovary for the mucus-shrouded egg. He uses a laparoscope, which illuminates and magnifies the area. Near the moment of ovulation, the egg is sucked through a long needle (middle instrument) to a plastic tube, then into a small aspirating bottle.

gar Jones, longtime acquaintances of Steptoe and Edwards, reported their first successful pregnancy last May.

At Louise Brown's third birthday this July, in vitro fertilization, or extracorporeal (out of the body) conception, seems to be making slow but sure progress toward establishing itself as more than just a medical curiosity. Last year, for example, two Harvard Medical School researchers reported development of a hormonal assay of follicular fluid that could potentially improve the odds of a successful implantation by allowing selection of the ova that have the best chance.

Two Australian groups that have induced 20 pregnancies in the last two years seem to be making the best progress so far. They have found that they can use an ultrasound scan to determine exactly when ovulation is about to occur.

While much of the world's attention has been focused on restoring the fertility of women with blocked fallopian tubes, 40 percent of couples who are unwillingly childless are so because the man cannot produce sperm in sufficient numbers or with sufficient motility to guarantee that one will survive the journey from vagina to fallopian tube and then fertilize the waiting ovum. In these cases, if surgery or drugs are unsuccessful in solving the problem, the only answer is to use some other man's sperm.

A few years ago, a doctor who practiced artificial insemination always had a

few donors on call. When a woman was ready to be impregnated, the call went out to one of these men.

But times have changed. Semen for artificial insemination can now be stored frozen in one of more than 17 sperm banks scattered throughout the country. Freezing allows a man to save his sperm prior to vasectomy or testicular surgery for use at a later date. This form of artificial insemination is called AIH: artificial insemination—husband.

When the husband has never had his sperm banked, or if the woman is single and desires to have a child by herself, use of donor sperm is required. This is called AID: artificial insemination—donor.

When donor sperm is banked, it is classified according to the physical characteristics of the donor. Thus, if a woman's husband is six feet tall, weighs 180 pounds, has black hair and Italian ancestry, the chances are that a perfect donor match will be found.

Two to six ejaculates of donor's or husband's semen are required to give a woman a good chance of becoming pregnant. She might get pregnant after the first insemination, but the odds are against it. Most doctors like to have enough semen for at least six menstrual cycles. One ejaculate can be provided and frozen every two to three days, giving the sperm count a chance to build up in between. Six ejaculates can thus take 12 to 18 days to collect. "Getting pregnant is not as easy as people think it is," says fertility specialist Dr. Wayne Decker.

The donated semen is mixed with glycerol, a preservative, and divided into 0.5 milliliter portions—about five or six per ejaculate—and placed in small straws or glass ampules. The straws are labeled and placed under liquid nitrogen at −384 degrees Fahrenheit. Two straws are used per menstrual cycle, one in each of two separate insemination sessions. Twelve straws are the minimum required for each woman, but many doctors like to have as many as 50 on hand to be safe.

When hormone tests determine that the woman is at her peak of fertility, the doctor thaws one of the straws, draws the semen up into a long glass pipette and inserts the pipette into the vagina near the cervix—the tiny opening into the uterus. The doctor forces the sperm out of the pipette by squeezing a rubber bulb on the other end. A rubber or plastic disc closes the vagina for several hours to seal in the valuable cargo.

The conception rate from frozen sperm is 90 percent, but the figure is deceiving because it represents only men whose sperm will survive the freeze-thaw analysis that is always done on a potential depositor's sperm. Only about 37 percent of men can have their semen frozen and thawed and still have a minimum of 40 percent of their sperm motile in the end.

And what of the children of artificial insemination? Are they normal? Physically, yes. There is no increase in birth defects attributable to this procedure, and there might even be a slight decrease.

Nor is there any evidence of long-term psychological harm, but this is difficult to know for sure. Most children of AID do not know their backgrounds, and no systematic records are kept. One who did learn of her unusual origin and who now writes under the name Lillian Atallah said, "Knowing about my AID origin did nothing to alter my feelings for my family. Instead, I felt grateful for the trouble they had taken to give me life."

SURROGATE MOTHERS

Our understanding of the world is based on our experience, which, in the case of human reproduction, has always been the natural process by which the father inseminates the mother during sexual intercourse; the mother carries the child for nine months and then gives birth. But science is changing our experience, and with that change will come a change in our perception of who we are as human beings on this planet in this Universe. As test-tube babies become more commonplace, so also will surrogate mothers, who carry the children that will be claimed at birth by other couples. Inevitably embryos will be transferred from one mother to another and ovaries and testes will be transplanted just as hearts and kidneys are now, but with more far-reaching ethical and legal ramifications.

Dr. Robert Francoeur, author of *Utopian Motherhood*, discusses the kind of science-fiction scenarios that await us as we continue to alter the reproductive process to suit our needs and desires: "A barren woman, citizen of Russia, receives an ovarian transplant from a black citizen of Nigeria. Married to a sterile . . . native of the Australian bush country, she is artificially inseminated with frozen semen from an Eskimo. . . . But the Russian woman has difficulty carrying the child, so she arranges for an American Indian woman to serve as a substitute mother. Puzzle out, if you will—and if you can—the racial and national constitution of the offspring, its citizenship, and its two (?) parents."

A PERFECT BABY

VIRGINIA APGAR, M.D., M.P.H.,
and JOAN BECK

Much more is known today than ever before about the diseases
and abnormalities, inherited and acquired, that cause
birth defects. There are still great gaps in our understanding, of course. But
if all the knowledge now available could be put into use by physicians,
by public health officials and especially by men and
women who are still to become parents, probably more than half of the
birth defects which now occur could be prevented.

The prevention of birth defects should begin long before a baby is born—ideally, even before he is conceived. For example, a man or woman who thinks that a close relative has a disorder which might be hereditary should take advantage of genetic counseling. This consultation should be obtained before marriage, but certainly before the conception of a child. It is particularly important for parents who have already had an infant with a genetic disorder.

Many people worry for years about the possibility of passing on to children a defect which has affected a parent or grandparent, an uncle or cousin, niece or nephew. Yet, very often, genetic counseling can prove such fears groundless or greatly exaggerated.

Often, the defect that a person fears transmitting is not hereditary at all, or is caused by a combination of hereditary factors with something that goes wrong during prenatal life. Even if a family disorder is hereditary, a genetic counselor may be able to determine from a family medical history that a particular individual could not possibly be a carrier of the abnormality. Or, if the prospective parent could be a carrier, the counselor may be able to suggest specific laboratory tests which will confirm or deny this possibility. For carriers, a genetic counselor can spell out in percentages how much risk each child would face.

A genetic counselor is also a good source of information about ways in which some birth defects can be diagnosed early in prenatal life, while the pregnancy can still be terminated if the prospective parents so decide. The counselor can also report on new treatments that may make the risk of having a baby with a specific birth defect seem less devastating to potential parents.

A considerable number of couples faced with the risk of having a baby with a major birth defect decide not to bear children but to form their family by adoption.

As more studies are done, researchers note a definite connection between the timing of pregnancy in the lives of parents and the occurrence of birth defects, prematurity, and stillbirths. Recent findings indicate that the ideal age for a woman to bear children is between twenty and 35. If possible, it is best not to begin having babies before the age of eighteen and to complete childbearing before 40. Countless mothers younger than eighteen and older than 40 have given birth to perfectly normal healthy babies. But young girls who become pregnant often do so in circumstances which make it unlikely they will have good prenatal care from the beginning of pregnancy. Many such girls are not adequately nourished, and many are exposed to other conditions which are associated with prematurity, high infant mortality, and an increase in certain birth defects.

Mothers older than 40 run greatly increased risks of having a child with a chromosomal abnormality, particularly Down's syndrome.

Many physicians now suggest that for women who become pregnant after 40, amniocentesis—an examination of the fluid in the amniotic sac—be used to discover if there are any chromosomal errors in the unborn infant's cells. New techniques make it possible to diagnose these conditions in time to terminate the pregnancy if the mother wishes.

It's desirable for a man to father his children before he reaches the age of 45. The chances are somewhat greater that a baby will be stillborn or have a congenital malformation if the father is older than 45, regardless of the age of the infant's mother. However, the risks to the baby are not as great with an older father as with an older mother.

Ideally, there should be an interval of at least two years between the end of one pregnancy and the beginning of another. The shorter the time period between pregnancies, the greater the likelihood of birth defects and obstetrical difficulties. The younger the mother is, the greater the risks to which she exposes her offspring by having them too close together.

The more children a mother has, beginning with the third, the fewer the chances that each will be born healthy and normal. In part, these risks are related to factors such as the increasing age of the mother, short spacing between pregnancies, and poor living conditions.

When a couple plans to conceive a child, intercourse should take place at intervals of no more than twenty-four hours for several days just preceding and about the time of ovulation. Some birth defects occur because the ovum is fertilized late in the monthly cycle, just as it is beginning to disintegrate. This delayed fertilization greatly increases the likelihood of chromosomal abnormalities and miscarriage.

The chances that conception will occur and that the resulting infant will be normal and healthy are greatest when the uniting sperm and ovum are both fresh. Frequent intercourse during the time when conception is possible is thought to increase the odds that neither sperm nor egg will be "overripe" at the time they join.

It can be difficult to determine precisely when ovulation takes place during a particular menstrual cycle. It is usually estimated that ovulation occurs approximately fourteen days before the beginning of a menstrual period, but this varies from one woman to another and, sometimes, even from one month to another in the same woman.

One method of approximating the day of ovulation is for a woman to take her temperature every morning when she wakes up and to keep a chart of the readings. In many women, the temperature increases by a small percentage of a degree at the time of ovulation and remains higher until the beginning of the next period. If conception occurs, the temperature stays at the higher level. This method is not completely reliable, however.

A few women are aware when ovulation occurs because they feel a pain in the lower abdomen when the tiny follicle containing the maturing ovum bursts to release the egg cell. This pain or discomfort, about midpoint in the menstrual cycle, is called "mittelschmerz."

Because a mother provides the total prenatal environment for an unborn baby during the first, most critical period of his existence, her health and wellbeing are inextricably linked with his. There is much a woman can do—not only during this crucial nine months, but before—to make this environment healthy, nourishing, and free of the hazards that can produce defects in her unborn baby.

Ideally, the kind of medical care that helps a woman provide a healthy, nourishing environment for her unborn child begins long before pregnancy. Before she marries, a woman—and her future husband—should be given adequate information about family planning in accordance with their needs and beliefs. Their family histories may suggest the need for genetic counseling, not so much because it might influence the decision to marry but for its relevance in planning ahead for children.

When she is ready to have a baby, a woman should have a medical checkup before conceiving, to make sure that she has no infections, nutritional deficiency, or physical abnormality that might interfere with the baby's development or safe birth. At this pre-pregnancy checkup, a woman should be warned against the dangers of drugs, radiation, and infections during the earliest weeks of pregnancy. Her doctor should make sure that her immunizations are up to date, to protect her and the baby she hopes to conceive against as many viral infections as possible. Medical conditions which might harm an unborn infant, such as thyroid deficiency, venereal disease, tuberculosis, and diabetes should be checked for and, if present, treated before pregnancy begins. Disorders like sickle cell anemia and heart disease, which are more hazardous to a pregnant woman than to her unborn infant, should also be evaluated before pregnancy starts.

If either the husband or wife has a history of occupational exposure to radiation, or if either has been taking drugs, the doctor may decide that an examination of their chromosomes is desirable to detect any possible abnormalities. A few studies link the father's exposure to radar equipment within a few weeks prior to conception to an increase in mongolism in their babies.

Regular checkups are essential during pregnancy, too, even if they seem routine and unnecessary. This medical monitoring provides an early warning system to detect the possibility of conditions such as toxemia, Rh incompatibility, premature separation of the placenta, and premature birth. It can also alert the physician to the presence of twins, which place extra strain on the mother's body and complicate delivery.

To encourage prenatal care, most obstetricians and family doctors arrange a fee in advance to cover prenatal supervision, delivery, hospital visits, and postnatal checkups. The fee remains the same, even if the mother requires more of the doctor's time than usual because of a complication during pregnancy or at the time of birth. Often, medical insurance plans cover most of these costs, or the physician may work out an installment type of payment program if a couple wishes.

City, county, and state health departments often provide free or low-cost prenatal care in neighborhood clinics, along with health and nutrition information. Many hospitals, especially those affiliated with a medical school, often give free prenatal services and obstetrical care. The U.S. Children's Bureau has made grants of many millions of dollars to help finance these municipal and hospital services. In many states, some prospective parents are also eligible for Medicaid funds for prenatal and obstetrical care.

There are several sources prospective parents seeking free or low-cost prenatal care can contact for information. These include: local, county, or state health departments; the nearest office of the U.S. Department of Health, Education, and Welfare; the closest clinic or chapter of The National Foundation—March of Dimes; the nearest hospital, particularly if it is connected with a medical school; the local community referral agency or Community Fund headquarters.

No woman should become pregnant unless she is sure she has had rubella (German measles) or has been immunized against it. This cause of serious birth defects can now be eliminated completely by means of a vaccine, but such protection must be assured before pregnancy begins.

The rubella vaccine contains live virus, greatly weakened so that it is not strong enough to produce a full-blown infection but will still trigger the body to manufacture antibodies as protection against the disease. No one knows whether these attenuated viruses could harm an unborn baby if a prospective mother were vaccinated early in pregnancy. Physicians, therefore, won't give rubella vaccine to any woman who might possibly be pregnant, or who might become pregnant within two or three months. To make sure that no woman in early pregnancy is inadvertently vaccinated, most doctors will not immunize any adolescent girl unless she is known to them as a regular patient. Women are immunized only if a physician can be sure they are using a reliable method of birth control and understand the necessity for avoiding conception for at least two months following vaccination.

Before the rubella vaccine was developed, it was estimated that about twenty percent of women reached adulthood without ever having had the disease. Their unborn infants were thus in danger should they be exposed to the virus during the early months of pregnancy.

With the development of a simple blood test for rubella antibodies in 1966, doctors discovered, however, that a large percentage of women were mistaken about whether or not they had had the disease. Many women who assumed they were immune to rubella had apparently had a brief illness with a mild rash caused by another virus. Antibodies were found in the blood of another large group of women who were sure they had never had the disease, indicating that they must have had such a light case that there were no noticeable symptoms at all.

Because it is so easy to be mistaken about rubella, a woman should either have the vaccination or a blood test proving antibodies are present before she becomes pregnant.

From the very beginning of pregnancy, a woman should do everything possible to keep herself in good health and to avoid exposure to contagious diseases. This is particularly important during the first three months of pregnancy, when all of the new baby's organs and body structures are being formed and when the hazards of malformations are greatest.

An unborn infant, particularly during the first eight to thirteen weeks of pregnancy, is very vulnerable to certain viral infections. Destruction of just a few cells in his tiny body so early in his development can cause major malformations or disorders, while a similar loss in an adult would not even be noticeable. Even viruses which produce only brief, mild symptoms in an adult, can result in severe and lifelong handicaps for an unborn child.

To protect an unborn infant against the hazards of viral infections, a woman should make sure she is immunized, not only against rubella, but also against whooping cough, measles, mumps, polio, diphtheria, and smallpox before she becomes pregnant. During pregnancy, she should avoid exposure to any persons who might have a viral infection. Should she become ill during pregnancy, she should consult her physician immediately. Avoiding illness also lessens the likelihood that she might need medication during pregnancy—another hazard to the unborn child.

All during pregnancy, a woman should avoid eating undercooked red meat or contact with any cat which might be the source of a toxoplasmosis infection. Toxoplasmosis is usually a mild disease in adults. Many individuals may have it without even being aware of it, although it may produce a brief rash, cough, swollen glands, and other symptoms much like the common cold. But if a woman has toxoplasmosis during pregnancy, the organism may also attack her unborn baby. The mother recovers quickly from the disease. The unborn infant may not, but may continue to have active infection all during the months before birth and afterward.

Of the unborn infants who have toxoplasmosis during pregnancy, about twenty percent are born with major defects, including mental retardation, hydrocephalus, epilepsy, eye damage, and hearing loss. Some may also be premature.

A pregnant woman should not take any drugs whatever unless absolutely essential—and then only when prescribed by a physician who is aware of her pregnancy. This prohibition is particularly important during the first two or three months of pregnancy when the unborn infant's body and organs are developing. The reason this ruling has to be so strict and inclusive is that scientists now think many birth defects are caused by the action of a drug taken by a pregnant woman on the vulnerable tissues of her unborn child whose particular, individual, genetic make-up makes these tissues susceptible to damage.

Most drugs—over the counter as well as those sold by prescription—are tested on experimental animals under laboratory conditions before they are given to human beings. But the unborn offspring of laboratory species do not consistently react the same way to medications as unborn human children. So this kind of research cannot provide enough answers to protect all infants.

Drugs, in this sense, include not only medicines, such as aspirin, sleeping pills, tranquilizers, but also such things as nose drops and sprays, laxatives, mineral oil, douches, reducing aids, and even baking soda, vitamin supplements, and other common remedies for various conditions. Spray-can insecticides are also forbidden, along with other potent substances which can be inhaled.

X-ray examinations or radiation treatments should not be given to a pregnant woman; this warning applies particularly to the abdominal area during the first three months of pregnancy.

So hazardous is radiation to an unborn infant during the earliest weeks of his life that many physicians and hospitals make it a rule not to X-ray the abdominal area of any woman of childbearing age except in serious emergencies or during the first ten days following the start of a menstrual period. There is much less danger to an unborn child during the last part of pregnancy, after all of the infant's organs and bodily structures have been formed. X-rays at this stage may be essential to diagnose the condition of the unborn infant, or to help ensure his safe birth.

Another hazard of radiation during pregnancy is the possibility of damage to genes and chromosomes in the egg cells already formed within the tiny body of an unborn baby girl. This kind of abnormality would not show up for at least another generation, until this girl herself began to have children or perhaps for several generations.

It's best to avoid cigarettes during pregnancy. The babies born to mothers who smoke average about half a pound less in weight than the infants of women who don't smoke.

Researchers aren't sure precisely how cigarette smoking affects an unborn infant. They theorize that the growth retardation may be caused by the nicotine, which is known to pass through the placenta into the body of the developing infant, or by the high level of carbon monoxide in the mother's blood which reduces the amount of oxygen the blood brings to the unborn infant.

A nourishing diet, rich in proteins, vitamins, and minerals, and adequate in total calories, is essential during pregnancy. It is also important all of the years of a girl's life before she has children.

The body of an unborn infant must be built out of the nutrients in his mother's body. If she is gravely undernourished, her child will be, too.

In the United States, there are still many prospective mothers who do not have an adequate diet. Poor nutrition in pregnancy usually reflects a lifetime of undernourishment due primarily to poverty, but also to lack of information about good nutrition and sometimes to cultural customs.

Poor women are not the only ones who are inadequately nourished. A woman who diets too strictly during pregnancy for the sake of her appearance may be exposing her unborn infant to unnecessary risk, too. According to a three-year study by the National Research Council's committee on maternal nutrition, severe caloric restrictions during pregnancy may have harmful effects on the unborn baby's neurological development and may make his birth weight hazardously low. Ideal weight gain during pregnancy should be twenty-four pounds, or a range of twenty to 25 pounds, the Council concluded.

A prospective mother who is Rh-negative should make sure her physician takes the necessary steps to protect her unborn baby and subsequent children from Rh disease.

An Rh-negative woman who has never been pregnant with an Rh-positive baby and who has never received a transfusion of Rh-positive blood can now almost always be protected against the danger of having a child with Rh disease. All that is necessary is to have an injection of a special gamma globulin containing antibodies against Rh-positive blood within 72 hours after she's given birth to an Rh-positive infant. The Rh antibodies in the vaccine attack any Rh-positive red blood cells which might have entered the mother's circulation at the time of birth and destroy them before they can trigger the mother's own immune system to produce antibodies. Should she become pregnant again with an Rh-positive infant, she will not have any of the dangerous antibodies which could destroy the baby's red blood cells before birth.

It is essential, however, that every Rh-negative mother receive the vaccine following the birth of every Rh-positive infant, every miscarriage, or every abortion, spontaneous or induced.

Unfortunately, the Rh vaccine cannot help an Rh-negative mother who has already begun to produce antibodies because she had an Rh-positive baby or an abortion or a miscarriage before the vaccine was developed. If she becomes pregnant, her physician should monitor the well-being of her unborn infant carefully by checking the level of antibodies in the mother's blood and, if necessary, by amniocentesis. If the baby is in danger, he can often be helped by an intrauterine blood transfusion.

Every precaution should be taken to prevent a baby from being born prematurely. This caution applies to all weighing less than five-and-a-half pounds at birth.

The handicaps of prematurity extend from subtle forms of learning difficulties and behavior problems in the almost-normal ranges of birth weight to severe retardation, blindness, hearing loss, and even death in the tiniest newborns. Prematurity is often linked, too, with cerebral palsy and retarded physical development.

Prematurity is related to many direct and indirect causes: poor nutrition, illness of the mother during pregnancy, poverty, lack of good prenatal care, too short an interval following a previous pregnancy, cigarette smoking, anemia, the mother's age, unfavorable living conditions, and twins. Most of the recommendations already made will help to reduce the possibility of prematurity.

Good, regular, prenatal care is probably the most important of these recommendations, for there is much a physician can do to prevent prematurity. He can prescribe supplementary proteins, irons, and vitamins, if necessary. He can treat toxemia, bleeding, anemia, infections and other disorders in the mother before they become a serious threat to her unborn child. Sometimes, he can stop a premature labor so that the pregnancy can continue until close to full term. He can diagnose the

2. THE PRENATAL PERIOD

presence of twins and advise the mother to get extra rest, especially during the last three months of pregnancy, to help postpone labor as long as possible.

A good physician also knows how to balance any need the mother may have for pain-relieving drugs with the safety of her child. For all of the medications given to the mother also affect her infant as long as blood is circulating through the umbilical cord. Normally, the processes of labor and birth decrease the amount of oxygen that reaches the infant; too much anesthetic or anesthetic given at the wrong time can cause brain injury or even death from the drastically lowered oxygen supply. Medications such as muscle relaxants and depressants given to the mother during labor also affect her child. Because they don't wear off as quickly in the baby as they do in the mother, their effect can be an extra handicap for the newborn who is struggling to survive on his own immediately after birth, especially if he has other handicaps.

Education-for-childbirth classes which teach a prospective mother what to expect during labor and delivery are beneficial to many women. By easing tensions and fears about the unknown, this instruction can help to reduce the amount of anesthetic a woman needs, show her ways to cooperate with her physician, and teach her how to work with the powerful muscular forces of her body—all important to the safety of her baby.

An infant changes faster during these first nine months than he ever will again. He is more vulnerable to injury before birth than he ever will be after.

Following these recommendations may seem tedious and unnecessary, especially to women who have already given birth to healthy children. But each pregnancy is different. Each child has a unique make-up. No effort is too great to increase the chances that a baby will be born without handicaps.

Information about family planning, prenatal care and genetic counseling can usually be found by contacting a large medical center or university-affiliated medical school, or from The National Foundation—March of Dimes, 1275 Mamaroneck Avenue, White Plains, New York 10605.

Premature Birth: Consequences for the Parent-Infant Relationship

The normal pattern of interaction in which both infant and parent initiate and respond to mutually complementary behavior is difficult to establish when the infant is premature

Susan Goldberg

Susan Goldberg is Assistant Professor of Psychology at Brandeis University. She has been doing research in infant development since 1967, including studies of infant cognitive development and parent-infant interaction. Her research on the effects of prematurity on early social relations has been carried out over the past four years with the cooperation of the Boston Hospital for Women. Address: Psychology Department, Brandeis University, Waltham, MA 02154.

Imagine, if you will, the sound of a young infant crying. For most adults it is a disturbing and compelling sound. If it is made by your own infant or one in your care, you are likely to feel impelled to do something about it. Most likely, when the crying has reached a particular intensity and has lasted for some (usually short) period of time, someone will pick the baby up for a bit of cuddling and walking. Usually, this terminates the crying and will bring the infant to a state of visual alertness. If the baby makes eye contact with the adult while in this alert state, the caregiver is likely to begin head-nodding and talking to the baby with the exaggerated expressions and inflections that are used only for talking to babies. Babies are usually very attentive to this kind of display and will often smile and coo. Most adults find this rapt attention and smiling exceedingly attractive in young infants and will do quite ridiculous things for these seemingly small rewards.

I have used this example to illustrate that normal infant behaviors and the behaviors adults direct toward infants seem to be mutually complementary in a way that leads to repeated social interactions enjoyed by both infants and adults. Consider now the experiences of a baby whose cry is weak and fails to compel adult attention, or the baby (or adult) who is blind and cannot make the eye contacts that normally lead to social play. When the behavior of either the infant or the adult is not within the range of normal competence, the pair is likely to have difficulties establishing rewarding social interactions. Premature birth is one particular situation in which the interactive skills of both parents and infants are hampered.

Recent studies comparing interactions of preterm and full-term parent-infant pairs have found consistently different patterns of behavior in the two groups. Before we turn to these studies, it will be useful to introduce a conceptual framework for understanding parent-infant interaction and a model within which the findings can be interpreted.

A conceptual framework

In most mammalian species, the care of an adult is necessary for the survival, growth, and development of the young. One would therefore expect that such species have evolved an adaptive system of parent-infant interaction which guarantees that newborns will be capable of soliciting care from adults and that adults will respond appropriately to infant signals for care. Where immaturity is prolonged and the young require the care of parents even after they are capable of moving about and feeding without assistance, one would also expect the interactive system to be organized in a way that guarantees the occurrence of social (as opposed to caregiving) interactions that can form the basis for a prolonged parent-child relationship. It is not surprising to find that when these conditions are met, the parent-infant interaction system appears to be one of finely tuned reciprocal behaviors that are mutually complementary and that appear to be preadapted to facilitate social interaction. Furthermore, as the example given earlier illustrates, both parents and infants are initiators and responders in bouts of interaction.

This view is quite different from that taken by psychologists in most studies of child development. For most of the relatively short history of developmental psychology it was commonly assumed that the infant was a passive, helpless organism who was acted upon by parents (and others) in a process that resulted in the "socialization" of the child into mature forms of behavior. In popular psychology this emphasis appeared as the belief that parents (especially mothers) were *responsible* for their child's development. They were to take the credit for successes as well as the blame for failures.

In the last fifteen years, the study of infant development has shown that the young infant is by no means passive, inert, or helpless when we consider the environment for which he or she is adapted—that is, an environment which includes a responsive caregiver. Indeed, we have discovered that infants are far more skilled and competent than we originally thought. First, the sensory systems of human infants are well developed at birth, and their initial perceptual capacities are well matched to the kind of stimulation that adults normally present to them. Infants see and discriminate visual patterns from birth, although their visual acuity is not up to adult standards. Young infants are especially attentive to visual movement, to borders of high con-

Reprinted by permission of *American Scientist*, journal of Sigma Xi, The Scientific Research Society.

59

trast, and to relatively complex stimuli. When face to face with infants, adults will normally present their faces at the distance where newborns are best able to focus (17–22 cm) and exaggerate their facial expressions and movements. The result is a visual display with constant movement of high contrast borders.

A similar phenomenon is observed in the auditory domain. Young infants are most sensitive to sound frequencies within the human vocal range, especially the higher pitches, and they can discriminate many initial consonants and vocal inflections. When adults talk to infants, they spontaneously raise the pitch of their voices, slow their speech, repeat frequently, and exaggerate articulation and inflection. Small wonder that young infants are fascinated by the games adults play with them!

In addition, researchers have found that when adults are engaged in this type of face-to-face play they pace their behavior according to the infant's pattern of waxing and waning attention. Thus the infant is able to "control" the display by the use of selective attention. At the same time, studies have found that babies are most likely to smile and coo first to events over which they have control. Thus, infants are highly likely to smile and gurgle during face-to-face play with adults, thus providing experiences which lead the adult to feel that he or she is "controlling" an interesting display. We will return to the notion of control and the sense of being effective as an important ingredient in parent-infant relationships.

A second respect in which infants are more skilled and competent than we might think is their ability to initiate and continue both caregiving and social interactions. Although the repertoire of the young infant is very limited, it includes behaviors such as crying, visual attention, and (after the first few weeks) smiling, which have compelling and powerful effects on adult behavior. Almost all parents will tell you that in the first weeks at home with a new baby they spent an inordinate amount of time trying to stop the baby's crying.

Crying is, at first, the most effective behavior in the infant's repertoire for getting adult attention. When social smiling and eye contact begin, they too become extremely effective in maintaining adult attention. In one study, by Moss and Robson (1968), about 80 percent of the parent-infant interactions in the early months were initiated by the infant. Thus, the normally competent infant plays a role in establishing contacts and interactions with adults that provide the conditions necessary for growth and development.

Competence motivation: a model

The actual process by which this relationship develops is not clearly understood, but we can outline a plausible model that is consistent with most of the available data. A central concept in this model is that of competence motivation, as defined by White (1959). In a now-classic review of research on learning and motivation in many species, White concluded that behaviors that are selective, directed, and persistent occur with high frequency in the absence of extrinsic rewards. He therefore proposed an intrinsic motive, which he called competence motivation, arising from a need to cope effectively with the environment, to account for behavioral phenomena such as play, exploration, and curiosity. Behavior that enables the organism to control or influence the environment gives rise to feelings of efficacy that strengthen competence motivation. White pointed out that much of the behavior of young infants appears to be motivated in this manner. Why else, for example, would infants persist in learning to walk when they are repeatedly punished by falls and bruises?

At the other extreme, Seligman (1975) has demonstrated that animals, including humans, can quickly learn to be helpless when placed in an unpleasant situation over which they have no control. This learned helplessness prevents effective behavior in subsequent situations where control is possible. It has been suggested that an important part of typical parent-infant interaction in the early

months is the prompt and appropriate responses of the parent to the infant's behavior, which enable the infant to feel effective. The retarded development often seen in institutionalized infants may arise from learned helplessness in a situation where, though apparent needs are met, this occurs on schedule rather than in response to the infant's expression of needs and signals for attention. There is a general consensus among researchers in infant development that the infant's early experiences of being effective support competence motivation, which in turn leads to the exploration, practice of skills, and "discovery" of new behaviors important for normal development.

I have suggested elsewhere (1977) that competence motivation is important to parents as well. Parents bring to their experiences with an infant some history that determines their level of competence motivation. However, their experiences with a particular infant will enhance, maintain, or depress feelings of competence in the parental role. Unlike infants, parents have some goals by which they evaluate their effectiveness. Parents monitor infant behavior, make decisions about caregiving or social interaction, and evaluate their own effectiveness in terms of the infant's subsequent behavior.

When parents are able to make decisions quickly and easily and when subsequent infant behavior is more enjoyable or less noxious than that which prompted them to act, they will consider themselves successful in that episode. When parents cannot make decisions quickly and easily and when subsequent infant behavior is more aversive or less enjoyable than that which led them to intervene, they will evaluate that episode as a failure. Figure 1 illustrates this process, and the following discussion is intended to clarify the model depicted.

The normally competent infant helps adults to be effective parents by being readable, predictable, and responsive. Readability refers to the clarity of the infant's signaling—that is, how easily the adult can observe the infant and conclude that he or she is tired, hun-

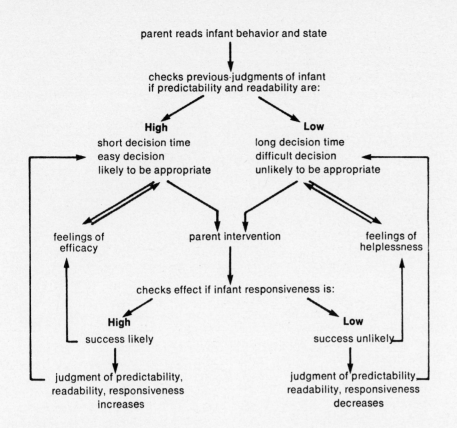

Figure 1. An adult who has experienced a successful interaction with an infant (*left*) perceives the infant as "readable" and predictable and acquires a feeling of competence in further interactions. The good and sensitive care that results causes the infant to feel more competent in turn at eliciting the appropriate responses, and thus a cycle of successful interaction is established. The reverse of this pattern is illustrated in the right side of the figure.

gry, eager to play, etc. Although there may be some infants who are easier for everyone to read than others, readability within the parent-infant pair is a joint function of infant behavior and the adult's skill in recognizing behavior patterns.

Predictability refers to the regularity of the infant's behavior—whether sleeping, waking, feeding, and elimination follow a recognizable pattern and whether the infant repeatedly responds to similar situations in a similar fashion. Again, both infant behavior and adult behavior and sensitivity to the infant determine predictability within a given pair. Responsiveness is the infant's ability to react to external stimulation, whether animate or inanimate. To the extent that an infant responds promptly and reliably to adult behavior he or she contributes directly to the adult's feelings of effectiveness as a caregiver.

The left side of Figure 1 shows that when an infant is readable and pre-dictable the adult is able to make caregiving decisions quickly and easily and is highly likely to make decisions that lead to successful or desirable outcomes. When an adult has interacted with an infant in ways that have led to an evaluation of success, the adult is likely to perceive the infant as more readable and predictable than before. Thus, the infant who is readable, predictable, and responsive can capture an initially disinterested adult in cycles of mutually rewarding and effective interaction. Notice also that, in this part of the figure, the adult is able to respond promptly and appropriately to the infant's behavior, providing the infant with what we would describe as good or sensitive care that enhances the infant's feelings of competence. In addition, since these successes make the adult feel efficacious, he or she now has more confidence and is better able to make judgments about infant behavior and caregiving in the future. The right side of the figure illustrates the situation in which the infant is

unreadable, unpredictable, and unresponsive as a joint function of poorly organized infant behavior and/or poorly developed adult skills.

Problems of preterm pairs

Under normal conditions, the natural reciprocity of adult and infant behavior guarantees that each member of the pair is provided with frequent opportunities to feel effective. A review of what is known about preterm infants and their parents will indicate that such pairs have a greater probability of falling into the patterns on the right side of the figure than do their full-term counterparts. Most preterm pairs eventually do develop successful relationships. However, the available data also indicate that they must make compensatory adjustments to enable them to overcome initial disadvantages.

Premature infants are those who are born after fewer than 37 weeks of gestation and weigh under 2,500 g. Infants who were born small for their age or with known congenital defects are not included in the samples of the studies I am describing. The most obvious fact of premature birth is that parents are confronted with an infant who is relatively immature and may not have developed the care-soliciting or social behaviors available to the full-term infant.

Several studies, including my own (Goldberg et al., in press), which have systematically evaluated the behavior of preterm infants (close to term or hospital discharge), have reported that they spent less time alert, were more difficult to keep in alert states, and were less responsive to sights and sounds (a ball, a rattle, a moving face, and a voice) than the full-term comparison group. Furthermore, preterm infants who had experienced respiratory problems following birth rarely cried during the newborn examination, even though some of the procedures (e.g. undressing, testing reflexes) are mildly stressful and provoke crying from full-term infants. This suggests that these preterm infants are not likely to give adults clear distress signals.

The effectiveness of the preterm infant's cry in compelling adult attention has not been studied extensively. However, at the University of Wisconsin (Frodi et al. 1978), mothers and fathers were shown videotapes of full-term and preterm infants in crying and quiescent states. A dubbed sound track made it possible to pair the sound and the picture independently. Physiological recordings taken from the viewing parents indicated that the cry of the premature infant was physiologically more arousing than that of the full-term infant, and particularly so when paired with the picture of the preterm baby. Furthermore, ratings of the cries indicated that parents found that of the premature baby more aversive than that of the full-term infant. Thus, although the preterm infant may cry less often, this can be somewhat compensated for by the more urgent and aversive sound of these cries. If a parent is able to quiet these cries promptly, they clearly serve an adaptive function. If, however, the infant is difficult to pacify or frequently irritable, it is possible that the aversive experience will exceed the parent's level of tolerance or that he or she will experience repeated feelings of helplessness that can be damaging to the interactive relationship.

Thus far, we have assumed that the less competent behavior of the preterm infant is primarily attributable to immaturity. Often prematurity is associated with other medical problems that depress behavioral competence. In addition, the early extrauterine experiences of preterm infants in intensive-care nurseries probably do little to foster interactive competence and may, in fact, hinder its occurrence. Procedures such as tube feedings, repeated drawing of blood samples, temperature taking, and instrument monitoring often constitute a large proportion of the preterm infant's first encounters with adults. There are few data on the effects of specific medical procedures, and since these procedures cannot ethically be withheld on a random schedule, this is a difficult area to study. However, numerous studies have attempted to foster early growth and development of preterm infants by adding specific kinds of experiences.

An example of a study from the first category is one in which 31 preterm infants were gently rocked for 30 minutes, three times each day, from their fifth postnatal day until they reached the age of 36 weeks postconception. They were compared to 31 unrocked preterm babies of similar gestational age, weight, and medical condition. The experimental infants were more responsive to visual and auditory stimulation and showed better motor skills as well.

Other studies have tried to treat preterm infants more like their full-term counterparts. In one study 30 preterm infants weighing 1,300–1,800 grams at birth were randomly assigned to experimental and control groups. The infants in the experimental group were given extra visual stimulation by placing mobiles over their cribs and were handled in the same manner as full-term infants for feeding, changing, and play. The control group received hospital care standard for the preterm nursery, which meant that handling was kept to a minimum. Although initial weights and behavioral assessments had favored the control group, at 4 weeks postnatal age, the experimental group had gained more weight and showed better performance on the behavioral assessment than the controls.

Like these two examples, all of the other studies which provided extra stimulation to preterm infants showed gains in growth and/or development for the babies in the experimental group beyond those of the control group. Thus, although we do not know whether routines of intensive care interfere with early development, we do know that the behavioral competence of preterm infants can be enhanced by appropriate supplemental experiences.

On the parents' side, premature birth means that parenthood is unexpectedly thrust upon individuals who may not yet be fully prepared for it. Beyond the facts of not having finished childbirth preparation classes or having bought the baby's crib, it may be that more fundamental biological and psychological processes are disrupted. A beautiful series of studies

by Rosenblatt (1969) has explored the development of maternal behavior in rats. As in humans, both male and female adult rats are capable of responding appropriately to infants. However, the hormonal state of the adult determines how readily the presence of infants elicits such behaviors. Furthermore, hormonal changes during pregnancy serve to bring female rats to a state of peak responsiveness to infants close to the time of delivery. Other animal studies indicate that experiences immediately after delivery are important for the initiation of maternal behavior. In many mammalian species removal of the young during this period may lead to subsequent rejection by the mother.

We do not have comparable hormonal studies of human mothers, but it seems likely that hormonal changes during pregnancy may serve similar functions. There is some evidence that among full-term births, immediate postpartum experiences contribute to subsequent maternal behavior. A series of studies by Klaus and Kennell (1976) and their colleagues provided some mothers with extra contact with their infants soon after birth. In comparison with control groups, these mothers were observed to stay closer to their babies, to touch and cuddle them more, and to express more reluctance to letting others care for their babies after leaving the hospital. Klaus and Kennell have summarized these studies and interpreted them as indicating that there is an optimal or "sensitive" period for initiating maternal behavior in humans. As further evidence they cite studies in which preterm infants are found to be overrepresented among reported cases of child abuse, neglect, and failure to thrive. These disturbing statistics, they suggest, reflect the effects of parent-infant separation during the sensitive period.

Even if one does not accept the idea of the sensitive period as described by Klaus and Kennell (and many developmental psychologists do not), it is clear that parents whose preterm infants must undergo prolonged hospitalization have few opportunities to interact with them. Even in the many hospitals that encourage parents to visit, handle, and care for their babies in intensive care, the experiences of parents with preterm infants are in no way comparable to those of parents with full-term infants.

If you have ever visited a friend under intensive care in the hospital, you will have some idea of the circumstances under which these parents must become acquainted with their infants. Neither parents nor infants in this situation have much opportunity to practice or develop interactive skills or to experience the feelings of competence that normally accompany them. Parents also have little opportunity to learn to read, predict, or recognize salient infant behaviors. In a study conducted at Stanford University, Seashore and her colleagues (1973) asked mothers to choose themselves or one of five other caregivers (e.g. nurse, grandmother) as best able to meet their infants' needs in numerous caregiving and social situations. Mothers who had not been able to handle their first-born preterm infants chose themselves less often than mothers in any other group sampled.

Thus, both infants and parents in preterm pairs are likely to be less skilled social partners than their full-term counterparts, because the development of interactive capacities has been disrupted and because they have had only limited opportunities to get acquainted and to practice. In addition, during the hospital stay, parents of preterm infants already have little self-confidence and lack the feeling of competence. Ordinarily, an interactive pair in which one member has limited competence can continue to function effectively if the partner is able to compensate for the inadequate or missing skills. In the case of parent-infant pairs, because the infant's repertoire and flexibility are limited, the burden of such compensatory adjustments necessarily falls upon the parent.

Observations of interactions

Six studies to date have compared parent-infant interaction in full-term and preterm pairs. They were carried out in different parts of the country

with different populations and different research methodologies. Yet there seems to be some consistency in findings that is related to the age of the infant at the time of observation (which also reflects the duration of the parent-infant relationship). Each study involved repeated observation of the same parent-infant pairs, though the number of observations and the length of the studies vary.

Those studies which observed parents and infants in the newborn period typically report that parents of preterm infants are less actively involved with their babies than parents of full-term infants. Relative to full-term infants, preterm infants were held farther from the parent's body (Fig. 2), touched less, talked to less, and placed in the face-to-face position less often. Subsequent observations of the same pairs usually indicated that the differences between preterm and full-term pairs diminished with time, as parents in the preterm group became more active. Thus, it appears that the initiation of interaction patterns considered "normal" for full-term pairs is delayed in preterm pairs. In my own study (Di Vitto and Goldberg, in press) I found that for one kind of parental behavior—cuddling the baby—the preterm infants never received as much attention as the full-term infants in spite of increases over time. Over the first four months, parents cuddled preterm infants more at later feeding observations, but they were never cuddled as much as the full-term infants at the very first (hospital) observation. Thus, the development of some kinds of interactions in the preterm group can be both delayed and depressed.

In contrast with these observations of very young infants, studies of older infants reported a very different pattern. Regardless of the observation situation (feeding, social play, or object play), preterm infants were less actively engaged in the task than were full-term infants, and their parents were more active than those of full-term infants. In one study of this type, Field (1977) placed each mother face to face with her baby, who sat in an infant seat, and asked her to "talk to your baby the way you would at

home." Infant attention and parent activity were coded. Infants in the preterm group squirmed, fussed, and turned away from their mothers more than those in the full-term group, and preterm mothers were more active than full-term mothers. Instructions that decreased maternal activity ("Try to imitate everything your baby does") increased infant attention in both groups, while those that increased maternal activity ("Try to get your infant to look at you as much as possible") decreased infant attention in both groups.

Field's interpretation of these findings assumed that infants used gaze aversion to maintain their exposure to stimulation within a range that would not overtax their capacities for processing information. Thus, when mothers' activity decreased, infants were able to process the information provided without the need to reduce stimulation. Field also suggested that since the *imitation* condition provided stimulation that was matched to the infant's behavior, it might be more familiar and thus easier for the infant to process. It is possible that the greater initial fussing and gaze aversion reflected information-processing skills that were less developed than those of full-term infants.

Brown and Bakeman (in press) observed feedings in the hospital, one month after discharge, and three months after discharge. Their findings are somewhat different from the overall trend because they were similar at all observations. Behavior segments were assigned to four categories: *mother acts alone, baby acts alone, both act,* and *neither acts.* In comparing preterm and full-term pairs, they reported that preterm infants acted alone less frequently than full-term infants, while mothers of preterm infants acted alone more often than those of full-term infants. Furthermore, in preterm pairs, the *neither acts* state was most likely to be followed by *mother acts alone,* while in the full-term pairs, it was equally likely to be followed by activity by the baby or the mother.

In my own research (DiVitto and Goldberg, in press; Brachfeld and Goldberg 1978) there are two sets of data consistent with these findings. First, we found that parent behavior during feedings in the hospital, and at the 4-month home and laboratory visits, was related to infant behavior in the newborn period. Regardless of their condition at birth, infants who had been difficult to rouse as newborns received a high level of functional stimulation from parents (e.g. position changes, jiggling the nipple). Infants who had been unresponsive to auditory stimulation as newborns received high levels of vocal and tactile stimulation during feedings. Thus, the parents of infants who were unresponsive as newborns appeared to work harder during feedings in the first four months than did the parents whose newborns were more responsive.

We also observed the same pairs at 8 months of age in a free-play situation. Four toys were provided and parents were asked to "do what you usually do when [name] is playing." In this situation, both at home and in the laboratory, preterm infants (particularly those who had been very young and small at birth and had respiratory problems) played with toys less and fussed more than the full-term group. Parents in the preterm group stayed closer to their babies, touched them more, demonstrated and offered toys more, and smiled less than those in the full-term group.

Another study with somewhat younger infants also fits this pattern. Beckwith and Cohen (1978) observed one wake–sleep cycle at home one month after discharge. Since babies were born and discharged at different ages, the age of the infants varied: some were relatively young, while others were closer in age to the older groups in other studies. All were born prematurely. However, Beckwith and Cohen found that mothers whose babies had experienced many early complications devoted more time to caregiving than those who had babies with fewer problems.

All these studies concur in indicating that parents with preterm infants or preterm infants with more serious early problems devote more effort to interacting with their babies than do their full-term counterparts. In most

Figure 2. Parents of preterm infants seem, in general, to be less actively involved with their babies in the early postnatal period than parents of full-term infants. For example, this tendency is sometimes revealed in the distances at which mothers hold their preterm babies (*left*) relative to mothers of full-term babies (*right*), as shown in these posed pictures. (Photographs by B. Di Vitto.)

of the studies this was coupled with a less responsive or less active baby in the preterm pairs. Thus, it appears that parents adapt to the less responsive preterm baby by investing more effort in the interaction themselves. As Brown and Bakeman put it, the mother of the preterm infant "carries more of the interactive burden" than her full-term counterpart. From our own laboratory, there is some evidence that other adults have a similar experience with preterm infants. At our regular developmental assessments at 4, 8, and 12 months, staff members rated the preterm group as being less attentive to the tasks, less persistent in solving them, and less interested in manipulating objects than the full-term group. In addition, staff members found it necessary to spend more time with the preterm group to complete the required tasks.

The consistency of these findings suggests that in pairs with a preterm infant, adults use a common strategy of investing extra time and effort to compensate for their less responsive social partner. It is important to note that while this seems to be a widely adopted strategy, it is not necessarily the most successful one. In Field's study (1977) a decrease in maternal activity evoked infant attention more effectively than an increase. In our own observations of 8-month-old infants, increased parent involvement did not reduce the unhappiness of the sick preterm group, and some play sessions had to be terminated to alleviate infant distress. Hence, while there seem to be some consistent strategies by which parents compensate for the limited skills of their preterm infants, these pairs may continue to experience interactive stress in spite of or even because of these efforts. Continuation of such unrewarding interactions, as Figure 1 indicates, is a threat to continued effective functioning of the interactive system.

The data reviewed above provide little evidence on the duration of interactive differences between full-term and preterm pairs. Among researchers in the field, there seems to be an informal consensus which holds that such differences gradually disappear, probably by the end of the first year. In my own research, a repetition of the play sessions at 12 months revealed no group differences. At 11–15 months, Leiderman and Seashore (1975) report only one difference: mothers of preterm babies smile less frequently than those of full-term babies. However, in Brown and Bakeman's study, group differences were observed as late as preschool age in rated competence in social interactions with adults (teachers) and peers. These data are too meager and scattered to support a firm conclusion on the duration of group differences.

This review has focused only upon the ways in which premature birth may stress the parent-infant interaction system. Preterm infants are generally considered to be at higher risk for subsequent developmental and medical problems than their full-term counterparts. In order to understand the reasons for less than optimal developmental outcomes, it is important to bear in mind that premature births occur with high frequency among population subgroups where family stress is already high (e.g. young, single, black, lower-class mothers). Most of the research designs which would allow us to disentangle the independent contributions of each medical and social variable to long-term development are unethical, impractical, or impossible to carry out with human subjects.

The early approach to studying the consequences of prematurity was to consider each of these medical and social variables as "causes" and the physical and intellectual development of the child as the "effect." The data reviewed here indicate that we cannot think in such simple terms. Prematurity (or any other event which stresses the infant) stresses the parent-infant interaction system and indeed the entire family. The way in which the family is able to cope with these stresses then has important consequences for the child's development. A major finding of the UCLA study was that for preterm infants, as for full-term infants, a harmoniously functioning parent-infant relation-ship has beneficial effects on development in other areas, such as language, cognition, motor skills, and general health. Prematurity, like many other developmental phenomena, can best be understood as a complex biosocial event with multiple consequences for the child and the family.

Furthermore, in the absence of sophisticated medical technology, the vast majority of the births we have been discussing would not have produced live offspring. In evolutionary history, though it would have been adaptive for infants' initial social skills to be functional some time before birth was imminent, there was no reason for these preadapted social skills to be functioning at 6 or 7 months gestation. Premature births include only a small proportion of the population, but our ability to make such infants viable at younger and younger gestational ages by means of artificial support systems may be creating new pressures for differential selection. The fact that the majority of preterm pairs do make relatively successful adaptations indicates that the capacity to compensate for early interactive stress is one of the features of the parent-infant interaction system.

References

Beckwith, L., and S. E. Cohen. 1978. Preterm birth: Hazardous obstetrical and postnatal events as related to caregiver-infant behavior. *Infant Behav. and Devel.* 1.

Brachfeld, S., and S. Goldberg. Parent-infant interaction: Effects of newborn medical status on free play at 8 and 12 months. Presented at Southeastern Conference on Human Development, Atlanta, GA, April 1978.

Brown, J. V., and R. Bakeman. In press. Relationships of human mothers with their infants during the first year of life. In *Maternal Influences and Early Behavior*, ed. R. W. Bell and W. P. Smotherman. Spectrum.

DiVitto, B., and S. Goldberg. In press. The development of early parent-infant interaction as a function of newborn medical status. In *Infants Born at Risk*, ed. T. Field, A. Sostek, S. Goldberg, and H. H. Shuman. Spectrum.

Field, T. M. 1977. Effects of early separation, interactive deficits, and experimental manipulations on mother-infant interaction. *Child Development* 48:763–71.

Frodi, A., M. Lamb, L. Leavitt, W. L. Donovan, C. Wolff, and C. Neff. 1978. Fathers' and mothers' responses to the faces and cries of normal and premature infants. *Devel. Psych.* 14.

Goldberg, S. 1977. Social competence in infancy: A model of parent-infant interaction. *Merrill-Palmer Quarterly* 23:163–77.

Goldberg, S., S. Brachfeld, and B. DiVitto. In press. Feeding, fussing and play: Parent-infant interaction in the first year as a function of newborn medical status. In *Interactions of High Risk Infants and Children*, ed. T. Field, S. Goldberg, D. Stern and A. Sostek, Academic Press.

Kennell, J. H., and M. H. Klaus. 1976. Caring for parents of a premature or sick infant. In *Maternal-Infant Bonding*, ed. M. H. Klaus and J. H. Kennell. Mosby.

Klaus, M. H., and J. H. Kennell. 1976. *Maternal-Infant Bonding.* Mosby.

Leiderman, P. H., and M. J. Seashore. 1975. Mother-infant separation: Some delayed consequences. In *Parent-Infant Interaction.* CIBA Foundation Symp. 33. Elsevier.

Moss, H. A., and K. S. Robson. The role of protest behavior in the development of parent-infant attachment. Symposium on attachment behavior in humans and animals. Am. Psych. Assoc. Sept. 1968.

Rosenblatt, J. S. 1969. The development of maternal responsiveness in the rat. *Am. J. Orthopsychiatry* 39:36–56.

Seashore, M. J., A. D. Leifer, C. R. Barnett, and P. H. Leiderman. 1973. The effects of denial of early mother-infant interaction on maternal self-confidence. *J. Pers. and Soc. Psych.* 26:369–78.

Seligman, M. R. 1975. *Helplessness: On Development, Depression and Death.* W. H. Freeman.

White, R. 1959. Motivation reconsidered: The concept of competence. *Psych. Review* 66:297–333.

BEFORE THEIR TIME

Jack Fincher

Although a critical care nurse, Ann Starkey had no idea there was any serious problem with her pregnancy. Neither did her doctor, until she came to him complaining of a frequent and uncontrollable but futile urge to urinate.

A bout of bleeding early in her pregnancy suggested that Starkey's was a high risk case, but when she had not miscarried by the fifth month, her doctor felt the danger was probably past. No, this was only a bladder inflammation, the 35-year-old California woman thought.

But when analysis of a urine specimen revealed nothing out of the ordinary, the doctor decided to examine her cervix, something usually not done until labor starts unless there are cramps or further bleeding. "When he looked at me, he didn't say anything for a long time," she remembers. "I knew something was terribly wrong."

Ann Starkey's cervix may have been dilated for days—three months too early. She had been walking around with an open cervix, exposing membranes that could rupture at any minute and lead to massive contamination that could menace both her and her baby. Ann Starkey was the victim of premature labor, a distressing and dangerous condition for both mother and child that strikes up to one in 10 expectant mothers in the United States every year.

Seventy-five per cent of all premature labor can be traced to some underlying factor such as multiple pregnancy, toxemia, infection, irritation due to partial separation of the placenta or—as in Ann Starkey's case—a cervix unable to hold and carry the baby to term. An association has also been established between badly nourished mothers and early delivery. Many symptoms of high risk pregnancy can be detected in advance, and efforts are being made to delay delivery in these cases. A recent study at the University of California at San Francisco reports that special care of high risk mothers can reduce preterm delivery by 64 percent.

Still, fully one in four such deliveries remains as medically mysterious as the timing of labor itself, normal or otherwise. What's more, it can happen to any pregnant woman. Says Stanford Medical Center's Director of Maternal Fetal Medicine, Kent Ueland, "No one knows what starts labor. We know prostaglandins [natural body substances that trigger the smooth muscles of the uterus to contract] are involved. You can release them by stretching open the cervix with your finger. Just before labor, some mammals, such as sheep, have a rapid drop of the sex hormone progesterone and a concurrent surge of estrogen. But that hasn't been documented in humans, probably because it occurs so rapidly we just haven't been able to measure it as it happens."

Ann Starkey's doctor had her signed in to the labor and delivery unit at the Stanford Medical Center in Palo Alto. She was lucky because Stanford also has a top ranked neonatal intensive care unit where special care is provided after birth for very low weight infants. Starkey was put to bed and injected with a betamimetic, a powerful drug that often stops labor. Her blood, unfortunately, showed an elevated white cell count, a disturbing sign that her membranes might have ruptured, permitting bacteria to invade the egg-shaped amniotic sac which contained the fetus floating in an aseptic cushion of fluid. The presence of an infection there would dramatically increase the chances that the labor suppressant might induce a fatal heart attack or stroke. So much so that she had been asked to sign a paper saying she knew she was consenting to take a drug that threatened her life. Ann Starkey signed.

The injections were unavailing. Her heart pounding because of the drug, she watched anxiously as a stylus scratching away on graph paper mapped the progress of her contractions. They persisted, but remained weak in intensity, so about 8:00 P.M. sutures were put around the cervix and drawn tight. No use. At 1:00 A.M. her membranes started leaking amniotic fluid. Labor was accelerating.

Five hours later her white blood cell count had doubled. If there were to be any hope of a normal baby, Ann Starkey knew, it could no longer remain in the uterus. The sutures were cut and pitocin, another natural body substance that causes the uterus to contract, was given intravenously.

She lay in tears as Ron Cohen, an attending neonatologist at Stanford's neonatal intensive care unit, told her and her social worker husband Larry that their first child's chances of survival were dim. The Starkeys made it clear that, after Ann's safety, they wanted what was best for the baby. "We didn't want it to survive if it was going to be handicapped beyond a productive life," says Ann.

Gently, Ron Cohen informed them that babies weighing less that 500 grams—a little over one pound and common for 24 weeks' gestation—were usually too small to try to save. Cohen, they realized, was reaching the crucial decision for them. Their baby had to make the weight or it would be all over.

Ann Starkey never got to the delivery room. At about 1:00 P.M., lying flat on her back under an anesthetic that enabled her to sense pressure but not pain, she felt the baby passing through the birth canal. Sterile towels were thrown under her, a crew from the intensive care nursery was summoned with the push of a bedside button. Less

than a minute later Matthew Starkey was born, one tiny wrinkled foot stirring the air as the doctor snipped the umbilical cord. "He opened his mouth, took a deep breath, and cried," says Ann, savoring that miraculous moment again with her husband. "He was pink, wasn't he pink? Usually kids that small come out blue, unable to breathe, with no muscle tone. They whisked him off on a portable ventilator and that was all I saw of him for the next nine hours."

The baby weighed 700 grams. Larry Starkey said, "When he popped out and cried, the thought that he might not make it just disappeared." That thought vanished too soon, the Starkeys would learn time and again to their frustration. But two hours later Ron Cohen roused Ann Starkey with the message she and her husband had been waiting for: "We've got a fighter."

Matthew Starkey had just joined the ranks of America's "Kilogram Kids," a legion of very premature infants weighing 2.3 pounds and under at birth. They are being saved by the advance of neonatal medicine and technology to face an uncertain future—sometimes normality if they are strong, well doctored, and lucky, sometimes vegetating disaster if they are not. The fate awaiting can be blindness, deafness, chronic heart and lung disease, or severe brain damage. It can also be limited to minor handicaps such as minimal nerve "insults" that can only be detected by the minutest muscle stiffness, the most subtly discriminating neurological work-up or machine test or cardiopulmonary function. But at birth the outcome cannot be judged by even the most experienced neonatologists.

The term *premature* can be misleading. In the case of a 500-gram baby, the medical profession is given the task of turning a fetus into a human being. Many of these very premature babies weigh less than fetuses that can be legally aborted. And the task of saving one is no easy matter. Though 98 percent of Stanford's premature babies survive, 32 percent of those between 750 and 1,000 grams and 76

percent of those below 750 don't. About 242,000 premature babies were born in the United States in 1979, more than 18,000 of them weighing less than 1,000 grams. Although national survival rates are increasing rapidly, those rates are based on all babies weighing under 2,500 grams.

Still, neonatal intensive care units report not only increased survival rates but decreases in the severity of handicap of those babies that suffer handicaps. At the Children's Hospital of Los Angeles, for example, the survival rate for babies under 2,500 grams, who suffer not only from prematurity but from respiratory and congenital diseases as well, has increased from 40 percent in 1960 to 85 percent in 1980. Of the survivors only 15 percent suffer any sort of handicap, and only one percent are stricken with severe handicaps.

The economic question is major. For a baby requiring five to six months of intensive hospital care, the cost can be as high as $200,000, though usually it is within five figures. But that such babies by definition are not flawed but merely perilously ahead of schedule only confuses the moral dilemma. "After its size and sex," says Ron Cohen, "the question parents of a premature like Matthew always ask is, 'What's wrong with my baby?' I tell them, 'Your baby is normal. His form, his needs, how he's behaving—everything is exactly normal for that stage.'

"The baby is no more sick than I am. But he's as close to death as you would be if you were suddenly transported to the surface of the moon or the bottom of the ocean. Being on the moon or the ocean floor is not a disease, but it sure as hell is life threatening. We've taken him from an environment to which he is beautifully adapted to one that can be deadly.

"In other words, without an amniotic sac to protect him, without a placenta to feed him, breathe for him, oxygenate his blood, and eliminate his waste, he needs us to give him a space suit with all those tubes and wires and needles, because Captain Kirk can't beam him back into the uterus."

Three "Kilo Kids"

Jeanette O'Kelly's fourth pregnancy was difficult from early on—a rupture of the amniotic sac, a swift infection that sent her temperature skyrocketing, an exhausting breech delivery. Still, the baby was alive and kicking. "About one pound, 11 ounces," says his mother, a former hairdresser. "I couldn't imagine anything so tiny. But he had everything: eyelashes, eyebrows, hair. The first time I saw him he was on his back with the respirator and three wires coming out of his umbilical cord. The IVs came later."

"The doctors were very gloomy," remembers her husband, Jerry, a structural engineer. "We didn't want to hear that." There were plenty of "red flag" complications. "But we couldn't visualize all those things," says Jeanette now.

The O'Kellys had to commute to the hospital at Stanford from a small coastal town 50 miles away. They made sure their three other children came with them whenever practical. "It was something happening to all of us, good or bad," Jerry says. "It was important for them to understand."

When one lung overexpanded and collapsed in a welter of cysts, the baby was put on a nerve-blocking drug that left him helpless, his tiny face swelling on the side where he lay, one eye bagging with gravity. "But then it got better," says Jeanette. "And we went on to something else." Michael's brittle bones kept breaking. "The nurses would put up signs saying 'Don't touch this leg,'" says Jerry. "Then some technician would take blood out of it and there would be more damage. It must have been very painful. As an engineer you get used to trade-offs. But with this kind of trade-off, look at what the baby has to go through. Some of it didn't seem worth it."

"There were times I wanted them just to leave him alone," Jeanette says. "But I don't think I could have quit."

At one point the O'Kellys had to watch helplessly as their baby went blind. "The doctors told us he would," says Jeanette. "You could see his eyes getting whiter and whiter. I felt then I could deal with anything. We had come so far."

At another point the carbon dioxide in Michael's blood soared so high the doctors confessed that most people aren't able to remain conscious with that much in the system. Suddenly his oxygen intake improved; suddenly it got much worse. The O'Kellys were told that if he didn't get off the ventilator then, he might never do so. Removed, the tiny infant labored mightily and reached a precarious balance with a breathing hood only. But he never came completely off the oxygen.

His parents decided to take him home to the small hospital where he had been born. Doctors concurred, informing them pointedly that Michael O'Kelly was going to require prolonged hospitalization even if he made it. The transfer went well, but for the O'Kellys, the aftermath remains a nightmare. They began to doubt the hospital was equipped to meet their child's special needs.

There are perhaps 50 to 75 top level neonatal intensive care units throughout North America, which like Stanford are laboratories outfitted to cope with the extreme highs and lows of this life-or-death confrontation. Banks of blipping lights, blinking numbers, and beeping alarms stand incessant sentry over water beds gently undulating in incubators controlled for temperature and humidity by the baby's own body. Indeed, so many electronic machines and computerized devices endlessly monitor, report, and sound warnings on such vital signs as brain waves, heartbeat, blood gases, and respiratory rate that a team of technicians must be retained to service them around the clock.

In 1980 Stanford admitted 339 prematures from throughout northern California. Forty-five were Kilogram Kids like Matthew Starkey, weighing less than 1,000 grams. Some were transported from dangerously less equipped rural areas by pre- and post-delivery mercy flights. The trend is to transfer high risk mothers before delivery so that babies like Matthew have the most sophisticated treatment at the outset. However, it is at the point of transfer to an intensive care unit when parents must make a major decision about their baby's future. When they move a child to a special facility they must be aware that the doctors and nurses there are trained to do everything possible to save the baby's life, whatever the handicaps.

There is something invincibly homey about Stanford's nursery despite the electronics. Shrewdly so, for the families'—and the staff's—sakes. Orange and yellow cats and dogs roam the fabrics of the curtains, and the woodwork and walls are painted in lollipop pastel. Tiny heads are covered with colorful wool caps to prevent heat loss. Crowns are fashioned from Styrofoam coffee cups to keep the wire leads of various telemetry carefully in place. Careful attention is paid to names. Gaily crayoned pink and blue signs proclaim, "My name is Juanita!" or "Happy Birthday, Jeffrey!" while platoons of green-gowned and blue-smocked nurses, doctors, and technicians troop easily from crib to crib with their clipboards, stethoscopes, and treatment paraphernalia. Checking and probing, laughing and questioning, conferring and weighing, deciding and prescribing.

Parents arrive for a visit to be offered an Easter or Christmas card "from" their baby. And most of the

In the midst of one feeding, Michael O'Kelly went limp and his color faded. Looking on, his mother panicked. She yelled at the nurse to call the doctor. "Machines were going off, monitors buzzing," remembers Jeanette. "The doctor was on the phone shouting for suction. She did and in a split second he came to. All he had was a mucus plug."

A few days later Jerry O'Kelly was phoned that their baby was very sick. He arrived at the hospital to find the machines disconnected. No one had told him that Michael was dead.

Having gone through the experience, the O'Kellys now feel they can handle anything—even another prematurity if it happened again. Nor do they have any doubts that things would proceed pretty much as they did before.

"As soon as you walk into that hospital and the baby gets into trouble, you lose rights as parents," Jeanette says. "They will try to save that baby."

"It has rights and they will do whatever they can to accommodate those," Jerry says. "It makes sense. There's a lot of things they can't know, don't know."

"People take that for granted," Jeanette says, "until everything goes wrong. You can try to bargain—anything over 30 weeks and we'll chance it, anything under and we won't. Doctors say we as parents don't have that choice. They say they delivered a lady 25 weeks along and her baby did fine. After Michael was born, people kept telling us stories of uncles born under two pounds who were put in the oven to keep warm and now they're over six feet tall. They made it on their own, they tell us, without technology."

Jerry O'Kelly says, "I guess it's man's nature to try to achieve more than he understands. That's what a lot of these doctors are trying to do. There's no way around that."

From the beginning, David and Elsie Sobel—not their real names—had a premonition that the birth of their daughter Dawn would not go well. "I had bad cramping and a discharge, but I didn't know how to evaluate them," recalls Elsie. "I think women need to be better educated to the early signs of premature labor. If we had alerted our doctor a few days earlier he might have been able to stop labor and give me more steroid for Dawn's lungs.

"We were told she was going to be small, but we didn't know what that meant. Frankly my fantasy was that either she would die and we would be sad or that she would live and be okay. I had no concept there was this long, serious middle ground. When we took the tour of the labor and delivery rooms, they didn't want us to see the intensive care nursery. We did and we were shocked, never believing we would be there in three weeks."

But they were. Dawn was hurried into intensive care and placed on a ventilator a few hours later. She fought it and had to be given a curarelike drug to relax her muscles so the machine could do its work. Taken off after her breathing had stabilized, she fell unconscious five days later with a large bleeder. A spinal tap found blood. Her brain waves grew abnormal, her reflexes erratic. The Sobels ⟶

homelike atmosphere in the nursery is provided by the nurses who not only serve as the babies' constant companions and day-to-day caretakers but as the major link between parents and doctors. Says Stanford's NICU head nurse Kathi Palange, "It's really hard to look at a 500-gram baby and think of it as a human being. We try to do everything we can to give parents and peers the sense of the baby as an individual." That includes hanging a profusion of snapshots amid the normal nursery mobiles. "After all," Palange continues, "many of these babies are here for six months. This is home."

Yet there remains something supernaturally eerie about it, too, something otherworldly the visitor notices only at the sudden piercing wail of a baby just graduating from a life-saving hookup: An enforced peace alien to normal infancy. For everywhere around you the desperate struggle for life rages quietly on. The fight is not only against death and trauma but also against the instruments designed to forestall them: lung and nasogastric tubes, needles, warm metal disks that can irritate sensitive skin as they coax blood to the surface and register its oxygen content. The Kilogram Kids do not protest aloud as their bigger brothers and sisters might. They cannot. Their cries are blocked by fat tubes of soft rubber and plastic.

Presiding over all this with a buoyant humanity is a chunky neonatologist with the improbable name of Philip Sunshine. At 52, Sunshine patrols the halls of his unit day and night, like some genial northside Chicago janitor, a ring of brassy keys jutting from his hip pocket. Sunshine is one of a group of doctors in the relatively new field of premature medicine who have taken it over several watersheds in the last generation.

Having accomplished this, however, neonatologists are quick to caution that nothing about the care and treatment of the extremely premature can be certain. Constant, difficult trade-offs are the rule. If you increase liquid feedings to offset weight loss, for example, fluid may build up and strain the heart and lungs. Remove it with diuretics and you risk dehydration and disruption of vital sodium and potassium balance. Add a saline solution intravenously to restore it, and the whole heart-lung-fluid strain is apt to start all over again.

At best, an infuriating paradox reigns. Robbed of their most rapid period of growth in utero (when body weight normally quadruples), Kilogram Kids have calcium-hungry bones that can be broken were told there was possibly serious brain damage. "Yet," says Elsie, "every time something else went wrong, and it did, they would try harder. More oxygen, more blood." The Sobels felt they were getting a mixed message: Dawn was bad off; Dawn might get better. "We didn't know if she would survive and, if she did, if she was so badly off that she wouldn't be any more than a vegetable. If we were going to end up with a severely damaged child, then maybe they shouldn't proceed with treatment so vigorously. I know it's a matter of personal values, but it comes down to a question of what quality of life is worth preserving. A lot of the nurses agreed with us."

"We were at our worst when we felt we were fighting the hospital," David adds. "I think they should say to parents, 'We really can't say if you're going to have a mentally disabled child or one in an institution. Think about this really carefully. This is what it might mean for the rest of your life.' And I think that's when parents should have input in which way to go."

The Sobels won what they thought was a firm, if, informal, commitment from the Stanford staff to let nature take its course. Told by a nurse the next night their daughter would probably not make it, the Sobels went to the hospital and held their first child for the first time. "It was a terribly ironic moment," remembers Elsie. "Knowing she wasn't going to make it, knowing that in many ways it was for the best." They left to sleep and make funeral arrangements, fully expecting to be awakened by a telephone call. It never came. The next morning

they learned Philip Sunshine had intervened.

"They were all ready for the baby to die," Sunshine says. "I listened to her and there was no question what the problem was. A big pneumothorax—air pocket in the chest surrounding the lung. I put a chest tube in, and she immediately came out of her decline."

"We had very mixed feelings," David Sobel recalls. "We met with him afterwards and expressed some anger that we hadn't been consulted. I learned later some sixth sense told him Dawn was going to be all right."

"Parents don't have all the perspective, but neither, in truth, do doctors," says Elsie Sobel. "They have very little perspective on what it's going to mean if the child comes out less than perfect."

"They also have a vested interest in saving lives," David adds. "So they're not neutral and independent. They have their own emotional needs and desires and drives too. I think there has to be independent adjudication. Suppose they could be sued for wrongful life? Suppose a court decided agressive treatment leading to lasting damage was grounds for a suit? Doing what they should not do—malpractice—is one thing. But what if nobody knows all the consequences of what they're doing and they do it anyway?"

"In a situation like that, if real financial responsibility were attached, I think hospital administrators would be right in there," Elsie says. "You have to make your feelings known in any case. Because in the absence of pressure from you, it will just go on and on. Even with pressure, it may."

almost by a rough glance. Yet their powers of healing and recuperation are so phenomenal that fractured bones left unset will spontaneously realign, knit, and X ray as normal by age two or three. Lungs, so ravaged by acute respiratory distress that they resemble those of terminal emphysema sufferers, heal by age three or four.

Even as they are eager to grow and develop, the preemies below 1,000 grams face another maddening hazard. They are not yet equipped to coordinate simple sucking and swallowing, much less digest and move all the food they need through the gut. Nothing in the vast and growing armamentarium of medicine can satisfy the preemie's need for calcium and other nutrients that would have been provided by the placenta. Put enough calcium in an IV and it precipitates out as "snow," minuscule

stones that can clog the tubes. Deliver it directly to the digestive tract with a tube, and the baby throws it up or the intestinal lining sloughs off, admitting bacteria which can lead to gangrene of the bowel. Hold back on calcium and the breaking bones mend but do not grow adequately. "There's no way we can get enough calcium into these kids," laments Ron Cohen. "By age three they may be developmentally on par with their peers. But sizewise, it's beginning to look as if they may never catch up."

Finally, there is the hazard of apnea, or respiratory arrest. A 26-week-old fetus in the womb does not breathe. Why should it, with a mother and placenta so ready to do it instead? "Why, then, should it know to breathe out here?" asks Cohen. "It's got a nervous system telling it it's 26 weeks old. Breathing is probably controlled by a re-

flex that's not fully developed at that gestational age. We've got kids out there who, if we turn off their ventilators, would stop breathing when they fall asleep. They don't know they're not supposed to."

Given such a mercurial prognosis, many troubled parents resent what they perceive as total hospital control over decision making. It is they after all who must live with the end results. It is a rare father or mother who doesn't at one point or another feel at least a twinge of angry resentment over this. At its most intense, according to Charlene Canger, one of the intensive care nursery's two social workers assigned full-time to such ongoing ordeals, the parental attitude can congeal into a mother's withering blast: "You want to kill my child!"

At Stanford, typically, the tougher medical decisions are the product of what is candidly con-

Sunshine agreed that before making any more major decisions the Sobels would be consulted. As it turned out, none had to be made. Today Dawn Sobel is three years old. She has a limp in her left leg and a stiff left hand that require ongoing physical therapy, and a shunt that runs beneath the skin from her brain to her intestinal cavity with a pressure-activated valve behind her ear keeping natural pathways free of excess spinal fluid that could cause hydrocephaly. If the shunt fails, the symptoms—grogginess, out-of-it behavior—look like flu, and Dawn must be raced to the hospital. She will either outgrow the need for the shunt or face further surgery to have it lengthened.

"Dawn didn't get off scot-free, and neither did we," says Elsie Sobel. "But we feel we have a delightful child. Meeting her, you can see she's perceptive, extremely verbal, and socially oriented. We've been lucky. The problems have been tough. We can tolerate living with the ones she has."

The wonder of it is," marvels Cathy Doolittle, "we have a boy who is healthy." Michael weighed 900 grams at birth, and when he came home from the Stanford hospital two weeks before his originally projected birthdate, he weighed roughly 2,200 grams (four pounds, 12 ounces). A decade later he is at the bottom of the weight chart but about average in height and retains as the only medical residue of his hazardous experience the remnants of a "lazy eye."

"He was 20/20 in his good eye, 20/200 in the other," says his mother. "Now, thanks to exercises, he can go without glasses."

Adds his father, Chuck, "He's right in there. His stamina is good and he's not a shrimp. He's on the soccer team, on the swim team. Coming out of the pool he really freezes. But you don't know if that's his normal body makeup or the prematurity."

Compared with many his size, Mike Doolittle had a relatively uncomplicated stay at Stanford despite the lack of much of today's technology. His only real peril was persisting apnea. "They had all those probes on him," remembers his mother, "and every time he stopped breathing they would yell at him to get it going again."

A crack reader who has since recovered from early dyslexia, Mike is known as the family cutup. Though he was highly excitable in kindergarten and still has problems concentrating, Mike has grown into a talkative, active, outgoing 10-year-old. His only crisis in development came when his parents decided, at the doctor's recommendation, to hold him back a year in school because of his size. Mike at first felt he had flunked, but now his grades are fine. He's had more professional care than most children, say the Doolittles, but they've always been careful to treat him like the normal child he has grown to be. Their doctor had assured them nothing can happen now to Mike that wouldn't happen to any other child. "But even though we never coddle him," says his mother, "like all preemie parents, you never stop wondering, will he really be okay?"   —J.F.

ceded to be a "benevolent despotism" operating on the venerable model of university administration—plenty of free speech for everyone, final authority coming from the top.

"The ultimate responsibility rests with one of the attending neonatologists," says David Stevenson, who divides that responsibility with two other doctors on a two-months-off, one-month-on basis. "You examine every patient, review all charts, several times a day. Ideally, you're not surprised by anything."

At Stanford the staff functions as a team. Doctors consult with each other, the social workers, and the nurses. Stevenson relies on the nursing staff for minute-to-minute guidance and information on the quick and subtle changes in the babies' conditions and for updates on the emotional status of the parents. Kathi Palange says that outsiders have difficulty thinking of their

unit as intensive care because the patients are so small, but points to the tremendous strain of watching for each sign of change in these babies coupled with advising and comforting parents. "And it isn't just parents," she says. "The babies change from better to worse, worse to better, so frequently we often have to bolster each other as well."

The Stanford teams—doctors, social workers, and nurses—often consult with parents together. Stevenson admits that parents are "hostage to circumstance" in a way that makes "choice" a misnomer. "It would be naive to think that informed consent means you give them every detail of the information you have and let them decide on the best opinion," he says. "I prefer to see informed consent as words nearer to their etymological root—helping form or shape parent thinking so they come to understand, accept, and support the ex-

pert consensus of a staff that has more *knowledge* than they do, in consultation with a physician whose competence they assume.

"What happens, finally, is the parents often borrow that opinion. We manage the medical decision making, absolutely. They depend on me for that. They would be terribly upset if because of something I knew and they didn't, I let them decide on something they would ultimately regret."

Even then, adds Ron Cohen, such decisions are difficult enough. "Seventy-five percent of the babies below 1,000 grams that we put on the ventilator survive, 25 percent don't. And on day one, we can't tell you which will be which. I do think a lot of so-called ethical issues are really questions of good or bad medicine. Not of letting a baby die or not, but of whether to treat or not treat."

Having a preemie, he goes on,

Watersheds in premature medicine

Intermittent Positive Pressure Ventilation (IPPV)

A stroke of serendipity in the late 1960s rescued the respirator, or ventilator, from its grisly reputation as a tacit kiss of death for prematures. So unsophisticated were the early machines with their simple on-off rhythm that doctors dared put only dying infants on them. Philip Sunshine and his associates suspected a self-fulfilling prophecy. Sure enough, when two more complex adult-sized models were scaled down and a policy of aggressive early intervention initiated, the data clearly indicated that babies who were ventilated did better than those who were not. What's more, curiously, those ventilated on one of the two machines did statistically better than those on the other. Why? Sunshine had both dismantled and found that the better respirator had a broken valve that would not shut entirely off. There remained always a mother's kiss of pressure that prevented the immature lung's air sacs from totally deflating once they had been forcibly evacuated. This is caused by the lack in preemies' lungs of a chemical called surfactant (surface-active agent). Production of this chemical can be stimulated by giving the mother a steroid hormone when premature labor starts, in conjunction with a labor-suppressing drug to hold off delivery long enough for the steroid to work.

The transcutaneous oxygen monitor

No larger than a nickel, this platinum cathode, when taped to the skin and heated, can monitor the level of oxygen in the blood drawn to the surface. The alternative method of periodically drawing blood gas samples with a hypodermic needle depletes little bodies of too much blood and fails to reflect moment-to-moment changes in oxygen content that can be critical in determining proper ventilator settings. Explains Cohen, "When you draw a blood gas sample you have no way of knowing where on the fluctuating oxygen curve you are getting it. If your timing is unfortunate and every time you take one you are looking at the bottom of the curve, you will continue to turn up the oxygen." Too much oxygen, doctors have discovered, could play a part in retrolental fibroplasia, blindness due to retinal detachment from damaged blood vessels. The transcutaneous monitor now enables continuous fine tuning of blood oxygen.

Ultrasound scanning

Devised in wartime to detect enemy ships, sonar has since been refined to give neonatologists a means of plumbing premature heads and hearts in search of life-menacing anomalies. Echo is the nickname of a lightweight probe that bounces a beam of sound waves off deep body structures to form a picture on a portable TV screen. Echo can find hidden "bleeders," cranial hemorrhages that can spread and devastate the brain. Bleeders afflict almost half of all Kilogram Kids, usually in an atrophying area unique to the newborn known as the germinal matrix, a capillary-packed factory where brain cells are manufactured before they migrate elsewhere. Fortunately, most bleeders stop short of being extensive, and the preemie usually escapes grave neural damage.

PDA drugs and surgery

Echo can also determine the dangerous persistence of a vestigial cardiac shunt called the PDA, patent ductus arteriosis. Nature intends the PDA as a temporary bypass to spare the developing heart the unnecessary job of pumping large volumes of blood to fetal lungs, which are strictly unused machinery before birth, since the mother breathes for her unborn child through the placenta. Everybody is born with a PDA, but it usually closes a day or so after birth—provided birth is full term. In preemies, however, the shunt remains partially open, pouring three times too much blood back through the lungs instead of routing it to the waiting body. The result may be severe heart failure. Now, Echo can be employed to pinpoint a PDA problem without inserting a catheter into the heart, and it can be corrected with an antiarthritis medication that hastens the closing by interfering with prostaglandin production. If medication doesn't correct the problem, the duct can be tied off surgically.

—J.F.

can be an immense blow, "probably as much of an emotional sledgehammer as death. The parents have just had their dream of a big, bouncing baby killed, after all. They're in shock. Mourning, grieving, going through denial, anger. There are days you come in knowing that they hate your guts and can't take it any more. But how many change their minds? After you pull the plug, it's too late."

In the end, Cohen tells you, many of the parents with handicapped kids end up saying, "I love my kid. He's not perfect, he's not going to grow up to be president, but he's the joy of my life." "Is it up to me," Cohen asks, "to say, 'Sorry, mom. He's not good enough for you,' even though you think he is?"

Phil Sunshine agrees but remembers the premature born to two Ph.D.s. The baby suffered no detectable permanent damage but his nervous system may have been affected by early oxygen deprivation. In any case, he had an average IQ—and a seven-year-old brother who tested as genius. The mother said, "I know you consider this a good outcome, but he can't do anything his brother can."

Sunshine didn't know what to say. The father said it for him: "Yeah, but he's pleasant to be around, happy, giving, and even-tempered. Maybe being able to do everything isn't all that important." Indeed, Phil Sunshine has his own fitting aphorism from the Indian savant Rabindranath Tagore: "Each newborn child brings the message that God is not yet discouraged with man."

Stevenson might agree. He says of the Starkey baby, "He is a miracle. With his birth weight, no one could have guessed he'd do so well. He surprised us all."

After PDA surgery (see box A/E p. 72) and complications that in-cluded brain hemorrhage, high bilirubin, fluid retention, dehydration, tube-caused infections, chronic lung disease, and distended bowel from forced feeding, Matthew Starkey was taken off the ventilator at seven and a half weeks and sent home a month later. At that time he weighed four pounds, four ounces (1,930 grams).

At just under six months old he weighed nine and a half pounds and has been gaining up to 12 ounces a week since he came home from the hospital. According to Ann Starkey, the only outward indication that he was a preemie is his size and a slight case of RLF disease in his eyes that may eventually lead to trouble with reading.

"He took incredible insults to his body," she says. "A preemie that small will usually be at death's door once he gets an infection. He will die before anyone figures out what's wrong. But he survived through a combination of natural resistance and the doctors' skill. For me, dealing with the doctors was one of the most positive experiences of my life. There was continual trust and caringness, and I always knew I was being well taken care of."

Development During Infancy

No age period in human development has received more attention during the past 20 years than that of infancy. To be sure, we are more certain than ever before that the first several years of life are of fundamental importance for subsequent human development. However, it is equally clear that events of infancy do not necessarily determine developmental outcome. For example, providing optimal care for infants lays the foundation for successful negotiation of the preschool and childhood years, but optimal care of the infant does not make the preschool or school-aged child any less vulnerable to inadequate caregiving. Child abuse first experienced during the school-age years can be as devastating to subsequent development as child abuse first experienced during infancy.

Despite massive research efforts, or perhaps because of them, many problems of early development remain to be solved. What are the long term effects of infant day care? What are the effects of fostercare placement on the infant's social and emotional development? Much developmental research is directed toward determining the kinds of experiences children should have, at what times these experiences should be provided, and by whom they should be provided. To what extent do sensitive periods (critical periods) set the course of development during infancy? Sensitive periods refer to times when the rate of organization occurs most rapidly. Presumably, it is during these times that the individual is most susceptible to environmental stress. For example, the sensitive period for structural differentiation of the organism is the period of the embryo, and it is during this period that the fetus is most susceptible to environmental insults. Similarly it has been suggested that the sensitive period for the organization of social attachments is from the third to the twelfth postnatal month. Studies of the effects of

maternal deprivation and poor institutional care suggest that failure to establish attachments during the first year of life are detrimental to the infant's subsequent social-emotional development. The events of a sensitive period are not irreversible as they once were thought to be. Presumably, however, the more one moves beyond a sensitive period the more difficult it is to develop the phenomenon unique to that period.

Part of the explosion in infant research involves the study of caregivers and infants in cultures other than Western ones. Cross-cultural research has broadened our concept of individual differences and has helped to clarify the relative influences of culture and species on behavioral organization. Not only are there cultural differences in rearing patterns, but there are differences in infant behavior as well. And, irrespective of culture, each infant's unique characteristics will play an important role in structuring the quality of interaction with his or her caregivers and caregiving environment.

Looking Ahead: Challenge Questions

Are there reasons why premature infants especially ought to be breast fed? What affect might it have on maternal bonding?

What sort of evidence would support the notion that infants are competent, active cognizers of the external world?

Why has it been so difficult to demonstrate behavioral continuity from the period of infancy to subsequent periods of development?

If the two-year-old shows empathy and concern for others, can this be taken as evidence to support the notion that the newborn enters the world intrinsically good, and then is corrupted by society?

The Importance of Mother's Milk

Graham Carpenter

Graham Carpenter is an assistant professor of biochemistry and medicine in the Department of Biochemistry of Vanderbilt University's School of Medicine in Nashville, Tennessee.

Reproduction of the species is considered to be the driving force in the evolution of biological systems, and nature has a large investment in a newborn organism. This is particularly true of humans and other large mammals that have relatively long gestation periods and usually produce only one or two offspring at each birth. Survival of these newborns is critical to the continuance of each species, and for almost all mammals, milk is the material that provides total nourishment during the initial stages of life. The exception is the human species, which in the last several decades has in large numbers shifted from milk to substitutes.

At the turn of the century approximately 50 percent of all newborn babies in the United States were breast-fed for at least the first twelve months of life. Recent surveys indicate that during the 1970s about one in three babies was nursed during the first month of life. Concurrently, the duration of breast-feeding declined rapidly, to the point that about 5 percent of all infants were nursed until six months of age and 1 percent until twelve months of age. At present there is a shift among new mothers to return to breast-feeding, but this group is small in relation to the total population. In today's era, when information is prized and decision making based on biological instinct is, perhaps unfortunately, frowned upon,

it would seem that data about such an important commodity as milk (and its commercial formula substitutes) should be of concern to both the public and the medical profession.

Too frequently the assumption is made that "milk is milk," and whether a newborn human drinks mother's milk or cow's milk is of no large consequence. A second assumption is that today's technology is so advanced that artificial formulas can duplicate the quality of natural human milk. Both of these assumptions are incorrect. Comparison of the composition of milk from various species shows that there exist significant qualitative and quantitative differences, which seem to reflect the varying needs of each species for proper development in early life. For example, compared to human milk, the milk of the bovine species has twice as much protein, which after digestion provides the newborn with a source of raw materials, that is, amino acids, for muscle growth. This increased protein content reflects the needs of almost all newborn animals (excluding humans) to grow rapidly in order to avoid predators, become independent quickly, and survive. A newborn cow, for instance, will double its birth weight in about 50 days, whereas a newborn human requires 180 days. Because human milk is relatively low in protein does not mean that it is insufficient in that respect. Human infants do not need to add bulk as rapidly as other newborn animals, but have different needs, including maintaining a higher rate of brain growth.

Myelination—the surrounding of nerve axons with a lipoprotein membrane, or sheath, necessary for the proper conduction of nerve impulses—is an important process of human brain growth in the first year of life. Myelination requires substantial quantities of lipid, and human milk has a relatively

high lipid content. Lipid intake is also important for the baby of lower weight who, to maintain a proper body temperature, must produce fat for insulation.

Comparative analyses of milk compositions provide many examples such as these and quite strongly demonstrate that each species has during its evolution devised a milk composition that is optimal for its specific needs. The high degree of sophistication of the biological mechanisms that control the composition of milk is demonstrated by the capacity of mothers of preterm babies to produce a milk with a higher content of protein and lipid than is found in the milk of mothers of full-term babies. Nature apparently provides the preterm, low-weight infant with extra protein to increase its body mass, or weight, and with extra lipid to stabilize body temperature and to provide more fuel for energy production.

Most of our present knowledge of milk composition concerns those components that are present in milk in the largest amounts—macronutrients such as protein, carbohydrate, and lipid. There is also a reasonable body of data describing the levels and different types of minerals and vitamins. Milk, however, is more complex than is currently understood, and there are increasing feelings in the scientific community that, in addition to satisfying nutritional needs, milk may provide other, subtle but important factors for growth and development in the newborn. For example, the antibodies passed through milk from mother to child help the newborn, whose ability to produce antibodies has not fully developed, resist microbial infections. Breast-fed babies do, in fact, suffer fewer infections, particularly of the gastrointestinal tract, than formula-fed babies.

Hormones, the body's chemical messengers, are other kinds of molecules present in milk. Most hormones are either proteins (insulin, for example) composed of many amino acids or have chemical structures related to steroids. A characteristic of all hormones is that they are present in body fluids in exceedingly small quantities compared with other components. Nevertheless, hormones play a vital role in regulating body chemistry and physiology. For instance, an individual can ingest large amounts of carbohydrates but unless insulin is present the carbohydrates will not be utilized properly. Similarly, other hormones control virtually all processes that the body carries out. There are a number of hormones known to be present in human milk, but their significance has not been demonstrated. This does not mean these molecules have no significance; it simply means that none is yet understood.

Also present in milk is an interesting class of hormones—often referred to as growth factors—that controls cell growth and differentiation. Research in this area is relatively new and it is very likely that many more growth factors will be identified in the future. Of those now known, one of the most thoroughly investigated is epidermal growth factor, or EGF. Epidermal growth factor is a small protein molecule composed of fifty-three amino acid residues. Discovered in the early 1960s in mice by Stanley Cohen, a biochemist at Vanderbilt University, this hormone has since been detected in many mammalian species. It is present in almost all human body fluids, including milk, where its concentration (approximately thirty nanograms per milliliter) is quite significant for a hormone.

The classic procedure for determining the function of a hormone has been to surgically remove the hormone-producing organ and record the resultant effects of the hormone deficit. The observed effects can be attributed to the hormone deficit if the effects are prevented or reversed by injection of the hormone into the animal. This experimental strategy is not always possible, however. In the case of EGF, it is not known where in the body the hormone is produced, and the available evidence suggests that there are probably several distinct sites. Therefore, it has not been possible to determine unequivocally what functions EGF serves. There are experiments, however, that demonstrate quite interesting biological effects when EGF is administered to animals. These results probably provide good clues to the natural function of this hormone.

Cohen's pioneering studies demonstrated that EGF had a pronounced stimulatory effect on the growth and differentiation of the outermost layer of the body, the epidermis of the skin—hence the name epidermal growth factor. In those initial experiments, newborn mice were injected daily with small quantities of EGF, and an intriguing result was observed. Normally, a newborn mouse is born with its eyelids shut and, without exception, its eyelids open at thirteen to fourteen days after birth. But baby mice injected with the epidermal growth factor opened their eyelids in seven days. The proliferation of skin cells in the eyelid area and their differentiation, a process called keratinization, had been accelerated. Later studies have demonstrated that the effect was not limited to the eyelid area; all areas of the epidermis were similarly stimulated to proliferate and keratinize in newborn animals treated with EGF.

More recent experiments have shown that EGF stimulates epithelial tissues other than the skin. The entire gastrointestinal tract is lined with epithelial tissue, and several studies have shown that EGF stimulates cell division and accelerates certain differentiation events in this tissue. During development in the perinatal period, the cells of the gastrointestinal tract begin to produce hydrolytic enzymes—protein molecules required for the digestion of food. The rates of activity of these enzymes are generally low at birth and increase as the infant matures. If these digestive enzymes do not develop at the correct time, the infant is less able to utilize food to sustain its nutritional requirements, and obviously, a long delay in the maturation of the digestive enzymes has serious consequences. A recent study by a Canadian group at the University of Sherbrooke in Quebec reports that when newborn mice are injected with EGF the maturation of several digestive enzymes is accelerated. Thus the hormone may have a significant function in the growth and development of this important system.

A second critical transition for the newborn infant occurs at birth, when maternal oxygen, which was delivered *in utero,* is no longer available; suddenly oxygen must be taken in from the air and, via the lungs and circulatory system, made available to the tissues. Failure to adjust successfully to atmospheric oxygen at birth creates a respiratory distress syndrome called hyaline membrane disease. This is, of course, a serious condition, and one that is seen not infrequently in the baby born prematurely. The premature infant is especially vulnerable to this problem because the final stages of lung maturation in the fetus normally occur just prior to full-term birth. Hyaline membrane disease cannot be predicted before birth, and the mortality rate is low but significant.

This respiratory syndrome has been studied in newborn lambs, and the results show that in cases where pregnant ewes are subjected to stress and their lambs delivered prematurely, many of the lambs (75 percent) die soon after birth of respiratory distress similar to the hyaline membrane disease seen in human infants. When the fetal lambs are infused *in utero* with EGF for a few days prior to premature delivery, however, development of the lung epitheliums is accelerated, respiratory distress is infrequent, and almost all of the lambs survive. Moreover, in these same experiments, accelerated growth of epithelial tissue is noted not only in the lungs but also in other areas of the pulmonary epithelium, such as the trachea and esophagus.

An epithelial tissue in adults that appears to be very sensitive to EGF is the corneal epithelium in the eye. This tissue is important for sight and can be easily injured. Research has shown that in both experimental animals and in humans, EGF accelerates the proliferation of cells in a wounded area of the corneal epithelium, thereby hastening the wound-healing process. Because EGF is present in milk, a natural fluid, clinical trials are being conducted to determine whether milk might be a feasible treatment for corneal lesions. In fact, the use of EGF as a general wound-healing agent is being considered. In this regard, it is interesting to note that folk medicine often prescribes the application of urine to wounds. And in war situations this practice has been employed when other treatments were not immediately available. Urine is usually a sterile solution and contains high amounts of EGF.

Nature is often remarkably ingenious in devising strategies to maximize the utility of its products. In the case of protein molecules, it is not unusual for one protein to be capable of carrying out more than one distinct function. At the level of molecular architecture this is not a trivial engineering task. In addition to its capacity to stimulate cell growth and differentiation, the EGF molecule has a second biological activity. When administered to experimental animals and to humans, this hormone blocks the release of excess gastric acid induced by a variety of chemicals, such as histamine or pentagastrin.

The ability of EGF to control acid secretion in the stomach was discovered unexpectedly in 1975 when a British research group at Imperial Chemical Industries isolated and determined the structure of urogastrone—a protein hormone known since the 1920s to be present in high quantities in the urine of pregnant women and to be an inhibitor of acid secretion. Computer comparisons of urogastrone with other known proteins revealed that the primary structures (that is, the sequences of amino acids) of urogastrone and EGF are so nearly identical (within the limits of experimental technology) that one can conclude they are the same molecule. Thus milk-fed infants receive a hormone that may help to prevent discomforts and injuries to the stomach lining (ulcers, for example) resulting from excess gastric acid.

Scientists have been increasingly successful at removing selected cells from the intact animal and maintaining these cells in a growing state for long periods of time in the laboratory. This technique, called cell culture, involves placing the cells in a plastic dish with a defined medium of glucose, minerals, vitamins, and amino acids. Under these conditions the cells remain viable but do not grow. For growth and cell division to occur, serum—a blood fraction—is added to the medium. Serum apparently contains hormones, or growth factors, necessary to regulate cell growth and division and for many years has been considered to be indispensable for this purpose. Recent experiments, however, have shown that milk is also able to stimulate cell proliferation in cell culture and can make up for approximately 95 percent of the serum requirement. Biologically, this suggests that milk is a fluid rich in the factors that control cell growth, and EGF appears to be a key ingredient in milk for the stimulation of cell division. This has been demonstrated by treating milk with antibodies to EGF.

Antibodies are highly specific reagents that are able to recognize one particular protein molecule in a mixture of thousands of slightly different protein molecules. Antibodies bind to the protein they recognize and often inactivate it. When milk is treated with antibodies to EGF, the capacity of the milk to stimulate cell growth is reduced by 90 percent. This has been demonstrated in cell culture with human fibroblasts (connective tissue cells) and human glia cells (brain-derived cells). Different types of cells are known to vary in their responsiveness to any particular hormone; therefore, it is possible that milk may contain additional growth factors other than EGF that stimulate different cell types. For example, erythropoietin, a protein growth factor that controls the development of red cells in the blood, is known to be present in milk.

In summary, we know that EGF is able to exert a significant influence on the proliferation and differentiation of various types of epithelial cells in the intact animal. We also know that this hormone is present in physiologically significant quantities in milk. Is there a connection? Is milk a physiological vector for the delivery of important hormones to the infant? These intriguing questions will have to wait for further research before answers can be provided. To resolve some obvious questions, however, a few additional comments can be made at this time. If the hormone is ingested in milk and affects the growth and development of tissue in the gastrointestinal tract, it must be able to resist conditions in the gastrointestinal tract that cause the digestion of most protein molecules. Studies of the chemistry of EGF have shown that the hormone's activity is not destroyed by exposure to strong acid or proteases (enzymes that digest protein molecules). Therefore, it is not unreasonable to suggest that this growth factor may remain biologically active in the normally adverse conditions, for a protein molecule, of the gastrointestinal tract.

If EGF also affects other epithelial tissues, such as that of the lungs, then there is a second problem: the growth factor would have to be absorbed into the circulatory system by passing through the lining of the gastrointestinal tract. That this apparently can occur has been demonstrated in the experiments conducted with newborn mice. The results showed that oral administration, as well as subcutaneous injection, of EGF resulted in precocious eyelid opening, indicating that the hormone was absorbed from the gastrointestinal tract into the systemic circulation. This has not, however, been demonstrated with humans, and animal species differ in terms of which proteins will be absorbed.

As already mentioned, large numbers of babies in the United States are not fed with mother's milk but receive commercial formulas with either a soybean or bovine milk base. Does this make a difference as far as growth factors are concerned? Cells grown in culture can be stimulated to grow and divide by either human or bovine milk. When various commercial formulas were tested, however, none were able to stimulate cell proliferation. This is not to be taken as an indictment of the commercial formulas—certainly many children have been raised on formula without apparent adverse consequences. These results indicate that human milk is not duplicated by the industrial products and that our scientific technology is not always able to better or even equal nature.

Biology is one key to the bonding of mothers and babies

Hara Estroff Marano

Hara Estroff Marano is a science writer living in New York City, and executive editor of American Health *magazine.*

Pink and plump, the infant shrieks his discomfort to the world he entered less than 48 hours before. Pediatrician T. Berry Brazelton materializes at one side of the wailing, flailing infant, and lowers his head to its level. "Hi there," he croons. "Can you turn over here if I talk to you?" The baby turns his head to the voice, seems to search for its source, and stops crying.

With this simple demonstration (although this youngster may be exceptionally responsive), Dr. Brazelton contradicts the old idea that babies can neither see nor hear at birth. He also dramatizes a major discovery about human development. It is a discovery only in the sense that science is beginning to recognize what sensitive mothers have suspected all along—that newborns come highly equipped for their first intense meetings with their parents, and in particular their mothers.

At birth, Dr. Brazelton and others have found, not only do many babies orient themselves to sound, they prefer the sound of the human voice, especially the high pitch of the female voice. They choose to look at faces over other objects and will follow with their eyes the turning of a nearby human face. They may imitate facial gestures such as sticking out a tongue, and they synchronize their body movements to the rhythm of the human voice.

Unable to cling to the fur of a highly mobile mother (as do monkeys), the human infant depends for all of its early needs on the strength of its mother's emotional attachment. How mother and infant become emotionally attached—some call it bonded—to each other is a subject of serious investigation by growing numbers of psychologists, psychiatrists and pediatricians in the United States. The current wave of interest began building about 15 years ago, as technological gains dramatically improved premature babies' chances of survival.

Drs. Marshall Klaus and John Kennell at Rainbow Babies' and Children's Hospital in Cleveland, and others who run the intensive-care nurseries that sprang up to treat premature infants, made a startling observation. They found that in spite of their near-heroic measures to save tiny premature infants, a disproportionate number of them wound up back in hospital emergency rooms, battered and abused by their parents, even though they had been sent home intact and thriving. One of the contributing factors seemed to them to be the prolonged separation of mothers and infants which was then routine following premature births. Such separations can sometimes interfere with the bond that usually forms under more natural circumstances, Drs. Klaus and Kennell believe.

Getting a handle on this bond was not easy, Dr. Klaus now admits. He first had to overcome the limitations of his training as a pediatrician. "It took me some time to turn my eyes from the baby to the mother; only then did I fully realize that the mother is the instrument through which the baby can thrive."

Nor is the problem limited to premature babies. Reports of child abuse and neglect are increasingly common. According to the National Center for Child Abuse, three of every hundred infants need medical attention for injuries suffered at the hands of parents. Then there are the subtler forms of abuse—neglect and growth failure without organic cause—that do not always find their way to hospitals or headlines. In addition, there is the growing sense that the ability to cope and handle stress is acquired through the parent-infant relationship.

Among those who are probing mother-infant bonds, some researchers adopt for their models monkeys and other animals, both in the wild and in the laboratory; but while mother-infant attachment occurs in many animals as well as humans, bonding in humans occurs in a very specific and complex way. Other investigators comb through the family histories of children for whom such bonds failed to develop. Still others chronicle the actions of normal mothers and children going about their daily routines at home, or observe them in special laboratories set up to film them during brief separations and reunions.

But all are aimed at gathering information to help improve the relations between parents and children in the United States. Taken together, their work constitutes the first major attempt to analyze scientifically what is often seen only through rose-colored glasses, if at all—how human relationships develop.

Dr. Brazelton is one of the numerous investigators parsing the relationship between mothers and infants and between fathers and infants as well. His observations at Harvard and at Boston Children's Hospital lead him to believe that a mother's emotional attachment to her infant does not descend on her by some obstetrical deus ex machina in the delivery room. It develops gradually, beginning in the feelings and dreams many women experience about themselves and their unborn babies during pregnancy.

Anxiety and disruption of old concepts through dreams, Dr. Brazelton thinks, may become part of a normal process, an "unwiring" of all the old connections to be ready for the new role. Prenatal anxiety whips up the energy a woman needs for greeting the individuality of the new baby. Evidence is amassing that as she does so, she is responding to the hormonal signals guiding her pregnancy to a close.

Evolutionary biologists, who take a long-range view of human behavior, see parenting as much too important to be left to whimsy. They hold that behavior that is so critical to the survival of both individuals and the species must have some biologic base, must somehow be wired into the nerve circuits of the brain. This notion strikes a strong chord with one of the emerging themes of modern neuroscience—that behavior has more innate components than most of us have been led to believe.

Most of the evidence supporting the idea of a "biologic base" comes from experiments with rats and sheep. As science proceeds by the careful building of inferences, scientists look to such animals for clues to what might be going on in humans. Not that we, like the experimental rat, are held in hormonal thrall. But the rigorous experiments that are possible with animals can lead to new insights, confirmed by close observation of human behavior. In looking at the earliest stages of maternal attachment in rats, Drs. Jay Rosenblatt and Harold Siegel of Rutgers University have discovered two distinct phases, a hormonally triggered burst of interest followed by a more psychologically based need for continued contact.

Hormones may trigger mothering in animals

About a day before mother rats give birth (ten days before birth in sheep and three weeks before birth in humans) their hormonal status changes dramatically. The blood level of progesterone, the hormone that sustains pregnancy by keeping the laden uterus quiescent, declines sharply, and the level of estrogen rises. The main point of his work, Dr. Rosenblatt says, is to show that "the onset of maternal behavior before delivery is based on this rise in estrogen." An animal facing a litter of pups, as young rats are called, before the change, stays as far away from them as possible. So do virgin rats. If, however, the virgins are caged with pups, left with them day in and out, then they become maternal toward them after four to seven days, and the smaller the cage, the faster it happens. That can be contrived in a laboratory, where it is possible to remove the litter each day and give them needed care while substituting a fresh batch of age-mates. But in real life, such animals would be dead within 48 hours. Yet when a virgin rat is given a transfusion of blood from a new mother, she becomes maternal within ten to 14 hours. She will preside over the litter as if it were her own. Although she cannot lactate, she assumes the nursing position, crouching over her pups. She will

do all in her power to keep the pups close, retrieve them when they stray. Blood taken from animals before the hormonal shift, or more than 24 hours after birth, has no effect on her.

"We know," says Dr. Rosenblatt, "that without the hormones, the rats' initial aversion to pups is a fear of them. It appears to be part of a basic fearfulness of anything new. And little pups are certainly something new and novel for them."

The hormones, he says, reduce the fearfulness. "They tip the balance of responding to the young, making the mother ignore or overcome the unattractive features." In essence, he says, the hormones change the animals' motivation. "Of all the stimuli a mother faces, she selects certain ones to attend to. Of all the things she can do, she does only certain things. If, before a rat gives birth, we offer her a baby and a piece of food, she chooses the food. Right after birth, she chooses the baby. That is a motivational shift."

Because all rats—virgins and even males, as well as new mothers—become maternal if given enough time with pups, Dr. Rosenblatt concludes that all rats share the neural system that underlies maternal behavior. He thinks the same is probably true of primates. Among the colony of rhesus monkeys at the Rutgers Institute of Animal Behavior, which he heads, it is not uncommon for a never-pregnant animal to adopt a baby. "Like the rat, rhesus monkeys have some inherent capacity to be maternal. But that doesn't mean there's no physiologic basis for it." Unfortunately, he notes, no one is testing hormones in monkeys.

Closeness keeps mothers maternal

Rosenblatt's rat studies show that hormones trigger a maternal response, but also that hormones don't keep the animals responsive. Only the pups themselves do that. A certain amount of close contact with the pups shortly after birth is needed for the mother to maintain the responsiveness that the hormones activated. If a rat gives birth but isn't allowed any contact with her litter, but is given her pups back later, she won't be maternal toward them. It will take her about a week to overcome her resistance to them, as if she had never been pregnant. But if a new mother is allowed several hours of contact with her new litter before they are removed, she will still be highly maternal if they are given back days or even weeks later.

Do Rosenblatt's studies throw any light on observations of human mothers and infants? Shortly after Klaus and Kennell suspected that mother-infant separation might be partly responsible for the unusually high rate of battering among premature babies, they opened the doors of the premature nursery to mothers, although in taking such a radical step they had no proof that what they were doing was safe or even helpful. Indeed, the medical canons of the era held that the mothers could contaminate their babies. (Dr. Klaus, with Drs. Cliff Barnet, Herbert Leiderman and

Rose Grobstein of Stanford University, demonstrated that the infection rate didn't change in preemie nurseries after mothers were let in.)

Invariably, the mothers approached their infants with a substantial amount of residual fear, as if precipitous birth had cut short their hormonal and psychological ripening. At first, they stalked the incubators, circling them for one to two visits; eventually, they would make an approach, poking their babies with their fingertips. Finally, they stroked their babies' arms and legs, moving, after four to eight visits, from the extremities to the babies' trunk—something mothers of full-term infants do exuberantly within minutes of greeting their babies, provided they are afforded the privacy and emotional support for a "rendezvous."

This period of rendezvous after normal births, which Rosenblatt's studies suggest is important, has been commonly overlooked in American obstetrical practice. Seen with the cool eye of clinical observation, what develops between mothers and babies who are permitted close contact after birth is a sort of "mating dance," an elaborate courtship in which, ideally, they link their behavior through every available channel of communication into a smooth pattern of signal and response.

A high state of alertness in both mother and infant is helpful in getting things rolling. Not only does the infant come headlong into the world unfurling such a repertoire of social skills that those who notice them are apt to refer to "the amazing newborn," but babies born to unmedicated mothers have an incredible capacity for alertness in the first hours after birth. Newborns, says Dr. Klaus, spend nearly 40 minutes of their first hour on Earth in a state of rapt attention. During this time, their eyes are shiny-bright, wide open, and capable of focusing and fixating on objects. During this state of high alertness newborns will follow with their eyes and head a slowly moving object, especially a face. This prolonged alertness, says the Cleveland pediatrician, "is especially suited for meeting parents. It often fosters parental feeling and a sense of ecstasy in parents."

In humans, it's love at first sight

It is the visual attentiveness that·seems to matter most to parents. When mothers talk to their babies just after birth, 80 percent of what they say is related to eyes. "Please open your eyes. If you open your eyes I'll know you're alive," is a phrase Dr. Klaus has heard many times. Most striking, when mothers are put together with their babies, they shift around to arrange themselves *en face* with their infants—that is, they align themselves so that their eyes and the babies' eyes are in the same plane of rotation. In doing so, mothers seem to be searching for a signal. "A mother can't easily become bonded to her infant unless the baby responds to her in some manner," explains Dr. Klaus,

who restates his observation as possibly one of the basic principles of bonding: "You can't love a dishrag."

Giving flesh to Yeats' declaration that "love comes in at the eye," mother and infant often move through a behavioral sequence which, Drs. Klaus and Kennell find, is not very different from what happens when a man and woman fall in love: mutual gazing, touching, fondling, nuzzling, kissing. Together, they fall into step with each other, their synchrony epitomized sometimes by a baby moving its head in rhythm to its mother's words.

Nothing better illustrates the interdependence of needs than the act of a mother breast-feeding her baby. There are both emotional and physical benefits, for mother and infant. Breast-fed infants, for example, have measurably fewer infections and develop fewer allergies than bottle-fed babies. "The most powerful way to forge a strong bond between mother and infant is through breast-feeding," says Dr. Kennell. "It continues the process begun early after birth. As a social exchange, it is rewarding for mother and baby over and over." His observations have convinced him that the more mothers and babies are together shortly after birth, the stronger is the attachment between them and the more natural mothering becomes. (At the same time, Dr. Klaus points out that it does not always happen instantly. He cites studies showing that about 25 percent of mothers "fall in love" with their babies before birth, from 25 to 30 percent in the first hours. For about 40 percent, it takes a week or even longer.) So powerful is the early attachment that its effects on both mothers and babies are discernible years later.

Drs. Klaus and Kennell have demonstrated this experimentally, in their own pediatric bailiwick. "The hospitals served as a natural laboratory," says Klaus. "In America, where hospital separation is routine, most of us look separately at mothers and babies. Being together is·biologic and natural. Separation is abnormal and frightening." They studied a group of mothers and babies who got routine care. For comparison, they followed another group of mothers and babies who were put in a warm room where they could lie together unclothed for an hour after birth and who were again together five more hours on each of the first three days after delivery.

Starting a month after birth and throughout the next five years—the study is still under way—the Cleveland pediatricians found important differences between the two groups of mothers and babies. A month after birth, when they came back for a special office visit, the early-contact mothers stood closer to their infants, picked up their crying babies more. During feedings (which were filmed), they more often stayed in the *en face* position and fondled their babies. Interviews revealed they were more reluctant to leave their infants with someone else. And they reported that when they did go out, they found themselves constantly thinking about the baby.

A year later, they still were more attentive to their babies during an uncomfortable office visit. They helped the pediatrician approach the reluctant babies. After two years, the early-contact mothers talked differently to their children from the control mothers, although there were no differences among the two groups of mothers that could account for such an observation—all were from the same socioeconomic class and scored about the same on I.Q. tests. Yet the early-contact mothers used richer language constructions and more words, especially descriptive adjectives. They issued fewer commands to their children but asked more questions. What is more, the early-contact mothers continued to speak to their children when other adults came into the room, while the control mothers talked more to the adult interviewer.

"The early-contact mothers presented a model of better learning," says Dr. Kennell. Their speech had more variety, more opportunity for response. "They gave more stimulation to the child's thinking. They seemed to be more aware of the needs of growing children. They could interpret the environment better to them.

"To think all that is the result of just 16 hours of being together in the first three days of life," sighs Dr. Kennell. "The hours after birth seem to comprise a sensitive period for maternal-infant attachment."

Early contact may reduce child abuse

At Nashville General Hospital, Dr. Susan O'Connor has found that, by putting mothers together with their babies during the hospital stay after birth, she can help a significant proportion of women to overcome some of the personal and cultural pulls that could lead them to neglect their infants. Dr. O'Connor, assistant professor of pediatrics at Vanderbilt University, feels that "this is an area of research that shows real promise." She cautions, however, that we must not "look upon it as the answer to all our problems." Indeed, none of the researchers feels early bonding solves all the problems of parenting. Nor do they believe that the lack of very early contact must preclude the forming of an affectionate bond. Dr. Klaus points out that adoptive mothers often do "a great job."

If the early falling in love is somewhat magical, coaxed out of a built-in bag of tricks, staying in love over the next months and years takes work. Even so, Harvard pediatrician Brazelton and Cornell University psychiatrist Daniel Stern see it, quite literally, as a form of child's play. They have recorded such play —in separate but similar studies—by videotaping several mothers and babies in face-to-face encounters, at home and in special laboratories, and later analyzing and reanalyzing the film. Both doctors find that mother-infant play is built on tiny advances and retreats, thrusts and parries, that go by too fast for most people to see what is happening but which sensitive mothers nevertheless apprehend. It has taken Dr. Brazelton as long as 28 hours to catch all there is to see in three minutes of film!

In the earliest stages, mother leads the game, reaching over to draw her baby out. Gradually, the baby essays a few smiles, throws out a few vocalizations, and starts up the game himself. He reaches out to get her, she brightens to his overtures, feeding him talk and facial expressions—the elements of communication—until, overloaded with stimulation, he averts his head to recover himself, before beginning again.

Throughout, the mother serves as a protective "envelope" for her baby, screening out the background noise of the world, letting through only as much stimulation and information as she learns to expect he can handle, enlarging the envelope as her baby signals his readiness for more before he turns away. (Fathers, Dr. Brazelton finds, do something different with their babies. They excite them more, even when they assume a primary care-taking role. Where mothers soothe, fathers tend to whisk their babies off onto gleeful excursions—and babies seem to expect it of them.)

As the mother forms a protective envelope for her baby, so does baby form one for her. In ways that are physiologically measurable, the attachment of mother and infant buffers them both from the effects of stress. The most striking evidence of this comes from studies with monkeys, showing that mother-infant contact lowers the levels of the "stress hormone" cortisol.

This buffering system, says Stanford University psychologist Seymour Levine, "permits a mother to focus on her infant and the baby to focus on his mother. Through the mother-infant relationship, he develops a coping response. He finds he can do something about his environment."

Biologically speaking, today's mothers and babies are two to three million years old. Are there behavioral characteristics that come to us as part of our genetic makeup, as do such characteristics as bone size and blood type? "A mother must take care of her baby, must be close to him," says Dr. Klaus. And mothers have been taking care of their babies for millions of years. "We think that when we put the body of a mother close to her baby, something is turned on that is part of her genetic makeup." The human infant, he concludes, seems to have been built to communicate with its mother. The evidence points to a sophisticated signaling system between them. "If this is so," he says, "then babies make sense. Then the puzzle of their unusual talents begins to unravel."

NEWBORN KNOWLEDGE

Richard M. Restak

Richard M. Restak is a Washington, D.C., neurologist whose book, The Self Seekers, *was published in June 1982.*

Infant researcher Louis W. Sander has a favorite home movie. It depicts a young married couple standing on the lawn outside their home. The woman is holding their eight-day-old baby who, as the film opens, turns fussy and restless. She hands the baby to her husband, who casually takes the child and places it in the crook of his arm while continuing an animated conversation with the cameraman. As the film unfolds, the father appears to ignore his newborn baby. The baby too seems to be unaware of the father. Nevertheless, after just a few seconds the infant stops crying, grows quiet, and finally, drops off to sleep.

A slow motion, frame-by-frame analysis of the movie reveals a different story. The father looks down several times at his baby, who returns the gaze. Infant and father begin to reach for each other. The baby clasps the little finger of the father's hand and, at that moment, falls asleep.

What delights Sander is the sensibility of the infant, a quality not generally associated with newborns. In light of a host of similar observations, partly made possible by innovative use of videotape, scientists are revising a long-held belief that newborns are passive creatures waiting for the world to imprint its wisdom on them. From at least the moment of birth, infants are enormously responsive.

This new knowledge is bringing about a quiet revolution that will affect everything from when and how a baby is delivered to the kind of advice obstetricians and pediatricians offer to new parents.

According to T. Berry Brazelton, Chief of the Child Development Unit of the Children's Hospital Medical Center in Boston, only moments out of the womb, infants are capable of a wide variety of behavior. Eyes alert, they turn their heads in the direction of a voice (they prefer a female pitch), inquisitively searching for the source of the sound that attracted them. Sander, professor of psychiatry at the University of Colorado Medical Center, and William Condon, a professor of psychiatry at Boston University Medical Center, have observed that the infant moves its arms and legs in synchrony to the rhythms of human speech. Disconnected vowel sounds, random noise, or tapping do not suffice; only the natural rhythms of speech will do. And it does not matter what language the infant initially hears: Infants in Sander and Condon's study responded to Chinese in the same way they responded to English. Such behavior provides support for theorists such as Massachusetts Institute of Technology linguist Noam Chomsky, who believes the human capacity for language is inborn and requires only appropriate exposure for normal speech development.

Newborns are particularly attracted to faces. A baby will turn its head and eyes while following a moving drawing of a face, but if pieces of the drawing are scrambled, it loses interest. Soon after birth it recognizes its parents and begins to fasten a special kind of attention on them.

At the Children's Hospital Medical Center in Boston, films of four-week-old infants demonstrate that babies behave differently with their parents than they do with other people and, not surprisingly, with objects. When a bright toy is brought within reach, the infant's attention is hooked, and its fingers and toes point toward the toy with gleeful expectation, but the baby quickly loses interest and gazes elsewhere. A few seconds later a second round of attention begins. The pattern of attention and loss of interest is jagged and irregular. With the mother, in contrast, the baby's movements are smooth and cyclic, and its attention pattern is more sustained.

Babies pay special attention to their fathers as well. "Amazingly enough," says Brazelton, "when several weeks old, an infant displays an entirely different attitude —more wide-eyed, playful, and bright-faced—towards its father than towards its mother." Brazelton describes these cycles with the father as "higher, deeper, and more jagged," corresponding to the father's "more playful, jazzed-up approach." One explanation for the infant's behavior, Brazelton says, is that fathers, on the whole, behave as if they expect more heightened, playful responses from their babies.

Researchers also are beginning to recognize something most relaxed parents have always known:

3. INFANCY

Playing with one's infant is a very important element in its normal, healthy development. This marks a refreshing change from the rather grim, tight-lipped preoccupation with feeding and elimination that has been fashionable in some circles in recent years.

"I think there are several assumptions about infants that we now have to question very seriously," says Daniel Stern, author of *The First Relationship: Infant and Mother*. In his laboratory at New York Hospital's Payne Whitney Clinic, Stern has captured on film delicate and evanescent exchanges between mother and infant. Often their responses occur within microseconds, suggesting, according to Stern, an inborn mutual readiness of both mother and infant to respond to each other.

Infant researcher Charles A. Ferguson, a linguist at Stanford University, agrees. In a whimsically entitled study, "Baby Talk in Six Languages," he finds that mothers of six different nationalities speaking their native languages all use a special version of baby talk with their infants. Sometimes the baby elicits from its mother behavior she has never practiced nor seen. Her speech is marked by short sentences, simplified syntax, and nonsense sounds, transforming phrases such as "pretty rabbit" into "pwitty wabbit." When talking to their babies, mothers invariably raise the pitch of their voices, with long stretches of speech in the falsetto range. They prolong eye contact with the infant well beyond what is normal between adults. Two grown-ups will stare at each other with the same intensity only when they are extremely aroused emotionally—enraptured lovers or fierce enemies.

There are other ways in which infants and parents establish their special relationships. Through trial and error, they establish routines that are mutually gratifying. For example, most parents do not enjoy waking at 3:00 A.M. to feed their babies, so they attempt to persuade the infants to sleep through the night. When the baby learns this routine, a sense of harmony is created not only between infant

and parents but with the rest of the household as well. At this point the baby has finally become an authentic family member.

Gradually and painstakingly, parent and infant establish other routines: mealtime, playtime, even time when it's all right to be cranky. As each mutual adjustment is negotiated, the bond between the two is strengthened. But when these routines are interrupted or, worse, never established, family life can become an unpleasant series of interrupted meals, hurt feelings, and short tempers. Anyone who has ever experienced jet lag knows what it's like to be out of phase with other people's biological rhythms—nodding asleep in a chair, for example, while others are ready for dinner. So, too, parents and baby all want to have something to say about when food is served, diapers changed, and games played.

Early on the infant learns a wide variety of useful skills; for instance, it combines sight, sound, and touch into meaningful patterns. A three-week-old, blindfolded and allowed to rub its tongue along a toy block, will later gaze at a picture of a block in preference to other objects, a neat demonstration that the infant already integrates sight and touch.

A three-month-old shown two cartoons simultaneously, with the sound track of one played in the background, will stare selectively at the movie that corresponds to the sound track. The infant's skill at matching sound with picture can be carried even further by superimposing the two movies on top of one another and then slowly separating them. The infant's attention turns to the film that matches the sound track.

In dealing with people the infant exhibits even more astonishing acumen. By one week of age a baby can pick out its mother's voice from a group of female voices and at two weeks can recognize that the mother's voice and face are part of a unit. British researcher Genevieve Carpenter tested two-week-old babies by exposing them to four different situations: 1) the mother speaking to her infant in her own

voice, 2) a strange woman speaking to the infant in her own voice, 3) the mother speaking in the female stranger's voice, and 4) the stranger speaking in mother's voice. The babies responded most favorably to the first situation, illustrating that as young as two weeks a baby can tell mother from stranger. More interesting, however, were the infants' responses to the third and fourth situations. They cried and turned away from this bizarre and frightening combination of the familiar and the strange.

Another fascinating study showed that infants and mothers respond to each other when the mother appears on closed-circuit TV screens nearly as effectively as when they are together. But if a baby watches a videotaped recording of its mother, it quickly loses interest, its eyes begin to wander, and it begins to fret. Infants evidently recognize that they get no personal response from their videotaped mothers, while in the live exchanges on closed-circuit TV, baby and mother can make eye contact.

One area of research that is particularly intriguing—and controversial—is whether it is essential for mothers and newborns to spend time together immediately after birth. Marshall Klaus and John Kennell of Case Western Reserve School of Medicine in Cleveland have demonstrated that mothers who are allowed an hour with their infants immediately following birth in addition to five hours in the next three days behave differently from other mothers denied the same amount of time with their newborns. During their first hour, infants may spend an astonishing 85 percent of the time in an alert, wakeful state, eyes wide open and inquisitive, a situation that may promote a bond between mother and child. When filmed during the infant's first exam at one month, for example, the mothers who were allowed more time with their infants (so-called extended contact mothers) were more reluctant to leave their babies with strangers and preferred to stay and watch the exam. When the babies were fussy, these mothers were more soothing. Feeding, too, was different: The extended contact mothers all held their babies so that they could look at them face to face.

When filmed during the infants' first-year checkups, the extended contact mothers continued to demonstrate active interest and participation, often helping the pediatrician if their babies were fearful or restless. At two years, these mothers tended to ask questions of their children rather than issue commands. The vocabulary the mothers used was richer and more stimulating, which according to some studies may result in higher infant IQs.

Intrigued with Klaus and Kennell's findings, other researchers extended their studies and found that increased contact between a mother and her healthy, full-term infant in the first few days and weeks after birth is associated with fewer instances of later child abuse. Increased contact also correlates with less infant crying, more rapid infant growth, increased affection,

and more self-confidence on the part of the mother.

In fact, many infant researchers now believe that increased contact between mother and infant in the first few days of life affects maternal behavior and infant development for periods of from one month to five years. Some believe the beneficial effects that stem from increased alertness and responsiveness last a lifetime. No one knows for sure. "We strongly believe that there is a sensitive period in the first few minutes and hours after the infant's birth which is optimal for infant-parent attachment," says Klaus.

Critics of the Klaus-Kennell theory feel there are other factors that contribute to optimal bonding. They argue that adopted children, premature babies, and infants born to mothers too sick to respond to them in their first few days still develop normal, affectionate relationships with their mothers. Nonetheless, even critics agree that allowing mother and infant to be

together during the first few hours is humane and natural. As a result, even though all the evidence is not in, hospitals throughout the world are beginning to allow mother and baby time together in the first hours after birth.

Doctors and hospital administrators are also beginning to realize that intensive care units and rigid hospital routines are potential disrupters of the natural interaction between mother and child. Robert N. Emde, professor of psychiatry at the University of Colorado Medical School, believes it is extremely important for parents and children to be together as much as possible. "For years, theories described how mothers shaped babies, but we are now beginning to appreciate how much babies shape mothers"—and fathers as well.

"No longer can we look upon a newborn as a lump of clay ready to be molded by the environment," says Brazelton. "We've come a long way in our understanding of just how marvelous a creature a human infant really is."

ETHNIC DIFFERENCES IN BABIES

Striking differences in temperament and behavior among ethnic groups show up in babies only a few days old.

DANIEL G. FREEDMAN

Daniel G. Freedman, *professor of the behavioral sciences at The University of Chicago, spent last fall in Australia as a visiting fellow in the department of anthropology at the Australian National University in Canberra. There he extended his research into the newborn capacities of Australian aborigines. His doctorate in psychology from Brandeis University was followed by a postdoctoral fellowship at Mt. Zion Psychiatric Clinic and the Langley Porter Neuropsychiatric Institute in San Francisco. Much of the information in this article appears in an expanded form in Freedman's book,* Human Sociobiology, *published by the Free Press. With Fred Strayer and Donald Omark, Freedman edited* Human Status Hierarchies.

The human species comes in an admirable variety of shapes and colors, as a walk through any cosmopolitan city amply demonstrates. Although the speculation has become politically and socially unpopular, it is difficult not to wonder whether the major differences in physical appearances are accompanied by standard differences in temperament or behavior. Recent studies by myself and others of babies only a few hours, days, or weeks old indicate that they are, and that such differences among human beings are biological as well as cultural.

These studies of newborns from different ethnic backgrounds actually had their inception with work on puppies, when I attempted to raise dogs in either an indulged or disciplined fashion in order to test the effects of such rearing on their later behavior.

I spent all my days and evenings with these puppies, and it soon became apparent that the breed of dog would become an important factor in my results. Even as the ears and eyes opened, the breeds differed in behavior. Little beagles were irrepressibly friendly from the moment they could detect me; Shetland sheepdogs were very, very sensitive to a loud voice or the slightest punishment; wire-haired terriers were so tough and aggressive, even as clumsy three-week-olds, that I had to wear gloves while playing with them; and finally, Basenjis, barkless dogs originating in Central Africa, were aloof and independent. To judge by where they spent their time, sniffing and investigating, I was no more important to them than if I were a rubber balloon.

When I later tested the dogs, the breed indeed made a difference in their behavior. I took them, when hungry, into a room with a bowl of meat. For three minutes I kept them from approaching the meat, then left each dog alone with the food. Indulged terriers and beagles waited longer before eating the meat than did disciplined dogs of the same breeds. None of the Shetlands ever ate any of the food, and all of the Basenjis ate as soon as I left.

I later studied 20 sets of identical and fraternal human twins, following them from infancy until they were 10 years old, and I became convinced that both puppies and human babies begin life along developmental pathways established by their genetic inheritance. But I still did not know whether infants of relatively inbred human groups showed differences comparable to the breed differences among puppies that had so impressed me. Clearly, the most direct way to find out was to examine very young infants, preferably newborns, of ethnic groups with widely divergent histories.

Since it was important to avoid projecting my own assumptions onto the babies' behavior, the first step was to develop some sort of objective test of newborn behavior. With T. Berry Brazelton, the Harvard pediatrician, I developed what I called the Cambridge Behavioral and Neurological Assessment Scales, a group of simple tests of basic human reactions that could be administered to any normal newborn in a hospital nursery.

In the first study, Nina Freedman and I compared Chinese and Caucasian babies. It was no accident that we chose those two groups, since my wife is Chinese, and in the course of learning about each other and our families, we came to believe that some character differences might well be related to differences in our respective gene pools and not just to individual differences.

Armed with our new baby test, Nina and I returned to San Francisco, and to the hospital where she had borne our first child. We examined, alternately, 24 Chinese and 24 Caucasian newborns. To keep things neat, we made sure that all the Chinese were of Cantonese (South Chinese) background, the Caucasians of Northern European origin, that the sexes in both groups were the same, that the mothers were the same age, that they had about the same number of previous children, and that both groups were administered the same drugs in the same amounts. Additionally, all of the families were members of the same health plan, all of the mothers had had approximately the same number of prenatal visits to a doctor, and all were in the same middle-income bracket.

It was almost immediately clear that we had struck pay dirt; Chinese and Caucasian babies indeed behaved like two different breeds. Caucasian babies cried more easily, and once started, they were harder to console. Chinese babies adapted to almost any position in which they were placed; for example, when placed face down in their cribs, they tended to keep their faces buried in the sheets rather than immediately turning to one side, as did the Caucasians. In a similar maneuver (called the "defense reaction" by neurologists), we briefly pressed the baby's nose with a cloth. Most Caucasian and black babies fight this maneuver by immediately turning away or swiping at the cloth with their hands, and this is reported in most Western pediatric textbooks as the normal, expected response. The average Chinese baby in our study, however, simply lay on his back and breathed through his mouth, "accept-

ing" the cloth without a fight. This finding is most impressive on film.

Other subtle differences were equally important, but less dramatic. For example, both Chinese and Caucasian babies started to cry at about the same points in the examination, especially when they were undressed, but the Chinese stopped sooner. When picked up and cuddled, Chinese babies stopped crying immediately, as if a light switch had been flipped, whereas the crying of Caucasian babies only gradually subsided.

In another part of the test, we repeatedly shone a light in the baby's eyes and counted the number of blinks until the baby "adapted" and no longer blinked. It should be no surprise that the Caucasian babies continued to blink long after the Chinese babies had adapted and stopped.

It began to look as if Chinese babies were simply more amenable and adaptable to the machinations of the examiners, and that the Caucasian babies were registering annoyance and complaint. It was as if the old stereotypes of the calm, inscrutable Chinese and the excitable, emotionally changeable Caucasian were appearing spontaneously in the first 48 hours of life. In other words, our hypothesis about human and puppy parallels seemed to be correct.

The results of our Chinese-Caucasian study have been confirmed by a student of ethologist Nick Blurton-Jones who worked in a Chinese community in Malaysia. At the time, however, our single study was hardly enough evidence for so general a conclusion, and we set out to look at other newborns in other places. Norbett Mintz, who was working among the Navaho in Tuba City, Arizona, arranged for us to come to the reservation in the spring of 1969. After two months we had tested 36 Navaho newborns, and the results paralleled the stereotype of the stoical, impassive American Indian. These babies outdid the Chinese, showing even more calmness and adaptability than we found among Oriental babies.

We filmed the babies as they were tested and found reactions in the film

we had not noticed. For example, the Moro response was clearly different among Navaho and Caucasians. This reaction occurs in newborns when support for the head and neck suddenly disappears. Tests for the Moro response usually consist of raising and then suddenly dropping the head portion of the bassinet. In most Caucasian newborns, after a four-inch drop the baby reflexively extends both arms and legs, cries, and moves in an agitated manner before he calms down. Among Navajo babies, crying was rare, the limb movements were reduced, and calming was almost immediate.

I have since spent considerable time among the Navaho, and it is clear that the traditional practice of tying the wrapped infant onto a cradle board (now practiced sporadically on the reservation) has in no way induced stoicism in the Navaho. In the halcyon days of anthropological environmentalism, this was a popular conjecture, but the other way around is more likely. Not all Navaho babies take to the cradle board, and those who complain about it are simply taken off. But most Navaho infants calmly accept the board; in fact, many begin to demand it by showing signs of unrest when off. When they are about six months old, however, Navaho babies do start complaining at being tied, and "weaning" from the board begins, with the baby taking the lead. The Navaho are the most "in touch" group of mothers we have yet seen, and the term mother-infant unit aptly describes what we saw among them.

James Chisholm of Rutgers University, who has studied infancy among the Navaho over the past several years, reports that his observations are much like my own. In addition, he followed a group of young Caucasian mothers in Flagstaff (some 80 miles south of the reservation) who had decided to use the cradle board. Their babies complained so persistently that they were off the board in a matter of weeks, a result that should not surprise us, given the differences observed at birth.

Assuming, then, that other investigators continue to confirm our findings, to what do we attribute the differences on the one hand, and the similari-

3. INFANCY

ties on the other? When we first presented the findings on Chinese and Caucasians, attempts were made to explain away the genetic implications by posing differences in prenatal diets as an obvious cause. But once we had completed the Navaho study, that explanation had to be dropped, because the Navaho diet is quite different from the diet of the Chinese, yet newborn behavior was strikingly similar in the two groups.

The point is often still made that the babies had nine months of experience within the uterus before we saw them, so that cultural differences in maternal attitudes and behavior might have been transferred to the unborn offspring via some, as yet unknown, mechanism. Chisholm, for example, thinks differences in maternal blood pressure may be responsible for some of the differences between Navahos and Caucasians, but the evidence is as yet sparse. Certainly Cantonese-American and Navaho cultures are substantially different and yet the infants are so much alike that such speculation might be dismissed on that score alone. But there is another, hidden issue here, and that involves our own cultural tendency to split apart inherited and acquired characteristics. Americans tend to eschew the inherited and promote the acquired, in a sort of "we are exactly what we make of ourselves" optimism.

My position on this issue is simple: We are totally biological, totally environmental; the two are as inseparable as is an object and its shadow. Or as psychologist Donald O. Hebb has expressed it, we are 100 percent innate, 100 percent acquired. One might add to Hebb's formulation, 100 percent biological, 100 percent cultural. As D. T. Suzuki, the Zen scholar, once told an audience of neuropsychiatrists, "You took heredity and environment apart and now you are stuck with the problem of putting them together again."

Navaho and Chinese newborns may be so much alike because the Navaho were part of a relatively recent emigration from Asia. Their language group is called Athabaskan, after a lake in Can-

ada. Although most of the Athabaskan immigrants from Asia settled along the Pacific coast of Canada, the Navaho and Apache contingents went on to their present location in about 1200 A.D. Even today, a significant number of words in Athabaskan and Chinese appear to have the same meaning, and if one looks back several thousand years into the written records of Sino-Tibetan, the number of similar words makes clear the common origin of these widely separated peoples.

When we say that some differences in human behavior may have a genetic basis, what do we mean? First of all, we are *not* talking about a gene for stoicism or a gene for irritability. If a behavioral trait is at all interesting, for example, smiling, anger, ease of sexual arousal, or altruism, it is most probably polygenic—that is, many genes contribute to its development. Furthermore, there is no way to count the exact number of genes involved in such a polygenic system because, as geneticist James Crow has summarized the situation, biological traits are controlled by one, two, or *many* genes.

Standing height, a polygenic human trait, can be easily measured and is also notoriously open to the influence of the environment. For this reason height can serve as a model for behavioral traits, which are genetically influenced but are even more prone to change with changing environment.

There are, however, limits to the way that a given trait responds to the environment, and this range of constraint imposed by the genes is called a *reaction range*. Behavioral geneticist Irving Gottesman has drawn up a series of semihypothetical graphs illustrating how this works with regard to human height; each genotype (the combination of genes that determine a particular trait) represents a relatively inbred human group. Even the most favorable environment produces little change in height for genotype A, whereas for genotype D a vast difference is seen as nutrition improves.

When I speak of potential genetic differences in human behavior, I do so with these notions in mind: There is overlap between most populations and

the overlap can become rather complete under changing conditions, as in genotypes D and C. Some genotypes, however, show no overlap and remain remote from the others over the entire reaction range, as in genotype A (actually a group of achondroplastic dwarfs; it is likely that some pygmy groups would exhibit a similarly isolated reaction range with regard to height).

At present we lack the data to construct such reaction-range curves for newborn behavior, but hypothetically there is nothing to prevent us from one day doing so.

The question naturally arises whether the group differences we have found are expressions of richer and poorer environments, rather than of genetically distinguishable groups. The similar performance yet substantial difference in socioeconomic status between Navaho and San Francisco Chinese on the one hand, and the dissimilar performance yet similar socioeconomic status of San Francisco Chinese and Caucasians on the other favors the genetic explanation. Try as one might, it is very difficult, conceptually and actually, to get rid of our biological constraints.

Research among newborns in other cultures shows how environment—in this case, cultural learning—affects reaction range. In Hawaii we met a Honolulu pediatrician who volunteered that he had found striking and consistent differences between Japanese and Polynesian babies in his practice. The Japanese babies consistently reacted more violently to their three-month immunizations than did the Polynesians. On subsequent visits, the Japanese gave every indication of remembering the last visit by crying violently; one mother said that her baby cried each time she drove by the clinic.

We then tested a series of Japanese newborns, and found that they were indeed more sensitive and irritable than either the Chinese or Navaho babies. In other respects, though, they were much like them, showing a similar response to consolation, and accommodating easily to a light on the eyes or a cloth over the nose. Prior to our work, social anthropologist William Caudill had made an extensive and thorough

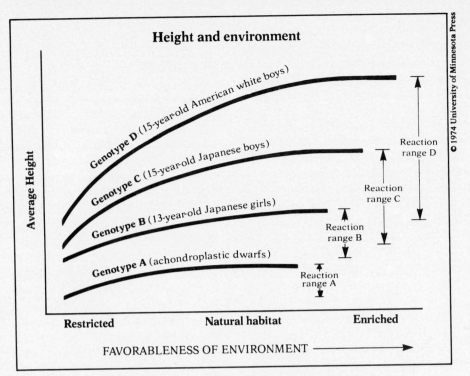

Height and environment

Genotype D (15-year-old American white boys)

Genotype C (15-year-old Japanese boys)

Genotype B (13-year-old Japanese girls)

Genotype A (achondroplastic dwarfs)

Average Height

Reaction range D

Reaction range C

Reaction range B

Reaction range A

Restricted   Natural habitat   Enriched

FAVORABLENESS OF ENVIRONMENT ⟶

© 1974 University of Minnesota Press

The concept of reaction range shows clearly in this comparison of adolescent groups: the better the environment, the taller the person. Although some groups show considerable overlap in height, no matter how favorable the environment, height cannot exceed the possible reaction range.

study of Japanese infants. He made careful observations of Japanese mother-infant pairs in Baltimore, from the third to the twelfth month of life. Having noted that both the Japanese infants and their mothers vocalized much less to one another than did Caucasian pairs, he assumed that the Japanese mothers were conditioning their babies toward quietude from a universal baseline at which all babies start. Caudill, of course, was in the American environmentalist tradition and, until our publication appeared, did not consider the biological alternative. We believe that the mothers and babies he studied were, in all probability, conditioning each other, that the naturally quiet Japanese babies affected their mothers' behavior as much as the mothers affected their babies'.

With this new interactive hypothesis in mind, one of my students, Joan Kuchner, studied mother-infant interactions among 10 Chinese and 10 Caucasian mother-infant pairs over the

first three months of life. The study was done in Chicago, and this time the Chinese were of North Chinese rather than South Chinese (Cantonese) ancestry. Kuchner started her study with the birth of the babies and found that the two groups were different from the start, much as in our study of newborns. Further, it soon became apparent that Chinese mothers were less intent on eliciting responses from their infants. By the third month, Chinese infants and mothers rarely engaged in bouts of mutual vocalizing as did the Caucasian pairs. This was exactly what the Caudill studies of Japanese and Caucasians had shown, but we now know that it was based on a developing coalition between mothers and babies and that it was not just a one-way street in which a mother "shapes" her infant's behavior.

Following our work, Caudill and Lois Frost repeated Caudill's original work, but this time they used third-generation Japanese-American moth-

16. Ethnic Differences in Babies

ers and their fourth-generation infants. The mothers had become "super" American and were vocalizing to their infants at almost twice the Caucasian rate of activity, and the infants were responding at an even greater rate of happy vocalization. Assuming that these are sound and repeatable results, my tendency is to reconcile these and our results in terms of the reaction-range concept. If Japanese height can change as dramatically as it has with emigration to the United States (and with post-World War II diets), it seems plausible that mother-infant behavior can do the same. On a variety of other measures, Caudill and Frost were able to discern continuing similarities to infant and mother pairs in the old country. Fourth-generation Japanese babies, like babies in Japan, sucked their fingers less and were less playful than Caucasian babies were, and the third-generation mothers lulled their babies and held them more than Caucasian American mothers did.

A student and colleague, John Callaghan, has recently completed a study comparing 15 Navaho and 19 Anglo mothers and their young infants (all under six months). Each mother was asked to "get the attention of the baby." When video tapes of the subsequent scene were analyzed, the differences in both babies and mothers were striking. The Navaho babies showed greater passivity than the Caucasian babies. Caucasian mothers "spoke" to their babies continually, using linguistic forms appropriate for someone who understands language; their babies responded by moving their arms and legs. The Navaho mothers were strikingly silent, using their eyes to attract their babies' gaze, and the relatively immobile infants responded by merely gazing back.

Despite their disparate methods, both groups were equally successful in getting their babies' attention. Besides keeping up a stream of chatter, Caucasian mothers tended to shift the baby's position radically, sometimes holding him or her close, sometimes at arm's length, as if experimenting to find the best focal distance for the baby. Most of the silent Navaho mothers used only subtle shifts on the lap, holding the baby at about the same distance throughout. As a result of the intense stimulation by the Caucasian mothers, the babies frequently turned their heads away, as if to moderate the intensity of the encounter. Consequently, eye contact among Caucasian pairs was of shorter duration (half that of the Navaho), but more frequent.

It was clear that the Caucasian mothers sought their babies' attention with verve and excitement, even as their babies tended to react to the stimulation with what can be described as ambivalence: The Caucasian infants turned both toward and away from the mother with far greater frequency than did the Navaho infants. The Navaho mothers and their infants engaged in relatively stoical, quiet, and steady encounters. On viewing the films of these sequences, we had the feeling that we were watching biocultural differences in the making.

Studies of older children bear out the theme of relative unexcitability in Chinese as compared to Anglos. In an independent research project at the University of Chicago, Nova Green studied a number of nursery schools. When she reached one in Chicago's Chinatown, she reported: "Although the majority of the Chinese-American children were in the 'high arousal age,' between three and five, they showed little intense emotional behavior. They ran and hopped, laughed and called to one another, rode bikes and roller-skated just as the children did in the other nursery schools, but the noise level stayed remarkably low, and the emotional atmosphere projected serenity instead of bedlam. The impassive facial expression certainly gave the children an air of dignity and self-possession, but this was only one element effecting the total impression. Physical movements seemed more coordinated, no tripping, falling, bumping, or bruising was observed, nor screams, crashes or wailing was heard, not even that common sound in other nurseries, voices raised in highly indignant moralistic dispute! No property disputes were observed, and only

the mildest version of 'fighting behavior,' some good-natured wrestling among the older boys. The adults evidently had different expectations about hostile or impulsive behavior; this was the only nursery school where it was observed that children were trusted to duel with sticks. Personal distance spacing seemed to be situational rather than compulsive or patterned, and the children appeared to make no effort to avoid physical contact."

It is ironic that many recent visitors to nursery schools in Red China have returned with ecstatic descriptions of the children, implying that the New Order knows something about child rearing that the West does not. When the *New Yorker* reported a visit to China by a group of developmental psychologists including William Kessen, Urie Bronfenbrenner, Jerome Kagan, and Eleanor Maccoby, they were described as baffled by the behavior of Chinese children: "They were won over by the Chinese children. They speak of an 'attractive mixture of affective spontaneity and an accommodating posture by the children: of the 'remarkable control of young Chinese children'— alert, animated, vigorous, responsive to the words of their elders, yet also unnervingly calm, even during happenings (games, classroom events, neighborhood play) that could create agitation and confusion. The children were far less restless, less intense in their motor actions, and displayed less crying and whining than American children in similar situations. We were constantly struck by [their] quiet, gentle, and controlled manner . . . and as constantly frustrated in our desire to understand its origins.' "

The report is strikingly similar to Nova Green's description of the nursery school in Chicago's Chinatown. When making these comparisons with "American" nursery schools, the psychologists obviously had in mind classrooms filled with Caucasian or Afro-American children.

As they get older, Chinese and Caucasian children continue to differ in roughly the same behavior that characterizes them in nursery school. Not surprisingly, San Francisco school-

teachers consider assignments in Chinatown as plums—the children are dutiful and studious, and the classrooms are quiet.

A reader might accept these data and observations and yet still have trouble imagining how such differences might have initially come about. The easiest explanation involves a historical accident based on different, small founding populations and at least partial geographic isolation. Peking man, some 500,000 years ago, already had shovel-shaped incisors, as only Orientals and American Indians have today. Modern-looking skulls of about the same age, found in England, lack this grooving on the inside of their upper incisors. Given such evidence, we can surmise that there has been substantial and long-standing isolation of East and West. Further, it is likely that, in addition to just plain "genetic drift," environmental demands and biocultural adaptations differed, yielding present-day differences.

Orientals and Euro-Americans are not the only newborn groups we have examined. We have recorded newborn behavior in Nigeria, Kenya, Sweden, Italy, Bali, India, and Australia, and in each place, it is fair to say, we observed some kind of uniqueness. The Australian aborigines, for example, struggled mightily against the cloth over the nose, resembling the most objecting Caucasian babies; their necks were exceptionally strong, and some could lift their heads up and look around, much like some of the African babies we saw. (Caucasian infants cannot do this until they are about one month old.) Further, aborigine infants were easy to calm, resembling in that respect our easy-going Chinese babies. They thus comprised a unique pattern of traits.

Given these data, I think it is a reasonable conclusion that we should drop two long-cherished myths: (1) No matter what our ethnic background, we are all born alike; (2) culture and biology are separate entities. Clearly, we are biosocial creatures in everything we do and say, and it is time that anthropologists, psychologists, and population geneticists start speaking the same language. In light of what we know, only a truly holistic, multidisciplinary approach makes sense.

For further information:

Caudill, W., and N. Frost. "A Comparison of Maternal Care and Infant Behavior in Japanese-American, American, and Japanese Families." *Influences on Human Development,* edited by Urie Bronfenbrenner and M. A. Mahoney. Dryden Press, 1972.

Chisholm, J. S., and Martin Richards. "Swaddling, Cradleboards and the Development of Children." *Early Human Development,* in press.

Freedman, D. G. "Constitutional and Environmental Interaction in Rearing of Four Breeds of Dogs." *Science,* Vol. 127, 1958, pp. 585-586.

Freedman, D. G. *Human Infancy: An Evolutionary Perspective.* Lawrence Erlbaum Associates, 1974.

Freedman, D. G., and B. Keller. "Inheritance of Behavior in Infants." *Science,* Vol. 140, 1963, pp. 196-198.

Gottesman, I. I. "Developmental Genetics and Ontogenetic Psychology." *Minnesota Symposia on Child Psychology,* Vol. 8, edited by A. D. Pick. University of Minnesota Press, 1974.

WE WANT YOUR ADVICE

Any anthology can be improved. This one will be—annually. But we need your help.

Annual Editions revisions depend on two major opinion sources: one is the academic advisers who work with us in scanning the thousands of articles published in the public press each year; the other is you—the person actually using the book.

Please help us and the users of the next edition by completing the prepaid article rating form on the last page of this book and returning it to us. Thank you.

Your Child's Self-Esteem

Paul Chance

Paul Chance, Ph.D., is a free-lance writer who specializes in psychology.

Consider Alice, age five. Alice attends kindergarten, where she is making excellent progress. Her teacher thinks she is one of the brightest children in the class, though in fact she has no more natural ability than most. She is often the first to raise her hand when the teacher asks a question, waving it eagerly and sometimes calling out, "I know! I know!" If called on when she does not know an answer, she does not hesitate to make a guess. Sometimes these answers sound foolish to her classmates, but their laughter doesn't bother Alice—she justs laughs right along with them. Alice tackles almost every assignment with enthusiasm. If one approach fails, she tries another. If her persistence does not pay off, she asks the teacher for help. Alice is as comfortable with other children as she is with her schoolwork. She is a popular child, and in group activities she often takes the lead. At home, Alice is eager to do things for herself. She is proud, for instance, that she can already dress herself completely, buttons, shoelaces, and all, without help.

Now consider Zelda, age six. Zelda is in the first grade. She did not do very well in kindergarten, and her progress continues to be slow. Her teacher believes that she is one of the least intelligent children in the class, though in fact she has as much ability as most. She never volunteers, and if called on she usually refuses to say more than "I don't know." Zelda works on most assignments in a lackluster, mechanical manner and often abandons them at the first sign of difficulty. When her teacher asks if she needs help, she says merely, "I can't do it." Zelda is no more adept socially than she is academically. She has few friends, and in group activities she is usually the quiet one on the sidelines. At home, Zelda is more at ease and more loquacious, but not more self-reliant. She waits for others to do things for her because she "can't" do them for herself. Her mother still checks her each morning to be sure that she has dressed herself properly.

Competence has little to do with natural ability.

Alice and Zelda are as far apart as the letters *a* and *z*. The differences that separate them are not, however, due to differences in native ability. The differences are emotional and motivational. Alice is obviously self-assured and self-reliant. She likes herself and her world. Although she could not put her philosophy into words, she is an optimist. She believes that she has some degree of control over her destiny, that success and happiness are goals an individual can achieve through effort. Zelda, on the other hand, is as filled with self-doubt as Alice is with self-confidence. Her self-esteem is low and she thinks the world a harsh, unfriendly place. A philosopher would describe her as a fatalist, a person who believes that what happens is largely a matter of fate or chance. Zelda believes that she can do little to shape her future, that success and happiness are things that "just happen" to people who get lucky. Although Alice and Zelda have about the same amount of intelligence, it is clear that Alice is making far better use of her abilities. The result is that Alice is a highly competent child, while Zelda is best described as helpless.

Why do some children become Alices, while others become Zeldas? This question has received intensive study over the past decade. Most researchers seem convinced that experiences in infancy and early childhood play an especially important role in the development of competence, so their research efforts have focused on experiences in the first three years of life. This is not to say, of course, that whether a person becomes highly competent or utterly helpless is unalterably fixed by age three. People can change at any age. Nevertheless, the evidence suggests that the kinds of experiences that are important to the development of competence typically *begin* in early childhood. What are those experiences? The research on this subject is complex and not easily reduced to a few simple, clear-cut statements. But over and over again, the studies reveal four elements common to the backgrounds of the most competent children but conspicuously missing from the backgrounds of the least competent.

The importance of a strong parent-child bond.

It may come as no surprise to most parents that one common element in the backgrounds of very competent children is a strong bond between the child and the primary care-giver—usually, but not necessarily, the mother. Dr. Alan Sroufe, professor of child development, and his co-workers at the University of Minnesota, Twin Cities, have found, for instance, that infants judged "securely attached" at eighteen months of age were more successful at solving problems, such as getting an object out of a tube, at age two. They were also better able to elicit the help of their mothers to solve problems that were too difficult for them. They were, in other words, already more competent than children who lacked a strong bond with their mothers.

The signs of a secure child.

Dr. Sroufe notes that it is possible to predict which children will be successful preschoolers by studying the relationship a child has with his caretaker at twelve to eighteen months of age. "Even by two years," he says, "secure children will be more enthusiastic, persistent, and cooperative in solving problems than insecure children will be." Children with a good, secure relationship with an adult can function well in a nursery school at a younger age than can children without such a relationship. "Apparently," Dr. Sroufe concludes, "secure children

have learned early how to explore and master their environment and function within clear, firm limits."

Perhaps the most extensive work on the relationship between a close attachment and child development is that of Dr. Burton White, former director of the Preschool Project at Harvard University, and his colleagues. Their research followed the progress of 40 children, beginning at age one or two. The researchers went into the homes of these children every other week, 26 times a year, for one or two years, and then retested the children again at the ages of three and five. The researchers concentrated on the interactions of the infants with their mothers and others in the home. They concluded that a close social relationship "was a conspicuous feature in the lives of children who developed best."

Another way to study the benefits of a love bond, as it might be called, is by looking at the development of children for whom such a bond is notably lacking. One sometimes finds such children in poorly staffed institutions. Dr. Sally Provence, professor of pediatrics at Yale University's Child Study Center, who has made a special study of such children, observes that they often become "subdued and apathetic." Given a little tender loving care, however, these children often liven up dramatically.

Providing a stimulating environment.

Another common element in the backgrounds of competent children is a stimulating environment. Dr. K. Alison Clarke-Stewart, associate professor of education and human development at the University of Chicago, studied the interactions of mothers with their firstborn infants, ages nine to thirteen months. She found, among other things, that mothers of competent children talked to or made other sounds when interacting with their babies more often than did the mothers of less competent infants. Dr. White and his co-workers were so impressed by the role of verbal stimulation in the development of competence that they wrote that "live language directed to the child is the most consistently favorable kind of educational experience an infant can have during the eleven- to sixteen-month period." They go on to point out that language from a television or radio or speech directed elsewhere that the

child overhears has little if any beneficial effect.

Freedom to explore can make even an ordinary environment more stimulating than it is from afar. An environment that is full of interesting objects a child cannot get to is less stimulating than one with fewer objects that are within reach. Dr. White and his collaborators found, in fact, that freedom of movement was characteristic of the homes of competent children. The more freedom to explore about the house (within the limits prescribed by safety, of course), the more competent a child was likely to be.

The evidence for the benefits of a stimulating environment suggests that a dull, monotonous environment is a prescription for helplessness. This theory seems to be borne out by the classic research of renowned psychiatrist René Spitz, who studied the development of children living in the thoroughly monotonous world of a badly understaffed foundling home. These children had little to do all day but sleep or stare at the blank walls about them. Needless to say, such children do not develop normally, but the degree to which their development is retarded is striking. Dr. Spitz offers this description of the typical child reared in such an impoverished environment: "These children would lie or sit with wide-open, expressionless eyes, frozen immobile face, and a faraway expression as if in a daze, apparently not perceiving what went on in their environment."

Fortunately for such children, a little bit of stimulation can have substantial benefits. For instance, psychologists Wayne Dennis and Yvonne Sayegh gave institutionalized infants in an otherwise impoverished environment items such as flowers, bits of colored sponge, and a chain of colored plastic discs to play with for as little as an hour each day. It is hard to believe that so little improvement in their thoroughly monotonous environment would make a great difference, yet their developmental ages jumped dramatically.

Interactions—with parents . . .

It is, of course, possible to get too much of a good thing. Dr. White believes that too much stimulation, too many things going on around the child, may merely confuse him. This idea is supported by a study conducted by Dr. Jerome Kagan, professor of human development at Harvard University, who watched mothers as they interacted with their four month-old infants. He noted when the mothers spoke to or cooed to their babies and what else they were doing at the time. He found that upper-middle-income mothers usually spoke to their children while facing them but did *not* simultaneously tickle them or provide other stimulation. Low-income mothers, on the other hand, were likely to talk to their infants while diapering, feeding, or burping them. It is probably not a coincidence, Dr. Kagan observes, that the children of upper-middle-income mothers typically show more precocious language development than do the children of low-income mothers.

Most researchers seem to agree that a varied environment is important to the development of competence, but the quality of the stimulation is more important than the amount.

A third characteristic of the backgrounds of competent children is frequent social interaction. Dr. White has found, for instance, that highly competent children have at least twice as many social experiences as their less competent peers. He says that "providing a rich social life for a twelve- to fifteen-month-old child is the best thing you can do to guarantee a good mind." He also notes that firstborn children have far more opportunities to interact with their parents than do later-born children. The rich social life of firstborns may have something to do with the fact that they are usually (though not always, of course) more competent than their siblings are. They are, for instance, more likely to obtain positions of leadership as adults than are later-born children.

...and with others.

Psychologist Michael Lewis, director of the Institute for the Study of Exceptional Children at the Educational Testing Service in Princeton, New Jersey, believes that the child's interactions with other people are more important than his interactions with any other part of the environment. "We learn about others through our interaction with them," he writes, "and at the same time we define ourselves." How does a child learn whether he is a boy or a girl, tall or short, strong or weak? Through his interactions with others who treat him as a boy rather than a girl, and who are taller or shorter, stronger or weaker, than he is. How does he learn whether

he is competent or helpless? Partly, argues Dr. Lewis, through his interactions with the people around him.

Studies of social isolation have shown that even when other forms of stimulation are available, a dearth of social experiences can have devastating effects. Dr. Harry Harlow and his colleagues at the University of Wisconsin at Madison found that monkeys reared alone grew up to be timid, wholly inadequate individuals. Monkeys reared by their mothers but separated from other youngsters of their kind fared better, but still developed abnormally. Thus it appears likely that the more opportunities for social encounters a child has, the better. It is even possible to see social competence emerge as a result of such experience. When, for example, California psychologist Jacqueline Becker gave pairs of nine-month-old babies the opportunity to play with one another, she found that they interacted more and more with each succeeding session. When these youngsters were introduced to a new baby, they were much more likely to approach him than were infants who had had less social experience.

A world that responds.

Probably the most important element in the environments of highly competent children is something that researchers call *responsivity*. A responsive environment is one that *responds to* the behavior of the child. There is, in other words, some correspondence between what the child does and what happens to him. Under ordinary circumstances there is at least a minimal amount of responsivity in the life of every child. Take, for example, the baby nursing at his mother's breast. As Dr. Martin Seligman, professor of psychology at the University of Pennsylvania, writes: "He sucks, the world responds with warm milk. He pats the breast, his mother tenderly squeezes him back. He takes a break and coos, his mother coos back. . . . Each step he takes is synchronized with a response from the world." When a child's behavior has clear, unequivocal consequences, he not only learns about those consequences but "over and above this," writes Dr. Seligman, "he learns that responding works, that in general there is *synchrony* between responses and outcomes." This means, in turn, that the child exerts some control over his environment, and many

researchers agree with Dr. Seligman that "how readily a person believes in his own helplessness or mastery is shaped by his experience with controllable and uncontrollable events."

A responsive environment, then, inclines a child toward competence, while an unresponsive environment inclines a child toward helplessness. Dr. Lewis illustrates the difference by describing the experiences of two infants, Sharon and Toby. One morning Sharon wakes up wet, hungry, or perhaps just lonely, and cries. Nothing happens. She cries again. Still no response. She continues crying for several minutes, but no one comes. Finally she falls asleep, exhausted. On the same morning another infant, Toby, awakes. She, too, is wet, hungry, or lonely, and cries. Within seconds she has the attention of a warm hand, a smiling face, and the food or dry diaper she needs. Sharon's world is unresponsive; her behavior has no effect. Toby's world is highly responsive; her behavior gets results almost immediately. Now, what is the lesson each child is taught by her respective experience? Sharon learns that making an effort to affect one's condition is useless. Things happen or they don't; what she does is unimportant. Toby learns that her efforts are worthwhile. What happens depends, in part, upon what she does.

Some readers may think at this point that responsivity is just another name for permissiveness. Give the child what he wants, pander to his every whim, deny him nothing. In other words, spoil him. Not so. A responsive environment is not one that gives a child everything and anything he wants. Responsivity means merely that an act produces clear, consistent consequences. Sometimes those consequences will be negative. For example, a four-year-old child who insists upon having cookies for breakfast may send his bowl of cereal flying. A parent might respond to this behavior by saying, "Since you've thrown away your breakfast, you'll have to go without." Another parent might insist that the child clean up the mess he has made. In each case the child's behavior has some effect, but the effect does not necessarily include getting a plate of cookies.

Handling a baby's cry.

But what about Toby's crying? Sure, Toby learns that she can master her environment, but doesn't she inevitably become a crybaby in the process? Doesn't she learn that the way to get what you want is by making a fuss? Interestingly enough, the answer is no. Psychologists Silvia Bell and Mary Ainsworth conducted a study of the effects of responsiveness on crying. They observed the interactions of mothers and their infants during the first year of the child's life. There were wide variations among the mothers in how often and how quickly they responded to their baby's cries. The most responsive mother, for instance, responded 96 percent of the time, while the least responsive mother answered only 3 percent of her baby's cries. Many parents would predict that the first infant would cry constantly. What actually happened, though, was that the children who could control their environment by crying soon learned to use more subtle tactics to exert control, and they also learned to do things for themselves. The researchers conclude that "an infant whose mother's responsiveness helps him to achieve his ends develops confidence in his own ability to control what happens to him." This means that he comes to do more things for himself, which means there are fewer occasions for calling upon Mom.

Other research supports the notion that a responsive environment leads to competence. In one study, for example, Dr. Lewis and psychologist Susan Goldberg watched mothers interact with their three-month-old infants. They noticed that the behavior of some mothers was likely to be a reaction to what the baby did, while the behavior of other mothers tended to be independent of the baby's activity. The researchers found that the first infants, those whose mothers were responsive, were more interested in the world around them and were more attentive.

Toys that foster competence.

Dr. John S. Watson of the University of California at Berkeley demonstrated that the responsiveness of the physical world also is beneficial. Dr. Watson designed a mobile that would rotate whenever a baby exerted pressure on a pillow. When an infant turned his head this way or that, the mobile would spin. Dr. Watson found that with just ten minutes of practice a day, the infants learned to control the mobile within a few days. They also smiled and cooed as the mobile spun to and fro, apparently enjoying the

control they exerted over the object. Other babies who saw the mobile spin but had no control over its movement did not show the same reaction.

Providing a child with responsive toys does not necessarily require anything so elaborate as Watson's motorized mobile. Psychologist Robert McCall notes that a mobile can be made responsive simply by tying a piece of soft cotton yarn loosely around a baby's wrist and tying the other end to the mobile. When the baby moves his hand, the mobile moves. Another inexpensive but highly responsive baby toy is the rattle, since it makes a noise only when and if the baby shakes it. Yet another example is a mirror, perhaps made of shiny metal so that there is no danger of broken glass. The child looks in the mirror and sees someone looking back. The person looking back does all sorts of things—smiling, laughing, frowning—but only if the child looking into the mirror does them first. As the child gets a bit older, a spoon and a pie pan provide responsive, if noisy, diversion. It may well be the case that the more responsive toys tend to be the least expensive. Toys that "do it all" rarely require much activity from the child. Thus, the *least* responsive toy available is probably the $500 color television set, while one of the most responsive toys around is the $1 rubber ball.

There is evidence that if a child's environment is thoroughly *un*responsive, he is almost certain to become helpless rather than competent. Dr. Seligman and his colleagues have conducted a number of studies that demonstrate just how devastating the lack of control over events can be. They have found that when a laboratory animal is unable to escape an unpleasant situation, it eventually quits trying. More important, when the animal is later put into another situation from which it could readily escape, it does not do so. In fact, it makes no effort to escape. Psychologist Donald Hiroto got similar results when he studied the effects of uncontrollable unpleasant events on college students. Some students heard an unpleasantly loud noise, which they could do nothing about. Other students heard the same noise but learned to control it by pushing a button. Afterward, the students were put into another situation in which they could turn off a noise simply by moving their hand from one part of a box

to another. Those who had learned to control the noise in the first situation did so in the second, but most of those who could do nothing about the first noise made no attempt to escape the second. They simply sat there and did nothing. They had been made helpless, at least momentarily.

Helping a child master his world.

Researchers have not, of course, deliberately set out to make children helpless by exposing them to unpleasant situations from which they cannot escape. They have, however, noted that children reared in unresponsive environments are not likely to become highly competent. Dr. Seligman points out that a lack of control was characteristic of the environment of Dr. Spitz's institutionalized children and may have been more important to their helplessness than the lack of stimulation they received.

All children are subjected to some unpleasant events that they cannot control. An infant's diaper rash is beyond his control, as is the misery of most childhood illnesses. And even the brightest child must eventually experience failure. But if the child is usually able to exert some control over the events in his life, this may give him some immunity against the adverse effects of unpleasant events he is powerless to control.

It appears, then, that the kind of experiences a child has in the first few years of life plays an important role in his development. The child who has a close, warm relationship with an adult; who lives in interesting surroundings; who has ample opportunity to interact with other people; and, most important, who lives in an environment that is responsive, has an excellent chance of becoming competent. The earlier these experiences begin, the better. "I believe," Dr. Seligman told me, "that motivation and emotion are more plastic than intelligence. I am no longer convinced that special kinds of experiences will raise a child's IQ by twenty points or induce him to write piano concertos at age five, as Mozart did. But I am convinced that certain kinds of experiences during childhood will produce a child who is helpless, while other experiences will produce a child who is competent."

There is in every child an Alice and a Zelda. The question is, which is to prevail?

Infant Day Care:
Toward a More Human Environment

Arminta Lee Jacobson

In planning optimal environments for infant day care, the human element is often minimized. Desirable caregiving competencies which can be used as a basis for evaluating day care personnel are derived from research findings.

What implications for infant caregiving in day care can be drawn from mother-infant interaction research? Few studies have been done on interpersonal caregiving competencies or the effect of discrete caregiving variables on infant development in day care settings. Yet the spiraling increase of out-of-home care for infants demands research attention, both for professionals concerned with infant day care and for parents needing such services. The following discussion examines mother-infant interaction research in order to delineate current areas of exploration and to synthesize findings into a helpful format for administrators, educators, researchers, and others interested in upgrading the quality of infant day care.

Importance of the Primary Caregiver

The importance of the primary caregiver in an infant's development is often overlooked, although several research studies have given evidence of the relationship between early caregiving experiences and competencies in later childhood. In a longitudinal study of environmental determinants related to human competency upon entering school, White and Watts (1973) found that ratings of competency of children at age six varied very little from ratings of competency of those children at age three. Further investigation pinpointed the period of 10 to 18 months as the most cru-

cial in determining a child's later competency, especially in the areas of social skills and attitudes.

Yarrow et al. (1973) studied the relationship between mothering experiences during the first six months of life and selected intellectual and personal-social characteristics at 10 years of age. For boys, the Wechsler Intelligence Scale for Children IQ and several aspects of a child's relationship to others at 10 years of age were related to variables of maternal behavior at six months of age. In another study (Yarrow et al. 1972), the social environment was shown to be highly significant in influencing infant functioning, independent of dimensions of the inanimate environment.

In a report by Bayley and Schaefer (1964), results of an analysis of data collected in the Berkeley Growth Study between 1928 and 1954 showed maternal and child behaviors to be intercorrelated over an 18-year span of growth. The relationship to maternal behaviors was more significant for boys. Coping capacities of older children were found to be significantly related to early mother-infant interactions in a study by Murphy (1973) of 31 children and mothers. These studies and others contribute to the growing recognition of the impact of human relations in the earliest years of development.

Research studies of mother-infant interaction have varied in the type of interrelationships studied as well as in research design, data collection, and analysis. Categories of maternal and infant variables chosen to enter into relationship models have only gross similarities among investigations. Study of interpersonal behavior by its very nature requires direct observation of behavior and is susceptible to subjectivity in measurement. Behavior patterns are often quite complex, and interrelationships not included in the research model are often overlooked. Although infants have a limited repertoire of relationship responses, adult transactions are practically unlimited in variety and complexity. Nevertheless, important information discerned from such studies helps to identify those interrela-

tionship variables which effect optimal development in the early formative years.

Although the mother-infant dyad has been the focus of most research seeking to explain social determinants of infant behavior and development, findings from such research can easily be generalized in terms of appropriate behavior for any adult serving as a primary caregiver of an infant, even for a limited part of the day, as in a day care setting. What is conducive to optimal development in one setting could logically be conceived as appropriate in another setting.

An exception which must be made in generalizing research findings of mother-infant interaction to day care is the area of attachment of infant to caregiver. In a series of ongoing studies of mother-infant relations, Ainsworth and Bell (1972) have pinpointed quality of attachment between mother and infant as being related to other aspects of infant and maternal behavior. Mutual attachment of infant and caregiver cannot be assumed in a day care setting. Nature and degree of attachment of primary caregivers and infants in day care have not been investigated and would be difficult to study due to the common instability of such relationships over time and the confounding effects of other adults and infants.

Areas of Adult Influence

Given the limitations of research methodology and generalizations, what evidence from recent research can serve as guidelines for infant day care personnel in providing an optimal human environment for infants?

Infants' physical, emotional, social, and cognitive development is shaped to a great extent by the behaviors of the primary caregivers in relation to the children. Primary caregivers can be conceived of not only as determinants of infants' physical survival but also as social agents against which infants test their growing competencies and

Reprinted by permission from *YOUNG CHILDREN*, Vol. 33, No. 5 (July 1978), pp. 14-23. Copyright ©1978, National Association for the Education of Young Children, 1834 Connecticut Avenue, N.W., Washington, DC 20009.

conceptions of self and the world. The extent to which adults initiate interactions with or respond to infants, the affective nature of those behaviors, their content and context, all have an influence on infants' developing responses and behaviors and the context within which different facets of their development emerge.

Infant Competence. Personality characteristics, control, involvement, responsiveness, and attachment are some of the many types of maternal influences found to be related to infant development. In a study of the mother-infant dyad (Stern et al. 1969), a sequence of relationships between personality characteristics of mother, modes of maternal behavior, and responses and development of the infant was defined. The nine factors resulting from this composite appear to be distributed along a continuum ranging from child-centered to mother-centered maternal functioning. Effective mothers were defined as those whose infants were lovingly responsive to them and accelerated in development. The characteristics these mothers seemed to have in common were: (1) attentive, loving involvement with their infants; (2) high levels of visual and vocal contact; and (3) play involvement. The mothers producing the more accelerated infants were characterized as self-confident and skilled in their caregiving and individualistic in style.

White and Watts (1973) found that infants assessed in their study as highly competent had mothers who differed significantly from mothers of infants judged less competent. Mothers of the more competent infants involved themselves in more mother-infant interactions. Even when their infants were as young as 12 to 15 months, these mothers spent more time with "highly intellectual" activities and used interaction techniques which taught or were facilitative in nature. These mothers decreased their use of restrictive techniques as children grew older while mothers of the less competent infants increased their use. From the analysis of attitudes and values of mothers in the study, characteristics related to optimal development of children included a positive attitude toward life in general; enjoyment of infants in the one-to-three-year age range; an acceptance of the incompatibility of infant needs and preservation of posessions and household order; and the willingness to take risks for the sake of infants' curiosity and development.

Ainsworth and Bell (1972) studied infants' competence in direct dealing with the physical environment as measured by developmental competence on the Griffiths Scale. Positive relationships were shown between infant competence and maternal factors of sensitivity, acceptance, cooperation, and the amount of floor freedom allowed the infant. Amount of playing with the baby by the mother was also positively correlated with developmental scores of the infant. Frequency of punishment was negatively related to infant competence.

Level and variety of social stimulation (Yarrow et al. 1972) provided by a primary caregiver in the home have been found to be positively related to functioning of five-month-old infants. Infant functioning which related significantly to social stimulation included goal-directed behaviors, reaching and grasping, and secondary circular reactions. Adult responses, contingent upon infant distress, were found to be significantly related to goal-directed behavior in the infant.

Other studies (Murphy 1973; Stern et al. 1969) exemplify findings which support an optimal level of interaction, reporting a curvilinear relationship between development and degree of attention. In studying the development of coping ability in young children, Murphy (1973) found that optimal early mother-infant interactions were characterized by a balance of attention and autonomy, of interaction and letting the infant alone part of the time. Too much or too little attention, body contact, and talking to infants were found to be not good for infant development. These findings concur with findings (Stern et al. 1969) which characterize mothers of slow-developing infants as exhibitionist, vigilant, and including both high and low levels of physical contact. Murphy (1973) also found that patterns of mothering were related to individual infant temperaments in different ways, indicating the need for flexibility in interaction patterns.

Infant Vocalization. Mother responsiveness and infant vocalization have been examined in several studies. Clarke-Stewart (1973) reported a high relation of responsive maternal speech and children's competence in a longitudinal study of infants from 9 to 18 months of age.

Responsive mothers—those who ignore few episodes and respond with little delay—have infants with more variety, subtlety, and clarity of noncrying communication. During the second, third, and fourth quarters of the first year, infants of responsive mothers cried significantly less than infants of unresponsive mothers. Beckwith (1971b) also reported a positive relationship between mothers' ignoring of infants and frequency of infant crying. Infants who cried little had a wider range of differentiated modes of communication than did infants who cried often (Ainsworth and Bell 1972). Amount of maternal play behavior has also been found to be positively related to amount of infant vocalization (Clarke-Stewart 1973).

Perceptual-Cognitive Development. In the last decade, perceptual-cognitive development of very young children has interested researchers and parents. A study of perceptual-cognitive development in infants 12 weeks of age (Lewis and Goldberg 1969) also stressed the importance of maternal responses which are contingent upon the infant's behavior. Perceptual-cognitive development was found to be moderately related to the overall response of mother to infant's crying and vocalization and the amount of touching, holding, and smiling exhibited by the mother, and highly related to the amount of looking by the mother. These findings concur with other studies (Stern et al. 1969; White and Watts 1973) which characterize effective mothers as being very responsive to and involved with their infants.

An investigation of the relationships between maternal behaviors, infant behaviors, and individual differences in infant IQ (Beckwith 1971a) was made with the same infants at two interviews, during age ranges from 7.2 to 9.7 months and 8.5 to 11.3 months. This study revealed that low maternal verbal and physical contact within the home were significantly related to lower IQ on the Cattell Infant Intelligence Scale. Maternal restriction of infant exploration was found to be related to decreased interest in attaining speech during the last quarter of the first year and was significantly related to lowering of IQ scores.

Clarke-Stewart (1973) also reported maternal restrictiveness to be negatively related to scores on the Bayley Scale of Mental Development at 18 months. In this study the Bayley measure was highly correlated with the mother's nonphysical stimulation—looking and talking. Responsiveness of the mother was also related to the child's Bayley score and to the child's speed of processing information, schema development, language, and social and emotional competence. Stimulation by mother to promote achievement has also been found to be related to Cattell IQ scores at six months of age (Yarrow et al. 1973).

Ainsworth and Bell (1972) have studied cognitive development in White middle socioeconomic status (SES) infants and Black lower SES infants in terms of development of the concept of object permanence and scores on the Griffiths Development Scale. Infants who had harmonious interactions with mothers sensitive to their signals and who had developed attachment relationships of normal quality tended to develop the concept of person permanence in advance of object permanence. At 8 to 11

Table 1. Characteristics of Competent Infant Caregivers.

Desired Caregiver Characteristics	Cues to Desirable Caregiver Characteristics
I. Personality Factors	
A. Child-centered	1. Attentive and loving to infants. 2. Meets infants' needs before own.
B. Self-confident	1. Relaxed and anxiety free. 2. Skilled in physical care of infants. 3. Individualistic caregiving style.
C. Flexible	1. Uses different styles of caregiving to meet individual needs of infants. 2. Spontaneous and open behavior. 3. Permits increasing freedom of infant with development.
D. Sensitive	1. Understands infants' cues readily. 2. Shows empathy for infants. 3. Acts purposefully in interactions with infants.
II. Attitudes and Values	
A. Displays positive outlook on life	1. Expresses positive affect. 2. No evidence of anger, unhappiness, or depression.
B. Enjoys infants	1. Affectionate to infants. 2. Shows obvious pleasure in involvement with infants.
C. Values infants more than possessions or immaculate appearance	1. Dresses practically and appropriately. 2. Places items not for infants' use out of reach. 3. Reacts to infant destruction or messiness with equanimity. 4. Takes risks with property in order to enhance infant development.
III. Behavior	
A. Interacts appropriately with infants	1. Frequent interactions with infants. 2. Balances interaction with leaving infants alone. 3. Optimum amounts of touching, holding, smiling, and looking. 4. Responds consistently and without delay to infants; is always accessible. 5. Speaks in positive tone of voice. 6. Shows clearly that infants are loved and accepted.
B. Facilitates development	1. Does not punish infants. 2. Plays with infants. 3. Provides stimulation with toys and objects. 4. Permits freedom to explore, including floor freedom. 5. Cooperates with infant-initiated activities and explorations. 6. Provides activities which stimulate achievement or goal orientation. 7. Acts purposefully in an educational role to teach and facilitate learning and development.

months these infants were also advanced in the level of object permanence achieved. Harmonious attachment relationship, as well as floor freedom, were highly related to development scores.

Infant Play Behavior. Another area of consideration is the development of infant play behavior. According to findings by Clarke-Stewart (1973), the best single predictor of play behavior in infants was the amount of stimulation with toys and objects received from the mother at home.

Other researchers have studied quality of investigative behavior and exploratory play and its relation both to maternal behavior and to the quality of infant-mother attachment relationships (Ainsworth and Bell 1972). They found a significant relationship during the last quarter of the first year between frequent harmonious transactions with the mother, mother responsiveness to infant-initiated interaction, and the infant's greater exploration of toys and advanced behavioral schemata in play.

Social Development. Social development and play appear to be enhanced by some of the same maternal behaviors. In studying relations between the mother's behavior and the quality of the child's attachment, Clarke-Stewart (1973) found a number of nonlinear relationships. Optimally securely attached children—those able to use mother as a secure base from which to explore the environment and to which to return periodically at times of stress or for reassurance—were associated with homes where there was not constant exposure to a great number of people and where mothers were socially stimulating, responsive, and affectionate. In particular, the children's attachment was highly related to frequency of maternal social behavior.

In studying the use of mother as a secure base from which to explore, Ainsworth and Bell (1972) studied quality of infant attachment in relation to maternal ratings. Infants rated as highest in actively seeking proximity and interaction with mothers all had scores above the median in sensitivity to infant signals, acceptance, cooperation, and accessibility.

The early manifestation of infant obedience indicates progress in social development. In a study by Stayton, Hogan, and Ainsworth (1971), maternal variables of sensitivity, acceptance, and cooperation were all highly intercorrelated with infants' compliance with commands during the last quarter of the first year. Frequency of verbal commands, frequency of physical intervention, and amount of floor freedom permitted the infant were not found to be related to compliance with commands.

Happiness. An obvious measure of effectiveness in interpersonal relations with infants is the degree to which positive affect or happiness is observed in the infant. Smiling and vocalizing and the absence of crying and fretting are seen as evidence of happiness. An infant's expression of happiness has been found to be most closely related to the mother's expression of positive emotions (Clarke-Stewart 1973). Mothers who vocalize and smile frequently have been found to have infants who vocalize and smile frequently. The more positive the maternal behaviors, the less frequently the infants fret and cry (Lewis and Wilson 1972). Infant fretfulness has been observed to be related to maternal rejection and self-control. Lower levels of infant fretfulness are associated with maternal effectiveness in physical, social, and instrumental behaviors (Clarke-Stewart 1973).

Implications for Infant Day Care Workers

Despite the inconsistency of focus and the nebulous nature of desirable maternal behaviors, mother-child interaction studies provide a sound research base for determining desirable caregiving attributes. In view of the empirical evidence on the importance of human interactions to infant development, it is clear that infant day care workers must be highly competent in interpersonal skills for quality caregiving. It is imperative that day care administrators hire and train infant caregivers on the basis of their attitudes and behaviors in interpersonal relations with infants.

Table 1 represents a synthesis of characteristics which provide an optimal human environment for infant caregiving, as generalized from the research findings. The categorization of caregiving behaviors can be used for further development of competency profiles for infant caregivers. Administrators of infant care centers will be most interested in those items helpful to selecting and evaluating infant caregivers; characteristics reflected in Table 1 provide possibilities for structuring interview or evaluation schedules. More specific attention to developmental levels of competence within behavior indexes could lead toward individualized training experiences for infant day care staff.

Further research, directed toward specification, assessment, and integration of infant caregiving behaviors, is needed, since only through delineation of these important human behaviors can child care personnel plan knowledgeably for the optimal care of infants.

Other implications for the placement of caregivers in day care settings come from research findings which highlight cultural, racial, and SES differences in maternal expectations for infants and in mother-infant interaction behaviors (Goldberg 1972; Lewis and Ban 1973; Lewis and Wilson 1972; Tulkin and Cohler 1973). Developmental differences in infants have been associated with caregiver differences. Consideration should be given to placing caregivers in day care settings where their cultural and SES values and expectations are similar to those of the families served.

Recognition of wide variations in caregivers' attitudes, sensitivities, and behaviors should also prompt day care professionals to work cooperatively with parents in setting caregiving goals for infants. Parents can help caregivers define the infant's nature and needs and the kind of environmental variables most effective in maximizing the infant's potential.

The crucial importance of the earliest experiences of life need continual emphasis and investigation. It is hoped that persons responsible for planning day care experiences for infants will be creatively sensitive to ways in which the quality of life for infants can be improved.

References

Ainsworth, M. D. S., and Bell, S. M. "Mother-Infant Interaction and the Development of Competence." ERIC Document Reproduction Service No. ED 065 180, 1972.

Ainsworth, M. D. S.; Bell, S. M.; and Stayton, D. J. "Individual Differences in Strange-Situation Behavior of One-Year-Olds." In The Competent Infant: Research and Commentary, edited by L. J. Stone, H. T. Smith, and L. B. Murphy. New York: Basic Books, 1973.

Bayley, N., and Schaefer, E. S. "Correlations of Maternal and Child Behaviors with the Development of Mental Abilities: Data from the Berkeley Growth Study." Monographs of the Society for Research in Child Development 29, no. 6 (1964), serial no. 97.

Beckwith, L. "Relationships Between Attributes of Mothers and Their Infants' IQ Scores." Child Development 42, no. 4 (1971a): 1083-1097.

Beckwith, L. "Relationships Between Infant's Vocalizations and Their Mother's Behaviors." Merrill-Palmer Quarterly 17 (1971b): 211-226.

Caudill, W., and Frost, L. "A Comparison of Maternal Care and Infant Behavior in Japanese-American, American, and Japanese Families." ERIC Document Reproduction Service No. ED 057 153, 1971, Honolulu, Hawaii.

Clarke-Stewart, K. A. "Interactions Between Mothers and Their Young Children: Characteristics and Consequences." Monographs of the Society for Research in Child Development 38, nos. 6-7 (1973), serial no. 153.

Goldberg, S. "Infant Care and Growth in Urban Zambia." Human Development 15 (1972): 77-89.

Lewis, M., and Ban, P. "Variance and Invariance in the Mother-Infant Interaction: A Cross-Cultural Study." ERIC Document Reproduction Service No. ED 084 006, 1973, Princeton, New Jersey.

Lewis, M., and Goldberg, S. "Perceptual-Cognitive Development in Infancy: A Generalized Expectancy Model as a Function of the Mother-Infant Interaction." Merrill-Palmer Quarterly 15 (1969): 81-100.

Lewis, M., and Wilson, C. D. "Infant Development in Lower-Class American Families." Human Development 15 (1972): 112-127.

Murphy, L. B. "Later Outcomes of Early Infant and Mother Relationships." In The Competent Infant: Research and Commentary, edited by L. J. Stone, H. T. Smith, and L. B. Murphy. New York: Basic Books, 1973.

Stayton, D. J.; Hogan, R.; and Ainsworth, M. D. S. "Infant Obedience and Maternal Behavior: The Origins of Socialization Reconsidered." Child Development 42 (1971): 1057-1069.

Stern, G. G.; Caldwell, B. M.; Hersher, L.; Lipton, E. L.; and Richmond, J. G. "A Factor Analytic Study of the Mother-Infant Dyad." Child Development 40 (1969): 163-181.

Tulkin, S. R., and Cohler, B. J. "Childbearing Attitudes and Mother-Child Interactions in the First Year of Life." Merrill-Palmer Quarterly 19 (1973): 95-106.

Tulkin, S. R., and Kagan, J. "Mother-Child Interaction in the First Year of Life." Child Development 43 (1972): 31-41.

White, B. L., and Watts, J. C. Experience and Environment: Major Influences on the Development of the Young Child. Englewood Cliffs, N.J.: Prentice-Hall, 1973.

Yarrow, L. G.; Goodwin, M. S.; Manheimer, H.; and Milowe, I. D. "Infancy Experiences and Cognitive and Personality Development at Ten Years." In The Competent Infant: Research and Commentary, edited by L. J. Stone, H. T. Smith, and L. B. Murphy. New York: Basic Books, 1973.

Yarrow, L. G.; Rubenstein, J. L.; Pedersen, F. A.; and Jankowski, J. J. "Dimensions of Early Stimulation and Their Differential Effects on Infant Development." Merrill-Palmer Quarterly 18 (1972): 205-218.

Development During Childhood

So pronounced are the cognitive and social changes occurring during the transition from preschool to childhood that one developmental psychologist refers to this time period as the "5-to-7 shift." During the 5-to-7 shift, significant changes occur in the child's attention span, recall memory, learning, and problem solving skills. Articulation improves, vocabulary size increases, and the child achieves a new understanding of syntactical aspects of language. Most of the changes that occur during the transition to childhood, as well as those that occur during childhood itself, involve social, emotional, cognitive, and language development.

Social-Emotional Development. During the school years the child's social network expands. School extends the child's peer group beyond the confines of the immediate neighborhood and exposes the child to a new set of authority figures. The quality of the child's interaction with each of his or her available role models will influence the structure of his or her sense of social and emotional competence. The extent to which conflict affects personality development during childhood is a topic of special interest to contemporary developmentalists.

Cognitive and Language Development. During the past two decades the study of cognitive development has been dominated by the theory of Jean Piaget. Piaget's theory attempts to explicate the structural elements of the mind by focusing on the functional abilities of the child at various stages of development. Although it provides a rich description of what the child can and cannot do during a particular stage of development, it is less adequate for explaining how the child acquires various cognitive skills. Thus, many developmentalists are using information processing models to integrate classic cognitive psychology with cognitive developmental theory.

Prior to the 1960s, theories of language development stressed environmental determinants. The theory of Noam Chomsky shifted emphasis to genetic explanations. Today, investigators stress organizational models that are based on the assumption that genetic and environmental factors work in concert to determine behavioral outcome, including the behavior we call language.

Education and Child Development. The family is the first major socialization force to which the child is exposed. However, during the period of childhood, children become involved with the second major socialization force, the school. New friendships develop as the child's peer network expands beyond his or her neighborhood. For many children, school entrance represents the first extended separation from the home. Most children experience little difficulty adapting to school, but for others, school adjustment is more problematic.

Educators are recognizing that learning processes are far more complex than previously imagined. Attempts to explain intellectual development independent of emotional development do not take into account the systemic nature of the organism. More and more, educators point out that many children suffer from various "learning disabilities," disturbances that prevent their functioning effectively in the traditional school environment. Seldom, however, do educators look within the educational system to assess the extent to which "learning disabilities" are generated by the school environment itself rather than originating from within the child or from within the home.

Looking Ahead: Challenge Questions

How do the cognitive competencies of the child differ from those of the infant or preschooler? Why would developmentalists be dissatisfied with stage theories of development?

Do cross-cultural similarities in language development support biological theories of language acquisition? If so, then why are there different languages?

Can educational institutions change, or have they become such conservative forces that the only way to change them is to design an entirely new system for the education of children?

Do you believe that schools should attempt to teach children correct moral behavior? If so, whose definition of right or wrong conduct is to be used? Mine or yours?

How Children Influence Children:
The Role of Peers in the Socialization Process

Emmy Elisabeth Werner

Emmy E. Werner, Ph.D., is a Professor of Human Development and Research and Child Psychologist at the University of California, Davis.

In his review on family structure, socialization and personality, John A. Clausen points out that an older sibling may be caretaker, teacher, pacesetter or confidant for a younger one. Yet such a reference work as the *Handbook of Socialization Theory and Research* by D. B. Goslin includes few references about caretaking of children by agemates. What cross-cultural evidence we can find, however, indicates that caretaking of children by siblings, cousins or other peers is a significant phenomenon in most societies of the developing world.

Sibling and Child Caretaking

Child caretaking is widespread cross-culturally, but relevant material about this topic is scattered throughout many ethnographic studies, which makes comparative analysis difficult. In one cross-cultural survey on the age of assignment of roles and responsibilities to children, based on ethnographies of 50 cultures, pancultural trends in the age of assignment of child care roles were observed.[1] These centered on the 5- to 7-year-old period, when care of siblings, peer play and the understanding of game rules are most frequently initiated. This is the same age when Western societies introduce formal schooling.

The most common worldwide pattern is informal child and sibling care that is part of the daily routine of children within the family and that is carried out without formalized organizational rules. Under these circumstances, child caretakers frequently operate under two simultaneous sets of pressures: one from their small charges, the other from their parents. In all non-Western societies investigated by the Whitings in their Six-Cultures Study, children were expected to do some child tending.[2] However, there were striking differences in the types of caretaking mothers were willing to delegate, the age at which they considered a child competent, and the amount of supervision considered necessary.

One question on the mothers interview indicates the value placed on the help given by the child nurse. When the mothers were asked who had helped them care for the sample child when he or she was an infant, 69 percent of the mothers from the East African community, 41 percent of the mothers from the Mexican barrio, 25 percent of the Filipino, 21 percent of the North Indian, but only 12 percent of the New England and Okinawan mothers reported having been helped with an infant by a child. The three highest-ranking societies, the East African, the Mexican and the Filipino communities, were also the societies that ranked highest in the nurturant behavior of their children, as observed independently in naturalistic settings.

There is usually a strong contrast between infancy and young childhood in terms of child and adult caretaking practices. The care of toddlers requires different skills and behaviors on the part of child caretakers than the care of an infant. Observations of the interaction of children with 2- to 4-year-old siblings in the Six-Cultures Study indicate that caretakers of toddlers were comparatively more apt to reprimand, criticize and punish. This is in some contrast to the predominant nurturant and responsive attitude shown toward the infants in these societies. Thus, the role of the child caretaker is a function of at least three factors: the physical maturation of the child; the availability of different caretakers; and the differing cultural conceptions of maturity of a child, which, in turn, leads to different patterns of caretaking by children.

Antecedents of Child Caretaking

The residence and size of a family, as well as the daily routines, subsistence economy and maternal workload, are related to the frequency of child caretaking in the developing world. Sibling caretaking is more common in societies where women have more work to do, where the work takes the mother from home or is difficult to interrupt, and where circumstances of residence, birth order and family size make alternative caretakers available. A domestic group with a large number of kin and cousins present, a mother with many offspring and a daily routine that keeps brothers, sisters and other adults available for caretaking would be the optimal situation for the development of nonparental and sibling caretaking.[3] . . .

Consequences of Child Caretaking

There is a great need for additional data that document the possible effect on a child of either providing or receiving child caretaking. Most of the data available deal with attachment behavior and differences in affiliation versus achievement motivation.

Sibling caretaking seems to be of special importance in cultures that are polygynous. Africa leads the world in polygynous societies. A study of Kikuyu children illustrates the importance of the sibling group in socialization.[4] After the child is raised by the mother for the first one or two years and is given a great deal of maternal care that fosters strong attachment, he or she will move in with the siblings when the mother is pregnant again. The sibling group is mostly responsible for the socialization of the young child and becomes the main source of the child's emotional involvement.

In a short-term longitudinal study of 3-year-old American preschoolers, one researcher found that secure attachment may play a dual role in children's relationships with other children.[5] It may directly promote peer competence by encouraging a positive orientation toward other children, and, insofar as mothers who foster secure attachment also encourage expanded interactions, it may indirectly promote social competence by giving children the opportunity to learn from peers.

Studying urban Japanese families, Caudill and Plath were impressed with the role of siblings in the instruction and care of the younger babies, and by how this responsibility for parenting appeared to diminish any sibling rivalry and to create close bonding between brothers and sisters.[6] They ascribed the strong affectionate bond in interdependence between different members of the family to the sleeping arrangements. When the baby is new, he or she sleeps with the mother; when another baby comes, the child sleeps with an older brother or sister. Sleeping with another member of the family apparently strengthens family bonds and expresses a strong nurturant family life, at the same time lessening the sexual aspects of sleeping together.

In their Six-Cultures Study, the Whitings found that children who interact with infants were more nurturant and less egotistic than children who did not care for infants. These authors suggest that caretaking of infants appears to affect overall interaction with peers.[7] This becomes quite apparent when we take a look at the consequences of sex differences in child caretaking. B. Whiting and C. P. Edwards compared boys and girls in seven societies, the six cultures mentioned earlier plus the Kikuyu of Kenya, and observed incidences of nurturant and responsible behavior.[8] Older girls, aged 7 to 11, offered help and support to others more often than did boys. There were no such sex differences for children aged 3 to 6. The authors interpret the increased nurturance of older girls as due to the assignment to girls of increased childrearing duties, particularly infant caretaking. Another researcher observed Luo boys in Kenya who were expected to perform child-caretaking chores usually assigned to girls.[9] Such boys displayed more feminine social behaviors than boys not needed for such tasks.

Thus, it appears that sex differences in nurturance and responsible behavior may only occur at particular ages and are not uniform across all cultures. The critical factor for the development of nurturant behavior seems to be the demand for child care tasks within the home. It would be interesting to see whether similar findings could be replicated in our own culture, as sex-role expectations change in the wake of a more egalitarian type of childrearing.

Several authors, including R. Levy and J. E. Ritchie, have attempted to generalize about the effects of child caretaking on the development of individual differences in children.[10] These authors have dealt with ethnographic accounts of child caretaking in Polynesian societies and have argued that sibling caretaking restricts the development of individual differences in both children and adults. The possible effects of child caretaking were presented by Levy as the development of an easygoing or apathetic "you can't fight City Hall" orientation to life. Weisner and Gallimore suggest that these consequences need to be interpreted in terms of the social context in which the child will live as an adult.[11] The socialization goal of the societies in which these observations were made is the integration of the child into the social context, rather than fostering individual achievement and independent skills. Thus, it may be that children raised in a sibling-caretaking system develop psychological and behavioral characteristics that are adaptive in some settings and not in others. Systematic differences can be expected in the learning experiences of young children when taught by siblings rather than parents.[12]

From a brief overview of the rather scarce data available on sibling caretaking in the Six-Cultures Study and in Polynesian groups in Hawaii, New Zealand and Tahiti, it appears that sibling caretaking in extended families anywhere in the world may be a functional adaptation of low-income groups that allows economically marginal families flexibility in coping with crises and increases the number of potential resource contributors. A case in point is the American Indian family in the American metropolis society, which differs significantly from the nuclear-family, conjugal pair and single-person types that predominate in White America.[13] The less stable and the lower the amount of income among American Indian families, the larger the household. Brothers or sisters of the husband and wife, and nieces and nephews, all join together to pool their meager resources. This grouping together also characterizes other poverty-stricken households among other ethnic and racial minorities within the industrialized urban West.

It remains to be seen what positive roles siblings can play in helping the younger child adapt to changes brought about by modernization and industrialization, since older children appear more open and exposed to modern influences than younger ones.

Affiliation Versus Achievement Motivation

Evidence of the effects on motive development of sibling caretaking is either severely limited or indirect . . . In the Polynesian, African, Asian and Latin American societies where child caretaking has been studied, it appears that early parental demand for non-dependence serves, in part, to shift independence training to older siblings. Thus, refusal of help by parents redirects the child's overtures to siblings, who provide nurturance and training and, in turn, pressure for independence.

Of critical importance is the fact that this shift from adult to sibling caretaking can occur without the toddler learning self-care skills, which may impose a rather strong burden on the young caretaker that may lessen the child's achievement motivation at the crucial age when it tends to crystallize. Given the mother's behavior, the child has no alternative but to turn to siblings; thus, achievement motivation may be sacrificed for the sake of affiliation.

Reliance on sibling caretakers as a factor in the development of affiliation motivation has been suggested by studies of Hawaiian-Americans.[14] The pattern of being interdependent and affiliating with others is a significant feature of Hawaiian life and may cause problems in the classroom. Accustomed to sibling care, Hawaiian children are inclined to attend to peers rather than teachers and individual work, behavior that is often interpreted by teachers in terms of motivational and attentional deficits.

On the positive side, S. MacDonald and R. Gallimore found in a number of classroom studies that Hawaiian-American students perform at high levels if allowed to interact or affiliate with peers in team work or in the sharing of earned privileges.[15] Whether peer interaction is more motivating for those from families in other cultures where there is a great deal of sibling care of children is a hypothesis that has not been directly tested.

To sum up, child caretaking appears to be an important antecedent to nurturant, responsible behavior and to behavior that leads to affiliation rather than achievement motivation. Though it is presently preponderant in the non-Western world, child caretaking may in the future play an important role as an alternative to maternal caretaking in the West. P.M. Greenfield suggests that day care centers should involve older children and siblings in child care and that schooling or tutoring of primary school children should involve children as well as adults.[16] The Whitings argue that whether a child is told to take care of younger siblings or whether he or she is sent to school instead may have a more profound effect upon the profile of the child's social behavior than the manipulation of reinforcement schedules by the parents. Thus, major attention needs to be paid in future cross-cultural studies to the role of child caretakers as transmitters of new social values and as links between the family and the rapidly changing outside world.

Children's Play Groups and Games

Children's play groups are not necessarily dependent on caretaking patterns, but the two variables are frequently closely related. Child caretaking affects the sex composition of play groups and their physical and social mobility. Where caretaking is not limited to one's own siblings, it shapes contacts with children not in one's immediate family.

In a review article on exploration and play, Weisler and McCall trace the developmental sequence in the nature of children's social play.[17] At first the child plays in isolation, without reference to what other children are doing. The first indication of a social element is the occurrence of parallel playing, in which the nature of the child's behavior is influenced by and may be similar to that of nearby children, but there is no direct social interaction. Subsequently, there may be short interactions between children consisting of socially instigated but not truly interactive play, as when the behavior of another child is imitated. Later, full-scale group play can be observed, in which one child interacts verbally and physically in a prolonged sequence with other children.

Several theoretical orientations have emphasized the role of play as a means of reducing tension and anxieties. Cross-cultural comparisons might reveal, in addition, different social and cultural values that are infused in the play of young children. . .

Children's games around the world appear to play an important part in resolving conflicts over socialization pressures and teach social values and social skills essential for successful adaptation in a given society, whether through

physical skills, taking chances or making rational choices in a deliberate strategy.

A number of ecological and child-training correlates appear associated with assertive, competitive and rivalrous behavior in children. Increasing modernization, as measured by exposure to school and city life, and the opportunity for social mobility and the removal of the inhibiting effects of traditional stress on obedience and control of aggression seem to contribute to an increase in these behaviors, more so among boys than girls and among older than younger children. Extrafamilial socializers can counteract this trend in societies where cooperation is stressed as part of a deliberate philosophy.

Summary

In sum, the influence of peers as mediators of social change cannot be underestimated. The results of studies of child caretaking, of games and of competitive versus cooperative behavior in the classroom seem to indicate that peers, with and without the direct support of teachers and the sociopolitical system of a given society, transmit social values that are important in the process of modernization. The young, as role models for still younger children, become important pacesetters in the developing world and in human cultural evolution.

---

[1]B. Rogoff, M.J. Sellers, S. Piorrata, N. Fox and S. White, "Age of Assignment of Roles and Responsibilities to Children: A Cross-Cultural Survey," *Human Development*, 1975, 18.

[2]B. Whiting and J.W. Whiting, *Children of Six Cultures*, Cambridge, Mass., Harvard University Press, 1975.

[3]L. A. Minturn, "A Survey of Cultural Differences in Sex-Role Training and Identification," in N. Kretschmer and D. Walcher (eds.), *Environmental Influences on Genetic Expression*, Washington, D.C., U.S. Government Printing Office, 1969.

[4]J. I. Carlebach, "Family Relationships of Deprived and Non-Deprived Kikuyu Children from Polygamous Marriages," *Journal of Tropical Pediatrics*, 1967, 13.

[5]A.F. Lieberman, "Preschoolers Competence with a Peer: Relations with Attachment and Peer Experience, *Child Development*, 1977, 48.

[6]W. Caudill and D.W. Plath, "Who Sleeps By Whom?: Parent-Child Involvement in Urban Japanese Families," *Psychiatry*, 1966, 29.

[7]Whiting and Whiting, 1975, op. cit.

[8]B. Whiting and C.P. Edwards, "A Cross-Cultural Analysis of Sex Differences in the Behavior of Children Aged Three Through Eleven," *Journal of Social Psychology*, 1973, 91.

[9]Carl R. Ember, "Female Task Assignment and Social Behavior of Boys," *Ethos*, 1973, 1.

[10]See, for example, R.I. Levy, "Child Management Structure and Its Implications in a Tahitian Family," in E. Vogel and N. Bell (eds.), *A Modern Introduction To The Family*, New York, Free Press, 1968 and J.E. Ritchie, *Basic Personality in Rakau*, New Zealand, Victoria University, 1956.

[11]T.S. Weisner and R. Gallimore, "My Brother's Keeper: Child and Sibling Caretaking," *Current Anthropology*, 1977, 18(2).

[12]M. Steward and D. Steward, "Parents and Siblings As Teachers," in E.J. Mash, L.C. Handy and L.A. Hamerlynek (eds.), *Behavior Modification Approaches to Parenting*, New York, Brunner/Mazel, 1976.

[13]J. Jorgensen, "Indians and the Metropolis," in J.O. Waddell and O.M. Watson (eds.). *The American Indian in Urban Society*, Boston, Little Brown, 1971.

[14]R. Gallimore, J.W. Boggs and C.E. Jordan, *Culture, Behavior and Education: A Study of Hawaiian-Americans*, Beverly Hills, Calif., Sage, 1974.

[15]S. MacDonald and R. Gallimore, *Battle in the Classroom: Innovations in Classroom Techniques*, Scranton, Intext, 1971.

[16]P.M. Greenfield, *What We Can Learn from Cultural Variation in Child Care*, paper presented at the American Association for the Advancement of Science, San Francisco, 1974.

[17]A. Weisler and R.B. McCall, "Exploration and Play: Resume and Redirection," *American Psychologist*, 1976, 31(7).

If your child doesn't get along with other kids

There are ways for parents to help kids who have chronic difficulties getting along with their peers. And if you think a problem may be in the making, there are things you can do before it gets serious.

THE PROBLEM may announce itself with a call from another parent. The voice is regretful but firm.

"Please don't send your child over to play anymore. He spends the whole time fighting."

Or it may be a baby-sitter, a principal or a teacher who's the first to tell you your child doesn't get along with other children.

No parent likes to get that kind of report, but is it really so important for children to get along well with their peers?

"Children get unique things from each other," says Dr. Willard W. Hartup, director of the University of Minnesota's Institute of Child Development and a leading researcher on children's peer relations. For one thing, he says, "it's better to practice and experience the consequences of aggression with someone your own size."

But if a child doesn't learn how to handle his feelings and communicate his ideas and opinions to his peers, says Chet Brodnicki of Child and Family Services in Hartford, Conn., "he'll probably encounter a great deal of difficulty as an adult along those very lines. And that will affect his ability to hold a job, complete his education and have stable relationships with other adults."

Other professionals agree. Furthermore, they agree that peer problems may go along with other problems, such as learning difficulties. And these troubles may be your best signal that all is not going well with your child.

Whether they are aggressive or shy and withdrawn, the youngsters who can't get along with children their age are isolated, and as various studies suggest, these children are more likely than others to drop out of school, become juvenile delinquents and have mental health problems.

The good news is that you can prepare your children—even very young ones—to get along with their peers and you can get help if you need it.

A healthy pattern

Granted, children need children. Does this mean you should worry about a child who wants to spend his recess reading? Not at all, says Elizabeth Jacob of the Virginia Frank Child Development Center of the Jewish Family Service in Chicago. "Maybe he is by temperament a quiet child. Maybe this year he happens to be fascinated with reading. Many children's development is uneven, and there's a wide range of 'normal unevenness,' as well as a wide range of temperaments."

With most children social development follows a predictable course. At first the baby grows attached to the parents. A secure child will soon start responding in friendly fashion to a strange adult or child. Two-year-olds usually enjoy playing alongside each other, but they're really not ready to play *with* each other. By the time a child is 3, he may be ready to take turns or share toys if an attentive adult is nearby to give occasional help.

Five-year-olds can often manage cooperative play by themselves. By the time a child is 6 to 8, he wants to be off with other children much of the time.

From then until adolescence and beyond, peers are king. If you say there's no Santa Claus and a peer says there is, your son or daughter will probably believe there is a Santa Claus.

What can you do to help along the healthy process of establishing peer friendships?

▶ Make sure your baby has a warm, secure, continuing relationship with the person who takes principal care of him. This is particularly important from five to 18 months. One study found that the security of a child's attachment to his mother at 15 months accurately predicted his competence with his peers at 3½.

▶ Let your child be with other children at a very early age. Infancy isn't too young for informal get-togethers in the mother's presence. Even children too young for

As Dr. Benjamin Spock puts it, "Children encountered for the first time can seem as strange and dangerous to inexperienced children as gorillas would to grownups."

▶ Pay special attention to early social experiences of an only child to make up for the practice he's not getting with a brother or sister. Spock suggests taking a first child to a playground or a friend's backyard several times a week, especially when the child begins to walk. "Let her learn all by herself how to meet push with push or how to hang on to a toy when another child is trying to grab it. . . . She gets her basic feelings about the meaning of aggressiveness of other children from her parents. If her parents consider it dangerous or cruel, she is frightened by it. If they take it casually, she learns to do the same."

▶ When a 3-year-old is ready for cooperative play, it's helpful if a responsible adult is around, not to take over but to see that the children learn, in Jacob's words, to "take turns, negotiate, moderate, wait." At this age children can benefit from a good nursery school or other regularized play situation.

▶ Try to spot developmental problems early. Mary MacCracken, a learning disability specialist who wrote *Lovey: A Very Special Child* and former chairperson of the National Association for Mental Health, favors screening tests in kindergarten or earlier to look at developmental indicators—motor, verbal and paper-and-pencil skills—and behavioral characteristics, such as how the child gets along with other children. If there is trouble with any of these indicators, MacCracken says, the child should be watched carefully and given one-to-one help.

▶ Try pairing a withdrawn preschooler with one other playmate. This worked especially well in a study in which the playmate was 15 months younger than the shy child.

▶ If your school-age child isn't making friends on his own, lend a hand. Spock suggests inviting children over, one by one, for a meal or a special outing. If it takes a bribe to get them to come, so be it. "You can't make an obnoxious child popular with bribes," he says, "but you can ensure that your child's good qualities will be given fair consideration."

▶ Read children's books with a friendship theme with your child. It gives him an opening to air his feelings about other children.

▶ Work with your child's teacher to find clubs and recreation groups that follow the youngster's interests.

Becoming better playmates

New research projects are throwing more light on qualities that make a child attractive to other children. Studies point to four social skills that seem to count in gaining acceptance. Dr. Sherri Oden of the University of Rochester and Dr. Steven Asher of the University of Illinois call these skills participating, cooperating, communicating, and validating or supporting.

Children earn acceptance by *participating* in a game or activity, initially by getting started and paying attention; by *cooperating,* as in taking turns and sharing materials; by *communicating,* through talking and listening; and by *validating or supporting,* as in looking or smiling at playmates and offering help or encouragement.

Oden and Asher set out to see whether coaching in these four skills would make unpopular third- and fourth-graders more acceptable to their classmates. After five coached play sessions over four weeks, the unpopular kids got higher ratings from their classmates. A year later their ratings were higher still.

Harvard researcher Dr. Robert L. Selman has been studying children's ideas about friendship. It is Selman's theory that children move through an overlapping five-stage sequence in understanding friendship and may get stuck at any stage along the way. The process begins at ages 3 to 7 with what Selman labels Momentary Playmateship, in which friends are valued because they're nearby and have nice toys. At ages 4 to 9 comes One-Way Assistance, in which a friend is a friend because he does what you want to do. Between 6 and 12 Two-Way Fair-Weather Cooperation may develop, followed at 9 to 15 by Intimate, Mutually Shared Relationships. Finally, at age 12 or older, children may gain enough perspective for Autonomous Interdependent Friendships to become possible.

Selman, who has used his research to help troubled youngsters make friends, observes that a child may not get along with his peers if his understanding of friendship is either delayed or too advanced. For instance, a youngster who's ready for intimate, possessive friendships may not be accepted by playmates who are still working their way through the one-way, self-interest stages.

Selman has been able to help disturbed children catch up to stages of friendship skills that fit their ages. He's also developing "friendship therapy" for children who have been too aggressive or too shy to get along with children of their age.

Stanford's Dr. Philip G. Zimbardo is another social psychologist working on the problems of shyness. He tells parents and teachers to head off shyness by helping the child discover his attractive qualities, and he recommends games and exercises for combating shyness in both children and adults.

Should you get help?

Dr. Charles R. Shaw, a child psychiatrist and author of *When Your Child Needs Help,* writes that "the time to take your child for professional help is when you feel he is unhappy. . . . If your child is happy, he is probably okay."

Dr. Spock says that "a child who can't make or keep friends by six or who is aggressive or cruel or timid with other children, should have help."

The Hartford Child and Family Services finds that peer problems are most often first identified in the classroom. This agency sees the largest concentration of peer problems in overaggressive 7- to 12-year-old boys, especially "just after the report cards come out and in the spring, when promotions for next year are being planned," says Brodnicki.

The agency may assign such a child to an activity group in which six or eight children with similar difficulties meet for an hour and a half each week for at least ten weeks with one or two therapists. Through group activities, including decision making and discussion, the children learn ways of dealing with anger and frustration.

At the same time a counselor meets with the family. This does not imply that the family is to blame. However, methods that worked with other children in the family may not work with this one, and possibly the counselor can suggest alternatives. Or the whole family, including the child, may be reacting to a traumatic family event—a death, a divorce, a move.

Community mental health centers and family service agencies like the one in Hartford get government or United Way funds as well as other public or private grants, so they can often adjust their fees to the family income. Charges are usually moderate compared with the fees of private practitioners. Look for family agencies in the Yellow Pages under "Marriage and Family." Ask whether they belong to the Family Service Association of America (there are about 270 members in 42 states). Community mental health centers set up with federal funds are required by law to have children's services. Look for them under "Health," "Mental Health," "Clinics" or "Social Services." Help or referral assistance may also be available through the child's school if your school system has social workers and psychologists on the staff, as many do.

Your health insurance may include counseling from private therapists or funded agencies.

It's a good idea to have a youngster who has behavior problems checked by a physician. There may be some medical problem that's causing the trouble—for instance, a vision or hearing defect. Dr. Lee Salk, a family psychologist, points out that even minimal dysfunction of the central nervous system, often easily treated, can bring on aggressive behavior, hyperactivity, temper tantrums— and the concomitant trouble with peers—if untreated.

Whatever is bothering a child who doesn't get along with other kids—fear or insecurity, lack of social skills, trouble in the home, medical problems—it's worth finding out what it is and doing something about it.

Most children respond well to help, says Dr. Rosemary Burns, director for Youth and Family Service at a Virginia community mental health center. "In the length of a school year in treatment, most children can work their way out of peer difficulties." □

BOOKS FOR PARENTS AND KIDS

The following publications are for parents.
- *Childhood and Adolescence: A Psychology of the Growing Person,* by L. Joseph Stone and Joseph Church (Random House; $14.95). Fourth ed.
- *Families: Applications of Social Learning to Family Life,* by Gerald R. Patterson (Research Press, Box 3177, Champaign, Ill. 61820; $4.95). Rev. ed.
- *Help for Your Child: A Parent's Guide to Mental Health Services,* by Sharon S. Brehm (Prentice-Hall; $10.95 hardcover, $4.95 paperback).
- *Raising Children in a Difficult Time,* by Benjamin Spock, M.D. (W. W. Norton; $7.95 hardcover. Pocket Books; $1.95 paperback).
- *Shyness: What It Is, What to Do About It,* by Philip G. Zimbardo (Addison-Wesley; $9.95 hardcover, $5.95 paperback).

These books are for children.
- *Amos and Boris,* by William Steig (Farrar, Straus & Giroux; $6.95 hardcover. Penguin; $1.95 paperback).
- *Frog and Toad Are Friends,* by Arnold Lobel (Harper & Row; $5.95 hardcover, $1.95 paperback).
- *Let's Be Enemies,* by J. M. Udry (Scholastic Book Service, 906 Sylvan Ave., Englewood Cliffs, N.J. 07632; 85 cents). Illustrated by Maurice Sendak.
- *Tales of a Fourth Grade Nothing,* by Judy Blume (Dutton; $6.95 hardcover. Dell; $1.25 paperback). See also other books by Blume.
- *Two Good Friends,* by Judy Delton (Crown; $5.50).
- *Will I Have a Friend?* by Miriam Cohen (Collier Books; $6.95 hardcover, $1.95 paperback).

Moral Education for Young Children

Susan R. Stengel

Susan R. Stengel, Ed.D., is a kindergarten teacher at the Colorado Academy in Denver.

The form that children's moral education should take and the values to be taught are controversial among parents and educators. Some feel that a few simple behaviors such as how to share and how to say thank you are sufficient. Others focus on the development of self-esteem. Still others believe in providing a maximum amount of independence for children to work out their own social arrangements and disputes.

Decisions about how to discipline and teach young children to cope in the world should be based on an understanding of the development of morality. Parents and teachers of young children can benefit from knowing about the stages of moral development through adulthood so that they can provide early experiences upon which later development can flourish.

What Is Morality?

Morality has been defined (Berkowitz 1964) as action that conforms to socially determined standards of right behavior. Moral education based on this framework involves identifying those right behaviors and then training children to act accordingly, either by rewarding, punishing, modeling, lecturing, or some combination of these.

Some philosophers assert that morality involves more than prescribed action (Wilson 1967, p. 60). The right action must be freely chosen, must be based on reasons that take into account the interests of others, and must be accompanied by appropriate feelings or attitudes. Moral education derived from this viewpoint suggests exposing children to a variety of moral codes from which they select one. Teaching the right reasons and how to apply those reasons to situations involving moral choice would be included.

The cognitive-developmental view of morality (Kohlberg 1969) maintains that morality is a developmental process. One's reasons for acting morally, and the kinds of motivation required to act morally, change with time and experience in a predictable way. For example, while rewarding appropriate action may be sufficient to elicit moral behavior in young children, good reasons are usually necessary to convince teenagers or adults that a given action is moral. For the developmentalist, moral education means facilitating children's progress through the stages of moral reasoning, leading to the adoption of freely chosen moral values.

The Development of Moral Reasoning

Inspired by Piaget, Kohlberg (1969) has spent 20 years investigating how people think about moral problems by presenting moral dilemmas and noting what kinds of reasons people use to back up their resolutions to the dilemmas.

Kohlberg found that moral reasoning develops in stages. The stages as summarized by Fenton (1976, pp. 189-190) are:

Stage 1. The punishment and obedience orientation: The physical consequences of doing something determine whether it is good or bad without regard for its human meaning or value. People at Stage 1 think about avoiding punishment or earning rewards, and they defer to authority figures with power over them.

Stage 2. The instrumental relativist orientation: At Stage 2 right reasoning leads to action which satisfies one's own needs and sometimes meet the needs of others. Stage 2 often involves elements of fairness, but always for pragmatic reasons rather than from a sense of justice or loyalty. Reciprocity, a key element of Stage 2 thought, is a matter of "you scratch my back and I'll scratch yours."

Stage 3. The interpersonal sharing orientation: At this stage, people equate good behavior with whatever pleases or helps others and of whatever others approve. Stage 3 thinkers often conform to stereotypical ideas of how the majority of people in their group behave. They often judge behaving by intentions, and they earn approval by being nice.

Stage 4. The societal maintenance orientation: Stage 4 thought orients toward authority, fixed rules, and the maintenance of the social order. Right behavior consists of doing one's duty, showing respect for authority, or maintaining the given social order for its own sake.

Stage 5. The social contract, human rights, and welfare orientation: Stage 5 thinkers tend to define right action in terms of general individual rights and standards which have been examined critically and agreed upon by the entire society. The legal point of view is stressed, but emphasis is placed on the possibility of changing laws after rational consideration of the welfare of the society. Free agreement and contract bind people together where no laws apply.

Kohlberg's theory describes a sixth stage, the universal ethical principle orientation, which was dropped from the measurement because he did not find examples of it in his experimental populations. However, the sixth stage which few people seem to attain, still is part of his moral development theory—a theory he is expanding to include a seventh stage (Kohlberg 1981).

The primary educational method suggested by Kohlberg is to produce cognitive conflict in the mind of an individual that will force her or him to use higher stage reasoning to solve a problem. If individuals are exposed to reasoning one stage higher than their own, the growth process will be enhanced. One of the best ways to promote children's thinking about moral problems is through peer interaction in the form of dilemma discussions or class meetings in which students can exchange and justify their points of view.

Since Kohlberg published the original formulation of his stages, many researchers and educators have studied, elaborated upon, and used stage theory in their own work. Damon (1977) investigated children's ideas of justice, friendship, rules, manners, sex-role conventions, and authority. His work supports stage theory and describes in greater detail the thought processes of young children.

Damon considers the development of the concept of positive justice to be the central aspect of morality. He interviewed 144 children four through eight years old and presented a problem to them in which four children are given ten candy bars in exchange for making bracelets. One child makes the most bracelets; one child is the biggest; and one is younger than the others. The subject is asked how to distribute the candy bars. The results show distinct stages that correlate with age.

Level O-A: Justice is equated with the child's wishes. "I should get it because I want it."

Level O-B: The child is still self-centered, but feels the need to justify her or his choices. Illogical external factors such as size, sex, or other physical characteristics are used as justification. "I should get four because I'm four."

Level 1-A: Strict equality. Everyone gets the same. No special consideration is given to anyone.

Level 1-B: Reciprocity and merit are important factors. Those who work harder deserve more.

Level 2-A: Different but equally valid claims to justice are weighed. Special consideration is given for special needs. "She shouldn't have to work as hard because she's little."

Level 2-B: The claims of the various people (need, merit, etc.) involved and the demands of the specific situation are considered. Everyone should be given a fair share.

"Justice level 0-A was found predominantly at age four; 0-B, at ages four and five; 1-A, at age five (with some subjects scattered at higher ages); 1-B, at ages six and seven; 2-A, at age eight; and 2-B, at age eight" (Damon 1977, p. 91). Damon's results indicate that young children are capable of making moral judgments and that they should be called upon to do so in a variety of circumstances. However, when he tried to administer Kohlberg's interviews to the same subjects, the younger children did not comprehend the dilemmas, and the older children exhibited nothing above Stage 1 reasoning.

It appears, then, that children need to be given meaningful opportunities to take the viewpoints of others (role taking). They also need to learn that reasons are important in stating their own viewpoint. Before suggesting ways to accomplish these goals in an early childhood program, we first need to look at conditioning—the commonly used method of controlling behavior (if not teaching morality).

How to Facilitate Moral Development

Why Conditioning Is Inadequate

Why not simply teach children good reasons for moral actions and then reward them for behaving morally in accordance with those reasons? Certainly in the early years children are not able to take into account all the facts of a situation, so they must learn some behaviors that have general applicability. However, conditioning children to behave in response to a reward is not acceptable as a long-term solution for several reasons.

Parents and teachers do not control rewards for very long. As soon as children begin to interact with other children, they begin responding to rewards outside of the home and family. How will children make decisions on their own and decide among the many rewards available to them outside the home? If adult reward is the only method used to elicit behavior, children may change their behavior as soon as the reward is no longer present or if a more enticing reward is offered.

Another problem with conditioning is that children cannot be conditioned to respond appropriately in all situations. For example, if a child has been conditioned not to take food from other people, this behavior may be totally inappropriate if the child sees a baby eating poisonous berries. Clearly, our aim should be to help children understand principles and reasons rather than to teach specific actions, because the appropriate action will depend upon the situation. Creating a moral atmosphere in the home or classroom is thus the first step to moral education.

4. CHILDHOOD

Create a Moral Atmosphere

How do teachers or parents refrain from indoctrinating and conditioning children in an environment that offers optimal learning experiences? Teachers must exercise some control in classrooms in order to ensure justice for individuals, creating an atmosphere in which moral education (and other learning) can take place. Children need examples of fair treatment and organized social arrangements (e.g., ensuring that everyone who wishes gets a turn at easel painting, or allowing only four to play at a time in the block corner) if they are to understand justice and choose it for themselves when they get older. Such structure gives children the idea of a moral framework—a set of rules organizing human behavior. This structure reduces anxiety for both children and teachers because it ensures that each child will have the maximum opportunity to learn without preventing other children from having the same opportunity. "To try to impose values is immoral, but to fail to create frameworks within which people can choose their own values is just as bad" (Wilson 1967, p. 143).

The way in which the framework is established, however, can affect the attainment of the long-range goals of moral education. Therefore, the long-range goals should be kept in mind when formulating and enforcing basic rules (see Stone 1978).

Teachers can begin by asking what kinds of ground rules will facilitate a safe atmosphere conducive to moral education and other kinds of education for all of the children. Early childhood teachers may want to begin with four or five simple rules stated positively, such as "In this classroom, we walk," or "We put away our materials at this school." Too many ground rules may confuse the children and make them afraid to do anything for fear of breaking a rule. Later, rules for specific activities can be introduced, such as "We wear smocks to paint." Ground rules must be based on good reasons that are aimed at optimum learning and development for all children and that take into account the interest of teachers and parents. Ground rules should promote justice in the classroom.

Once the ground rules are chosen, the rules and the reason for each rule should be explained clearly to the children. For example, "Here, we put our materials away so they will be ready for the next person to use." Try to acquaint the children with the thought processes you went through to determine the rule. Rules will be more meaningful if adults mention the viewpoints of others and how the rules will serve to meet the needs of everyone. A demonstration of the rule in action and opportunities to implement the rule may be helpful.

After the ground rules have been introduced, the adults must follow them and enforce them consistently. Unless the adults model appropriate behavior, children will test the limits constantly. For example, one of the ground rules may be "When we are indoors, we speak in low voices." If the teacher calls loudly across the room to a child, everyone will probably begin speaking louder, and it will become difficult to change the pattern of speaking louder in order to be heard.

However, even with modeling, there will be infractions of the rules. These are handled best through patient and consistent guidance, and, if necessary, the imposition of logical consequences (Dreikurs and Grey 1970). For example, suppose Kaylene has not put away her materials after she has finished working with them. The teacher would first remind Kaylene of her responsibility. Often a child simply will forget a rule if she is engrossed in activity, until she has repeated the action a number of times and it becomes a habit. If she does not respond to a reminder, the teacher may take her hand and guide her to the material, perhaps explaining again the reason for the rule as they walk. However, a child may refuse outright to comply, in which case a consequence logically related to the misbehavior will have to be imposed. For example, the teacher may require that a child not work with anything else until the materials are put away. Patient and consistent enforcement of the rules initially will result in a program in which children can work alone or in groups and can have the maximum opportunity for learning and cooperating with one another.

The logical consequences approach to discipline is based on the idea that children should experience the result of their own actions, whether pleasant or unpleasant. Depending on the situation, the parent or teacher may have to select a result that is distasteful or annoying to the child, but one that is not harmful. Logical consequences are not used as threats but are imposed in a matter-of-fact, even friendly, manner.

Enforcing the ground rules gives children some perspective on the social group and their relationship to the group. Teachers will probably want to explain to the child how her or his behavior affects others and will perhaps ask the child what would happen if everyone disobeyed that particular rule. Reasoning with children may help convince them to comply with the rules. But even if they do not change their behavior, giving reasons teaches children that reasons are important, and that some reasons are better than others, and it shows respect for the child as a person. Discipline by logical consequences appeals to children's sense of fairness and maintains their integrity.

Using reasoning and consistent and logical discipline prepares children for the times when they do not have coaches to tell them how to act. They soon establish appropriate behavior patterns, make some decisions for themselves, and begin to use reasoning to convince others of their viewpoint. As young adults, these children will probably begin to examine their own values and the values of others and will look for criteria to use in choosing their own values. Children who use reason as the ultimate authority become less egocentric more quickly than those who rely on adult authority.

Learning to take the point of view of another (role taking) can be facilitated also in the ways we communicate with children and by helping them communicate with each other effectively.

Use Communication Techniques

Based on some ideas from counseling psychology (Rogers 1951; Truax and Carkhuff 1967), Gordon's (1970; 1974) Parent Effectiveness Training (P.E.T) assists parents and teachers in becoming skilled communicators. The first skill is active listening, which requires not only listening, but also communicating with the speaker that you have heard her or him and that you understand what was said. The listener tries to repeat the essence of what the speaker has said in an attempt to check out the listener's perception. If the listener has interpreted the speaker correctly, the speaker will be encouraged to continue talking or to come up with a solution. Parents or teachers can help children think through and resolve a difficulty without telling them what to do. Note the differences between this typical exchange between student and teacher and the active listening alternative.

Typical exchange:
   Situation: First day of school. Eddie is gazing out of the window of his second-grade classroom.
   Teacher: What are you doing, Eddie?
   Eddie: Nothing. *(Pause)* Do we have to go to school all day?
   Teacher: Certainly we go all day. You went all day last year. Whatever made you think we didn't have to go all day? (Gordon 1974, pp. 102-103)

Active listening:
   Teacher: What are you doing, Eddie?
   Eddie: Nothing. *(Pause)* Do we have to go to school all day?
   Teacher: You really wish you were out there instead of sitting here in the classroom.
   Eddie: Uh-huh. There's nothing to do in here. You just have to sit in a seat all day and do papers and read.
   Teacher: You miss being able to play outside like you did all summer.
   Eddie: Yes. Playing games and swimming and climbing trees.
   Teacher: That was fun, so it's hard to give all that up and come back to school again.
   Eddie: Yes. I hope summer comes back soon.
   Teacher: You're really looking forward to next summer.
   Eddie: Yes, when next summer comes I can do what I want to do. (Gordon 1974, pp. 103-104)

Active listening respects children's integrity and their ability to solve their own problems. It demonstrates empathy and caring by showing children that their point of view is understood or, at least, that it is worth trying to understand. Furthermore, it provides a communication model for children that will assist them to be sensitive to others' points of view as they begin to use active listening themselves.

Active listening can be used with infants and toddlers as well as older children.

   Child: *(Crying)* Truck, truck—no truck.
   Parent: You want your truck, but you can't find it. (Active listening.)
   Child: *(Looks under sofa, but doesn't find truck)*
   Parent: The truck's not there. (Feeding back non-verbal message.)
   Child: *(Thinks; moves to back door)*
   Parent: The truck's not there. (Feeding back non-verbal message.)

   Parent: Maybe the truck's in the back yard. (Feeding back non-verbal message.)
   Child: *(Runs out, finds truck in sandbox, looks proud)* Truck!
   Parent: You found your truck yourself. (Active listening.) (Gordon 1970, pp. 101-102)

Note that the parent does not praise the child when he finds his truck. The child already feels happy because he knows he has done a good job. He has good feelings because the parent has not intervened but has allowed him to take responsibility and assisted him with the use of active listening to fulfill his responsibility by himself. In this case praise is not necessary and might be interpreted as patronizing. Active listening affirms children's sense of competence and helps them see that they feel good because they did it themselves. This child will begin to associate good feelings with finding something himself rather than with having a truck.

The second communication skill Gordon advocates is called sending an I-message. I-messages are used when there is a conflict between the teacher and child. An I message serves the purpose of describing as clearly as possible the speaker's point of view without threatening or blaming anyone for causing the problem. I-messages carry with them the assumption that the listener is willing to help the speaker solve the problem if possible. They include a feeling, a nonblameful description of the behavior or problem that is causing the feeling, and the tangible effect of the behavior on the parent or teacher. For example:

   Child comes to the table with very dirty hands and face. (Teacher:) "I can't enjoy my [lunch] when I see all that dirt. It makes me feel kind of sick and I lose my appetite (Gordon 1970, pp. 132-133)

I-messages can be sent to young children nonverbally as in these examples.

   Rob is squirming while Mother is putting his clothes on.

Mother gently but firmly restrains him and continues to dress him. (Message: "I can't dress you when you are squirming.")

While Dad is carrying Tim in the supermarket, he starts to kick Dad in the stomach. Dad immediately puts him down. (Message: "I don't like to carry you when you kick me.") (Gordon 1970, p. 134)

Both active listening and I-messages put the teacher and the child on the same side of the problem rather than on opposing sides. They promote trust and empathy and they help children do exactly what they need to do to develop moral reasoning, i.e., take the viewpoints of others. Active listening helps children clarify their own point of view; I-messages help them perceive another's point of view. Using these communication skills promotes dialogue and thought and an attitude of solving problems by reasoning. Because this attitude usually results in harmonious human interaction, the children feel good about themselves and others in the process, thus promoting cooperation in the classroom. In such an atmosphere children are given optimal opportunity for increasing their understanding of social relationships and moral issues.

Lead Group Discussions

Group meetings with children at least four years of age also can be used to promote moral growth in several ways. The basic principle is to stimulate children to think. A question asking *what* (What did you do over the weekend?) is not as thought provoking as a question asking *why* (Why did your father want you to help him with the dishes?)

The teacher will have to take the lead in most discussions, but the content and interaction will come from the children. Children will first need to learn how to have an effective group discussion, speaking in turn and listening to each other. One way of taking turns is to have a talk ticket. The child holding the ticket may talk, and when she or he is finished, gives the ticket to another child who wishes to speak. To promote listening and understanding, children can occasionally summarize the remarks of each speaker before the next child speaks.

Once the ground rules for talking and listening have been established, the teacher keeps the discussion going by enforcing the rules and keeping the discussion focused on one topic. New rules may have to be formulated from time to time. As the children find that some people make lengthy speeches, for example, they may see the need for a time limit rule. If they do not think of it, the teacher may want to suggest the idea.

Small groups—five or six children—are more effective at first. Teachers should speak as little as possible and encourage the children to explain *why* they hold a certain position, e.g., "Why do you think we should share the crayons?" Teachers may share their own point

of view in an objective manner ("When we share, then everyone gets a turn.") as long as they do not monopolize the discussion. Asking a child "Do you agree with the reason Sara gave?" is a good way of helping children to think and to focus on reasons. In this way the children will begin to see that their ideas count, that listening to each other is productive, and that they can solve problems.

To encourage children to express different points of view on a subject, teachers might want to ask questions such as "Does anyone have a different suggestion to make?" or "What do you think your mother (brother, friend) would say about this?" or "What would you think if you were the person who had to clean up everything?" Because children think more like each other than like adults, they will be able to understand their classmates' ideas, and perhaps their own thinking and ways of looking at the world will be challenged.

Simple social dilemmas also can be presented (*First Things: Social Reasoning*). Those that arise spontaneously in the classroom are usually more effective than hypothetical dilemmas because the children are more likely to understand the situation. Problems relating to sharing, taking turns, cleaning up, treating each other kindly, etc., can be discussed productively with young children.

Conclusion

The development of moral reasoning is an important goal for the education of young children. While teaching a specific set of values often is not acceptable to parents and is not particularly effective with children, ignoring moral education in early childhood programs is irresponsible and impossible.

Although young children tend to operate egocentrically, they can begin to apply their emerging intellectual abilities to moral and social issues, thus laying the groundwork for their future moral development. The pedagogical techniques suggested here will facilitate emergence from egocentricity into a world of satisfying human relationships.

Moral education is a part of every early childhood education program; we teach moral values with every action, every rule, and every activity. It is therefore necessary to plan consciously for moral education just as we plan in other areas of the curriculum.

References

Berkowitz, L. *Development of Motives and Values in a Child.* New York: Basic Books, 1964.

Damon, W. *The Social World of the Child.* San Francisco: Jossey-Bass, 1977.

Dreikurs, R., and Grey, L. *A Parents' Guide to Child Discipline.* New York: Hawthorn, 1970.

Duska, R., and Whelan, M. *Moral Development: A Guide to Piaget and Kohlberg.* New York: Paulist Press, 1975.

First Things: Social Reasoning. Filmstrip series. Pleasantville, N.Y.: Guidance Associates.

Fenton, E. "Moral Education: The Research Findings." *Social Education* 40 (April 1976): 189-193.

Gordon, T. *P.E.T.: Parent Effectiveness Training.* New York: New American Library, 1970.

Gordon, T. *T.E.T.: Teacher Effectiveness Training.* New York: David McKay, 1974.

Kohlberg, L. "Stage and Sequence: The Cognitive-Developmental Approach to Socialization." In *Handbook of Socialization Theory and Research,* ed. D.A. Goslin. Chicago: Rand McNally, 1969.

Kohlberg, L. *Philosophy of Moral Development.* New York: Harper & Row, 1981.

Rogers, C.R. *Client-Centered Therapy.* Boston: Houghton Mifflin, 1951.

Stone, J.G. *A Guide to Discipline.* Rev. ed. Washington, D.C.: National Association for the Education of Young Children, 1978.

Truax, C.B., and Carkhuff, R.R. *Toward Effective Counseling and Psychotherapy.* Chicago: Aldine Publishing Co., 1967.

Wilson, J. In *Introduction to Moral Education,* ed. J. Wilson, N. Williams, and B. Sugarman. Baltimore: Penguin, 1967.

My thanks to Tom Lickona for providing me with a summary of Damon's stages that I have adapted.

THE MYTH OF THE VULNERABLE CHILD

Arlene Skolnick

Arlene Skolnick is a research psychologist at the Institute of Human Development, University of California, Berkeley. Skolnick, who received her Ph.D from Yale, is chiefly interested in marital relationships and changes in self-concepts in later life. She has written *The Intimate Environment*, coauthored *Family in Transition* (both published by Little, Brown), and is now writing a developmental-psychology textbook for Harcourt Brace Jovanovich.

Anxious parents should relax. Despite what some psychologists have been telling them for years, they do not have make-or-break power over a child's development.

Americans have long been considered the most child-centered people in the world. In the 20th century, this traditional American obsession with children has generated new kinds of child-rearing experts—psychologists and psychiatrists, clothed in the authority of modern science, who issue prescriptions for child-rearing. Most child-care advice assumes that if the parents administer the proper prescriptions, the child will develop as planned. It places exaggerated faith not only in the perfectibility of the children and their parents, but in the infallibility of the particular child-rearing technique as well. But increasing evidence suggests that parents simply do not have that much control over their children's development; too many other factors are influencing it.

Popular and professional knowledge does not seem to have made parenting easier. On the contrary, the insights and guidelines provided by the experts seem to have made parents more anxious. Since modern child-rearing literature asserts that parents can do irreparable harm to their children's social and emotional development, modern parents must examine their words and actions for a significance that parents in the past had never imagined. Besides, psychological experts disagree among themselves. Not only have they been divided into competing schools, but they also have repeatedly shifted their emphasis from one developmental goal to another, from one technique to another.

Two Models of Parenting

Two basic models of parental influence emerge from all this competition and variety, however. One, loosely based on Freudian ideas, has presented an image of the vulnerable child: children are sensitive beings, easily damaged not only by traumatic events and emotional stress, but also by overdoses of affection. The second model is that of the behaviorists, whose intellectual ancestors, the empiricist philosophers, described the child's mind as a *tabula rasa*, or blank slate. The behaviorist model of child-rearing is based on the view that the child is malleable, and

parents are therefore cast in the role of Pygmalions who can shape their children however they wish. "Give me a dozen healthy infants, well-formed, and my own specified world to bring them up in," wrote J. B. Watson, the father of modern behaviorism, "and I'll guarantee to take any one at random and train him to be any type of specialist I might—doctor, lawyer, artist, merchant, chief, and yes, even beggar man and thief!"

The image of the vulnerable child calls for gentle parents who are sensitive to their child's innermost thoughts and feelings in order to protect him from trauma. The image of the malleable child requires stern parents who coolly follow the dictates of their own explicit training procedures: only the early eradication of bad habits in eating, sleeping, crying, can fend off permanent maladjustments.

Despite their disagreements, both models grant parents an omnipotent role in child development. Both stress that (1) only if parents do the right things at the right time will their children turn out to be happy, successful adults; (2) parents can raise superior beings, free of the mental frailties of previous generations; and (3) if something goes wrong with their child, the parents have only themselves to blame.

Contemporary research increasingly suggests, however, that both models greatly exaggerate the power of the parent and the passivity of the child. In fact, the children's own needs, their developing mental and physical qualities, influence the way they perceive and interpret external events. This is not to say that parents exercise no influence on their children's development. Like all myths, that of parental determinism contains a kernel of truth. But there is an important difference between influence and control. Finally, both models also fail to consider that parent-child relations do not occur in a social vacuum, but in the complex world of daily life.

Traditionally, child-study researchers have assumed that influence in the parent-child relationship flowed only one way, from active parent to passive child. For example, a large number of studies tested the assumption, derived from Freudian theory, that the decisive events of early childhood centered around feeding, weaning, and toilet-training. It is now generally conceded that such practices in themselves have few demonstrable effects on later development. Such studies may have erred because they assumed that children must experience and react to parental behavior in the same ways.

Even when studies *do* find connections between the behavior of the parents and the child, cause and effect are by no means clear. Psychologist Richard Bell argues that many studies claiming to show the effects of parents on children can just as well be interpreted as showing children's effects on parents. For instance, a study finding a correlation between severe punishment and children's aggressiveness is often taken to show that harsh discipline produces aggressive children; yet it could show instead that aggressive children evoke harsh child-rearing methods in their parents.

A Methodological Flaw

The image of a troubled adult scarred for life by an early trauma such as the loss of a parent, lack of love, or family tension has passed from the clinical literature to become a cliché of the popular media. The idea that childhood stress must inevitably result in psychological damage is a conclusion that rests on a methodological flaw inherent in the clinical literature: instead of studying development through time, these studies start with adult problems and trace them back to possible causes.

It's true that when researchers investigate the backgrounds of delinquents, mental patients, or psychiatric referrals from military service, they find that a large number come from "broken" or troubled homes, have overpossessive, domineering, or rejecting mothers, or have inadequate or violent fathers. The usual argument is that these circumstances cause maladjustments in the offspring. But most children who experience disorder and early sorrow grow up to be adequate adults. Further, studies sampling "normal" or "superior" people—college students, business executives, professionals, creative artists, and scientists—find such "pathological" conditions in similar or greater proportions. Thus, many studies trying to document the effects of early pathological and traumatic conditions have failed to demonstrate more than a weak link between them and later development.

The striking differences between retrospective studies that start with adult misfits and look back to childhood conditions, and longitudinal studies that start with children and follow them through time, were shown in a study at the University of California's Institute of Human Development, under the direction of Jean Macfarlane. Approximately 200 children were studied intensively from infancy through adolescence, and then were seen again at age 30. The researchers predicted that children from troubled homes would be troubled adults and, conversely, that those who had had happy, successful childhoods would be happy adults. They were wrong in two-thirds of their predictions. Not only had they overestimated the traumatic effects of stressful family situations, but even more surprisingly, they also had not anticipated that many of those who grew up under the best circumstances would turn out to be unhappy, strained, or immature adults (a pattern that seemed especially strong for boys who had been athletic leaders and girls who had been beautiful and popular in high school).

Psychologist Norman Garmezy's work on "invulnerability" offers more recent evidence that children can thrive in spite of genetic disadvantages and environmental deprivations. Garmezy began by studying adult schizophrenics and trying to trace the sources of their problems. Later, he turned to developmental studies of children who were judged high risks to develop schizophrenia and other disorders at a later age. When such children were studied over time, only 10 or 12 percent of the high-risk group became schizophrenic, while the majority did not.

Other Sources of Love

The term "invulnerables" is misleading. It suggests an imperviousness to pain. Yet, the ability to cope does not mean the child doesn't suffer. One woman, who successfully overcame a childhood marked by the death of her beloved but alcoholic and abusive father, and rejection by her mother and stepmother, put it this way: "We suffer, but we don't let it destroy us."

The term also seems to imply that the ability to cope is a trait, something internal to the child. One often finds in the case histories of those who have coped with their problems successfully that external supports softened the impact of the traumatic event. Often something in the child's environment provides alternative sources of love and gratification—one parent compensating for the inadequacy of the other, a loving sibling or grandparent, an understanding teacher, a hobby or strong interest, a pet, recreational opportunities, and so on.

Indeed, the local community may play an important role in modulating the effects of home environments. Erik Erikson, who worked on the study at the Institute of Human Development, was asked at a seminar, "How is it that so many of the people studied overcame the effects of truly awful homes?" He answered that it might have been the active street life in those days, which enabled children to enjoy the support of peers when parent-child relations got too difficult.

Psychologist Martin Seligman's learned-helplessness theory provides a further clue to what makes a child vulnerable to stress. Summarizing a vast array of data, including animal experiments, clinical studies, and reports from prisoner-of-war camps, Seligman proposes that people give up in despair not because of the actual severity of their situation, but because they feel they can have little or no effect in changing it. The feeling of helplessness is learned by actually experiencing events we cannot control, or by being led to believe that we have no control.

Seligman's theory helps to explain two puzzling phenomena: the biographies of eminent people that often reveal stressful family relations, and Macfarlane's findings that many children who did come from "ideal" homes failed to live up to their seeming potential. The theory of learned helplessness suggests that controllable stress may be better for a child's ego development than good things that happen without any effort on the child's part. Self-esteem and a sense of competence may not depend on whether we experience good or bad events, but rather on whether we perceive some control over what happens to us.

Parents Can't Be Pygmalions

Many of the same reasons that limit the effect of events on children also limit the ability of parents to shape their children according to behavioral prescription. The facts of cognition and environmental complexity get in the way of best-laid parental plans. There is no guarantee, for example, that children will interpret parental behavior accurately. Psychologist Jane Loevinger gives the example of a mother trying to discipline her five-year-old son for hitting his younger sister: if she spanks him, she may discourage the hitting, or she may be demonstrating that hitting is okay; if she reasons with the child, he may accept her view of hitting as bad, or he may conclude that hitting is something you can get away with and not be punished for.

Other factors, interacting with the child's cognitive processes and sense of self, limit the parents' ability to shape their children. Perhaps the most basic is that parents have their own temperamental qualities that may modify the message they convey to their children. One recurrent finding in the research literature, for example, is that parental warmth is important to a child's development. Yet warmth and acceptance cannot be created by following behavioral prescriptions, since they are spontaneous feelings.

Further, the parent-child relationship does not exist apart from other social contexts. A study of child-rearing in six cultures, directed by Harvard anthropologists John Whiting and Beatrice Whiting, found that parents' behavior toward children is based not so much on beliefs and principles as on a "horde of apparently irrelevant considerations": work pressures, the household work load, the availability of other adults to help with household tasks and child care, the design of houses and neighborhoods, the social structure of the community. All these influences, over which parents usually have little control, affect the resources of time, energy, attention, and affection they have for their children.

The effects of social class may also be very hard to overcome, even if the parent tries. Psychiatrist Robert Coles has written about poor and minority children who often come to learn from their families that they are persons of worth—only to have this belief shattered when they encounter the devaluing attitudes of the outside world. Conversely, middle-class children from troubled homes may take psychological nourishment from the social power and esteem that are enjoyed by their families in the community.

Science and the Family: Historical Roots

Given the lack of evidence for the parental-determinism model of child-rearing, why has it been so persistent? Why have we continued to believe that science can provide infallible prescriptions for raising happy, successful people and curing social problems?

As psychologist Sheldon White has recently observed, psychology's existence as a field of scientific research has rested upon "promissory notes" laid down at the turn of the century. The beginnings of modern academic psychology were closely tied to education and the growth of large public expenditures for the socialization of children. The first psychologists moved from philosophy departments to the newly forming education schools, expecting to provide scientific methods of education and child-rearing. The founding fathers of American psychology—J. B. Watson, G. S. Hall, L. M. Terman, and others—accepted the challenge. Thus, learning has always been a central focus of psychologists, even though the rat eventually came to compete with the child as the favored experimental animal.

If the behaviorists' social prescriptions conjure up images of *Brave New World* or *1984*, a more humane promise was implicit in Freudian theory. The earliest generations of Freudians encouraged the belief that if the new knowledge derived from psychoanalysis was applied to the upbringing of children, it would be possible to eliminate anxiety, conflict, and neurosis. The medical miracles achieved in the 19th and early 20th centuries gave the medical experts immense prestige in the eyes of parents. There seemed little reason to doubt that science could have as far-reaching effects on mental health as it had on physical health. Furthermore, as parents were becoming more certain of their children's physical survival, children's social futures were becoming less certain. When the family was no longer an economic unit, it could no longer initiate children directly into work. Middle-class parents had to educate their children to find their way in a complex job market. The coming of urban industrial society also changed women's roles. Women were removed from the world of work, and motherhood came to be defined as a separate task for women, the primary focus of their lives. Psychological ideas became an intrinsic part of the domestic-science movement that arose around the end of the 19th century; this ideology taught that scientific household management would result in perfected human relationships within the home, as well as in the improvement of the larger society.

The Limits of Perfectibility

As we approach the 1980s, Americans are coming to reject the idea that science and technology can guarantee limitless progress and solve all problems. Just as we have come to accept that there are limits to growth and to our natural resources, it is time we lowered our expectations about the perfectibility of family life. Instead of trying to rear perfectly happy, adjusted, creative, and successful children, we should recognize that few, if any, such people exist, and even if they did, it would be impossible to produce such a person by following a behavioral formula. Far from harming family relations, lowered expectations could greatly benefit them.

What is more, the belief in parental determinism has had an unfortunate influence on social policy. It has encouraged the hope that major social problems can be eradicated without major changes in society and its institutions. For example, we have in the past preferred to view the poor as victims of faulty child-rearing rather than of unemployment, inadequate income, or miserable housing. Ironically, while we have been obsessed with producing ideal child-rearing environments in our own homes, we have permitted millions of American children to suffer basic deprivations. A seemingly endless series of governmental and private commissions has documented the sorry statistics on infant mortality, child malnutrition, unattended health needs, and so on, but the problems persist. In short, the standards of perfection that have been applied to child-rearing and the family in this century have not only created guilt and anxiety in those who try to live up to them, but have also contributed to the neglect of children on a national scale.

For further information, read:
Clarke, Ann M and A. D. Clarke, eds *Early Experience Myth and Evidence,* Free Press. 1977. $13 95
Garmezy, Norman "Vulnerable and Invulnerable Children Theory, Research and Intervention." American Psychological Association, MS 1337. 1976
Goertzel, Victor and Mildred G. Goertzel *Cradles of Eminence,* Little, Brown. 1978. paper. $4.95
Macfarlane, Jean "Perspectives on Personality Consistency and Change from the Guidance Study." *Vita Humana,* Vol. 7. No. 2, 1964

WE WANT YOUR ADVICE

Any anthology can be improved. This one will be—annually. But we need your help.

Annual Editions revisions depend on two major opinion sources: one is the academic advisers who work with us in scanning the thousands of articles published in the public press each year; the other is you—the person actually using the book.

Please help us and the users of the next edition by completing the prepaid article rating form on the last page of this book and returning it to us. Thank you.

MOOD & MEMORY

GORDON H. BOWER

Gordon H. Bower is chairman of the psychology department at Stanford University. An experimental psychologist, he specializes in human learning and memory, and was coauthor, with Ernest Hilgard, of the textbook Theories of Learning *(Prentice-Hall), now in its fifth edition. Bower, a member of the National Academy of Sciences, describes his studies of the impact of emotion on learning as a recent sideline. This article is adapted from his Distinguished Scientific Contributions Award address given last year at a meeting of the American Psychological Association. The full address first appeared in the* American Psychologist.

An American soldier in Vietnam blacked out as he stared at the remains of his Vietnamese girlfriend, killed by Vietcong mortar fire. Vowing revenge, he plunged into the jungle. Five days later an American patrol discovered him wandering aimlessly, dazed, disoriented. His memory of the preceding week was a total blank. He had no idea where he'd been or what he'd been doing for that period. Even after his return to the U.S., he could not recall the blackout period.

Several years later, a psychiatrist treating him for depression put him under hypnosis and encouraged him to reconstruct events from his combat days, both before and during the blackout. He calmly recalled earlier events, but when he neared the traumatic episode, he suddenly became very agitated, and more memories came pouring out. He began to relive the trauma of seeing his girlfriend's body and felt again the revulsion, outrage, and lust for revenge. Then, for the first time, he remembered what had happened after the mortar attack. He had commandeered a jeep, traveled alone for days deep into Vietcong territory, stalked Vietcong in the jungles, and set scores of booby traps with captured weapons before stumbling upon the American patrol. Curiously, after awakening from his hypnotic trance, the patient could remember only a few incidents singled out by the psychiatrist. But further treatments, described in the book *Trance and Treatment* by psychiatrists Herbert and David Spiegel, enabled him to bring more details into consciousness.

This case illustrates an extreme memory dissociation; the blackout events could be recalled in one state (of hypnotic agitation) but not in another (normal consciousness). Hypnosis helped the person return to the psychic state he was in when the blackout started; at that point, the emotional feelings returned, as did memories of the details of the blacked-out events. Psychoanalysts might call this a case of severe repression, which refers to the avoidance of anxiety-provoking memories. I believe such a label equates an observation with an explanation that may or may not be correct. Instead, I believe the soldier's case is an example of state-dependent memory, a more encompassing theory that refers to people's difficulty in recovering during one psychological state any memories acquired in a different state. State-dependency and repression are competing theories of forgetting. Each offers an explanation of why the soldier's blacked-out memories returned as he relived his trauma. But repression could not explain why a happy person can find happy memories easier to recover than sad ones.

The idea of studying the efficiency of memory during different psychological states—for example, while in hypnosis, under the influence of drugs, or after sensory deprivation—has been around for more than 50 years. However, previous investigations have been limited both in method and scope. While many clinical examples of state-dependency occur—for instance, violent "crimes of passion" are often blocked out but hypnotically recoverable by the assailant—such cases are really too rare, inconvenient, and complex for an adequate scientific analysis. In an earlier article in *Psychology Today* ("I Can't Remember What I Said Last Night, But It Must Have Been Good," August 1976), Roland Fischer described several examples and conjectured that memories are bound up with specific levels of physiological arousal. But my research shows that arousal level is not nearly as critical as the type of emotion felt—whether fear, depression, anger, or happiness. The most common laboratory method in previous studies of state-dependency used rats, learning with or without an injection of a drug like Amytal and later tested in either a drugged or nondrugged state.

As an experimentalist, I was challenged to produce state-dependent memory in the laboratory, using normal people and trying to evoke commonly occurring emotions as "states." Two of my students, Steve Gilligan and Ken Monteiro, and I were especially interested in trying to produce such learning using different emotions, such as depression, joy, fear, and anger. This turned into a more ambitious project when we found evidence not only of state-dependent memory but also of related emotional influences on thinking, judging, and perceiving. First, I'll describe our work on state-dependent memory.

The technique we employed for inducing moods used our subjects' imaginations, guided by hypnotic suggestion. College students who were very hypnotizable volunteered for our study. After hypnotizing them, we asked them to get into a happy or sad mood by imagining or remembering a scene in which they had been delightfully happy or grievously sad. Often the happy scene was a moment of personal success or of close intimacy with someone; the sad scenes were often of personal failure or the loss of a loved one. We told them to adjust the intensity of their emotion until it was strong but not unbearable—it was important for them to function well enough to learn. After getting into a mood state, the subjects performed a learning experiment for 20 or 30 minutes, after which they were returned to a pleasantly relaxed state before debriefing. (These procedures are harmless and our subjects have willingly volunteered for further experiments.)

After some pilot work, we found that strong mood state-dependent memory could be produced by teaching people two sets of material (such as word lists)—one while happy, the other while sad—and then asking them to remember one set in a happy or a sad mood. In one study, groups of hypnotized subjects learned List A while happy or sad, then learned List B while happy or sad, and then recalled the List A while happy or sad. The lists were 16 words long; memory was always tested by free recall. The groups can be classified into three conditions. In the first, control subjects learned and recalled both lists in a single mood, happy for half of them and sad for the other half. In the second condition, the subjects learned List A in one mood, learned List B in a different mood, and recalled List A in their original mood; these subjects should have recalled more than the control subjects because their different learning moods helped them to isolate the two lists, thus reducing confusion and interference from List B when they tried to recall List A. The third, interference condition was just the reverse; those students tried to recall List A when they were in their second, List B mood. Their recall of List A should have suffered, because the recall mood evokes memories of the wrong List B rather than the target List A.

When we returned subjects to their original moods, we did so by having them call up scenes different from their original ones. For example, if a woman originally induced happiness by reliving a scene of herself scoring the winning goal in a soccer match, we would instruct her to return to the happy mood by imagining a different scene, such as riding a horse along the beach. We had subjects use a second imagined situation so that any memory advantage obtained for same-mood testing would be due to overlap of moods, not to overlap of imaginary scenes.

A person's retention score was calculated as the percentage of originally learned items that were recalled on the later test. The results are in the chart on page 64; there is an obvious state-dependent effect. People who were sad during recall remembered about 80 per-

cent of the material they had learned when they were sad, compared with 45 percent recall of the material they had learned when they were happy. Conversely, happy recallers remembered 78 percent of their happy list, versus 46 percent of their sad list. The state-dependent memory effect shows up in the crossover of these lines on the chart. A good metaphor for this is to suppose that you have one bulletin board for happy moods and another for sad moods. On each board you post the messages you learn while in that mood. You will be able to read off your messages from the happy bulletin board best if you first get into a happy mood, and the messages on the sad bulletin board best when you get into a sad mood.

Aside from the state-dependent effect, I am often asked whether people learn better when they are happy or when they are sad. Others have found that clinically depressed patients are often poor learners. However, in all of our experiments with word lists, we never have found a difference in overall learning rate or later retention that was due to the subject's mood. I suspect this reflects our control over the hypnotic subjects' motivation to do as well as possible in the learning task despite their happy or sad feelings.

We next addressed the issue of whether state-dependency would occur for recall of actual events drawn from a person's emotional life. We enlisted some volunteers who agreed to record such emotional events in a daily diary for a week. We gave these subjects a book-

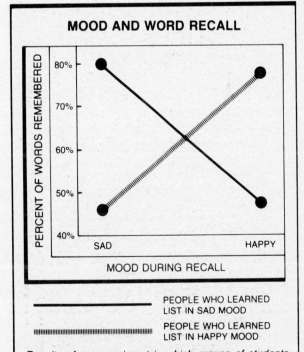

MOOD AND WORD RECALL

Results of an experiment in which groups of students learned a list of words while in one mood and later tried to recall as many as they could while in the same mood or a different mood. They were able to remember a much larger percentage when their learning mood matched their recall mood. This "state-dependency" effect is seen in the big difference between scores in the two recall situations, dramatized by the steep incline of the two lines connecting them. (The black dots show average percentages for both groups.)

let for recording emotional incidents and discussed what we meant by an emotional incident. Examples would be the joy they experienced at a friend's wedding or the anger they experienced in an argument at work. For each incident they were to record the time, place, participants, and gist of what happened and to rate the incident as pleasant or unpleasant on a 10-point intensity scale.

Conscientious diary-keeping is demanding, and we dropped nearly half of our subjects because they failed to record enough incidents in the proper manner consistently over the week. We collected usable diaries from 14 subjects and scheduled them to return a week later. At that one-week interval they were hypnotized; half were put into a pleasant mood and the other half into an unpleasant mood, and all were asked to recall every incident they could remember of those recorded in their diaries the week before.

The percentages of recall showed the expected results: people in a happy mood recalled a greater percentage of their recorded pleasant experiences than of their unpleasant experiences; people in a sad mood recalled a greater percentage of their unpleasant experiences than of their pleasant experiences.

Remember that when subjects originally recorded their experiences, they also rated the emotional intensity of each experience. These intensity ratings were somewhat predictive: recall of more intense experiences averaged 37 percent, and of less intense experiences 25 percent. The intensity effect is important, and I will return to it later.

After subjects had finished recalling, we asked them to rate the current emotional intensity of the incidents they recalled. We found that they simply shifted their rating scale toward their current mood: if they were feeling pleasant, the recalled incidents were judged as more pleasant (or less unpleasant); if they were feeling unpleasant, the incidents were judged more unpleasant (or less pleasant) than originally. That should be familiar—here are the rose-colored glasses of the optimist and the somber, gray outlook of the pessimist.

Is it possible that recording incidents in a diary and rating them as pleasant or unpleasant encourages subjects to label their experiences in this manner and in some way gives us the results we want? Perhaps. To avoid such contaminants, in our next experiment we simply asked people to recall childhood incidents. We induced a happy or sad mood in our subjects and asked them to write brief descriptions of many unrelated incidents of any kind from their pre-high school days. Subjects were asked to "hop around" through their memories for 10 minutes, describing an incident in just a sentence or two before moving on to some unrelated incident.

The next day, we had the subjects categorize their incidents as pleasant, unpleasant, or neutral while unhypnotized and in a normal mood (so that their mood would not influence how pleasant or unpleasant they rated an event). The few neutral incidents recalled were discarded, and the chart below shows the main results. Happy subjects retrieved many more pleasant than unpleasant memories (a 92 percent bias); sad subjects retrieved slightly more unpleasant than pleasant memories (a 55 percent bias in the reverse direction).

What the subjects reported was enormously dependent on their mood when recalling. That is state-dependent memory: the subjects presumably felt pleasant or unpleasant at the time the incidents were stored, and their current mood selectively retrieves the pleasant or the unpleasant memories.

What kind of theory can explain these mood-state dependent effects? A simple explanation can be cast within the old theory that memory depends upon associations between ideas. All we need to assume is that an emotion has the same effect as an "active idea unit" in the memory system. Each distinct emotion is presumed to have a distinct unit in memory that can be hooked up into the memory networks. The critical assumption is that an active emotion unit can enter into association with ideas we think about, or events that happened, at the time we are feeling that emotion. For instance, as the ideas recording the facts of a parent's funeral are stored in memory, a powerful association forms between these facts and the sadness one felt at the time.

Retrieval of some contents from memory depends upon activating other units or ideas that are associated with those contents. Thus, returning to the scene of a funeral, the associations activated by that place may cause one to reexperience the sadness felt earlier at the funeral. Conversely, if a person feels sad for some reason, activation of that emotion will bring into consciousness remembrances of associated ideas—most likely other sad events.

This theory easily explains state-dependent retrieval. In the first experiment, for example, the words of List A became associated both with the List A label and with the mood experienced at that time. Later, the words from List A can be retrieved best by reinstating the earlier List A mood, since that mood is a strongly associated cue for activating their memory. On the contrary, if a person had to recall List A while feeling in a different (List B) mood, that different mood would arouse associations that competed with recall of the correct items, thus reducing the memory scores. The same reasoning explains how one's current mood selectively retrieves personal episodes associated originally with pleasant or unpleasant emotions.

Beyond state-dependent memory, the network theory also helps to explain a number of influences of emotion on selective perception, learning, judgment, and thinking. When aroused, an emotion activates relevant concepts, thoughts, and frameworks for categorizing the social world. We have confirmed, for example, that people who are happy, sad, or angry produce free associations that are predominantly happy, sad, or angry, respectively. Similarly, when asked to fantasize or make up an imaginative story to pictures of the Thematic Apperception Test (TAT), they produce happy, sad, or hostile fantasies, depending on their emotional state. If asked for top-of-the-head opinions about their acquaintances, or the performance of their car or TV, they give highly flattering or negative evaluations, according to their mood. Also, their mood causes them to be optimistic or pessimistic in prognosticating future events about themselves and the nation. These influences can be seen as veiled forms of state-dependent retrieval of either the positive or negative memories about the person, event, or object.

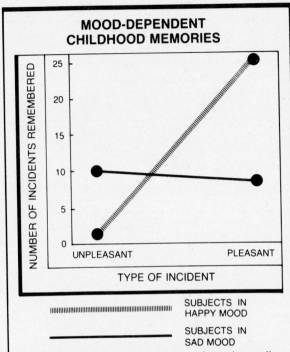

MOOD-DEPENDENT CHILDHOOD MEMORIES

SUBJECTS IN HAPPY MOOD

SUBJECTS IN SAD MOOD

Another experiment showing the state-dependency effect. Groups of students were put into a sad or a happy mood and then asked to remember incidents from childhood. Later, they labeled the incidents as either pleasant or unpleasant. Happy subjects recalled far more pleasant than unpleasant incidents. Sad subjects retrieved slightly more unpleasant memories. (The black dots show averages for both groups.)

Mood affects the way we "see" other people. Social interactions are often ambiguous, and we have to read the intentions hidden behind people's words and actions. Is that person being steadfast in arguing his position or is he being pigheaded and obstructive? Was his action courageous or reckless? Was that remark assertive or aggressive? In reading others' intentions the emotional premise from which we begin strongly influences what we conclude. Thus the happy person seems ready to give a charitable, benevolent interpretation of social events, whereas the grouch seems determined to find fault, to take offense, or to take the uncharitable view. We find that these effects appear just as strongly when people are judging themselves on competence or attractiveness as well as when they're judging others. For example, when our subjects were in a depressed mood, they tended to judge their actions moment-by-moment in a videotaped interview as inept, unsociable, and awkward; but if they were in a happy mood, they judged their behaviors as confident, competent, and warmly sociable. Thus, social "reality" is constructed in the eye of the beholder, and that eye is connected to the emotions.

The network theory further predicts that an emotion should act as a selective filter in perception, let-ting in signals of a certain emotional wavelength and filtering out others. The emotional state adjusts the filter so that the person will attend more to stimulus material that agrees with or supports the current emotion. An analogy is that our feelings are like a magnet that selects iron filings from a heap of dust, attracting to itself whatever incoming material it can use.

Emotional effects can de demonstrated in attention and perception as well as learning. Thus, a sad person will look at pictures of sad faces more than happy faces; a happy person will dwell longer on happy faces. People who are happy from having just succeeded at an intelligence task have lower thresholds for seeing "success" words; subjects who've failed have lower thresholds for "failure" words.

The main work we've done on this salience effect concerns selective learning. In one of our experiments, subjects were made happy or sad by a posthypnotic suggestion as they read a brief story about two college men getting together and playing a friendly game of tennis. André is happy—everything is going well for him; Jack is sad—nothing is going well for him. The events of the two men's lives and their emotional reactions are vividly described in the story, which is a balanced, third-person account. When our subjects finished reading the story, we asked them to tell us who they thought the central character was and who they identified with. We found that readers who were happy identified with the happy character, thought the story was about him, and thought the story contained more statements about him; readers who were sad identified with the sad character and thought there were more statements about him.

Our subjects tried to recall the text the next day while in a neutral mood. Eighty percent of the facts remembered by the sad readers were about the sad character; 55 percent of the facts remembered by the happy readers were about the happy character. This is a mood-congruity effect; readers attend more to the character whose mood matches their own. Since all recallers were in a neutral mood, their differing recall results from their selective learning; it is not a state-dependent effect, since that requires varying subjects' mood during recall as well as during learning.

How is the mood-congruity effect explained? Why is mood-congruent material more salient and better learned? Two explanations seem worth considering.

The first hypothesis is that when one is sad, a sad incident in a story is more likely than a happy incident to remind one of a similar incident in one's life; vice versa, when one is happy. (Note that this is simply the state-dependent retrieval hypothesis.) An additional assumption is that the reminding is itself an event that enhances memory of the prompting event. This may occur because the old memory allows one to elaborate on the prompting event or to infuse it with greater emotion. In other studies, we have found that people remember descriptions of events that remind them of a specific incident in their lives far better than they recall descriptions that don't cause such reminiscence. To summarize, this hypothesis states that the mood-congruity effect is produced by selective reminding.

The second hypothesis, which complements the first, is that the mood-congruity effect comes from the influence of emotional intensity on memory. We demonstrated this idea in a study in which subjects were put in a sad or happy mood during hypnosis and then asked to read a story that went from a happy incident to a sad incident to a happy incident, and so on. Although our hypnotized subjects in several experiments tried to maintain steady moods, they reported that a mood's intensity would wane when they read material of the opposite quality. Thus happy subjects would come down from their euphoria when they read about a funeral or about unjust suffering; those topics intensified the sad subjects' feelings.

But why are intense emotional experiences better remembered? At present, there are many explanations. One is that events that evoke strong emotional reactions in real life are typically events involving personally significant goals, such as attaining life ambitions, elevating self-esteem, reducing suffering, receiving love and respect, or avoiding harm to oneself or loved ones. Because of their central importance, those goal-satisfying events are thought about frequently and become connected to other personal plans and to one's self-concept.

Intense experiences may also be remembered better because they tend to be rare. Because they are distinctive, they are not easily confused with more numerous, ordinary experiences; they tend to be insulated from interference.

The explanation of the mood-congruity effect that fits our lab results best is that mood-congruous experiences may be rehearsed more often and elaborated or thought about more deeply than experiences that do not match our mood. Thus sad people may be quickly able to embroider and elaborate upon a sad incident, whereas they don't elaborate on happy incidents. Because their sad incidents are elaborated and processed more deeply, sad people learn their sad incidents better than their happy ones. The same principle explains why happy people learn happy incidents better.

Having reviewed some evidence for mood-congruity and mood-dependency effects, let me speculate a bit about the possible implications for other psychological phenomena.

One obvious phenomenon explained by mood dependency is mood perpetuation—the tendency for a dominant emotion to persist. A person in a depressed mood will tend to recall only unpleasant events and to project a bleak interpretation onto the common events of life. Depressing memories and interpretations feed back to intensify and prolong the depressed mood, encouraging the vicious circle of depression. One class of

therapies for depression aims at breaking the circle by restructuring the way depressed people evaluate personal events. Thus patients are taught to attend to and rehearse the positive, competent aspects of their lives and to change their negative evaluations.

State-dependent memory helps us to interpret several other puzzling phenomena. One is the impoverished quality of dream recall shown by most people. Most people forget their dreams, which is surprising considering that such bizarre, emotionally arousing events would be very memorable had they been witnessed in the waking state. But the sleep state (even the REM state of dreaming) seems psychologically distinct from the waking state, and dream memories may thus not be easily transferred from one state to the other.

State-dependent retention may also explain the fact that people have very few memories from the first year or two of their lives. In this view, as infants mature, their brains gradually change state, so that early memories become inaccessible in the more mature state. The problem with this hypothesis is that it leads to no novel predictions to distinguish it from the plethora of competing explanations of infantile amnesia, which generally range from Freud's repression theory to the theory that the infant's and adult's "languages of thought" mismatch so badly that adults can't "translate" records of infant memories.

State-dependent memory has been demonstrated previously with psychoactive drugs like marijuana, alcohol, amphetamines, and barbiturates. For example, after taking amphetamines, subjects remember material they have learned while high on the drug in the past better than when they are not high on it. Since such substances are also mood-altering drugs, a plausible hypothesis is that they achieve their state-dependent effect by virtue of their impact on mood.

To summarize, we have now found powerful influences of emotional states upon selective perception, learning, retrieval, judgments, thought, and imagination. The emotions studied have been quite strong, and their temporary psychological effects have been striking. What is surprising to me is that the emotional effects on thinking uncovered so far seem understandable in terms of relatively simple ideas—the notion that an aroused emotion can be viewed as an active unit in an associative memory and that it stimulates memories, thoughts, perceptual categories, and actions. Perhaps this is as it should be—that theories developed in one field (memory) aid our understanding of phenomena in another field (for example, emotional fantasies in the psychiatric clinic). Certainly that is the goal of all basic science.

THE VIOLENT BRAIN

DINA INGBER

Dina Ingber, science writer, recently covered an international conference about aggression.

A large crowd is waiting to board the bus. Most people hang back, shuffling along slowly with the group, but one woman shoves her way forward. Swinging her satchels, elbowing her way through, cursing at those who won't move, she makes her way in before the rest of us and grabs the last seat. She's aggressive, and for the duration of that uncomfortable ride, all the crowded standees wonder why they couldn't have been as aggressive as she had been.

Then there's the other scenario. Another long line, this time at the gas pumps during the gasoline shortage. There's pushing and shoving and honking of horns. But now someone pulls a gun and shoots.

That's aggression, too. What went wrong?

Our society has a mixed view of aggression. We all fear the mounting crime rate. Each year thousands of people are murdered in this country. And yet, we want our own lawyers to be aggressive on our behalf; we admire executives who claw their way to the top. Winners are called aggressive competitors, and employment ads seek aggressive salespeople.

As one who never gets that seat on the bus, and whose only violent confrontations are with paper and ink, I've always wondered what aggression really is. What is it that makes some people behave more forcefully? And will I ever be like them? Is it something in my blood, my upbringing, my brain, my genes that makes me hang back? Or are we all capable of aggression, of violence, even murder?

According to ethologists such as Konrad Lorenz and Robert Ardrey aggression is an instinct inherited from our prehuman ancestors. It survived evolutionary changes, they say, because it helped us survive.

Other researchers contend that people are not naturally aggressive. Rather, they say, society teaches us to be aggressive.

People who grow up in a more violent— or more frustrating—environment learn to respond with violence.

Yale neurologist Jonathan Pincus is not satisfied with that explanation, however. "We usually blame adverse socio-economic factors for violence—poverty, broken families, etc.," he says. "But very few poor people or those from broken homes are violent. Why?"

So today, scientists interested in aggression and violence think that something within each of our bodies—in our genes, our brains, our blood—may sow the seeds for violence. In their attempts to find out why one individual is more aggressive than another, they spend their days watching rats fight, shocking mice into action, dissecting brains, scrutinizing human wrestlers and hanging out with convicted killers.

SEX-HORMONE LINK

One of the earliest known links between physiology and aggression had to do with sex hormones. Centuries ago, farmers learned that they could calm an obstreperous male animal by castrating it, thus eliminating its supply of the hormone testosterone.

Testosterone levels also seem to be related to victory and defeat. In a recent study, Michael Elias, formerly of Harvard, studied hormone levels in university wrestlers and found that winners had higher levels of this hormone than the losers. "All the wrestlers showed increases in their testosterone levels after the match, which was expected, because testosterone should increase after exercise," Elias explains. "But winners had a greater percentage of increase than the losers, even if they started with the same level before the fight."

Elias believes his preliminary findings indicate that the changes in hormone levels must have had some adaptive value for our species. "I think there is a reason for having a lower testosterone level in defeat. It means that the losers—the less aggressive and less dominant of the species—have a lower sex-hormone level and therefore wouldn't have as many offspring as the victors," he says.

Are victory and dominance facets of aggression? Aggressors are the more

dominant. And in most societies, males (who always have higher testosterone levels than females) are the more aggressive and therefore the more dominant sex.

Does that mean males have evolved as the more aggressive of the species? That's an old issue. Am I off the hook as a killer just because I'm female? No such luck. Other sex hormones are also involved. Experiments show that both boys *and* girls born to women who had taken synthetic progestins (a hormone normally associated with females) during pregnancy were more aggressive than their nonexposed siblings.

Some women may be particularly inclined to violent behavior during about eight days each month, the days before and during menstruation, as a result of hormonal changes. In England, as a result of studies by British scientists, premenstrual syndrome (PMS) is now legally argued in the courts as a defense in criminal cases.

Can it be that aggression is defined in the individual at birth? Is it in the genes? Several studies both here and abroad have indicated that children of violent parents are more likely to be violent themselves, even if they are raised by nonviolent foster parents.

One study of violent patients by neurologist Frank Elliott, professor emeritus at the University of Pennsylvania Medical School, found that 94 of them out of 132 had a family history of violence. In some, violence could be traced back as far as four generations. And 12 adoptees who were children of violence-prone families were violence-prone themselves, even though their adoptive parents were not.

Geneticist Benson Ginsburg, of the University of Connecticut, and endocrinologist Michael Selmanoff, of the University of Maryland College of Medicine, contend that certain genes on the Y chromosome (the Y chromosome is the one that distinguishes males from females; males have the Y chromosome and females do not) are related to prepuberty surges of testosterone, and thereby of aggression, in certain genetic stocks of male mice.

"There are genes on the Y chromosome that are linked to aggression. But they don't cause aggressive behavior in every case, and they are not the only mechanism involved," Ginsburg hastens to add.

So if it's not just hormones or just heredity, what other mechanisms are involved? The most obvious place to start looking, a place through which all behavior seems to filter, is the brain.

Dr. Pincus of Yale divided juvenile offenders in a Connecticut reform school into two groups: more violent (that is, those who committed rapes, murders and personal assaults) and less violent (those arrested for break-ins, thefts or just the threat of assault).

NEUROLOGICAL ROOTS

He found that 46 percent of the more violent group had one or more major neurological problems, as compared with only 7 percent of the less violent group.

Other researchers have been able to pinpoint the problem area more specifically—narrowing it down to the brain's limbic system.

As brain researcher Dr. Paul MacLean, of the National Institutes of Health, emphasized several years ago, our brain is divided into three parts: the R-complex, or reptilian brain, inherited from the reptiles; the limbic brain, inherited from the early mammals; and the neocortex, which is prominent in the brains of higher mammals.

The neocortex is supposed to act as a control on the animal impulses generated by our more primitive brains. But damage to the limbic system can short-circuit that control.

"Cortical disease rarely produces aggression. But limbic damage does cause violent outbursts," says Elliott. So perhaps violence really is the animalistic part of our nature.

Specifically, the frontal and temporal lobes are most vulnerable. And located within those are the regions called the amygdala and the hypothalamus, both of which have been closely linked to aggressive behavior.

"If you stimulate the hypothalamus in an animal, you will get an immediate violent reaction," says Elliott. He calls this explosive rage "very primitive reptilian behavior."

To illustrate this, Harvard neurosurgeon Vernon Mark and colleagues have inserted electrodes into target areas of the brain in epileptic patients with violent behavior and then passed weak electric currents. When the currents reached the nucleus of the amygdala, the patients bared their teeth, grimaced and then lashed out like enraged animals.

Case histories showing the effects of brain damage on behavior are not lacking. Perhaps the most famous is the case of Charles Whitman, who in the 1960s climbed to the top of a tower in Austin,

Texas, and began shooting at passersby. He killed 17 people.

"Whitman had displayed a striking behavior change for the few months prior to the incident. He even went to see a psychiatrist. But in those days, nobody thought in terms of physiological causes," Mark explains. "A postmortem later showed that he had a brain tumor. But people were still reluctant to make the connection between the tumor and his violent behavior! Today, we know better than that."

Mark has handled a number of patients with abnormal aggression related to brain disease and has seen how treatment of the brain abnormality can usually clear up the problem.

"I once had a patient who tried to decapitate his wife and daughter with a meat cleaver. He was so violent, the police had to bring him in wrapped in a fishnet. His family explained that his personality had started undergoing a change about six months earlier. And he had been complaining of headache and blurred vision. A neurological exam showed that he had a tumor underneath the right frontal lobe, pressing directly on the limbic system. We removed the tumor and the patient had a dramatic reversal in behavior."

Tumors are not the only factors that can cause the brain to malfunction and lead to violence. Alcohol or mind-altering drugs can result in violence because of what Mark calls brain poisoning. The TV show *Quincy* recently dramatized a famous California case in which a policeman shot and killed a young man who, the officer claimed, had come at him in an unprovoked attack of rage. After an autopsy showed that the victim had been on angel dust (PCP) when killed, doctors testified that PCP can indeed cause violent behavior, and all charges against the policeman were dropped.

In an effort to find out just what is happening in the brain to cause these behavioral changes, biochemists are now studying the brain's chemistry to see what changes occur during aggressive behavior. It has been found that a group of chemicals known as amines are at a low level just before the onset of aggression and that they increase as the aggression is acted out. Some doctors have therefore taken to using the drug propranolol to treat violent patients because it seems to block the action of some amines and so prevent rage.

To get an even closer look at what's happening in the brain during aggressive behavior, neurochemist Bruce Morton, of the department of biochemistry at the University of Hawaii, has utilized a unique system for zeroing in on the different parts of the brain responsible for different behaviors.

"The brain is very selective about what it uses for energy in doing its work," explains Morton. "It likes to use only glucose." So Morton injects mice with a small dose of a radioactive glucose analogue, which is absorbed by the cells—including the brain cells—in a very short period of time. He then induces aggressive behavior in the colony male by introducing an intruder male. After 30 minutes of aggressive behavior by the mice, he removes the brain of the resident male, sections it and places these sections against X-ray film. Three weeks later the film is developed to reveal an activity map of the brain during aggression. This map points out the areas of the brain that have been activated or inhibited to produce the aggressive behavior.

Drs. Caroline and Robert Blanchard of the University of Hawaii, as well as other researchers, are finding that animals appear to have different kinds of aggressive patterns. They have very generally grouped the patterns into offensive and defensive behavior. And in the case of rodents, these behaviors can be identified by very specific sets of actions. If a rat is placed in another rat's cage, the home rat sees the new one as an intruder and attacks offensively. The hair on his back stands up. He chases the other rat, smells his genitals, jumps him from the side and bites his back. The intruder rat reacts defensively. He tries to flee, and when he finds this is not possible, he emits a high-pitched scream and freezes. Then he gives up and gives in to defeat. The two animals roll around the floor of the cage, with the attacking rat ending up on top and the intruder badly bruised or bitten.

GENETICALLY BASED

Preliminary evidence from another researcher shows that each of these two kinds of aggression is associated with activity in a different part of the brain. And biochemists think that different chemical reactions may also be at work. Moreover, genetic researchers think they may have come up with differing chromosomal patterns for each reaction. Dr. Stephen Maxson, of the department of biobehavioral sciences at the University of Connecticut, believes that offensive attack behavior may be coded on the Y chromosome. A strain of mice bred with specific genes on the Y chromosome exhibited certain aspects of the offensive behavior more than other mice. They charged, attacked and wrestled the intruder and inflicted more bites per minute on the enemy.

The Blanchards believe this offensive-defensive breakdown can be applied to humans. In humans, most aggression includes a combination of both offensive behavior (which results from anger) and defensive behavior (which results from fear). "When we're fearful, we emit a high-pitched scream, like a cornered rat," they say. "When we're angry, we yell. Biting and clawing are defensive."

Pain causes a defensive reaction, the Blanchards continue. Thus the violent lashing out of patients whose brains were given electric shocks is defensive. That would account, perhaps, for their animal-like reactions.

Certainly there are many discomforting stimuli that can cause violence in humans. Heat is one; more riots occur during heat waves than at any other time. Overcrowding, loud noises, noxious fumes—all have links with aggression.

The Blanchards theorize that defensive violence cannot be treated with punishment, because punishment merely serves as yet another painful stimulation and increases the violence.

But offensive attacks are something different again. An offensive attack, they think, occurs when the person perceives that his rights are being violated. Like the rat who attacks an intruder, people attack when they think their own rights are being intruded upon. It may be that a perceived breach of the right to a job or a decent place to live would account for the anger and violence among the unemployed and the poor.

But the key word here is *perceived*. The aggressive person reacts to what he perceives as a threat, and sometimes his perception is impaired. And that brings us full-cycle back to the physiological causes of aggression. If a person's physiology is unbalanced because of brain damage, hormonal irregularities or genetic abnormalities, then his ability to judge a threat is also off balance. What may seem to the normal person to be a minor intrusion becomes a major threat to the person with a low aggression threshold.

"I've had cases of a man attacking his wife because she burned the toast or a boy shooting a grocer because he didn't say 'thank you,' " says psychiatrist Frank Ervin, of McGill University in Montreal. "These are often misinterpreted as cases of unprovoked violence. But there is no such thing as violence without a cause. What happens is that the brain misperceives some incoming stimulus—a harmless gesture or a joking remark—as extremely threatening or enraging."

Is all violent behavior physiologically controlled? Well, yes . . . and no.

In that study done by Pincus of juvenile offenders, the more violent youths did tend to come from more violent environments. Seventy-five percent of the violent youngsters had been physically abused by their parents, and 70 percent had seen extreme violence in the home.

But studies have shown that experience does affect the brain. "Experience can create aggressive neural pathways in the brain," says Ervin.

Learning, environment, limbic brain, genes, hormones, chemicals . . . I am still not sure I can explain the lady who got the seat on the bus or understand the shoot-out on the gas line. But what seems obvious is that scientists are making headway in understanding and treating aggression. Relieve the painful stimuli in our society, give kids nonaggressive role models, treat limbic disorders with medication and surgery—and we may have a nonaggressive society. That's a fantastic thought. But what are the implications of such control? Consider what psychologist Bryan Robinson, formerly of Florida State University, said at a symposium several years ago:

BEHAVIOR MOD

"Aggression is not inherently bad. What is bad is too much of it, or too little, or misdirected aggressivity. It is conceivable that experiments such as we have heard about will lead to techniques or drugs that will selectively modify, or perhaps manipulate is a more honest word, human aggression. A very real problem then arises of who will do that manipulating and of exactly *what* will be modified . . . can certain individuals, classes of peoples or nations be made more or less aggressive? . . . The problem is a real problem and, before too many more years have passed, will be an *immediate* real problem."

THE INSTINCT TO LEARN

Birds do it, bees do it, perhaps even humans are programmed to acquire critical information at specific times.

James L. and Carol Grant Gould

James L. Gould, professor of biology at Princeton University, studies the navigation and communication of the honey bee. Carol Grant Gould is a writer and research associate in Princeton's biology department.

When a month-old human infant begins to smile, its world lights up. People reward these particular facial muscle movements with the things a baby prizes—kisses, hugs, eye contact, and more smiles. That first smile appears to be a powerful ingredient in the emotional glue that bonds parent to child. But scientists wonder whether that smile is merely a chance occurrence, which subsequently gets reinforced by tangible rewards, or an inexorable and predetermined process by which infants ingratiate themselves with their parents.

If this sounds like another chapter in the old nature/nurture controversy, it is—but a chapter with a difference. Ethologists, specialists in the mechanisms behind animal behavior, are taking a new look at old—and some new—evidence and are finding that even while skirmishing on a bloody battleground, the two camps of instinctive and learned behavior seem to be heading with stunning rapidity and inevitability toward an honorable truce.

Fortunately for the discord that keeps disciplines alive and fit, animal behavior may be approached from two vantage points. One of these sees instinct as the moving force behind behavior: Animals resemble automatons preordained by their genetic makeup to behave in prescribed ways. The other views animals as basically naive, passive creatures whose behavior is shaped, through the agency of punishment and reinforcement, by chance, experience, and environmental forces.

In the last few years, however, these two views have edged towards reconciliation and, perhaps, eventual union. Case after case has come to light of environmentally influenced learning which is nonetheless rigidly controlled by genetic programming. Many animals, ethologists are convinced, survive through learning—but learning that is an integral part of their programming, learning as immutable and as stereotyped as the most instinctive of behavioral responses. Furthermore, neurobiologists are beginning to discover the nerve circuits responsible for the effects.

Plenty of scientists are still opposed to this new synthesis. The most vociferous are those who view the idea of programmed learning as a threat to humanity's treasured ideas of free will. However, it now appears that much of what we learn is forced upon us by innate drives and that even much of our "culture" is deeply rooted in biology.

As though this were not enough of a shock to our ingrained ideas of man's place in the universe, it looks as though the reverse is true, too: Man is not the sole, lofty proprietor of culture; "lower" animals—notably monkeys and birds—also have evolved various complicated ways of transferring environmentally learned information to others of their own kind.

The honey bee provides entrancing insights into the lengths to which nature goes in its effort to program learning. These little animals must learn a great many things about their world: what flowers yield nectar at what specific times of day, what their home hives look like under the changes of season and circumstance, where water is to be found.

But new work reveals that all this learning, though marvelous in its variety and complexity, is at the same time curiously constrained and machinelike. Certain things that bees learn well and easily, they can learn only at certain specific "critical periods." For example, they must relearn the appearance and location of their hives on their first flight out every morning; at no other time will this information register in the bee's brain. Beekeepers have known for centuries that if they move a hive at night the bees come and go effortlessly the next day. But if they move the hive even a few meters at any time after the foraging bees' first flight of the day, the animals are disoriented and confused. Only at this one time is the home-learning program turned on: Evidently this is nature's way of compensating for changing seasons and circumstances in an animal whose vision is so poor that its only means of locating the hive is by identifying the landmarks around it.

Since bees generally harvest nectar from one species of flower at a time, it seems clear that they must learn to recognize flower species individually. Karl von Frisch, the noted Austrian zoologist, found that bees can distinguish any color, from yellow to green and blue and into the ultraviolet. However, they learn the color of a flower only in the two seconds before they land on it. Von Frisch also discovered that bees can discriminate a single odor out of several hundred. Experimentation reveals that this remarkable ability is similarly constrained: Bees can learn odor only while they are actually standing on the flower. And finally, only as they are flying away can they memorize any notable landmarks there might be around the flower.

Learning then, at least for bees, has thus become specialized to the extent that specific cues can be learned only at specific times, and then only in specific contexts.

The bees' learning programs turn out to be restricted even further. Once the bits of knowledge that make up a behavior have been acquired, such as the location, color, odor, shape, and surrounding landmarks of a food source, together with the time it is likely to yield the most nectar, they form a coherent, holistic set. If a single component of the set is changed, the bee must learn the whole set over again.

In a very real sense, then, honey bees are carefully tuned learning machines. They learn just what they are programmed to learn, exactly when and under exactly the circumstances they are programmed to learn it. Though this seems fundamentally different from the sort of learning we are used to seeing in higher animals such as birds and mammals—and, of course, ourselves—careful research is uncovering more and more humbling similarities. Programmed memorization in vertebrates, though deceptively subtle, is widespread. The process by which many species of birds learn their often complex and highly species-specific songs is a compelling case in point.

Long before the birds begin to vocalize, their species' song is being learned, meticulously "taped" and stored somewhere in their memory banks. As the bird grows, the lengthening days of spring trigger the release of specific hormones in the males which in turn spur them to reproduce first the individual elements of syllables and later the sequence of the stored song. By a trial and error process the birds slowly learn to manipulate their vocal musculature to produce a match between their output and the recording in their brains. Once learned, the sequence becomes a hardwired motor program, so fixed and independent of feedback that if the bird is deafened his song production remains unaffected.

This prodigious feat of learning, even down to the regional dialects which some species have developed, can be looked at as the gradual unfolding of automatic processes. Peter Marler of the Rockefeller University and his students, for instance, have determined that there are rigorous time constraints on the song learning. They have discovered that in the white-crowned sparrow the "taping" of the parental song can be done only between the chicks' 10th and 50th days. No amount of coaching either before or after this critical period will affect the young birds. If they hear the correct song during this time, they will be able to produce it themselves later (or, if females, to respond to it); if not, they will produce only crude, vaguely patterned vocalizations.

In addition, the white-crowned sparrow, though reared in nature in an auditory environment filled with the songs of other sparrows and songbirds with rich vocal repertoires, learns *only* the white-crowned sparrow song. Marler has recently been able to confirm that the parental song in another species—the swamp sparrow—contains key sounds that serve as auditory releasers, the cues that order the chicks' internal tape recorders to switch on. Ethologists refer to any simple signal from the outside world that triggers a complex series of actions in an animal as a releaser.

Here again, amazing feats of learning, particularly the sorts of learning that are crucial to the perpetuation of an animal's genes, are rigidly controlled by biology.

The kind of programmed learning that ethologists have studied most is imprinting, which calls to mind a picture of Konrad Lorenz leading a line of adoring goslings across a Bavarian meadow. Newborn animals that must be able to keep up with ever-moving parents —antelope and sheep, for example, as well as chicks and geese— must rapidly learn to recognize those parents if they are to survive. To achieve this noble aim evolution has built into these creatures an elegant learning routine. Young birds are driven to follow the parent out of the nest by an exodus call. Though the key element in the call varies from species to species—a particular repetition rate for one, a specific downward frequency sweep for another—it is always strikingly simple, and it invariably triggers the chicks' characteristic following response.

As the chicks follow the sound they begin memorizing the distinguishing characteristics of the parent, with two curious but powerful constraints. First, the physical act of following is essential: Chicks passively transported behind a calling model do not learn; in fact, barriers in a chick's path that force it to work harder speed and strengthen the imprinting. Second, the cues that the chick memorizes are also species-specific: One species will

127

concentrate on the inflections and tone of the parent's voice but fail to recall physical appearance, while a closely related species memorizes minute details of physical appearance to the exclusion of sounds. In some species of mammals, the learning focuses almost entirely on individual odor. In each case, the critical period for imprinting lasts only a day or two. In this short but crucial period an ineradicable picture of the only individual who will feed and protect them is inscribed in the young animals' memories.

By contrast, when there is no advantage to the animal in learning specific details, the genes don't waste their efforts in programming them in. In that case, blindness to detail is equally curious and constrained. For instance, species of gulls that nest cheek by jowl are programmed to memorize the most minute details of their eggs' size and speckling and to spot at a glance any eggs which a careless neighbor might have added to their nest—eggs which to a human observer look identical in every respect. Herring gulls, on the other hand, nest far enough apart that they are unlikely ever to get their eggs confused with those of other pairs. As a result, they are unconscious of the appearance of their eggs. The parents will complacently continue to incubate even large black eggs that an experimenter substitutes for their small speckled ones. The herring gulls' insouciance, however, ends there: They recognize their chicks as individuals soon after hatching. By that time, their neighbors' youngsters are capable of wandering in. Rather than feed the genes of their neighbors, the parents recognize foreign chicks and often eat *them*.

The kittiwake gull, on the other hand, nests in narrow pockets on cliff faces, and so the possibility that a neighbor's chick will wander down the cliff into its nest is remote. As a result kittiwakes are not programmed to learn the appearance of either eggs or young, and even large black cormorant chicks may be substituted for the small, white, infant kittiwakes.

Simply from observing animals in action, ethologists have learned a great deal about the innate bases of behavior. Now, however, neurobiologists are even tracing the circuitry of many of the mechanisms that control some of these elements. The circuits responsible for simple motor programs, for example, have been located and mapped out on a cell-by-cell basis in some cases and isolated to a single ganglion in others.

A recent and crucial discovery is that the releasers imagined by ethologists are actually the so-called feature detectors that neurobiologists have been turning up in the auditory and visual systems. In recent years, neurobiologists have discovered that there are certain combinations of nerve cells, built into the eyes and brains of all creatures, that respond only to highly specific features: spots of a certain size, horizontal or vertical lines, and movement, for example. In case after case, the basic stimulus required to elicit an innate response in animals corresponds to one or a very simple combination of discrete features systematically sought out by these specialized cells in the visual system.

The parent herring gull, for instance, wears a single red spot near the tip of its lower bill, which it waves back and forth in front of its chicks when it has food for them. The baby gulls for their part peck at the waving spot which, in turn, causes the parent to release the food. First, Niko Tinbergen, the Dutch Nobel Prize winner and cofounder of the science of ethology with Lorenz and von Frisch, and later the American ethologist Jack Hailman have been able to show that the chicks are driven to peck not by the sight of their parent but at that swinging vertical bill with its red spot. The moving vertical line and the spot are the essential features that guide the chicks, which actually prefer a schematic, disembodied stimulus—a knitting needle with a spot, for example.

Though the use of two releasers to direct their pecking must greatly sharpen the specificity of the baby gulls' behavior, chicks do quickly learn to recognize their parents, and the mental pictures thus formed soon replace the crude releasers. Genes apparently build in releasers not only to trigger innate behavior but, more important, to direct the attention of animals to things they must learn flawlessly and immediately to survive.

Even some of what we know as culture has been shown to be partially rooted in programmed learning, or instinct. Many birds, for instance, mob or attack potential nest predators in force, and they do this generation after generation. But how could these birds innately know their enemies? In 1978 the German ethologist Eberhard Curio placed two cages of blackbirds on opposite sides of a hallway, so that they could see and hear each other. Between the two cages he installed a compartmented box, which allowed the occupants of one cage to see an object on their side but not the object on the other. Curio presented a stuffed owl, a familiar predator, on one side, and an innocuous foreign bird, the Australian honey guide, on the other. The birds that saw the owl went berserk with rage and tried to mob it through the bars of the cage. The birds on the other side, seeing only an unfamiliar animal and the enraged birds, began to mob the stuffed honey guide. Astonishingly, these birds then passed on this prejudice against honey guides through a chain of six blackbirds, all of which mobbed honey guides whenever they encountered one. Using the same technique, Curio has raised generations of birds whose great-great-grandparents were tricked into mobbing milk bottles and who consequently teach their young to do the same.

What instigates the birds—even birds raised in total isolation—to pay so much attention to one instance of mobbing that they pass the information on to their offspring as a sort of taboo, something so crucial to their survival that they never question if or why these predators must be attacked? The mobbing call, it turns out, serves as yet another releaser that switches on a learning routine.

Certain sounds in the mobbing calls are so similar among different species that they all profit from each other's experience. This is why we often see crows or other large birds being mobbed by many species of small birds at once. So deeply ingrained in the birds is this call that birds raised alone in the laboratory are able to recognize it, and the calls of one species serve to direct and release enemy-learning in others. Something as critical to an animal's survival as the recognition of enemies, then, even though its finer points must be learned and transmitted culturally, rests on a fail-safe basis of innately guided, programmed learning.

The striking food-avoidance phenomenon is also a good place to look for the kind of innately directed learning that is critical to survival. Many animals, including humans, will refuse to eat a novel substance which has previously made them ill. Once a blue jay has tasted one monarch butterfly, which as a caterpillar fills itself with milkweed's poisonous glycosides, it will sedulously avoid not only monarchs but also viceroys—monarch look-alikes that flaunt the monarchs' colors to cash in on their protective toxicity. This programmed avoidance is based on the sickness which must appear within a species-specific interval after an animal eats, and the subsequent food avoidance is equally strong even if the subject knows from experience that the effect has been artificially induced.

But what is the innate mechanism when one blue tit discovers how to pierce the foil caps of milk bottles left on doorsteps to reach the cream, and shortly afterwards blue tits all over England are doing the same thing? How are theories of genetic programming to be invoked when one young Japanese macaque monkey discovers that sweet potatoes and handfuls of grain gleaned from a sandy shore are tastier when washed off in the ocean, and the whole troop (except for an entrenched party of old dominant males) slowly follows suit? Surely these are examples pure and simple of the cultural transmission of knowledge that has been environmentally gained.

Perhaps not. What the blue tits and the monkeys pass on to their colleagues may have an innate basis as well. The reason for this precocious behavior—and we say this guardedly—may be in a strong in-

The cells that bring you the world

There was a time when the visual system was thought of as little more than a pair of cameras (the eyes), cables (the optic nerves), and television screens (the visual cortex of the brain). Nothing could be farther from the truth. We now know that the visual system is no mere passive network of wires but an elaborately organized and highly refined processing system that actively analyzes what we see, systematically exaggerating one aspect of the visual world, ignoring or discarding another.

The processing begins right in the retina. There the information from 130 million rods and cones is sifted, distorted, and combined to fit into the four or so million fibers that go to the brain. The retinas of higher vertebrates employ one layer of cells to sum up the outputs of the rod-and-cone receptors. The next layer of retinal cells compares the outputs of adjacent cells in the preceding tier. The result is what is known as a spot detector: One type of cell in the second layer signals the brain when its compare/contrast strategy discovers a bright field surrounded by darkness (corresponding to a bright spot in the world). Another class of cell in the same layer has the opposite preference and fires off when it encounters dark spots.

The next processing step takes this spot information and, operating on precisely the same comparison strategy, wires cells that are sensitive only to spots moving in particular directions at specific speeds. The output of these spot detector cells also provides the raw material from which an array of more sophisticated feature detectors sort for

lines of each particular orientation. These feature detectors derive their name from their ability to register the presence or absence of one particular sort of stimulus in the environment. Building on these cells, the next layer of processing sorts for the speed and direction of moving lines, each cell with its own special preference. Other layers judge distance by comparing what the two eyes see.

The specific information that cells sort for in other retinal layers and visual areas of the brain is not yet understood. Research will probably reveal that these extremely complex feature detectors provide us with what we know as conscious visual experience. Our awareness of all this subconscious processing, along with the willful distortions and tricks it plays on us, comes from the phenomenon of optical illusions. When we experience an optical illusion, it is the result of a particular (and, in the world to which we evolved, useful) quirk in the visual mechanism.

Feature detectors are by no means restricted to the visual system. In birds and bats, for instance, specialized cells have been found that recognize many nuances in sound—locations, repetition rates, time intervals, and precise changes in pitch— that allow the creatures to form an auditory picture of the world.

There is every reason to suppose that our experience of the world is based on the results of this massive editing. Since neural circuits differ dramatically from species to species according to the needs of each, the world must look and sound different to bees, birds, cats, and people.
—*J.L.G. and C.G.G.*

stinctive drive on the part of all animals to copy mindlessly certain special aspects of what they see going on around them. Chicks, for instance, peck at seeds their mother has been trained to select, appar-

ently by watching her choices and copying them. In the case of many mammals, this drive is probably combined with an innate urge to experiment. The proclivity of young animals, particularly human children, to play with food, along with their distressing eagerness to put virtually anything into their mouths, lends support to the experimentation theory. Perhaps it is the young, too naive to know any better, who are destined by nature to be the primary source of cultural innovation. The more mature become the equally indispensable defenders of the faith, the vehicles of cultural transmission.

Patterns, then, however subtle, are beginning to emerge that unify the previously unrelated studies of instinct and learning. Virtually every case of learning in animals that has been analyzed so far depends in at least some rudimentary way on releasers that turn on the learning routine. And that routine is generally crucial to the perpetuation of the animal's genes.

Even the malleable learning we as humans pride ourselves on, then, may have ineradicable roots in genetic programming, although we may have difficulty identifying the programs, blind as we are to our own blindness. For example, you cannot keep a normal, healthy child from learning to talk. Even a child born deaf goes through the same babbling practice phase the hearing child does. Chimpanzees, by contrast, can be inveigled into mastering some sort of linguistic communications skills, but they really could not care less about language: The drive just is not there.

This view of human insight and creativity may be unromantic, minimizing as it does the revered role of self-awareness in our everyday lives, but the pursuit of this line of thinking could yield rich rewards, providing us with invaluable insights into our own intellectual development. The times we are most susceptible to particular sorts of input, for instance, may be more constrained than we like to think. The discovery of the sorts of cues or releasers that might turn on a drive to learn specific things could open up new ways of teaching and better methods for helping those who are culturally deprived. Best of all, analyzing and understanding those cues could greatly enrich our understanding of ourselves and of our place in the natural order.

Learning about Learning

Jane Stein

Preschool children are always counting, says Rochel Gelman, a University of Pennsylvania psychologist who studies cognitive development. It helps them to make sense of at least some of the puzzles—the arithmetic ones—they face in learning to cope with what for them must be an incredibly complex world. According to traditional developmental theory, however, they are not supposed to be able to count; they fail to comprehend the concept of conservation, or constancy, of numbers: that eight eggs in eight cups will still total eight when they are taken out of the cups and placed in a pile. Nevertheless, as Gelman observes, "They are always counting...practicing whatever they learn."

Those who, like Rochel Gelman, study cognitive development are dealing with the process by which children develop the ability to solve problems and to form complex concepts. That process is a basis for intelligent behavior and involves the child's interactions with the world. Until recently, preschoolers were viewed as cognitive incompetents. But it is now known that nonperformance—not being able to conserve numbers, for example—does not necessarily mean noncompetence.

Recent research into the development of cognition shows that children as young as six months of age are interested in numbers; by the time they are three, they have already developed a system of classifying sets of numbers. In addition, preschoolers can construct order, make inferences, explain cau-sality—all cognitive concepts once thought to be beyond them.

One reason for the growing awareness of preschoolers' cognitive competence is a change in research perspective. Instead of testing preschoolers' cognitive capacities against tasks they will be able to do when they are older, cognitive researchers are now focusing on what the youngsters are actually able to do at a given point in their development.

By observing how children solve problems—even when they solve them incorrectly—researchers are getting a better understanding of the wide range of strategies that are used, the complexities of the learning process and how cognitive abilities at one stage of development relate to abilities developed earlier and to those still to come. Though many studies address the development of cognition through mathematical concepts, many others do not; researchers in each area feel that they are all attacking something more fundamental, that the target is the nature of cognitive development itself, regardless of the route the investigator takes.

Early problem solving

"Children learn about problem solving even without direct instruction," says psychologist David Klahr of Carnegie-Mellon University. Although these early problem-solving capacities are typically called common sense, they are complicated processes involving considerable information and the use of multiple steps to reach a goal.

Consider the example of a four-year-old boy who is playing in the backyard. He wants to ride his bike, but he asks his father to unlock the basement door because "my socks are in the dryer." This seemingly bizarre statement is in fact, says Klahr, a fine example of logical problem solving. The problem is simple: The boy wants to ride his bike but is barefoot; he needs shoes so he won't hurt his feet on the pedals. He has to get his shoes—which is easy to accomplish since they are on the porch. He also has to get socks so his shoes won't rub his feet. This presents a secondary problem, that there are no more socks in his drawer. A search of memory produces a promising lead: A load of laundry was done recently, and the socks are likely to be in the dryer in the basement.

The boy seeks the most efficient way of getting the socks. He could walk around the house and go in by the front door. Or he could go in through the basement door, which is nearby, except that it is locked. He observes that his father is nearby and knows that Daddy usually has the keys with him. The final solution for the child is to ask his father to unlock the door so he can get his socks out of the dryer so he can put on his shoes in order to ride his bike.

This exercise in problem solving takes split seconds, and not one step is verbalized. It represents in capsule form a reasoning process we often call "intuitive."

To test the "intuitive" ability of preschoolers to solve problems, Klahr designed a game for young children in which they are asked to move one set of three inverted cans—each can of a different size and color—onto pegs so that they match the arrangement of another identical set of cans. Only one can is to be moved at a time, and a small can must not be placed on a larger one.

The youngsters come to Klahr with no prior knowledge of his puzzle. Yet, as his data show, all the youngsters tested—ranging in age from 3 to 6—came to the test already knowing the three basic strategies that they needed to solve the problem:

- If they want object X to be in location B and it is currently in location A, then try to move it from A to B.
- If they want to move object X from A to B and object Y is in the way, then remove object Y.
- If the approach they are trying is too hard, then do some part of it that is easier.

The children used a combination of these strategies to solve the simplest of Klahr's puzzles, those that involved moving only one object to achieve the correct configuration. They also used the strategies in other combinations for more complicated puzzles, some involving at least seven moves. "There are many ways to skin a cat, even in this mini-task," Klahr observes.

Indeed, some children solve his puzzle more effectively—with fewer steps—than others. Although most of the youngsters did improve their skills during the course of the testing, this did not add to their problem-solving skills in general. "I don't think they would be any better at playing chess because they know how to do this puzzle," Klahr says. But teaching specific problem-solving skills wasn't the point of his work. What Klahr did successfully was to show that young children solve problems using what we call intuition and that the rich repertoire of problem-solving methods used by adults—means-ends analysis, search, evaluation, planning—exist in rudimentary forms in youngsters as well.

Holistic to analytic

As children get older, their intuitive problem solving and other cognitive abilities become more sophisticated. Deborah Kemler, a psychologist at Swarthmore College, is documenting some of the cognitive changes that take place in children. "Young children have first the task of making sense of natural categories of objects in the world," she says. "These tend to be categories of objects that resemble one another, so overall similarity—mutual resemblance—is a useful criterion for establishing these categories." A boat, for example, is a natural category; all boats generally resemble each other. But young children, unlike older children and adults, find it difficult, and at times impossible, to form categories of diverse objects by isolating a property they have in common. Scientific categories tend to have this structure, says Kemler, but putting a boat and a sponge together because they both float may be beyond young children.

Kemler has followed the shifts in thinking patterns among a group of elementary schoolchildren ranging from kindergarten to fifth grade. A test she uses consists of cards of varying sizes and shades of gray. She selects three cards from a pack; two of the cards are identical in size but are very different in shade (light gray and dark gray). The third card is close but not identical in size and close but not identical in shade to the dark gray card.

When asked which two cards go together, the kindergarten children uniformly pick the two that are similar overall but which are not identical in any way. Fifth graders naturally select the two cards that share one identical component. Data on the second graders were typically ambiguous; they were in transition between the holistic and analytical categorization strategies.

Why do youngsters make this cognitive shift? Perhaps, Kemler hypothesizes, there is a natural predisposition to deal with wholes first and switch to abstract properties later. She suggests that this way of grouping objects may better prepare children to deal with complex concepts.

Daily experience and formal schooling in which children's learning becomes more and more governed by rules also play important roles in the switch. The rules that govern reading, for example, are based in part on the sounds of common components of words. In an experimental test conducted by Rebecca Treiman and Jonathan Baron of the University of Pennsylvania, they report, kindergartners with minimal reading skills tended to group syllables like "poo" and "boo" because they sound alike overall. But at the same age, children with more advanced reading skills classify on the basis of a common segment. They put "bee" and "boo" together instead because of the identical phonetic component with which each begins.

Adapting to this propensity to see wholes first and then properties might point the way to strategies for the teaching of reading. Indeed, several existing strategies do take such a direction. But research into cognition is far from validating one approach or another. New educational tools are likely to develop, however, as more pieces of the cognitive-development puzzle are explained and as a better picture develops of what children know and how they learn.

More and less

There is a considerable range of things that children can do well, according to psychologist Rochel Gelman. She has focused much of her work on numbers because she believes they represent a uniquely human

cognitive ability, just as is early language. "There must be something innate in counting," she says. "Babies at six months dete a difference between two and three [object when different sets are flashed on a scree Chimpanzees can't do it after hours ar hours of training. Perhaps counting is r stricted to humans...it is found universall in all cultures, among young children an unschooled adults."

Complex rules about how to count an what to count develop without the benef of specific formal instruction. Gelman h found that, by age three, preschoolers kno addition and substraction, see the differenc between more and less and can do simp mathematical reasoning.

A three-year-old participating in a sub traction game with Gelman said, "There wa three animals in the can." He looked aroun pointed to her and said, "Took one cuz there two now." In a game of "more and less," four-year-old picked a five-item display the winner "cause there's one, two, thre four, five." The loser was clearly the three item display "cause only one, two, three. Not surprisingly, the counting rules an mathematical reasoning encompass mor complex concepts as children get olde "You're not supposed to count somethin twice," said a five-year-old to Gelman. "Yo can't make it six if there are only five."

Gelman is focusing on what children ca do well at given stages. In the process, she also discovering what they are not very goo at. A group of three-year-olds, for exampl scored poorly—only 49 percent of thei answers were correct—when asked to coun a three-item display that was under clea plastic. The youngsters scored 87 percer correct, however, when they were asked t count the same items without the covering According to Gelman, "stimulus variable affect counting....The younger the childrer the more they need to point at or touch wha they count."

Ingrained errors

But more to the point of cognitive deve opment, Gelman's work shows that three year-old children know how to count. The might count in an idiosyncratic way, such a 2, 6, 10 instead of 1, 2, 3, but they count in stable order, thus proving they have mas tered one of the basic how-to-count princi ples. The one-one principle—each item in a array must be tagged with one and only on unique tag—is another index of emerging counting skills.

Gelman compares idiosyncratic errors i counting to the errors made by young lan guage learners, such as "I runned." Thes

rors show that the child's use of language—
ad numbers—is rule governed. The child
dheres to these rules, regardless of their
orrectness, and may develop poor language
ad mathematic skills not only because the
ale was learned incorrectly, but because of
ae consistency with which it is applied.

One of the problems facing cognitive
searchers is to better understand the rules
y which children learn and the ways those
ales are applied. Most children will self-
orrect language and counting errors that
evelop spontaneously. But sometimes er-
ors become ingrained when rules that in-
erently make sense but contain errors are
arned and applied, or when valid rules are
pplied incorrectly. Lauren Resnick, co-
irector of the Learning Research and De-
elopment Center at the University of Pitts-
urgh, is studying the erroneous strategies
aat children use in solving arithmetic prob-
ms. She compares them to computer pro-
rams with bugs and calls them "buggy
lgorithms."

Several dozen buggy algorithms have been
lentified for subtraction, most of which
evelop because the children have never
arned the complete standard strategy, or
lgorithm, or have forgotten parts of it. For
xample, when zero is taught, it may not be
aught carefully enough or explained well
nough. And when children do not fully
nderstand it as a concept, they end up
olving in unique ways problems in which it
ppears.

Resnick has found that children, when
naking a mathematical error, tend to follow
 rule, but often one that incorporates their
wn modifications. In subtraction, for exam-
le, they might take a smaller digit from a
arger one regardless of which one is on top.
Or sometimes they follow only part of the
ule. For example, when borrowing from a
olumn whose top digit is a zero, the student
vrites "9" but does not continue to borrow
rom the column to the left of the zero. At
ther times, rules may be completely made
up; whenever there is a zero on the bot-
om, zero is written as the answer. No mat-
er how buggy the algorithm, it is system-
tically used, Resnick observes.

Resnick has had some success with three
hildren who needed remedial instruction to
help correct their buggy subtraction algo-
ithms. She gave the youngsters a subtrac-
ion problem to solve:

$$300$$
$$-139$$

To test the contention that understanding
of an abstraction—in this case that a number
can be built out of a variety of sets of

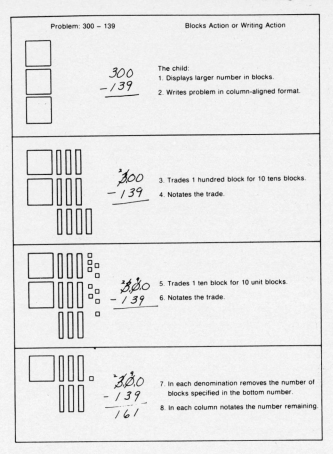

quantities—is enhanced if there are at least
two representations of the idea, Resnick sup-
plemented the written subtraction problem
with concrete forms such as number blocks,
color coded chips, bundles of sticks or coins
of different sizes. "They were not allowed
to write anything down without making a
corresponding move with a set of blocks,"
she explains. In order to do this, they had to
understand that the top number in subtraction is made up of several components, each
of a different value dictated by place, and
that these quantities can be exchanged among
each other as long as the total value remains
the same. A hundred-block can be traded
for 10 ten-blocks and a ten-block can be
converted into 10 unit-blocks, for instance.
"The possibility exists that we forced them
to do it right because this system actually
prohibits wrong moves," says Resnick.

The real test of whether or not there were
cognitive changes will come during the next
stage of her research, when the childen are
tested without the use of a second representation—the number blocks—several months
after the remedial teaching. Resnick's research
on buggy algorithms—knowing what the bugs
are, what they represent in developmental
cognition and how they get in—will ultimately lead to redesigned teaching manuals.

Persistent bugs

Not only young children, but college students majoring in science and mathematics
too, and even graduate engineers, are plagued
by buggy algorithms they carry into adulthood with them. Two University of Massachusetts investigators have found that many
students have carried their bugs through
four years of high school math without getting rid of them.

The scientists, John Clement and Jack
Lochhead, discovered that though students
could easily solve equations, they did not
know how to formulate them from word
problems. The most common error that
Clement and Lochhead found was a simple
reversal in translating word problems to
equations. Students also made repeated
errors in translating pictures or data tables
to equations and words to graphs.

The errors, moreover, were not caused by
carelessness but rather by self-generated
and persistent misconceptions. After testing students with a variety of algebra problems, Clement and Lochhead concluded that
the students have real cognitive difficulty
with a semantic understanding of algebra.

Consider the following example: Freshmen engineering students were asked to write
an equation that said the same thing as the
English sentence: There are six times as many

students as professors at a university. Nearly 40 percent of the students wrote $6S=P$, which says exactly the opposite of the sentence. Students often made a syntactical error by mechanically translating the words directly into symbols in the same order as they appeared in the sentence—six times the number of students, or $6 \times S$—or they made a semantic error by assuming that six times something had to represent the largest group—6 associates with S. In either case, they acted without fully understanding the most fundamental concepts of algebra: variables and equations.

Letters in algebra are called variables, and they stand for numbers that make an algebraic equation true rather than for the names of objects. An equation is a statement in which one side is the numerical equal of the other side. "Because the students were confused about the meaning of variable," says Clement, "many portrayed S as a symbol for 'student' rather than for 'number of students.' And since they were confused about how to write an equation, they had the equal sign express an association rather than an equivalence."

Students who understood the principles involved wrote the correct equations, $S=6P$, and translated it back into English as "The number of students is six times the number of professors." The key to understanding the correct equation is to recognize that it does not describe the situation in a literal sense; instead it describes a hypothetical relationship of equivalence.

The reason so many advanced students got the problem wrong, according to Clement and Lochhead, was that they had had little experience in testing their cognitive understanding of algebra. High school textbooks, they say, usually give a formula or a choice of formulas and ask the student to solve an algebra problem with it, rather than ask them to conceptualize the problem and then construct the formula.

The University of Massachusetts professors are concerned about enhancing the intuitive reasoning processes in students. "I am less interested in the procedure [of doing the problem correctly] than in the discovery of the procedure," says Lochhead. "If students are conscious of why they set up an equation and how it works, then they can use it for other kinds of problems. Then their knowledge will be more flexible." (See "Test yourself," accompanying this article, for additional algebra problems that stump engineering students.)

Professionals, too

A curious finding for Clement and Lochhead was that 17 professional engineers, each

Test yourself

Test your problem-solving abilities: Can you do better than freshmen engineering students did?

1.) Write an equation using the variables C and S to represent the following statement: "At Mindy's restaurant, for every four people who order cheesecake, there are five people who order strudel." Let C represent the number of cheesecakes and S represent the number of strudels ordered.

2.) Write an equation of the form $P_a = $ _____ for the price you should charge adults to ride your ferry boat in order to take in an average of D dollars on each trip. You have the following information: Your customers average one child for every two adults; children's tickets are half priced; your average load is L people (adults and children). Write your equation for P_a in terms of the variables D and L only.

3.) Write a sentence in English that gives the same information as the following equation: $A=7S$. A is the number of assemblers in a factory. S is the number of solderers in a factory.

4.) Spies fly over the Norun Airplane Manufacturers and return with an aerial photograph of the new planes in the yard.

B   W

They are fairly certain that they have photographed a sample of one week's production. Write an equation using the letters B and W that describes the relationship between the number of black airplanes and the number of white airplanes produced. The equation should allow you to calculate the number of white planes produced in a month if you know the number of black planes produced in a month.

Answers (and percent of freshmen engineering students getting it correct):

1.) $5C=4S$ (27%)

2.) $P_a = \dfrac{6D}{5L}$ (2%)

3.) There are seven assemblers for every solderer (29%)

4.) $5B=8W$ (32%)

Source: John Clement and Jack Lochhead, University of Massachusetts. ●

with between 10 and 30 years' experience, were given the translation problem in a slightly more difficult form, and eight missed it. When they were given the same problem to program on a computer, however, they all did it correctly. Chief among the reasons for the engineers' success with the problem on a computer is the unambiguous semantics of programming language. The interpretation of variables in computer language is clear; they stand for specific numbers. "College students working out algebra problems are not as precise [as computers]," says Lochhead. They tend to use a multi-purpose variable—for example, letting B in one part of a problem equal the number of books sold, then switching to let B equal the price of a book later on. "Poetically it's nice," Lochhead observes, "but scientifically it has to be precise."

In order to find out how to help students become more precise about their algebra reasoning, Clement and Lochhead conducted audio- and video-taped clinical interviews in which students were asked to think aloud as they worked through a series of algebra problems. One student, while grappling with a problem, said in frustration: "I think I'd like to kill my sixth-grade teacher because he didn't teach me this....All these little letters

that I've been working with for years in algebra and I can't [solve the problem]."

Clement and Lochhead use the tapes as a scientific tool—"just as a microscope is used in biology." As Clement explains: "We are actually recording evidence that can be used to construct maps of mental processes. We can study a ten-second reasoning segment in detail. We watch students explain an answer, hesitate, then change their minds." In more than one case, the two professors saw students write down the correct equation and then switch to an incorrect one. This illustrates how deep the cognitive misconception is; for these students, the incorrect solution is more compelling than the correct one. But by knowing the cognitive source of the problem, remedial teaching strategies could be designed to deal specifically—and perhaps finally—with the buggy equation.

Computers that learn

It is fascinating to speculate why one student intuitively solves a problem better than another. By identifying specific conceptual stumbling blocks, Clement and Lochhead have offered some clues. Additionally, computer models of mental processes are increasingly offering additional tools for knowing how people reason and ultimately learn.

ABLE is a computer program at Carnegie-Mellon University that actually learns physics. When it starts off as a novice, the Barely ABLE model finds the right answer only after a considerable search—much the way a beginning student stumbles slowly and clumsily when solving textbook problems. But once a problem is solved, the computer "learns" and stores the new information or rules so that it can subsequently solve similar problems rapidly and directly, thus becoming a More ABLE model. The ABLE model is a kind of computer program incorporating a system of rules called a production system. Each production in the system encapsulates some small part of the knowledge and is recalled or evoked at just those times when it is relevant to the problem.

Real people learn essentially the same way, though more slowly, according to Jill Larkin, formerly a physicist but now a psychologist working in cognitive research at Carnegie-Mellon University. In fact, ABLE learns *too* quickly. Once ABLE has learned to measure the speed of a block on an inclined plane, then it can always do it. It is an automated piece of new knowledge. "People aren't as automated," says Larkin, "and they learn slowly."

Larkin compared the way first-year college physics students and physics profes-sors solve problems and found them to be very similar to the way that the novice Barely ABLE and the expert More ABLE solve them. "The novice student showed considerably more variability in seeking out principles to use," says Larkin, "while the experts knew what would be useful and didn't have to search [their minds] for everything to find it." (See "Programmed to Think," *Mosaic*, Volume 11, Number 5.)

Computers, however, are limited instruments. "They can take one small domain," Larkin says, "and solve problems in that area as well as very good students can. But the problems we are giving the computers are relatively simple—such as a lever problem involving a ladder leaning against a bridge. Compare this with the complexity of what an engineer has to know to design a bridge. Computers fail to capture much of the richness in human knowledge and learning."

Psychologist John Anderson, also at CMU, agrees that to get a computer to model human cognition, it must be provided with a large amount of prior knowledge. But Anderson does not consider this a barrier to developing models. He is experimenting with a computer program that he calls ACT, which has been used to model geometry-problem solving, the learning of concepts, and language acquisition. "ACT is true to life," Anderson says. "It is cautious and does not take leaps based on little evidence."

In short, ACT learns as if it were human. To demonstrate this, Anderson timed experimental subjects as they solved geometry problems. "It might take human subjects two to five minutes with the first application of a postulate in geometry," he recalls. "After several tries using it, they can solve the problem in less than five seconds."

The ACT model, according to Anderson, shows that a basic key to learning is the development of concepts of pattern recognition and the appropriateness of using a particular theorem. For example, "There are more than ten ways to prove that triangles are congruent, and the students have to learn which ones are relevant to a particular problem," he notes. But one of the most common complaints from students about their problem-solving ability is that they "don't know how to get started," or "don't know how to decide what to do." And if they don't learn which conditions are appropriate for applying given principles, they too often learn inappropriate ones.

The National Science Foundation contributes to the support of the research reported in this article through its Research in Science Education and Memory and Cognitive Processes Programs.

Are Young Children Really Egocentric?

Janet K. Black

Janet K. Black, Ph.D., is Assistant Professor of Education, College of Education, North Texas State University, Denton.

Recently a friend decided it was best if she gave away her dog. After screening responses to an ad she had placed in the newspaper, three-year-old Julie and her parents were invited to visit Zoe. Upon becoming satisfactorily acquainted with Zoe, Julie's mother and father asked her if she would like to take Zoe home. Julie replied in a concerned tone, "But if we take Zoe, she (Zoe's owner) won't have a dog."

Another child, two years of age, accidentally knocked off his grandmother's glasses while she was reading to him. Marc patted her and said, "Sowy Grandma." This behavior was repeated several times throughout the afternoon.

Five-year-old Jonathan asked his mother how many quarters there were in a football game. After internalizing her explanation he said, "Five quarters would make one game and one quarter, and eight quarters would make two games."

The above behaviors are typical of observations that parents, teachers, and caregivers have made while interacting with young children. These behaviors pose some questions about theories of child development which suggest that young children are totally egocentric. According to Piaget, egocentric behavior prevents young children from conserving and from acting altruistically. However, there is a growing body of research evidence that indicates even young children are not always egocentric.

Piagetian and recent research on egocentrism

Yarrow and Zahn-Waxler (1977) conducted a detailed study of children's altruistic behavior between the ages of ten months and two-and-one-half years. After analyzing some 1,500 incidents, Yarrow and Zahn-Waxler conclude that children, from at least the age of one, have a capacity for compassion and various kinds of prosocial behavior. Pines (1979) discusses Flavell's conclusions about young children's egocentric behavior. As a result of his research, Flavell concludes that Piaget overestimated how egocentric young children are. His investigations with three-year-olds indicate that they behave in a consistently nonegocentric manner. Flavell believes that some of the role taking exercises used in earlier research may have been too complicated for young children, while simpler, more relevant tests are more reliable indicators of their true ability. For example, if children are shown a card with a dog on one side and a cat on the other, they will be able to tell you correctly what animal you see and ignore the one that faces them. Flavell concludes, "Though young children may not completely understand, they can pay attention to how other people feel" (Pines 1979, p. 77).

One of Piaget's best known experiments which allegedly documents young children's inability to decenter is the mountain task. Piaget used a three-dimensional model of three mountains (Piaget and Inhelder 1967) which are distinguished from one another by color, as well as the presence of snow on one mountain, a house on another, and a red cross on the third.

A child is seated at one side of the table upon which the above model is placed. The experimenter then stands a doll at varying positions around the mountains and asks the child, "What does the doll see?" Because it is hard for the child to give a verbal description, she or he is given a set of ten pictures and is asked to choose the one that shows what the doll sees. Generally, children up to the age of eight or nine cannot successfully do this task. Piaget (Piaget and Inhelder 1967, p. 212) concluded that these responses indicate that young children are unable to decenter.

Donaldson (1979) states:

We are urged by Piaget to believe that the child's behavior in this situation gives us deep insight into the nature of the world. This world is held to be one that is composed largely of "false absolutes." That is to say the child does not appreciate that what he sees is relative to his own position; he takes it to represent truth or reality—*the world as it really is*. . . . Piaget believes that this is how it is for the young child: that he lives in the state of the moment, not bothering himself with how things were just previously, with the relation of one state to those which came before or after it. . . . The issue for Piaget is how the momentary states are linked or fail to be linked in the child's mind. The issue is how well the child can deal conceptually with the transitions between them. (pp. 12-13).

A task, similar to yet different from Piaget's mountain experiment, designed by Hughes (1975) demonstrates that there are important considerations in the experimenter's, as well as in children's, behavior which Piaget failed to take into account. After acquainting the child with a square board divided by barriers into four equal sectors, a doll was put in each of the sectors one at a time and a policeman was positioned at points of the sectors. The child was asked if the policeman could see the doll. Then another policeman was introduced and the child was told to hide the doll from both policemen. This was repeated three times so that each time a different sector was left as the only hiding place. Thirty children between the ages of three-and-one-half and five were given this task with 90 percent of their responses correct. Even the ten youngest children (average age, three years nine months) achieved a success rate of 88 percent. Thus, it seems that young children are capable of considering and coordinating two different points of view.

Donaldson (1979) explains the differences in children's behaviors on the mountain and policeman tasks from an experiential perspective. In short, 'the mountain task is abstract in a psychologically very important sense: in the sense that it is abstracted from all basic human purposes, feelings, and endeavors" (p. 17). However, "young children know what it is to try to hide. Also they know what it is to be naughty and to want to evade the consequences" (p. 17).

In the policeman task, the motives and intentions of the characters are comprehensible even to three-year-olds. If tasks require children to act in ways which make human sense, that is, are in line with very basic human purposes, interactions, and intentions, children show none of the difficulties in decentering which Piaget maintained. Thus, while adults, as well as children, are egocentric in certain situations throughout life, the extent to which young children are egocentric seems to be much less than Piaget suggested.

Related to the issue of basic human purpose and feeling is the nature and context of the language used by the experimenter. Once again Donaldson raises valid questions about various Piagetian class-inclusion tasks. In one of these tasks a child is presented with four red flowers and two white flowers and asked: Are there more red flowers or flowers? Children of five usually respond that there are more red flowers. Donaldson (1979) states:

> There is not much doubt about what a child *does* when he makes the standard type of error and says there are more red flowers than flowers; he compares one subclass with the other subclass. . . . The question is why does he compare subclass with subclass? Is it because he *cannot* compare subclass with class as Piaget maintains? Or is it because he thinks that this is what he is meant to do? Is there. . . a failure of communication? (p. 39)

In discussing a variety of task-inclusion experiments in which there was perceptual and/or language modification, Donaldson (1979) concludes that the questions the children were answering were very often not the questions the experimenter was asking. In short, the children's interpretations did not correspond to the experimenter's intentions. The children either did not know what the experimenter meant, what the language meant, or had expectations about questions or the experimental material which shaped their interpretation. In other words, when children hear words that refer to a situation which they are at the same time perceiving, their interpretation of the words is influenced by the expectations they bring to the situation. While Piaget was aware of the differences of what language is for the adult and what language is for the child, he failed to keep these differences in perspective in using language for studying children's thinking (Donaldson, 1979).

Gelman (1979) believes that if researchers stopped using incorrect assumptions and inappropriate measures, they would learn that the cognitive skills of younger children are far greater than has been assumed. She developed a magic task which does not ask a child to distinguish between more or less but rather to designate a winner or loser in number conservation activities. "According to the results of the 'magic task,' preschoolers know full well that lengthening or shortening the array does not alter the numerical value of a display" (p. 903).

Conclusions

There is a growing body of evidence which indicates that young children are not as egocentric as Piaget suggested. If children are in contexts where they can use their knowledge of very basic human purposes, intentions, and interactions, they show no difficulty in decentering. Likewise, children's interpretation of the language of others is dependent upon (1) their knowledge of language; (2) their assessment of the experimenter's, caregiver's, teacher's, and parent's nonverbal intentions; and (3) the manner in which children would represent the physical situation if the adults were not present.

Because Julie had had very basic human experiences of relinquishing prized possessions or opportunities, she understood how people might feel if they had their pets taken away. Because Mac had had the very basic human experience of being hurt and comforted, he understood how his grandmother felt and what he could do to comfort her. Because Jonathan had had the very basic human experience of acquiring desired possessions with his allowance frequently given to him in four quarters, he readily indicated his ability to decenter when discussing the quarters in a football game. Contrary to Piaget, these three children's behavior indicates that they are not completely egocentric if the context is meaningful to them. While Piaget's vast contribution to the understanding of young children's cognitive development cannot be denied, no theory is final. Early childhood researchers and practitioners need to add to and clarify the roots of later cognitive and prosocial competence.

Implications

Astute and observant adults can renew their faith in their abilities to observe and know children in ways that researchers often misinterpret. Perhaps there should be more action research on the part of early childhood teachers or more dialogues between teachers and researchers.

Providing situations in which young children can demonstrate their knowledge of very basic human purposes and interactions is necessary to make a more accurate assessment of their competencies. Young children demonstrate varying competencies in different environments. There are contexts in which children indicate they do not know, when, in fact, they do (Black, 1979a, 1979b; Cazden 1975).

A third implication concerns the language adults use with children. Teachers and parents constantly need to be aware of young children's knowledge of language, of our nonverbal behavior, and children's probably understanding of physical situations.

By acknowledging that children in basic human situations and meaningful communicative contexts are more capable than previously thought, teachers, caregivers, and parents can obtain more accurate information about children's abilities. An awareness of these competencies facilitates provision of more appropriate experiences for young children.

Finally, researchers need to become cognizant of inappropriate methodology in studying young children. Conclusions and recommendations emanating from misguided research do not help practitioners provide appropriate experiences for young children. In fact, practices based on misinformation may actually impede children's development. Gelman (1979) cautions professionals about continuing to measure children with tasks that are more appropriate to older children (and even adults): "The time has come for us to turn our attention to what young children can do as well as what they cannot do. We should study preschoolers in their own right" (p. 904).

References

Black, J.K. "Formal and Informal Means of Assessing the Competence of Kindergarten Children." *Research in the Teaching of English* 13, no. 1 (1979a): 49-68.

Black, J.K. "There's More to Language Than Meets the Ear: Implications for Evaluation." *Language Arts* 56, no. 5 (1979b): 526-533.

Cazden, C. "Hypercorrection in Test Responses." *Theory into Practice* 14 (1975): 343-346.

Donaldson, M. *Children's Minds.* New York: Norton, 1979.

Gelman, R. "Preschool Thought." *American Psychologist* 34 (1979): 900-905.

Hughes, M. "Egocentrism in Pre-School Children." Unpublished doctoral dissertation, Edinburgh University, 1975.

Piaget, J., and Inhelder, B. *The Child's Conception of Space,* New York: Norton, 1967.

Pines, M. "Good Samaritans at Age Two?" *Psychology Today* (June 1979): 66-77.

Yarrow, M.R., and Zahn-Waxler, C. "The Emergence and Functions of Prosocial Behaviors in Young Children." In *Readings in Child Development and Relationships,* ed. R. Smart and M. Smart, New York: Macmillan, 1977.

WHO'S INTELLIGENT?

ROBERT J. STERNBERG

Robert J. Sternberg is associate professor of psychology at Yale. He received his Ph.D. in psychology in 1975 from Stanford, where he won the Sidney Siegel Memorial Award for his dissertation on human intelligence. In 1981, he received an American Psychological Association Distinguished Scientific Award for an Early Career Contribution to Psychology. The citation recognized his "major theoretical contributions to our understanding of human intelligence and mental abilities."

When experts try to define intelligence, they generally consult one another or their own intuition. But to the layman, the definitions they come up with often seem to be rarefied abstractions, unconnected with real people or real life. And formal IQ tests frequently seem unfair or beside the point.

Almost everyone likes to think that he or she pretty much knows what intelligence is and how to judge who has it and who doesn't. Indeed, people make informal judgments about others' intelligence all the time, and don't seem to need intelligence tests to do so. One could argue that the bulk of intelligence testing is not the kind that takes place in schoolrooms and psychologists' consulting rooms, but the kind that goes on in face-to-face encounters between people: in job and admission interviews, in classrooms, in meetings, at cocktail parties, during coffee breaks, and in initial encounters with strangers. As Ulric Neisser of Cornell has pointed out, psychologists have done many studies of intelligence as measured by IQ tests, but they have done practically none of intelligence as judged by people in everyday encounters.

Some research that my colleagues and I have recently done was designed to find out what laymen mean when they speak of intelligence. Our main conclusion is a simple one: Ordinary people have very definite ideas about what intelligence is, and their ideas are not too different from those of the experts. Moreover, the conception of intelligence held by scientists and nonscientists alike is not abstruse or theoretical but is firmly and clearly anchored in the real world.

Laymen Know What Intelligence Is

We drew several other conclusions from our research. First, despite the general agreement of experts and laymen, intelligence does not mean precisely the same thing to everyone; there are some differences between the views of laymen and those of experts, and among different groups of laymen. Second, the confidence of nonscientists in their ability to judge intelligence seems justified. Third, it is possible to predict people's IQ scores from the kinds of intelligent or unintelligent behavior that they list as characteristic of themselves. This last finding leads to the provocative idea that a simple behavioral checklist might some day be used as a formal device for estimating intelligence. Such a checklist could perhaps supplement traditional IQ tests in situations where cultural differences and test anxiety obscure real abilities.

The best-known example of the experts-only approach to defining intelligence is a symposium published in the *Journal of Educational Psychology* in 1921. That year, 14 psychologists and educators gave their views on the nature of intelligence. Lewis M. Terman said that intelligence is "the ability to carry on abstract thinking." Herbert Woodrow called it "the capacity to acquire capacity." S. S. Colvin said that a person "possesses intelligence insofar as he has learned, or can learn, to adjust himself to his environment."

Three years later, in a *Psychological Review* article that is still frequently quoted, Edward L. Thorndike offered yet another definition. "Let intellect," he wrote, "be defined as that quality of mind (or brain, or behavior if one prefers) in respect to which Aristotle, Plato, Thucydides, and the like, differed most from Athenian idiots of their day, or in respect to which the lawyers, physicians, scientists, scholars, and editors of reputed greatest ability at constant age differ most from idiots of that age in asylums."

In 1978, Barbara Conway, Jerry Ketron, Morty Bernstein, and I began asking laymen for *their* views on intelligence. In a series of experiments carried out over a year, we personally interviewed or questioned by mail 476 men and women, including students, commuters, supermarket shoppers, and people who answered newspaper advertisements or whose names we selected at random from the phone book. To compare the ideas of our lay subjects with those of experts, we also sent questionnaires to 140 research psychologists specializing in intelligence.

We did not think it would be useful to ask laymen directly for their definitions of intelligence. Such a request seemed less likely to elicit genuine convictions than to produce platitudes: stale ideas dredged up, perhaps, from memories of old courses taken in school or college, or from articles read long ago. We decided instead on an indirect approach. In our first experiment, for instance, we gave people a blank sheet of paper and asked them to list behaviors that they considered to be characteristic of "intelligence," "academic intelligence," "everyday intelligence," or "unintelligence."

We found our subjects in natural

COMPARING IDEAS ABOUT INTELLIGENCE

Intelligence researchers and laymen who participated in the final phase of the author's study agreed on many characteristics of intelligent behavior, but gave them somewhat different emphases. The columns below reflect the two groups' ratings. They are based on a statistical analysis of expert and lay responses to a list of characteristics mentioned by a group of laymen in the study's initial phase.

LAYMEN

I. Practical problem-solving ability

Reasons logically and well.
Identifies connections among ideas.
Sees all aspects of a problem.
Keeps an open mind.
Responds thoughtfully to others' ideas.
Sizes up situations well.
Gets to the heart of problems.
Interprets information accurately.
Makes good decisions.
Goes to original sources for basic
   information.
Poses problems in an optimal way.
Is a good source of ideas.
Perceives implied assumptions and
   conclusions.
Listens to all sides of an argument.
Deals with problems resourcefully.

II. Verbal ability

Speaks clearly and articulately.
Is verbally fluent.
Converses well.
Is knowledgeable about a particular field.
Studies hard.
Reads with high comprehension.
Reads widely.
Deals effectively with people.
Writes without difficulty.
Sets aside time for reading.
Displays a good vocabulary.
Accepts social norms.
Tries new things.

III. Social competence

Accepts others for what they are.
Admits mistakes.
Displays interest in the world at large.
Is on time for appointments.
Has social conscience.
Thinks before speaking and doing.
Displays curiosity.
Does not make snap judgments.
Makes fair judgments.
Assesses well the relevance of
   information to a problem at hand.
Is sensitive to other people's needs
   and desires.
Is frank and honest with self and others.
Displays interest in the immediate
   environment.

EXPERTS

I. Verbal intelligence

Displays a good vocabulary.
Reads with high comprehension.
Displays curiosity.
Is intellectually curious.
Sees all aspects of a problem.
Learns rapidly.
Appreciates knowledge for its own sake.
Is verbally fluent.
Listens to all sides of an argument
   before deciding.
Displays alertness.
Thinks deeply.
Shows creativity.
Converses easily on a variety of subjects.
Reads widely.
Likes to read.
Identifies connections among ideas.

II. Problem-solving ability

Is able to apply knowledge to problems
   at hand.
Makes good decisions.
Poses problems in an optimal way.
Displays common sense.
Displays objectivity.
Solves problems well.
Plans ahead.
Has good intuition.
Gets to the heart of problems.
Appreciates truth.
Considers the result of actions.
Approaches problems thoughtfully.

III. Practical intelligence

Sizes up situations well.
Determines how to achieve goals.
Displays awareness to world
   around him or her.
Displays interest in the world at large.

settings. Sixty-three of them were commuters about to board trains at the New Haven station; 62 were housewives and others about to enter a New Haven supermarket; and 61 were students studying in a Yale library. Almost no one had trouble with our request; people were apparently convinced that certain kinds of behavior indicated certain kinds of intelligence—or the lack of it.

From people's responses we compiled a master list of 250 behaviors, 170 that had been named as characteristic of intelligence and 80 that had been called signs of unintelligence. Some of the behaviors most frequently listed as intelligent were "reasons logically and well," "reads widely," "displays common sense," "keeps an open mind," and "reads with high comprehension." For unintelligence, the most commonly listed behaviors included "does not tolerate diversity of views," "does not display curiosity," and "behaves with insufficient consideration of others." The great diversity of the behaviors cited showed that our subjects held eclectic views of intelligent and unintelligent behavior, and suggested that people probably do not consider any one-dimensional scale adequate for measuring intelligence.

A study of this kind runs the risk of finding some idiosyncratic responses that reflect just one or two people's peculiar notions. For example, one person listed "bores people" as characteristic of an intelligent person, whereas another person listed "is fun to be with"—almost the opposite. In order to deal with this problem, we had 28 people from the New Haven area—nonstudents answering a newspaper advertisement—rate on a scale of 1 (low) to 9 (high) how characteristic they thought each of the 250 behaviors on the master list was of an ideally intelligent person, an ideally academically intelligent person, and an ideally everyday-intelligent person. We then applied a statistical technique called "factor analysis," which analyzes people's tendencies to view certain subsets of behaviors as related. The method grouped together all the behaviors that people viewed as similar and grouped separately all those that they viewed as dissimilar, and allowed us to determine the few basic factors underlying people's diverse

and, in a few instances, highly unusual responses. The result was to give us, in effect, a simple characterization of intelligence as viewed by our subjects.

It turned out that people conceived of intelligence as having three facets, which we labeled *practical problem-solving ability, verbal ability*, and *social competence*. Practical problem-solving ability included such behaviors as "reasons logically and well," "identifies connections among ideas," "sees all aspects of a problem," and "keeps an open mind." Under the heading of verbal ability came such behaviors as "speaks clearly and articulately," "is verbally fluent," "converses well," and "reads with high comprehension." Social competence was marked by such behaviors as "accepts others for what they are," "admits mistakes," "displays interest in the world at large," and "thinks before speaking and doing."

Since we had asked people not only about intelligence in general but also about academic intelligence and everyday intelligence, we also factor-analyzed the behaviors that had been cited as evidence for these two additional qualities. Our subjects, we learned, conceived of academic intelligence as composed of *verbal ability, problem-solving ability*, and *social competence*. These factors sound almost identical to the ones that emerged for intelligence in general; they were, in fact, quite similar, but the specific behaviors that had been listed reflected greater emphasis on academic skills, such as studying hard. The factors that emerged for everyday intelligence we called *practical problem-solving ability, social competence, character*, and *interest in learning and culture*. These, too, overlapped with those for intelligence in general, but less so, and had more of an everyday slant.

The Experts Emphasize Motivation

The resemblance between the views of scientists and nonscientists is surprisingly clear. On the whole, the informal theories of intelligence that laymen carry around in their heads—without even realizing that their ideas constitute theories—conform fairly closely to the most widely accepted formal theories of intelli-

gence that scientists have constructed. That is, what psychologists study as intelligence seems to correspond, in general, to what people untrained in psychology mean by intelligence. On the other hand, what psychologists study corresponds to only *part* of what people mean by intelligence in our society, which includes a lot more than IQ tests measure.

The data on which these conclusions are based come from two questionnaires that we sent to a group of laymen and to a group of recognized authorities in the field of intelligence. The latter hold doctorates in psychology and teach in major American universities; each has published several major books or articles about intelligence. The two questionnaires named the 250 behaviors on our master list. One questionnaire asked respondents to rate how characteristic each behavior was of an ideally intelligent, ideally academically intelligent, and ideally everyday-intelligent person. The other asked respondents to rate how important each behavior was to defining the respondents' conceptions of each of these three kinds of people.

Taking into account both the characteristicness and the importance ratings for the three kinds of intelligence (academic, everyday, and general), the median correlation between the response patterns of experts and those of laymen was .82 (on a scale where 0 indicates no relationship and 1 indicates a perfect correspondence).

There were two main differences between the groups. One was that the experts considered motivation to be an important ingredient in academic intelligence—an ingredient that did not emerge when we factor-analyzed the responses of the laymen. Behaviors central to this motivational factor included "displays dedication and motivation in chosen pursuits," "gets involved in what he or she is doing," "studies hard," and "is persistent."

The second difference was that laymen seemed to place somewhat greater emphasis on the social-cultural aspects of intelligence than did the experts. Behaviors such as "sensitivity to other people's needs and desires" and "is frank and honest with self and others" showed up in the "social competence" factor for laymen but not in the analogous "practical intelligence" factor for experts.

In order to get a better sense of just how experts and laymen differ in their views of intelligence, I went back to the original ratings of the importance of the various behaviors to people's conceptions of intelligence. I was particularly interested in those kinds of behaviors that received higher ratings from laymen than from experts, and in those that received higher ratings from experts than from laymen. The pattern was clear. Consider first some of the behaviors that laymen emphasized more than experts did in defining intelligence: "acts politely," "displays patience with self and others," "gets along well with others," "is frank and honest with self and others," and "emotions are appropriate to situations." These behaviors, which are typical of those rated higher by laymen, clearly show an emphasis on *inter*personal competence in a *social* context. Consider next some of the behaviors that experts typically emphasized more than laymen did in defining intelligence: "reads with high comprehension," "shows flexibility in thought and action," "reasons logically and well," "displays curiosity," "learns rapidly," "thinks deeply," and "solves problems well." These behaviors clearly show an emphasis on *intra*personal competence in an *individual* context. To the extent that there is a difference, therefore, it is clearly in the greater emphasis among laymen on intelligence as an interpersonal and social construct.

Another way of comparing the views of experts with those of laymen is to ask in what specific ways laymen's informal conceptions of intelligence resemble formal scientific theories. Some theorists, like most laymen, consider social competence an element of intelligence. In addition, many theorists have proposed a fundamental distinction between problem-solving abilities on the one hand (also called, in the psychological literature, "fluid" abilities) and verbal abilities on the other (also called "crystallized" abilities). This distinction is basic to the conception of intelligence held by our lay subjects.

Why, if we know people's informal theories of intelligence, do we need formal scientific theories at all? A careful examination of the kinds of behaviors people have listed will show why we do. Consider some examples of such behaviors: "reasons logically and well," "makes good decisions," "is verbally fluent," and "reads with high comprehension." One might well ask just what it means to do any of these things. These descriptions label behaviors without really explaining them or even defining what goes into them. What does it mean, psychologically, to reason logically and well, or to read with high comprehension? What makes some people reason or read better than others? These are the kinds of questions psychologists must address in their scientific theories. Thus, the informal theories of laymen can be seen as setting up a framework within which scientists can work; the detailed contents falling within that framework can be filled in only by scientific research.

Yet another comparison can be made by considering the content of IQ tests. In particular, how do people's conceptions of intelligence correspond to what IQ tests measure? The correspondence is striking indeed. Behaviors such as "reads with high comprehension" are measured by tests that ask people to remember facts and make inferences from short reading passages. "Is verbally fluent" is measured by word-fluency tests, such as those that ask people to think of as many words as they can beginning with the letter *r* in a brief time period. "Displays a good vocabulary" is directly measured by vocabulary tests. "Displays a good memory" is measured by memory tests, like those that ask a person to remember a string of digits such as 3-5-1-8-6-2. "Is knowledgeable about a broad range of things" is measured by tests of world knowledge. "Works puzzles well" is measured by tests such as anagrams, which present scrambled words (r-t-d-o-o-c) to be unscrambled (doctor). "Solves problems well" is measured by tests such as arithmetic word problems, which require people to solve real-world types of problems by using numerical calculations.

What's Smart for the Baganda Is Dumb for the Batoro

A fine-grained analysis of our data reveals not only differences between experts and laymen, but also distinguishable subpopulations among laymen. Students, we found, gave greater weight to academic ability as a component of general intelligence than commuters did. Commuters, on the other hand, considered everyday intelligence—the ability to function well in daily life— more important.

The differences in conceptions of intelligence become much greater if one goes outside our own culture. Mallory Wober, an African psychologist, investigated conceptions of intelligence among members of different tribes in Uganda and found considerable variation. The Baganda, for example, tended to associate intelligence with mental order, whereas the Batoro associated it with some degree of mental turmoil. When Wober asked his subjects to associate descriptive words with intelligence, he found that members of the Baganda tribe thought of intelligence as persistent, hard, and obdurate, whereas the Batoro thought of it as soft, obedient, and yielding.

Cross-cultural differences in conceptions of intelligence can have practical as well as theoretical implications, as I have discovered from my own experience. I recently attended a meeting on intelligence in Venezuela, where the government has established a Ministry for the Development of Intelligence to raise the intellectual level of the Venezuelan population. The meeting consisted of morning, afternoon, and evening sessions, with speakers and listeners representing a wide range of cultural backgrounds. In the early days of the meeting, my North American colleagues and I consistently arrived promptly at the time that a given session was scheduled to begin. We were acting in a way that is adaptive in meetings we have attended in the United States: If one wishes to hear a whole session, one arrives on time. Indeed, a behavior that was rated as very highly characteristic of intelligence by people in our experiments was being on time for appointments. But we quickly learned that what was adaptive and intelligent in the United States was quite maladaptive and unintelligent in Venezuela. Meetings simply never started on time, and delays of an hour or two were quite common. Someone who arrived on time for every session (or any session!) would waste countless hours waiting for meetings to begin— hours that could be better spent doing any of a number of other things.

That kind of difference has practical implications for me because I have been asked to conduct a training course in intellectual skills for Venezuelan schoolchildren. Obviously I will have to study Venezuelan ideas of intelligence before instituting the training; wholesale importation of North American conceptions of intelligence into the Venezuelan culture would make no sense at all.

We Use Our Theories of Intelligence

Just as psychologists administering IQ tests can measure intelligence on the basis of some (at least allegedly) scientific theory of what intelligence is, so ordinary people should be able to assess intelligence—their own and others'—on the basis of their own theories of what intelligence is. Indeed, we found that laymen not only *have* internalized conceptions of intelligence, but that they make good use of them in evaluating intelligence.

To find out whether or not what people say they think about intelligence is actually reflected in their judgments of intelligence, we sent lay subjects a series of character sketches of fictitious people, employing behaviors taken from our master list. Here are two typical sketches:

Susan:
She keeps an open mind.
She is knowledgeable about a particular field.
She converses well.
She shows a lack of independence.
She is on time for appointments.

Adam:
He deals effectively with people.
He thinks he knows everything.
He shows a lack of independence.
He lacks interest in solving problems.
He speaks clearly and articulately.
He fails to ask questions.
He is on time for appointments.

The respondent's task was to rate the intelligence of each person on a scale of 1 to 9. Our task was to find out whether or not the respondent's ratings were consistent with laymen's theoretical conceptions of intelligence as revealed in one of our earlier studies—the one described on page 140, in which we asked subjects to rate the degree to which each of the 250 master behaviors is characteristic of intelligent or unintelligent people. "Keeps

an open mind," for example, had been rated 7.7, while "shows a lack of independence" was worth 2.7. Averaging the ratings for each fictitious person, we came up with a score of 6 for Susan and of 4.3 for Adam. By comparison, our respondents rated Susan's intelligence at 5.8 (above average) and Adam's at 4.3 (below average). Overall, when we calculated the correlation between the two sets of ratings, it was an extremely high .96 (on a scale where 1 would mean a perfect relationship). In other words, laymen's ratings of people's intelligence are firmly grounded in their theories about intelligence.

In the course of doing this part of our study, we found that unfavorable characterizations of people—"fears the unfamiliar," "likes to argue but not to think about arguments," "is slow to learn," "acts indecisively," and "succumbs to propaganda"—carry more weight in reducing an evaluation of someone's intelligence than do favorable characterizations in increasing an evaluation of the person's intelligence. That is, ordinary people can be very harsh in their judgments of unintelligent behavior; when people do something stupid, they may find that others brand them as stupid without giving them full credit for the intelligent things they do.

As for people's ability to assess their own intelligence, we found a correlation of .23 between self-ratings on general intelligence and actual IQ. That correlation is not impressive; it is higher than chance, but it shows that most people have only a very modest ability to assess their own intelligence.

However, we found that people's self-*descriptions* can tell us much more about their intelligence than their self-*ratings*. Specifically, we discovered that if we presented people with our master list of 250 intelligent and unintelligent behaviors and asked them to rate how characteristic each behavior is of themselves, we could then estimate, from their responses, not only their overall IQ, but their subscores on such aspects of intelligence as problem-solving ability, verbal ability, and social competence. The correlation between overall scores on the checklist for intelligence and IQ was .52, more than twice as high as the correlation of self-rating with IQ. Moreover, this correlation compares

favorably with correlations obtained by psychologists in the laboratory using "cognitive measures," such as the time it takes to complete intellectual tasks: for example, analogies and anagrams. In other words, we seem to have found a potential measure of intelligence that could supplement, though not replace, conventional IQ tests. This, we think, is the major value of our research.

The estimates of intelligence that we can calculate from the master list of behaviors are only fairly accurate, not absolutely so. For that reason, I would not go so far as to suggest that the checklist replace IQ tests. But the checklist does have several desirable features as a supplementary measure of intelligence. First, its questions deal with *typical performance*, rather than with the *maximal performance* required by IQ test questions. There are few situations in one's life that require quite the expenditure of mental effort that is involved in taking an IQ test. Second, the checklist is not stressful, or at least it is much less stressful than an IQ test, making it especially appropriate for people who for one reason or another do not show their true abilities in an IQ testing situation. Third, the items on the checklist deal with real-world behaviors rather than with the highly artificial behaviors required by IQ tests.

Fourth, the checklist is more wide-ranging in the kinds of behaviors it inquires about than are IQ tests. For example, the checklist includes items assessing the kinds of social competence all but ignored by IQ tests. Moreover, the checklist can be tailored to different cultural groups by constructing and scoring it on the basis of behaviors that members of a given group consider to be important ingredients of intelligence. Both the content and the scoring are thereby made culturally relevant for the particular person whose intelligence is being assessed. Finally, the circumstances of administering the checklist would not have the inherent biases found in IQ testing situations, which place a premium on rapid solution of test items little resembling the tasks in ordinary people's lives.

One might attempt to dismiss the behavioral checklist by arguing that people would simply rate themselves as showing a maximum of desirable behaviors and a minimum of undesirable ones. But such a dismissal would be ill-advised. The scoring system we have developed calls for figuring out how much resemblance there is between a person's self-description and other people's descriptions of the ideally intelligent person; the greater the resemblance, the higher the real person's IQ. Thus, what matters is not the *level* of people's responses (on the 1 to 9 scale), but the *pattern* of responses; the correlational resemblance is indifferent to the magnitude of the ratings. Moreover, we know that subjects do not, in fact, simply check off for themselves the "ideal" pattern. No subjects came anywhere near depicting themselves as ideal.

On a theoretical level, our research can help enrich scientifically based theories of intelligence with intuitively based ones. The two kinds of research are complementary. Conducted in tandem, with each informing the other, they can provide greater understanding of the nature of intelligence than can either kind pursued alone. At the very least, the research we have done on people's conceptions of intelligence has taught us that what psychologists study as intelligence does have some connection with what people mean by intelligence in everyday life.

For further information, read:

Neisser, Ulric. "The Concept of Intelligence," in *Human Intelligence: Perspectives on Its Theory and Measurement.* Robert J. Sternberg and Douglas K. Detterman, eds., Ablex, 1979, $16.50.

Sternberg, Robert J. "The Nature of Intelligence," *New York University Education Quarterly,* Vol. 12, No. 3, pp. 10-17, 1981.

Sternberg, Robert J. "Testing and Cognitive Psychology," *American Psychologist,* 36(1981): 1181-1189.

Sternberg, Robert J. et al. "People's Conceptions of Intelligence," *Journal of Personality and Social Psychology,* 41(1981): 37-55.

Wober, Mallory. "Towards an Understanding of the Kiganda Concept of Intelligence," in *Culture and Cognition: Readings in Cross-Cultural Psychology,* J. W. Berry and P. R. Dasen, eds., Methuen, 1974, paper, $10.95.

Yussen, Steven R. and Patrick Kane. "Children's Conceptions of Intelligence," in *The Development of Insight in Children,* Academic Press, in press.

ISLANDS OF GENIUS

Richard Restak

Richard M. Restak is a Washington D.C. neurologist and author of The Brain *and* The Self Seekers.

Michael Hickey is 19. He has never spoken an intelligible word. Yet he seems to know what is going on around him. His eyes are clear, even penetrating, but at the same time strangely preoccupied. It is as if he is thinking about something profoundly important that he cannot or must not convey to others. Michael has a habit of rocking his muscular body back and forth in his chair, often accompanying the rocking movements with a variety of grunting sounds or quick, nervous gestures.

Michael suffers from autism, a mysterious and disabling disease that affects communication, concentration, learning, and emotions. Its cause is unknown. While Michael is in many ways typical of autistic young adults, he has some extraordinary talents many of them don't have. For example, on his first try Michael managed to realign a scrambled Rubik's Cube in less than 40 seconds.

No one has any idea how Michael does it. He is among about 10 percent of autistics who exhibit genius in some highly circumscribed area. A person like Michael, extraordinarily gifted in some areas, backward in others, is called an idiot savant. The term is an unfortunate one, originally coined to describe the 0.6 percent of mentally retarded people who also possess extraordinary talents. Autistics are not necessarily retarded, however,

and some have high IQs.

Bernard Rimland, a bearded 53-year-old San Diego psychologist and a leading authority on autism, has an intensely personal interest in the disease. His own son, Mark, now 25, is autistic. "Our son, definitely planned and wanted, has been a source of pride and despair from the moment of birth. Physically perfect and startlingly alert, he screamed so vigorously while he was in the hospital that it was extremely difficult for my wife to nurse him. At eight months he suddenly began walking. At one year he was clearly articulating whole sentences, but he never said mommy or daddy, and when he wasn't screaming, he seemed to be lost in a perpetual daydream."

Challenged to learn as much as possible about autism, Rimland has worked evenings and weekends on his own time over the past 22 years to establish the Institute for Child Behavior Research in San Diego, a world registry and information clearinghouse for more than 7,500 autistic children in the United States and more than 40 foreign countries. Rimland corresponds with parents of autistic children around the world and lectures at international meetings on autism.

From this correspondence, Rimland has turned up some common patterns of behavior. He reads from a typical mother's letter: "Joe understands books on electronics and uses the theories to build devices. He recently put together a tape recorder, fluorescent light, and a small transistor radio with some other components so that music from the tape was changed to light energy in the light and then back to music in the radio. By pass-

ing his hand between the recorder and the light, he could stop the music. He understands the concepts of electronics, astronomy, music, navigation, and mechanics. He knows an astonishing amount about how things work and is familiar with technical terms. By the age of 12, he could find his way all over the city on his bike with a map and compass. He reads Bowditch on navigation. Joe is supposed to have an IQ of 80. He does assembly work in a Goodwill store."

"This is a story that I've heard hundreds of times," Rimland says. "An enhanced ability to play music, do mathematics, memorize obscure facts, or construct elaborate mechanical devices coexists with profound deficiencies in activities that come naturally to most people.

"Think of it this way," he continues. "Imagine we're in a totally dark room right now, and I turn on a flashlight and illuminate a part of the room with a wide beam. We immediately put the illuminated portion into the context of our concept of a room. But the autistic person can't do that. His flashlight is incapable of a wider beam. Forced to use the narrow one, he can only deal with minute details. He never sees the whole room."

One autistic young man, for example, travels around the country recording and cataloguing the numbers on telephone poles. Another savant has taped thousands of feet of sewer noises by attaching a microphone at the upper end of a hose, which he inserts down the kitchen sink past the trap and into manholes in the street. Others put together jigsaw puzzles with the picture side down equally as well as when the puzzle is right side up.

4. CHILDHOOD

Some savants seem to store this kind of spatial detail in permanent memory. John Swezey, a classmate of Michael Hickey's in Los Altos, California, can draw a complete floor plan, including placement of windows and doors, of every house he's lived in since he was two and sketch the layout of a baby-sitter's house he went to a few times as a toddler. In contrast to Michael, John now talks but in an abrupt, truncated manner reflecting the difficulty he has in finding the right words.

Some savants are able to earn a living with their peculiar talents. A young man with perfect pitch worked for awhile as a piano tuner, but since it is difficult to tune a piano perfectly, he was unable to stop tinkering. He finally lost his job when he left a series of stains on the piano where he had put down a soda he was drinking. "He couldn't understand how the owner could get upset over such a little thing when he was doing such an excellent job tuning," Rimland says with a wry smile.

Further insight on the special talents of savants comes from A. Lewis Hill, who works with retarded people across the country on Staten Island, outside New York City. While the needs and abilities of retarded savants differ markedly from autistic savants, both groups nevertheless share similar touches of genius. Hill, a psychologist at the New York State Institute for Basic Research in Developmental Disabilities, groups all savants into one of seven categories: calendar calculation, artistic talent, mechanical dexterity, musical ability, unusual mathematical skills, memorization of obscure facts, and—extremely rare—the capacity to make fine sensory discriminations such as an extraordinary ability to identify substances by smell.

J. H. Pullen, "the genius of Earlswood Asylum," for example, had an amazing mechanical and engineering talent. Pullen, who died in 1918, built a seaworthy scale model of the ship the *Great Eastern*, complete in every detail including more than one and a quarter million handmade wooden pins that fix the planks to the 10-foot-long

model. Pullen never saw the sea, a river, or a ship. His only guide was the representation of the ship on a handkerchief.

Blind Tom, a black slave born in Georgia in 1849, excelled in languages and music. He could repeat word for word conversations in English, French, and Italian despite his inability to communicate with others except with grunts and other inarticulate sounds. He could imitate piano improvisations and play intricate piano compositions he had heard only once. He was said to know more than 5,000 musical pieces.

In an attempt to explain such rare abilities, Hill has spent seven years investigating a calendar savant named Robert, now 60, who lives in a foster home on Staten Island. Robert plays 11 musical instruments by ear, remembers important dates, and draws elaborate and detailed sketches of homes, but his most impressive ability is calendar calculation. He can name the day of the week any given date falls on going back to 1937, as well as the reverse, naming the correct date for a given day.

From his work with Robert, Hill raises questions about some of the myths surrounding the way savants make calendar calculations. According to Hill, Robert's ability is not based on photographic memory as other investigators have claimed. When Hill shows Robert a series of pictures, Robert later recalls few of the items in them.

Nor does his ability seem to be based on enhanced learning capacity. Hill showed Robert pictures of 16 women and told him their birth dates. After three reviews of the pictures and dates, Robert could not correlate any picture with the right birth date. "Just as you would expect with a mentally retarded person," says Hill, "he is not learning at an accelerated rate; he isn't even learning at a normal rate."

During one arduous calendar calculating session, Hill began to get a glimmer of how Robert operates. "I gave him 168 dates between 1943 and 1969 and asked him to identify the day of the week corresponding to those dates. Robert sat quietly and displayed no fatigue

while performing remarkably well on the task. But in an hour, I found myself exhausted and could no longer concentrate on the experiment," says Hill. "The 10-minute break we took at that time was for my benefit not his." He concluded that Robert's special talent may be an extraordinary ability to concentrate without getting distracted, tired, or bored.

"I think retarded savants tune out everything else in the world but the one thing that is of interest to them," says Hill. But he has no idea how they do it.

Some scientists have speculated that autistic and retarded savants have brain injuries that force them to use normally underused portions of their brains, thus developing special talents. Most savants, however, have no brain injuries, at least none that doctors can identify.

Since savants tend to be socially isolated, some theorists hypothesize that boredom sensitizes them to tiny variations in their environments. But many other retarded and autistic people are just as alone, and yet they never develop any special talents.

It is not even clear who qualifies as a savant, nor is it easy to tell the difference between a mentally retarded savant and an autistic savant, though there are some distinguishing features. IQ is one. Retarded savants generally have an IQ of 50 to 70 while some autistic savants have IQs of 140 and above. Another difference is that autistic savants often go on to successful careers as musicians and mathematics teachers, for example, while retarded savants rarely find jobs related to their skills.

The two groups also respond differently to institutionalization. The mentally retarded savant is apt to do well in a special school, often developing even greater savant talents there. The autistic savant, however, frequently loses his special abilities when he is forced to live in an institution.

This difference may be a result of the different treatment each receives. The abilities of retarded people are considered a sign of intellectual potential that should be encouraged, while the autistic savant's talents are sometimes seen as troublesome symptoms of emotional disturbance that should be discouraged. In fact, autistic savants often improve socially at about the same time their savant abilities begin to diminish. Too much emphasis on their skills may interfere with their budding ability to get along with others.

In an autistic child the special skills often emerge when the child is first learning about his environment. The child selects, say, numbers as a unifying element in the midst of a confusing world and then fits every experience and person he encounters into that numbers scheme. But later, as the child begins to feel less threatened, he begins to relinquish numbers, and eventually the savant abilities may disappear altogether, much to the autistic person's overall benefit. But in a retarded savant, such development never takes place.

Mentally retarded and autistic savants may also differ in the way they accomplish their remarkable feats. Robert evidently does not have a photographic memory, but Michael may, for he used to read by taking his teacher's finger and running it down the page. Now he scans a page in a second or two without moving his eyes as most of us do when we read. He then answers correctly almost all questions on what he just read. Later, sitting outside the schoolyard, Michael may stare into space with an intelligent, knowing expression. Perhaps he is reading—in his mind's eye—the pages he scanned just a few moments before.

In the absence of data, speculations about savants abound. Art, memory, music, and the construction of intricate mechanical devices—the special abilities of savants—are tasks that most normal people process in the right hemispheres of their brains. So far, though, savants reveal no preferential hemisphere activity.

"When people ask me how savants do such difficult things, I reply that I can't even tell them how I do such simple things as write my name or bring a spoon to my mouth," says Rimland. "I just think of what I want to do, and my hand does the rest. The difference with the savants is that when they think of something, they use 100 percent of their concentration not just the feeble 50 percent or so you and I can muster."

Rimland is convinced, at least in the case of autistic savants, that a defect exists within the brain, resulting in the savant's inability to associate incoming stimuli with stored memories. This limits the repertoire of responses, impeding the savant's ability to make generalizations or to think abstractly, but it might account for the heightened powers of concentration the savants display. Rimland speculates that such a defective filter may lie somewhere in the brain's reticular activating system, an area usually associated with alertness. Harry Klopf, neurophysiologist and artificial intelligence expert, has independently proposed the same thing. But if such a filter exists, neuroscientists have not yet been able to find it.

"We're just beginning to look at these fascinating people scientifically," says Hill, "and we hope we're getting closer to finding some answers." CAT and PET scans, developing knowledge of brain chemistry, and more sophisticated psychological and neurological probes should contribute to those answers. "But just how much we're going to learn and how quickly is anybody's guess. The savant is a dramatic example of just how little we really know about the mysteries of the human brain."

RITES OF PASSAGE

JOSEPH ADELSON

Joseph Adelson is professor of psychology at the University of Michigan at Ann Arbor. This article is adapted from a speech given in March by Adelson at the Urban Development Forum, which was sponsored by Research for Better Schools in Philadelphia.

HOW DO youngsters in the vital transitional period of pre- and early adolescence deal with the ideas of the social sciences and the humanities? How do they cope with the concepts they must absorb in learning about history or civics or political science or literary studies? Does psychology have anything useful to tell us about how to teach those subjects during that difficult age? Do we know something that would help us accelerate learning or deepen it or strengthen the child's grasp on what he has been taught?

The work I will report here is based on two major investigations, one cross-national, comparing over three hundred youngsters in our country, England, and Germany, ranging in age from ten or eleven to eighteen, from the fifth grade to the twelfth. The second study, in which we interviewed about 450 adolescents, covered the ages from eleven and twelve to eighteen. This study was directed and analyzed by my colleague, Judith Gallatin. The second study concentrated upon youngsters in an urban area, largely blue collar in origin, with an equal number of blacks and whites.

Our research instrument was the open-ended interview. After a great deal of trial and error, we hit upon an interview format that began with the following premise: a thousand people leave their country and move to a Pacific island to start a new society. We hoped that the use of an imaginary society would help free some of the children, the young ones particularly, from their preoccupation with getting "the right answer." Given this framework, we then offered our youngsters a great many questions on a wide variety of political, social, and moral issues: the scope and proper limits of political authority; the reciprocal obligations of the individual and the community; the nature of crime and justice; the collision between personal freedom and the common good; the prospects for

utopia; and so on. Put this way, it all sounds rather formidable, but the questions themselves were straightforward and generally quite concrete. In the second of the studies, we also introduced a number of questions having to do with urban tensions: the sources and outcomes of poverty, the relations between citizens and the police, and the proper channels for citizen protest. The interviews took, on the average, an hour to complete—the older the child, the longer the interview. We tape-recorded and then transcribed faithfully, including silences, uhs, "you knows," and grammatical incoherence, since we felt that the process of achieving a response might in some cases be as interesting as the response itself.

Since there are far too many findings to report even in summary form, I have identified five topics that I think are of central importance, since they influence so many other areas of social thought: the conceptions of community and of law, the growth of principles, and the grasp of human psychology and of social reality. In each of these topics we see some significant and at times startling changes in children's understanding during the adolescent years. I will concentrate here particularly upon those taking place in the earlier part of that period.

The Community

The first piece of advice to give any teacher preparing to work with ten, eleven, and twelve-year-olds is that one ought not to assume the child is talking about the same things you are. With respect to such concepts as "government" or "society" or "the state," the youngster may talk in a seemingly appropriate fashion; yet, when you extend the conversation or query him a bit, you may likely find something close to a conceptual void. At the threshold of adolescence, children find it difficult to imagine impalpable social collectivities; they do not yet enjoy the sense of community.

We can illustrate this graphically by looking at the answers eleven and twelve-year-olds give to the question "What is the purpose of government?" To begin with, many of them cannot answer the question at all. Either they fall mute entirely or provide obviously confused or irrelevant responses. In our cross-national study, we found that 15 percent of eleven-year-olds could give no answer at all to that question. More revealing yet is the number who are unable to give adequate answers—that is, answers of sufficient coherence and complexity to allow their being coded. The category "Simplistic, Missing the Point, Confused, Vague" accounts for 43 percent of responses among twelve-year-olds. A certain confusion about politics, government, law, and society is endemic among pre-adolescent youngsters. But the failure to understand the idea of government—and similar concepts of the collectivity—is especially significant because these are the regnant ideas in thinking about social, moral, and historical issues, and confusion, murkiness, error, and failure to grasp these concepts makes itself felt throughout a much larger domain of cognition.

BUT TO say that these youngsters are mistaken or confused does not take us very far, since it does not tell us about the specific nature of the cognitive flaw. To understand that, it may be best to turn to some specific responses, chosen at random, from eleven-year-olds of average intelligence, to the question on the purpose of government:

> To handle the state or whatever it is so it won't get out of hand, because if it gets out of hand you might have to...people might get mad or something.
> Well...buildings, they have to look over buildings that would be...um, that wouldn't be any use of the land if they had crops on it or something like that. And when they have highways the government would have to inspect them, certain details. I guess that's about all.
> So everything won't go wrong in the country. They want to have a government because they respect him and they think he's a good man.

What strikes us first about these statements is that, in each case, the speaker seems unable to rise securely above the particular. The child feels most comfortable in remaining concrete, by turning to specific and tangible persons, events, and objects—hence "government" becomes a "him," or the child talks about crops and buildings and highways. Of course an effort is made to transcend particularity, to discover a general principle or idea, but the reach exceeds the grasp, as we can see vividly in the first of these excerpts in which the speaker, seeking a general principle ("to handle the state"), gives up and subsides into concreteness ("people might get mad or something").

The shift from concrete to abstract modes of expression during the course of adolescence is a dramatic one. In our cross-national study, no eleven-year-old child was able to attain high-level abstractness in discussing the purpose of government; and no eighteen-year-old gave an answer as entirely concrete. Most eleven-year-olds (57 percent) can give only concrete responses. At thirteen and fifteen, a low level of abstractness is the dominant mode of conceptualizing government. And at eighteen, a strong majority of youngsters achieve a high level of abstractness.

The findings immediately above are based on our cross-national survey. In other studies we have tried different ways of categorizing responses, but the pattern remains essentially the same.

Unable to imagine "the community"—that is, the invisible network of rules and obligations binding citizens together—the child at the threshold of adolescence does not quite understand the mutuality joining the individual and the larger society. He does understand power, authority, coercion; indeed, he understands those all too well, in that his spontaneous discourse on "government" and the like relies heavily—at times exclusively—on the idea of force, authority being seen as the entitlement to coerce. Yet even that is imagined only concretely: it is the *policeman* who pursues and arrests the criminal, the *judge* who sentences him, and the *jailer* who keeps him. The less punitive purposes of the state are less readily discussed in large part, we believe, because the child, lacking a differentiated, textured view of collectivities, cannot quite grasp how they function or what their larger goals might be. The child at this stage may know that the government does things—fixes the streets, let us say—and that it does so in order to benefit the citizenry as a whole. But beyond such tangible activities leading to such tangible benefits, the need and purposes of the community remain a mystery, impenetrable.

Perhaps the most consistent finding we have is that the adolescent years witness a shift from a personalized, egocentric to a sociocentric mode of understanding social, political, historical, and moral issues. The sociocentric outlook is essentially absent at the beginning of adolescence—that is, when the child is ten, eleven, or twelve; yet, it is more or less universal by the time the child is seventeen or eighteen, with most of the movement taking place in the period we are talking about, somewhere between thirteen and fifteen years of age. The shift is dramatic in that it involves a fairly complete reorganization of how these issues are perceived and interpreted. We have here an expanding *capacity* to think in terms of the community. It does not mean that the youngster, having achieved that capacity, is held captive by it. It does not mean that discourse about society, from that point on, ignores individual needs and perspectives. It does mean, however, that the youngster, having achieved sociocentrism, is able to weigh the competing claims for ego and other, of the individual and the state, or the larger community. Until that point is achieved, social perceptions tend to be truncated, and social judgments and ratiocenation are vulnerable to the distortion of a narrow individualism.

The Law

Perhaps the most unnerving discovery we made upon first reading the interview transcripts was that a substantial minority of our youngest respondents were capable, on occasion, of the moral purview of Attila the Hun. On questions of crime and punishment, they were able—without seeming to bat an eyelash—to propose the most sanguinary means of achieving peace and harmony across the land. Here are three examples, all from the discourse of nice, clean-cut middle American thirteen-year-old boys, telling us their views on the control of crime:

> [On the best reason for sending people to jail]: Well, these people who are in jail for about five years must still own the same grudge, then I would put them in for triple or double the time. I think they would learn their lesson then.

4. CHILDHOOD

[On how to teach people not to commit crimes in the future]: Jail is usually the best thing, but there are others...in the nineteenth century they used to torture people for doing things. Now I think the best place to teach people is in solitary confinement.

[On methods of eliminating or reducing crime]: I think that I would...well, like if you murder somebody you would punish them with death or something like this. But I don't think that would help because they wouldn't learn their lesson. I think I would give them some kind of scare or something.

These excerpts are *not* randomly chosen, since we have selected cases marked by colorful language and thought. Yet neither are they altogether atypical, in this sense—they represent only the more extreme expressions of a far more general social and moral outlook: the tendency to see law, government, indeed most other social institutions, as committed *primarily* to the suppression of wayward behavior. In this view, human behavior tends toward pillage and carnage, and the social order is characteristically on the brink of anarchy. That may overstate it a bit, but not by much. Gradually but steadily, however, an entirely different view of the purpose of law emerges in later adolescence. Toward the end of the period we are dealing with, and certainly by the time children are fifteen and sixteen, the dominant stress upon violence and injury has begun to diminish markedly, and it will more or less vanish by the time the child reaches the age of eighteen.

Two other motifs similarly signal the end of the pre- and early adolescent period. One of these is the tendency to see laws as *benevolent* as against restrictive, as designed to help people. A characteristic statement: "The purpose of laws is to protect people and help them out." Another motif, somewhat related, we suspect, is one that links law to the larger notion of community, that sees law as providing a means for interpersonal harmony, either among competing social groups or in the nation or the state as a whole ("...so that the country will be a better place to live"). These changes, from a purely restrictive to a benevolent or normative view of law, are as fundamental and quantitatively decisive as a shift from the concrete thinking to the abstract.

Principles

We have so far observed two major developments in political thought from the onset of adolescence to its end: the achievement of a sociocentric perspective, the ability to think about social and moral and philosophical issues while keeping the total community in mind; and the gradual abandonment of an authoritarian, punitive view of morality and the law. We now add a third theme: the youngster's capacity to make use of moral and political principles—ideas and ideals—in organizing his thinking about social issues. Once available, that capacity alters—decisively and irrevocably—the youngster's definition of social issues, and at the same time it alters the child's sense of himself as a social and political actor. Most current theories of political attitudes and thinking stress the central significance of more or less stable, more or less complex systems of belief, the presence of which allows the person to organize his understanding of social and political reality. It is in the period we now

have under consideration that we first see the emergence of those systems, as the child begins to use principles in coming to legal, moral, political and social judgments. To judge by our interviews, however, it is a rather late development in adolescence. We seem to see the first signs of it when the child is between fourteen and sixteen, and the use of principles does not make itself felt fully until the end of the adolescent period.

Perhaps we best begin by showing just how the older adolescent makes use of principles in making judgments on social issues. Here is an eighteen-year-old who has just been asked what the government ought to do about a religious group opposed to compulsory vaccination:

Well, anyone's religious beliefs have to be tolerated if not respected, unless it comes down to where they have the basic freedoms. Well, anyone is free until he starts interfering with someone else's freedom. Now, they don't have to get their children vaccinated, but they shouldn't have anything to say what the other islanders do, if they want their children vaccinated. If they're not vaccinated, they have the chance they may infect some of the other children. But then that's isolated, that's them, so if they don't get vaccinated, they don't have anyone else to blame. (Do you think that the government should insist these people go along with what the majority has to say, since they're such a small minority?) No, I don't think that the government should insist, but I think that the government should do its best to make sure that these people are well informed. A well-informed person will generally act in his own interest. I never heard of religion that was against vaccination. (There are religions that are against blood transfusions.) If they want to keep their bodies pure...well, like I said, I think that a well-informed citizen will act in his own best interest. If he doesn't, at least he should know what the possibilities are, you know, the consequences. So I think the government's job is to inform the people. In that case, at least, to inform them and not force them.

Younger children, when faced by a question of this type, find it difficult to reason on the issue. They come down hard on one side or the other or cannot make up their minds and therefore hedge; in support of their position, they may put forward a principle-like phrase, such as "freedom of religion," but they cannot do much with the idea except to assert it. What we see in the excerpt we have given—which we choose not because it is "brilliant" but because it is characteristic in late adolescence—is the capacity to advance a general and generalizing principle, which then allows the youngster to talk about specific issues with some flexibility. These formulae need not be absolute in nature, nor rigidly applied; indeed, in many cases the youngster brings forward circumstances that call for a suspension or modification of the principle.

HOW DOES the youngster come into possession of these principles? As far as we can tell, they are not constructed *de novo* but are acquired by the most mundane processes of learning, in the classroom or through the media, in the church or at home. At moments one can almost see the civics or history textbook before the child's inner eye as he struggles with the question. Here is a youngster trying to answer a question as to which law should be made permanent and unchangeable:

Well, freedom of speech is one, as you said. And then one law, well, I don't think you should be in prison for a longer time than twenty-four hours without them telling the charge against you. Or freedom of the press or freedom of the religion, that should never be changed, because anybody can pick any religion they want. There's no certain religion that everybody has to go by. (Can you think of any other kind of law that should not be changed or is that about it?) There are some more laws, but I know what they are, but I can't really put it into words because...you know, I really know what they are, like the laws, the Bill of Rights, you know, the first ten amendments of the Constitution, uh, them laws, you know, that I haven't mentioned. They should be put in there, in the United States Constitution. I can't remember what they were exactly, but if I had a history book, I'd look them up, you know.

Obviously, he has absorbed some of the principles of constitutional democracy, albeit a bit imperfectly. Nevertheless, it is almost certain that the mode of discourse we see here is not exclusively a function of learning; it depends also upon the growth of cognitive capacity. If we take a look at the interviews of average children in the early and middle-adolescent period, we get some sense of the limits of learning before the child is intellectually ready. Ninth and tenth graders have also been exposed to the fundamental ideas of constitutional government, at least in the students we worked with; yet, it seemed to us that the learning does not quite "take," not completely, not sufficiently to allow the child to make use of it in ordinary conversation. The principles do not "come to mind," even when the child is primed by how the question is phrased. In writing the interview item on permanent laws, we were aware that younger children would not spontaneously think of laws or constitutional provisions guaranteeing fundamental freedoms, and so we decided to prime the pump, so to speak, by mentioning "freedom of speech" as an example. Nevertheless, very few of our younger subjects took the hint. Instead, they concentrated on those issues—crime and punishment, violence and injury—that most concerned them and generally in the straightforwardly authoritarian manner we mentioned earlier:

They should have a law, like people should stop stealing, and if they do steal, they would have to stay in jail for about a year until they settled down and stopped doing that. And they should stop killing each other because that's not right.

And even when the child is not entirely obsessed with fantasies of danger, the response to this question usually betrays an inability to make general statements:

Don't litter. Don't steal. Keep off the grass. Don't break windows. Don't run up the stairs. Don't play with matches. Keep matches out of reach of little children.

We do not want to make either too much or too little of the child's acquisition of principle. It does not usher in a golden era of humanistic wisdom. The ordinary youngster acquires the conventional ideas and ideals of the world about him, and unless he is intensely interested in social or philosophical or literary topics, he is unlikely to have ideas that are discernibly unique or penetrating. Yet on the other hand, it is a development of some importance. One obvious reason is that until the child acquires a capacity for general ideas, he does not understand most of the language of social and moral discourse that envelopes him. He is in that sense like the tourist in a foreign land, unable to speak or read the indigenous language, and not quite

sure what the customs signify. If he is facile enough, he may be able to mimic some of the argot and conduct of the natives around him, yet studied inquiry would soon reveal the lacunae and confusions. Time and again in our interviews with pre- and early adolescents—those, let us say, between eleven and fourteen—we come upon such instances wherein the child's mimetic talent allowed him to talk as though he knew the language when, in fact, he did not. The majority rules, the child says. Ah, we say in turn, so tell us about the majority. Then the child replies, oh, that's when everybody agrees.

Achieving a grasp of principle also means that the child can resist the appeal of the immediate, hence is less vulnerable to mere sentiment. The government wants to build a highway and needs some farm land. The farmer resists; the authorities insist. Who is right? Without some general idea to aid him—either the virtues of property or the common good or eminent domain or some such—the youngster is not far from helpless in telling us what ought to be done, and why. Either he sides with the farmer, sentimentalized as the underdog, or with the government, sentimentalized as the guardian of the public weal. Without the guidance of principle, he is, we feel, so subject to the tug of emotion, and thus of demagoguery, that he cannot make reasoned—and hence reliable—decisions. He is much too responsive to the *evident* good.

One more comment before we leave this topic. It may be worth repeating that the term "principles" refers to both ideas and ideals. The increasing conceptual grasp of the adolescent allows him to come to an understanding of the conventions of social and moral reality as understood by the community at large. At the same time he becomes capable of cognizing the "irreal" as well, and hence of being in touch with the values, hopes, and utopian beliefs of the culture as a whole. Hence the grasp of principles means that the child can become both more "realistic" and "idealistic." It has been our unfortunate habit to concentrate upon "adolescent idealism" as though that were a dominant moral outlook of the adolescent period. In fact, the child's realism, the child's becoming socialized to the conventions of the culture, is a far more conspicuous feature of this era. But what is perhaps most important is that we see a dialectic between these attitudes, between being realistic and being idealistic.

Understanding Human Behavior

Near the beginning of the interview schedule we introduced a series of questions about law and laws, some of which we have already mentioned. What is the function of law? What would happen in a world without law? How and why do people get into trouble with the law? In developing the topic, we want to get some sense of how youngsters understand the psychology of malfeasance. One of our questions put forth the following proposition: some percentage of people need laws to keep them from getting into trouble, while others "follow their consciences naturally and do not need laws." We then asked what accounted for the difference between these two types of people.

What interests us here are not the particular theories proposed—these are fairly commonplace—but rather the somewhat abrupt shift in the child's capacity to talk about human psychology, a shift that in its rudiments seems to take place fairly early in adolescence—most of the time it is visible between the ages of eleven and thirteen. Here are some typical eleven-year-olds trying to distinguish between those who are naturally law abiding and those who need laws to guide them:

Well...most people, some people they don't like, like speeding, they don't like to do this, but some people like...maybe...grownup people some people like to speed a lot.

Well about the person I think he had been pushed around and people don't like him and stuff. The people that do not like the laws—well they probably had friends and he didn't get into much trouble so they just got used to it.

Well...(pause, question repeated) well, it could be that the person who thinks that they were law abiding, I mean the criminals, they see things wrong. (How do you mean?) Well I mean they see...I can't explain it.

One is struck immediately by the sheer confusion of these comments: ideas—even phrases—do not quite connect to each other. There are gaps in discourse. Our experience has been that this sort of confusion suggests not so much ignorance, or fool's knowledge, as it does the child's earnest attempts to reach something just out of his grasp. He does not quite have the conceptual means to achieve a dimly sensed end. We sense that our third respondent is trying to say something about the social outlook of the delinquent ("they see things wrong"), while the second is speaking psycho-historically, that is, trying to link miscreancy to past experience ("he had been pushed around...and stuff"). In these instances we feel that the child's essential problem is a difficulty linking part to whole, particular to general, and vice versa. We may imagine that given the category "law abiding," the child's mind hits upon "speeding" as an instance of that larger category but cannot go beyond that, that is, cannot yet link speeding to other forms of social malfeasance, nor can he develop a differentiated view of the category "law abiding" that will allow him to classify different instances within it.

Even when the eleven-year-old's response is not quite so confused, it generally reveals some distinct limitations in the appraisal of human behavior. Here is a more typical response from a child at this age—it is neither the least nor the most advanced:

Oh, well, someone—their mom and dad might separate or something and neither one wanted them or something like that, didn't like them very much and oh, if they happened to turn bad, I mean just, and they had trouble—pretty soon if they keep doing that and pretty bad conditions they'll probably get in a lot of trouble.

ONCE WE get into this long, meandering sentence, we discover that it contains not one but two theories of miscreancy and its sources—the first of these having to do with parental rejection, the second suggesting that trivial sins that go uncorrected lead implacably to larger ones. But here we see even more

clearly the problem in being unable to find a suitable language. Our youngster speaks only about specific acts or feelings—as though he were the most naive type of behaviorist, one who had vowed to avoid all speculation about internal states of mind. In a year or two this very youngster, proposing the same theory, will almost certainly be able to tell us that kids who come from broken families feel bad about themselves and become trouble makers; but at this moment, although the child seems to have that general idea in mind, even the concept "broken family" may be a bit too abstract (or too unfamiliar) to state. Similarly, even such familiar denominatives as "trouble maker" or "delinquent" may be difficult either to understand or to express comfortably. At any rate, we note at this age level—although not universal even here—a common reliance on action language, the child being unable to talk about "traits" or "character" or other structures or tendencies of the personality. Instead he talks about specific acts of malfeasance.

Children at this age have no stable idea of the personality nor an understanding of motives beyond the most simple (getting mad, getting even, teaching a lesson). The youngster cannot think in terms of *gradations* of motives nor of *variations* in personality. Nor can he formulate the impact of the situation upon the personality. Nor can he propose a theory of incentives beyond simple coercion, nor can he recognize the symbolic or indirect effects of rewards and punishment.

What we have, in short, is a markedly impoverished conception of the personality. Motives are few and starkly simple—fear, anger, revenge, envy, the wish to be liked. Motives tend to be either/or in character—the child cannot easily think in terms of conflict of motives, of compromises among them, or of other dialectical processes that would ultimately determine behavior.

We also see a sharp limitation in time perspective. The child at this age seems unable to grasp fully the effect of the past upon the present, in that he does not seem to consider the effect of personal history upon current conduct. That statement needs some qualification. The child may mention the immediate precipitants of a course of current conduct but finds it difficult to link the present to more remote events in the person's past. Equally striking is the difficulty the youngster shows in tracing out spontaneously the potential effect of current conduct upon later events. Again, we do not want to overstate this: if the question clearly asks for future consequences (what would happen if there were no laws?), the child will imagine those consequences. But in ordinary discourse, the "time window" seems quite narrow. Beyond that, the youngster is rarely able to imagine dialectical processes taking place in the future as the result of decisions taken today—that, for example, an unpopular law may ultimately generate law breaking or other forms of underground opposition.

It may seem to be loading the dice somewhat to take our examples so exclusively from the realm of crime and punishment, given the child's obsessive involvement with these issues. Yet we see these difficulties elsewhere, even when the child is discussing virtue or merit, and for some of the same reasons—an uncertain sense of major and minor, relevant and irrelevant.

Appraising Social Reality

There are some surprising similarities between the preadolescent patterns in learning to understand human psychology and the gradual, at times faltering, steps he takes in developing a sense of social reality. In both instances we come across problems in classification: what belongs to what; how to construct a hierarchy of types and functions; how to specify boundaries and limits. In both instances we perceive a shortness of time perspective, the youngster being unable initially to imagine the effect of the past upon the present, or more than the immediate effect of current social events upon the more or less remote future. And in both instances we note what can only be called a thinness of texture; the child does not seem to grasp ambiguity, complexity, or interaction.

We want to begin by looking at a specific social institution in order to describe the changes that take place in the youngster's grasp of a structure and function and of its relation to larger social processes. We chose the idea of "political party" for several reasons; to begin with, almost all children raised in democratic countries are exposed to information about political parties, and in the fullness of time, achieve an adequate understanding of them; secondly, as an institution, it is neither so diffuse nor so various that different youngsters may have had entirely different experiences of it.

It comes as a surprise to most people how little children at the onset of adolescence actually understand about the nature and purpose of the political party. Since the knowledge of parties seems to be so ubiquitous and since the child is exposed to that knowledge regularly in the mass media, at home, or in school, we are likely to assume that that exposure has resulted in some learning, especially so if the child is the kind who is alert to current events. Nevertheless, a distinct majority of children at the age of eleven, twelve, and thirteen cannot give satisfactory answers to straightforward questions on the purpose and functioning of political parties—and by "satisfactory" we mean no exalted standards of comprehension. Either they cannot answer the questions at all (about 15 percent at age eleven) or they give answers that are either too diffuse to be coded or plainly in error. What is of particular interest is the kind of mistake the child is liable to make when he does venture an opinion. The most common of these is the tendency to confuse the functions of the political party with those of government as a whole. The party is seen as making laws or carrying out either the general or specific tasks of the state. But here are some characteristic expressions of that misunderstanding from some twelve-year-old boys chosen randomly:

Ah, what, like the United States? I think they have these parties because they want to help the United States be a better state, I mean a better country and things like that. And then that's why they have one every one or two years.

I guess because if they wanted a law a certain way then they could have it that way. (probe) I guess if they had a law that people couldn't kill, I guess they didn't like it that way. (Didn't like what?) Some people don't like laws and some people do.
To keep people in order. (What else?) That's all I have to say. (Further probe) To keep people in order like I just said.

In these examples we sense that the child cannot yet classify, that is, cannot yet establish boundaries between the separate functions and structures of the political process. Since he has heard that parties are involved in elections, he may see them as carrying out elections; since he grasps vaguely that they are connected to government, he imputes to them some of the functions of government.

We might mention here, somewhat parenthetically, that these confusions and errors are by no means limited to the topic of the political party. We find much the same pattern in the early years of adolescence, when the child is addressing more general questions about governing. They can find it difficult to distinguish among the legislative, executive, and judicial apparatuses of the state; for that matter, they can find it difficult to distinguish between the government, the state, and the nation, all of which seem to blend into each other. That confusion of element, part standing for wholes and vice versa, characterizes the child's early apprehension of social and governmental institutions.

The next stage is marked by an accurate, although rudimentary, grasp of institutional function. It is a distinct advance over the confusion and error we have seen in the examples just given, and yet compared with what the child will later be capable of, it is marked by what we will call *thin* texture. The child will fasten upon a single, at most two, aspect of structure or function. With respect to political parties, we will be told that the party puts forward candidates or stands for certain ideas or supports candidates. From the interview:

To help the candidates running to have a better chance of getting the office.
Well, so that the people can express their views.
It's to help the people find their candidates and to back the people when they are candidates.

The change from thin to thick texture is difficult to describe succinctly, since it may involve somewhat different processes. In the most simple form, we find a capacity to describe multiple aspects or functions of the institution being discussed. Thus, in relation to political parties, the youngster may tell us that parties both represent positions *and* support candidates, or that they both finance *and* organize for issues *and* their nominees. A step beyond that level is the ability to synthesize several ideas in a single statement. Here is an eighteen-year-old speaking on the advantages of political parties:

A well, if you have a whole bunch of people with different ideas but have a government that's to be run, you are not going to get much accomplished, but if you put them together in a group, and then they pool their assets and ideas, then they have enough power to do something about what they want, than everybody just talking about what they want.

Now this is by no means an extraordinary statement;

the ordinary citizen would make it. And yet its very or-dinariness may conceal from us that an important conceptual advance has taken place. She is telling us that parties are both efficient and potent in that they are able to unify otherwise disparate political voices: ideas in unison can be powerful, as they are not when voiced separately.

For reasons that are still obscure, at least to me, the degree of achievement of hypothetico-deductive reasoning that Piaget and other cognitive theorists have demonstrated to be involved in advance modes of reasoning in relation to scientific problems seems to be far less widespread in the social and philosophical reasoning of adolescents. When this degree of achievement occurs, it seems to take place much later in the child's development. The kind of cognitive operations that many children can perform at the ages of thirteen to fifteen when confronted with the mathematical and scientific problems seem to elude the grasp of all but the most exceptional youngsters when they confront problems of equivalent difficulty in the realm of social and humanistic ideas, and even among that exceptional group the level is not achieved until the age of eighteen.

Some Conclusions for Teaching

To return to the question we began from: Can the teacher of adolescents learn something from these findings? Can they improve the way we teach social and humanistic subjects?

In the course of preparing this essay, I read a good deal of the technical literature on learning, on concept formation, on whatever seemed germane, giving especially close scrutiny to those writings—few in number, alas—that make some effort to apply what we have learned in the laboratory to the actualities of teaching the young. It is not an edifying experience. The will is there, the earnestness, even a certain bumptiousness. Yet almost invariably something seems to be lost in translation, and with the best will in the world, we seem generally unable to use empirical findings, even reliable ones, to provide useful counsel to the educator. I think it can be done, but it will not be done easily, and it will certainly not be done by those who, like myself, are not directly engaged in teaching primary and secondary school youngsters. For that reason, what follows is offered modestly, indeed timidly.

When I first began doing the studies reported in this paper, my next-door neighbor was a man who taught social studies at our local junior high school. I soon found myself trying out my findings on him, and although I don't know whether my observations improved his teaching, his observations on my findings certainly sharpened my research. One day I consulted him about the following problem. The interview schedule contained several questions on taxes through which we had hoped to explore the child's understanding of the larger social functions of taxation, for example, to provide incentives or deterrents for certain economic or social activities, or to redistribute income. The power to tax is the power to destroy, as we all have been told; when does the

youngster grasp this and equivalent ideas about the indirect functions of the taxing authority?

As soon as we began doing the interviews we became aware that we had overshot the mark, in that the child's understanding of taxes was far less developed than we had expected it to be. Some of the younger children among the ten and eleven-year-olds understood next to nothing, only that the tax was something collected at the store when you bought something or something that one's parents had to pay to someone. More commonly, children did understand that the function of taxes was to raise revenue for government, but few of them could tell us more than that, and only a handful understood much about the use of taxes as a means of channeling economic and other behavior. One day I mentioned to my neighbor the general nature of these findings and how surprised our research group had been to discover how little children understood about this topic. He thought for a moment, then said that he himself was not surprised. Taxation was a required subject matter in the ninth grade civics course he taught, and he had found that children had trouble with it, indeed so much so that he tended to give the topic short shrift, moving on to more engaging issues as soon as he had covered the fundamentals. But why do the children have trouble, I asked. He wasn't sure, but he suspected it was because they did not find taxes to be of any direct importance to them. It was seen as an "adult" concern, and as a consequence they were bored. Being bored, they would not learn the information. That was, I should say, a characteristic formulation by my neighbor; he tended strongly to a motivational theory of learning, holding that if the child's interest could be captured, learning would follow as the night the day. As for myself, I was then in the first flush of a newly acquired Piagetism and urged that perspective on him, suggesting that the youngsters were not cognitively ready for those materials and that their boredom and inability to learn reflected an underlying confusion due to conceptual immaturity.

I am now not at all sure that I was right and my neighbor wrong, or vice versa. I suspect that we were both partly right, in that we had touched upon the right dimensions: interest or motivation, cognitive capacity, and information (or knowledge). In this essay I have stressed cognitive growth almost to the exclusion of other determinants of learning. I think that stress legitimate given the general neglect of that outlook until recently. Yet it must be understood to represent only one element of a more complex process wherein capacity, knowledge, and motivation interact continuously. If the child is not ready cognitively to grasp a particular concept, he will be unsteady in his grasp of related information, and he will also fail to show much interest in the general topic; at the same time, a high level of interest may stimulate the acquisition of knowledge and enhance cognitive capacity. Within limits, the mind stretches to fulfill its intellectual needs. In that sense the approach represented here—cognitive developmental—does not represent anything new so far as education is concerned. To the contrary, if one reads Piaget's writings on education, for example, one is immediately struck by its closeness in spirit to the work of John Dewey.

WHAT, THEN, can this approach do for us? With respect to practical teaching it can alert us to the sources of specific difficulties the child is likely to experience in learning new information and ideas. Conversely, it may alert us to otherwise unrecognized intellectual opportunities the child is ready for and may teach us how to teach the child to grasp those opportunities. Let me offer an example. We found that at the outset of adolescence the youngster cannot adopt an as-if or conditional attitude to social or psychological phenomena. What is, is, now and forever. Bad people are bad and good people are good. If a law is passed, the child assumes it will stay in place eternally, and he has a hard time understanding that it can be overturned; he has an even harder time grasping that it might be amended, that one part of a law might be retained and another part rejected: it is all or nothing. One of the unrecognized achievements of the adolescent period is the acquisition of the concept of amendment, which is itself part of a larger movement of the mind away from static, either/or conceptions of events, structures, and persons. The more inclusive concept of *mutability*—for example, of persons changing or institutions in flux, is not easily grasped until middle to late adolescence.

Now it seems to be vitally important that a teacher charged with the instruction of young adolescents would do well to keep that knowledge in mind, particularly since he is charged with teaching dynamic processes—that is, processes involving change—relating to persons and societies. If he is teaching about "laws" he ought, at the least, remain aware that although he may have in mind modifiable statutes passed by a legislative body, the eleven-year-olds he is talking to have in mind something like the Ten Commandments. One might, in general, want to avoid certain topics as being too difficult conceptually; or one might try to develop methods of finessing those limitations, doing an end run around them; or one might want to develop methods of overcoming them. That choice is up to the teacher, and to the deviser of curricula.

Probably the most common problem the child experiences in dealing with social and humanistic materials is achieving the proper degree of abstractness; and the most common error the teacher makes comes from a failure to recognize the child's problem or to take account of it. As I suggested earlier in this essay, the child has a remarkable mimetic capacity, an ability to use the language of abstractness without genuine understanding. He may use a word like "majority" confidently, yet once we begin to query him we find he has only the vaguest idea of its meaning. Another such word is "government." Another is "election." By the former term, the ten- or eleven- or twelve-year-old child may very well have in mind the governor or the mayor or some other figure cloaked in the robes of authority. The child at the same age may not really know what it means to be "elected." He does not necessarily connect it with an electoral process but confuses it with being appointed, or perhaps even being anointed, that is, with having somehow assumed the cloak of authority.

Looking back, it is painfully clear that many of our first interviewees did not understand the meaning of these and other terms; nevertheless, it took us a long time to realize it. A youngster would half recognize a term and answer with some appropriate cliche or stark response, one sufficiently plausible to allow the conversation to continue. After we had examined several of these half-on, half-off responses, it would dawn on us that something was not quite right, and we would then discern that there was a concept present somewhat beyond the ken of the youngsters in question.

Why did we not see this immediately? Because the language of social and humanistic disciplines so largely overlaps common parlance, and its principles so largely overlap both common sense and common experience. That is not likely to happen in more technical disciplines. If I quiz a youngster on the properties of the isosceles triangle, his ignorance and confusion will be evident immediately; but if I quiz him about law and government, he may well be able to improvise sufficiently to conceal these states of mind. It is not that the youngster aims to deceive his interlocutor; rather, he may only be aiming to please, to give the answers that are wanted. It is the examiner who does the rest, filling in the gaps and elisions, imputing to the child a level of understanding that is largely in the mind of the beholder.

I might say here, a bit parenthetically, that there seems to be a general tendency among adults to inflate the understanding of the child in these areas. I have no firm idea why this is so, but I've seen this tendency in myself—it took me a long time to accept what the transcripts were clearly saying about the cognitive capacities of the children. I have since seen other adults, with few exceptions, make the same error, generally saying something along these lines: the findings may be true for this particular sample of children but would not be true for the children they knew, referring tacitly to their own children. But if they were to give the interview to their own children, as I did to mine, they would discover, as I did, that the intellectual gestalt that the child offers, via an overall aura of brightness, simply conceals the actual (lower) level of cognitive capacity. I suspect that classroom teachers, who deal with a variety of youngsters through the day, are less likely to misappraise cognitive level quite so often or to the usual degree; yet, I also suspect that the direction of error is similar, that they perceive in the child a more advanced grasp than is truly the case.

That may not be a bad thing, so far as education is concerned, to teach up rather than down in terms of cognitive level. It seems to me it may be helpful to introduce concepts just beyond the easy reach of the youngster. The cautions here are obvious: the concepts should not be too advanced nor should there be so many of them to cope with that the child feels overwhelmed. But keeping these cautions in mind, the teacher ought not to refrain from the use of, let us say, abstract ideas, notions of historical influence, or any of the other concepts or perspectives we have found to be difficult for children at the threshold of adolescence. In some cases, these are helpful in providing a framework—albeit a loose or hazy one—to help the child organize the more concrete ideas he is more comfortable with.

Take as an example the concept of democracy. If a youngster between the ages of ten and twelve is asked to give a definition of that word he will almost certainly be unable to do so satisfactorily. He may address the question in strictly emotive terms, pronouncing on its merits, or he may mix up specific aspects of democratic systems—elections of the legislature or the presidency—with the system itself. Yet, if you extend the conversation with the child, you may find that he has in his grasp most of the specific elements that make up democratic modes of government. It seems to me that the teacher would at this point do well to help the child connect what he can grasp—the more or less concrete aspects of government—to the more general concepts, such as democracy. Often the problem is less in the child than it is in the adult, because adults—almost reflexively—think abstractly when thinking about abstract matters, and when faced with incomprehension, tend to explain things by piling abstraction upon abstraction.

THERE IS another reason why we may want to teach concepts the child is not quite prepared to grasp fully—when they embody values we deem vital. Many American youngsters at this age will, when prompted, use such phrases as "freedom of speech" or "freedom of religion" or—in a few cases—"Bill of Rights." Further discussion reveals that their understanding is incomplete or incorrect in important ways. They are certainly unable to grasp these ideas as abstractions. Yet these concepts are by no means empty of meaning to them. The child may well have an idea of First Amendment rights that is overblown or absurd; he may, for example, think that it means an utterly untrammeled tolerance for freedom of expression; but what is more important is that he has grasped, in however inchoate a fashion, the kernel of the idea of rights, and in time that idea will be placed in context, given resonance, qualified, and so on. What is more important is that some of the American reverence for "rights" has been communicated to the child.

Much the same can be said for the democratic rituals that the child is exposed to as part of his schooling. In trying to discuss the electoral process, some of our children adverted to the elections for student council or class president or most popular boy or girl that they had experienced. It was clear enough that the younger ones had only the dimmest notion of the connections, if any, between those processes and the electoral politics they learned about in the mass media. It is tempting to dismiss those exercises, precisely because they seem to be so hollow, so absent of genuine understanding. But talking to so many dozens of adolescent children myself and reading so many hundreds of their interviews has persuaded me that these presumably empty rituals do have an important socializing effect in habituating the child to the practices of democratic politics.

Diet and Schoolchildren

*Like medical doctors, educators have been slow to realize how
often there is a direct relationship between the kinds of food kids consume
today and their behavior and academic achievement.*

Fred L. Phlegar and Barbara Phlegar

*"Let thy food be thy medicine
and thy medicine be thy food."*
— Hippocrates

Recently a Radford University professor said to us, "We have taken our son off sugar-coated cereals. He is much calmer now and is getting along much better in school."

Did this professor know what he was talking about? If so, how many of our young people are adversely affected by eating popular, highly processed foods? How many students are creating problems for themselves and their teachers, school administrators, and parents?

Although definitive studies are still scarce, suspicion is aroused by cases like the following:

In San Jose, California, a mother reported that one of her foster children became aggressive and hostile after she stopped her home cooking and started using bakery products. Then other foster children in her home started having the same behavior problems. One had to be put on tranquilizers. After she learned about the possible effects of some foods on behavior, this foster mother adjusted the diets of all of her children. She reports that the changes were "unbelievable." All the children became much more serene and made better grades in school.

Hugh W. S. Powers, Jr., a physician in Dallas, Texas, has adjusted the diets of many students with a significant success

P.M. McCall '79

rate. One 16-year-old boy had emotional problems and little energy; he was failing some of his classes. Seven months after he was given a special diet he was doing very well in school.[1]

One of our learning-disabled 15-year-olds was so hyperactive he was constantly moving, pecking, drumming his fingers, and annoying other students. After we discussed the problem with him and his parents, his diet was adjusted. He has now calmed down, his attention span has increased, and he is achieving more academically.

What foods and substances influence behavior? The list is long — and loaded with commonly used items. Unfortunately, individual reactions to these substances vary greatly, so that it is impossible to

establish a forbidden list. For most young people the effects are generally negligible and are tolerated without much trouble. However, these same foods and substances may be devastating for others.

One couple reported a daughter with constant physical problems, including infected ears. A son was hysterical and destructive. The daughter's problem was milk; the son's was wheat. After dietary adjustments, the mother reported a happy home and regarded the change as miraculous.

Sugar, milk, eggs, corn, wheat, citrus products, beef, pork, caffeine, and additives (in the form of flavorings, coloring, preservatives, and stabilizers) are on the list of troublemakers. William G. Crook, a physician in Jackson, Tennessee, states that he has treated over 160 new hyperactive patients by adjusting diet. When certain foods are eliminated, most patients show significant improvement — usually within one week. He says, "I know, beyond any shadow of a doubt, based on what parents of my patients tell me, that many, and perhaps most, hyperactive children can be helped by changing their diets."

Dr. Crook also believes that as many as 50% to 75% of the population suffer from food allergies and that most of them don't know it. Common symptoms in children are headaches, abdominal pains, runny noses, fatigue, bed-wetting, and hyperactivity. Food-related allergies also affect the nervous system, causing aggressiveness, temper tantrums, depression, and poor coordination, Dr. Crook reports.

One of Dr. Crook's patients was thought to be mentally retarded at the age of 3. Now he is a normal teenager and is getting good grades in school. His problem was chocolate. One candy bar caused

FRED L. PHLEGAR (Radford Virginia Chapter) is chairman, Secondary Education Department, Radford University, Va. BARBARA PHLEGAR (Radford Virginia Chapter) teaches learning-disabled children in the Radford City Schools.

serious effects for two days. He became jittery and nervous and could not concentrate.[2]

Benjamin Feingold, a physician at Kaiser Permanente in San Francisco, believes that dramatic changes can be made in student behavior and achievement through diet. When synthetic food coloring and flavoring are eliminated from patients' diets, he says, remarkable personality and behavioral changes occur. Hyperactive children become calmer and more responsive, have a longer attention span, and are better able to cope with their environment. These changes are followed by an improvement in scholastic achievement. Drugs are not needed to cure these students.[3]

In March 1976 the 2,000 delegates to the New York State United Teachers Association (NYSUT) thought so much of Dr. Feingold's theory that they passed a resolution ending as follows:

Resolved, that NYSUT go on record in opposition to the use of any artificial food coloring or food flavoring that contributes to hyperkinesis; and further be it

Resolved, that NYSUT bring all possible and necessary pressure to bear on food processing and food distributing companies (including the sponsorship of legislation) to cease and desist from the use of any artificial food colorings and food flavorings that have been shown to contribute to hyperkinesis; and further be it

Resolved, that all NYSUT members be encouraged to refrain from purchasing and/or use of food products that contain artificial food colorings or artificial food flavorings that have been shown to contribute to hyperkinesis.[4]

Barbara Reed, chief probation officer of the Municipal Court of Cuyahoga Falls, Ohio, discovered that young offenders consumed great quantities of sugar, soft drinks, and starch. She recommended sugar-free, low-starch, no-junk-food diets. Those who followed her recommendations were never back in court. One judge was so amazed at the changes in these offenders that he began to order defendants to eat nutritional diets.[5]

Leonard J. Hippchen, a professor at Virginia Commonwealth University, reports biochemical research showing that the brain is affected by molecular substances that are normally there. The optimum amounts differ from person to person. Abnormal levels can lead to a variety of pathological thought and behavior patterns. For example, a student with a vitamin deficiency, a dependency disease, can become violent.

Hippchen also found a significant relationship between hypoglycemia (low blood sugar) and criminal behavior. Studying juvenile delinquents, he found that most of them suffered from hypoglycemia. They were arrested for disorderly conduct, assault and battery, attempted suicide and homicide, cruelty, embezzlement, larceny, and arson. These delinquents were former hyperactive students who were too restless to learn. They were behavior problems in school and at home. They grew up without a salable skill. Many became failures, truants, dropouts, and, finally, criminals.[6]

The above discussion should, we think, persuade educators to do something about the diet of hyperactive students. Many of these students end up in the principal's office, in alternative schools, in special education classes, or in jail. However, if more evidence is needed, then our discussion should include what is most important in many schools (whether educators admit it or not) — athletics.

At the University of Montreal, the Department of Nutrition and Dietetics conducted a year-long experiment with an amateur hockey team. The team was divided into two groups. One group was free to eat candy and chocolate bars. The second group was to eat sugar-free foods. The sugar eaters' play deteriorated as more and more sugar and sugar-related products were consumed. This group had weakened metabolism. Its members were physically inferior to those in the sugar-free group. Concentration, resistance to illness, and overall ability decreased, even with small amounts of sugar. The sugar-free group's performance improved as the year progressed.[7]

Some classroom teachers give candy as a reward for good behavior or correct responses to questions. The device may be counterproductive. Fortunately, some teachers are aware of what happens when students eat lots of candy. In Roanoke, Virginia, an attempt was made in 1976 to move Halloween from Saturday night back to Friday night so that students would have two days to get the sugar out of their systems. One council member who is also a teacher observed that the candy in the children's bloodstream made them uncontrollable in the classroom.[8]

Alan C. Levin, director of the New York Institute for Child Development, says that his office was chaotic the day after Halloween. His patients, who were hyperactive and learning disabled, could not participate in the therapy sessions after they had eaten so much candy. Their attention spans were limited; they were almost unmanageable.[9]

Nearly all surveys of problems in education, including those made by Phi Delta Kappa, list student discipline as number one. Motivation is usually number two. Both of these problems have a direct bearing upon scholastic achievement. But poor discipline and bad motivation are only symptoms of a deeper malaise. It will do little good to treat the symptoms alone. We use conferences, detention, corporal punishment, and suspension to help the student conform. Sometimes counselors and school psychologists help find academic, psychological, and/or sociological causes. Referrals are then made to physicians — and students end up on tranquilizers.

For some of these students, the cause of disruptive behavior is the food they are eating. If we changed their diets, their behavior and scholastic achievement should improve. Does this mean that most of the students who are referred to the principal should have their diets checked?

We believe it does. All students and their parents should be made aware of the importance of foods for physical and mental health. Special attention should be given to students in special education, to behavior problems, and to those students with physical problems, especially allergies. Furthermore, it should be emphasized that it is the students' and parents' responsibilities to do something about changing the diet. Psychologically, it is much better for students to take responsibility for their own actions and their own health.

Interestingly enough, typical school lunch menus contribute to poor nutrition. The usual fare in school cafeterias is as follows: devitalized white bread with additives; polished white rice; canned sweetened fruits; chocolate milk; hot dogs and luncheon meats loaded with nitrates, nitrites, and artificial colors; artificially flavored fruit punches; chemically made ice cream; instant foods, such as potatoes; and prepared frozen and canned foods preserved and doctored with additives.

Some school systems and state education authorities have made changes in the foods served in lunch programs and in vending machines. On 13 November 1975, for example, the West Virginia Board of Education passed a resolution prohibiting the sale of candy, soft drinks, chewing gum, and flavored ice bars in the public schools of the state.[10]

In Denver, Colorado, school lunches include freshly baked breads, fresh produce, and meat entrees low in fat. Junk foods are not available. A la carte alternatives include vegetarian plates. The program includes inservice training for food service employees, nutrition education, and a student advisory council.[11]

In Fulton County, Georgia, under the direction of Sara Sloan, the food program includes inservice training for employees.

Elementary schools conduct weekly mini-classes on nutrition. The lunch programs include freshly prepared foods free of additives and sugar. They are also low in cholesterol. Thirty of the 79 county schools now offer lunches prepared from natural foods.[12] Reportedly, students who eat these lunches regularly are absent less often than other students. The coaches report increased stamina and endurance among their athletes.

At Helix High School, in La Mesa, California, students on a similar luncheon regimen excelled in athletics and won more trophies and scholarships than before. Insurance rates were lowered because the students had fewer accidents.

In Montreal, Canada, the school council has banned the sale of junk foods in vending machines in all the schools. The school lunches are prepared "from scratch" and include freshly prepared baked goods.[13]

The Milwaukee Public Schools have improved the foods they serve. Thomas J. Farley, food technologist and director of food services there, makes several worthwhile points about the program. First, in January 1977 the Board of Directors banned all foods and beverages of any kind except school lunches between the hours of 8 a.m. and 3:30 p.m. The Type A lunch was effectively upgraded by tailoring menus to the students' tastes. Students were involved in workshops for a year, helping to work out procedures and menus. Good Type A lunches are essential if junk foods are to be eliminated.

Students in Milwaukee serve on taste test panels, participate in menu planning, and serve on committees that write menus. Only one meal a day is served in all 160 Milwaukee schools. There are no à la carte menus, no vending machines, and no alternative menus. No bread, rolls, muffins, cakes, or cookies have been purchased for over 16 years. Everything comes fresh from the system's own ovens at half the cost of purchased products.[14]

There are many reasons why it will be difficult for all school systems to do much about the foods they serve, and about student eating habits. First, there are the multi-billion-dollar food-packing companies, soft drink corporations, and vending machine operators. They don't want the eating habits of students changed. As a rule, profits are greatest where nutritional values are least. These corporations have the resources to advertise, publish propaganda, and lobby at both state and national levels. Furthermore, they contribute money to certain departments in large universities, so that research will be done to support their position.

Second, there are huge profits in these products for the schools themselves. Many districts profit from their lunch programs, and they profit especially from the vending machines. So it is the administrators who clamor for carbonated drinks, peanuts, potato chips, chewing gum, candies, and new junk foods. In West Virginia school administrators opposed the ruling that eliminated junk food in their schools. No doubt the profits are used for a variety of good causes. In 1974-75 over $1.4 million worth of candy was sold in the junior and senior high schools of Los Angeles. When dentists expressed a concern about cavities, the sale of candy was defended by school officials because the profits were needed to buy band uniforms.[15]

A third reason why it will be difficult to change eating habits is that parents often work outside the home and are busy with outside activities. Packaged and processed foods save time. Fast-food restaurants are also popular with busy people. Most of these restaurant foods contain preservatives, flavorings, food colors, and stabilizers. Many frozen foods contain large quantities of chemical additives. Ice cream, in most cases, is a chemical mixture. Too much candy, sugar, and salt and too many colas and snacks are consumed. If the family eats out, the chances are that they will patronize a fast-food restaurant. But these foods are as bad as or worse than the convenience foods purchased in grocery stores.

Fourth, most people do not believe that products that contain sugar, caffeine, additives, salt, corn, and wheat can do much damage. Moreover, they say, "What if they do? We want to enjoy what we eat. We eat foods because they taste good, not because they are good for us. We are used to nice packages of processed foods that have been sugared and colored." Even baby foods have added sugar. It is no wonder that our tastes and addictions begin early.

Finally, the medical profession itself does not understand or support the primary thesis that behavior can be changed by changing the diet. Orthomolecular physicians agree wholeheartedly, but the hypotheses we have offered here are not well accepted by the medical establishment in general.

Orthomolecular medicine is basically the treatment and the prevention of disease by the adjustment of the natural constituents of our bodies. It emphasizes these natural substances in the body and not the chemicals and drugs that are foreign to us.

The term "orthomolecular" was first used by Linus Pauling in 1968. It means "right molecule." Orthomolecular physicians attempt to create the optimum molecular environment for the cells of the body, which helps prevent disease. The ideal goal of medicine should be disease prevention. Curative treatment is an admission of failure. Yet the medical establishment seems to be more interested in treating symptoms than in dealing with the causes of disease.[16]

Clinical nutrition is not even taught in most medical schools. In fact, one survey found that the typical physician knew no more about nutrition than his receptionist. However, when she had a weight problem she knew more about nutrition than he did.

Orthomolecular physicians and psychiatrists have successfully treated patients with most of the degenerative diseases by using changes in nutrition. Last fall the CBS 60 Minutes program featured the Longevity Center in Santa Monica, California, directed by Nathan Pritikin. It successfully treats very serious heart patients with diet, vitamin and mineral supplements, and exercise.[17]

Orthomolecular doctors have also helped many students who are hyperactive, hostile, learning disabled, and schizophrenic. Students with dyslexia, hyperkinesis, phobias, obsessions, hallucinations, delusions, time distortions, and gross perceptual distortions also have been helped.

What are the implications of this for educators? First, students, teachers, administrators, and parents need to be educated about nutrition and about the relationships that exist between nutrition and physical and mental health. The very popular maxim, "You are what you eat," is often quoted in articles about natural foods. Yet few people select their foods rationally. Teaching people what to eat while they are children should make a powerful impact upon their health. Cooperation from the media and food industry would be beneficial, of course. Without it, successful nutrition education will be very difficult. But we must do what we can.

Nutrition minicourses should be conducted in the schools. Students need to have regular input into the menu planning for the cafeteria. The formation of nutrition clubs in the schools can foster further growth in wholesome eating habits. These clubs can sponsor communitywide nutrition workshops to educate parents and the general public.

Second, state legislatures and state boards of education need to pass laws and adopt policies that will restrict the distribution of soft drinks and junk foods in schools. Education lobbies that have been regarded as hypocritical when they say they seek more money "because children need good schools" might regain some credibility by sponsoring such laws and policies.

4. CHILDHOOD

Third, since educators are concerned about the health and behavior of all students, they should change the foods that are available in school. More juices, whole grain products, raw fruits, and raw vegetables should be served. Sugar, soft drinks, candy, chocolate milk, processed convenience foods, prepared frozen and canned foods, flavored ice bars, and vending machines for dispensing junk foods should *not* be used in the schools. Freshly prepared foods and baked goods should be served in the cafeterias. Preparing food "from scratch" tends to keep them additive free and low in cholesterol. If vending machines are used, they should dispense snacks such as nuts, seeds, and fruit juices.

Fourth, all students being considered for special education should have a physical examination from an orthomolecular physician, or at least from a physician who is aware of the values expressed and the diagnostic procedures used by orthomolecular-trained physicians.

Finally, the 2% to 5% of the students who are chronic discipline problems and students who continuously fail school subjects should be checked by an orthomolecular physician or a physician using the orthomolecular approach. Many students with discipline problems will also have scholastic problems, and they may be the same ones who are being considered for special education.

---

1. Hugh W. S. Powers, "Dietary Measures to Improve Behavior and Achievement," *Academic Therapy*, Winter 1973-74.

2. William G. Crook, "Adverse Reactions to Food Can Cause Hyperkinesis," 12 December 1977 letter to the editor of the *American Journal of Diseases of Children*.

3. Benjamin F. Feingold, *Why Your Child Is Hyperactive* (New York: Random House, 1975).

4. New York State United Teachers Association, "Hyperkinesis," Resolution 89, March 1976.

5. Barbara Reed (as cited by Timothy Schellhardt), "Can Chocolate Turn You into a Criminal? Some Experts Say So," *Wall Street Journal*, 2 June 1977.

6. Leonard J. Hippchen, "Contributions of Biochemical Research to Criminological Theory," Department of Administration of Justice and Public Safety, Virginia Commonwealth University in 31 January 1978 letter.

7. Robert Rodale, "Winning by Eating Right," *Prevention*, October 1977, pp. 25-30.

8. Fran Coumbs, "County's Halloween Scheduled Saturday," *Roanoke Times and World-News*, 28 October 1976.

9. Alan C. Levin, "Kid Food — Key to Problem Behavior," *Woman's Day*, 23 August 1977.

10. Faith Gravenmier, Hearings before the Subcommittee on Elementary and Secondary Education, U.S. House of Representatives, Washington, D.C., August 1976.

11. Fran Smith, "School Lunch: Local Activists Make Headway," *Nutrition Action*, October 1977, pp. 6-8.

12. Sara Sloan, *A Guide for Nutra-Lunches and Natural Foods* (Atlanta: Fulton County Schools Food Service Program, 1977).

13. Jane Kinderlehrer, "A Tale of Two Cities," *Prevention*, February 1977, pp. 60-63.

14. Personal communication.

15. "Candy Profits Buy Band Uniforms for L.A. Kids," *National Health Federation Bulletin*, April 1976, pp. 16, 17.

16. Linus Pauling, "On the Orthomolecular Environment of the Mind: Orthomolecular Medicine," in *A Physician's Handbook on Orthomolecular Medicine* (New York: Pergamon Press, 1977).

17. Nathan Pritikin, *Pritikin Diet Book* (New York: Grosset and Dunlap, 1979).

THE MISMATCH BETWEEN SCHOOL AND CHILDREN'S MINDS

Because neither theorists nor teachers understand children's minds, many students learn to hate school.

MARGARET DONALDSON

Margaret Donaldson, professor of psychology at the University of Edinburgh, has worked at Piaget's Research Institute in Geneva and with Jerome Bruner at Oxford. Her book, Children's Minds, *was published by W.W. Norton.*

Visitors to any elementary school would notice that most children in the kindergarten and first-grade classrooms are excited, happy, and eager to learn. But if they were to continue their visit to classrooms of the higher grades, they would find many who are unhappy, unresponsive and bored. Yet from infancy all normal human beings show signs of a keen desire to learn—a desire that does not appear to depend on any reward apart from the satisfaction of achieving competence and control. This desire is still strong in most children when they enter school. How is it that something that starts off so well regularly ends up so badly? Why do many children learn to hate school?

The answer cannot be that most children are stupid after the age of six, nor can it be that teachers enjoy making children miserable. Recent research into the nature of children's language and thinking can help us to see what goes wrong.

It is now clear that we have tended both to underestimate children's competence as thinkers and to overestimate their understanding of language.

The underestimations are in large measure a result of the theories of the most influential of all students of child development, Jean Piaget. From his experiments with young children he concluded that until the age of about seven, though competent in practical skills, children are extremely limited thinkers.

The overestimation of children's understanding of language is, in part, a result of the theories of linguist Noam Chomsky. In the 1960s Chomsky caused a wave of excitement among psychologists by drawing attention to the significance of one simple fact: Children who are only two or three years old can utter complicated sentences *that they have never heard before.*

Since these sentences generally conform to the rules of syntax, the children must, in some sense, know them. And even sentences that are not fully correct by adult standards still show that rules of some kind are at work in their construction. In fact the errors frequently reveal rules, as when "bringed" is used instead of "brought." We can be fairly sure that children who say "bringed" have not heard adults say it. They must have generated the form for themselves by applying the rule for forming past tenses in weak verbs in English.

The implications of these facts presented psychologists with a highly challenging question: How is it possible for a young child to master such a complex system of rules? There seemed to be only two possibilities: The child either has remarkable skills as a thinker, or some very special skills as a language learner. Chomsky argued for the second of these explanations. He proposed that human beings are endowed with a highly specialized faculty for learning language, which he called a language-acquisition device. This idea enjoyed widespread popularity for a while, and at least part of the reason was that the other explanation seemed implausible. There was evidence around—weighty, respectable evidence obtained by careful systematic study and experiment—that appeared to imply that the young child is not much of a thinker.

Yet there was other evidence, freely available but largely neglected, that pointed to a different conclusion. Anyone who talks with young children seriously and attentively knows that they say a great many thoughtful and seemingly intelligent things. The curious thing is that while so much attention was being paid to the grammatical sophistication of children's speech, very little attention was being paid to its meaning.

The following examples are remarks made by very young children (all younger than five, and some barely three years old) as they were listening to stories:

"The nails will tore his trousers." (A prediction about what will happen to a character who is putting nails in his pocket. Uttered in tones of concern.)

"You can't sew a turnip." (A confusion of "sew" and "sow." Uttered with scorn.)

"He's got sharp teeth and sharp claws. He must be a wild cat."

These examples are typical. Yet they are remarkable for the awareness of possibility and impossibility, of contingency and necessity revealed. They establish beyond doubt a well-developed ability to make sense of a highly complex world. And the impression of good sense gleaned from these isolated re-

Reprinted from *Human Nature*, March 1979. Reprinted by permission of A.P. Watt, Ltd., England.

marks becomes even greater when we are aware of the context in which they were made.

The problem is to reconcile these observations with experimental evidence that seems to show that children of this age are quite limited in their ability to deal with possibility, to reason inferentially, and to think intelligently in general. Although the evidence comes from diverse sources, the source that has been the most influential over the past few decades is the work of Piaget and his colleagues in Geneva. The reason for Piaget's great influence is not only his ingenious studies of children, but also the fact that he has woven his findings into a theory of great internal consistency and beauty, so that the mind is dazzled.

Once adopted, a theory tends to make us disregard evidence that conflicts with it. This is true even of a theory that is not very impressive, let alone one like Piaget's. But the most entrenched theory can be dislodged in the face of overwhelming evidence that it is wrong.

In the case of our theories about children's thinking, such evidence has been mounting for some time. Recent research, much of it concerned with the comprehension of language, throws new light on the reasons children can seem so limited as thinkers when they are tackling Piaget's tasks, yet so skilled when we watch them and listen to them in their spontaneous behavior.

In the early days after Chomsky's revolution in the field of linguistics, almost all those who were doing research on child language concentrated on studies of what children said. The reason was simply that the evidence needed in order to work out the rules of grammar that the children in some sense knew and used was evidence about language production. As long as this was the main concern, the question of what children could understand was largely ignored. But over the past few years there has been a marked shift of interest from syntax to semantics, and studies of comprehension have come into their own.

My own interest in language comprehension began in 1968 with a study of the ways in which children interpret the words "less" and "more." For this research we built two large cardboard apple trees, each equipped with six hooks on which beautiful red apples could be hung. Putting different numbers of apples on each tree, we asked which tree had more apples, which less. Then the children were asked to put more (or less) on one tree than on the other. The results surprised us. We had thought it likely that they would understand "more" better than they understood "less." What we found was that the two words appeared to be treated as synonyms. No matter which word we used, we tended to get the same responses—and they were the responses that were correct for "more."

This result was provocative in many ways, and it led to a series of further studies. One of these, by David Palermo of Pennsylvania State University, replicated the original results; but others, including research by Susan Carey of M.I.T., used different methods and cast doubt on the interpretation of these first findings.

My own view now is that we were asking the wrong question. Instead of asking how the children understood the words "less" and "more," we should have been looking at their interpretation of the utterances in which these words were used. I was led to see this by the results of a series of further studies, the first of which was still planned as an investigation of the development of word meanings. I wanted to study the children's understanding of words like "all" and "some." Naïvely, as it now seems to me, I hoped to discover the meanings of these words for the children by inserting them in statements like "All the doors are shut" or "All the cars are in the garages," and presenting the statements along with objects that rendered them true or false. What I discovered was that the children seemed to have no single meaning for "all." They judged all the doors to be shut if there was no door open, but often they judged all the cars to be in the garages when one car was sitting in full view outside. In the latter case the question they seemed to be considering was not where the cars were but whether all the garages were occupied. So we tried another configuration. We used two rows of garages, one row having four and the other six; and two rows of cars, one with four and one with five. In this study we again looked at the interpretation of sentences with the word "more" in them.

We were going to ask the children to make a comparison, and we wanted to make it as easy as possible for them, so we arranged the cars one above another on two shelves, with the extra car in one row always projecting on the right-hand side.

When the two rows of cars were presented alone, without garages, most of the children said there were more cars in the row of five than in the row of four. However, we also presented the cars enclosed in garages: four cars in the row of four garages, and five cars in the row of six garages (so that one garage was empty). About one third of the children now changed their judgments, saying there were more cars in the row of four. Again the question the children appeared to be answering was whether all the garages were filled: This was the thing that seemed to stand out, and no matter what we asked, this was the question they answered. Clearly "fullness" was what they expected to be asked about.

An important feature of this last experiment was that the task the children were given was, in its logical structure, the same as a Piagetian conservation test. Of all the tests that Piaget devised to reveal the nature of children's thinking in the preschool and early school years, the conservation tests are probably the best known. There are many such tests—tests of conservation of number, weight, volume, and length—but they all make use of the same key elements. Conservation of number will serve as an example.

First, the experimenter shows the child two rows of objects, equal in number and laid out opposite one another in one-to-one correspondence. The child is asked whether there is the same number in the two rows. Unless the child agrees that this is so, the test cannot proceed.

In the next step the experimenter destroys the perceptual equivalence of the two rows, by moving the objects in one row closer together, for instance. Usually this action is accompanied by a remark like "Now watch what I do," which ensures that the child is paying attention.

Once the new configuration is in place, the original question is repeated, usually in the same words. Children who continue to say that the two rows are equal are said to conserve and are called conservers. If they claim that one row now has more objects than the other, they are not conserving and are called nonconservers. According to Piaget, a child's ability or inability to conserve is an indication of his or her stage of mental development.

Clearly the task involving two rows of cars, with and without enclosing garages, has the structure of a conservation task, although it is an unorthodox one. First the child is asked a question that calls for a comparison, then something irrelevant to the meaning of the words in the question is changed, then the original question is asked again.

Some may say that many of the children in our study were not conserving. But *what* were they not conserving? The most plausible and generally applicable notion seems to be that what the children were failing to conserve was their interpretation of the words of the experimenter. The same question was put to them twice, but *in a different context*. Adults would have discounted the shift in context. They would have known that in this kind of formal task they were meant to discount it and to base their replies on the meaning of the words. But perhaps the children did not know they were meant to do this, or perhaps they could not do it because the context was too powerful for them. In either event, it looked as though some nonlinguistic feature was strong enough to cause a shift in interpretation of what, for an adult, was a repetition of the same question.

At this stage my attention was drawn to the possibility that part of the reason for the shift in interpretation had to do not with the physical context of the experiment, like fullness of garages or length of rows, but with what the children thought was the intention underlying the experimenter's behavior. I owe this insight to James McGarrigle, who devised an ingenious experiment to test it.

The experiment made use of a number-conservation task and a small teddy bear called Naughty Teddy. The task proceeded in the usual way up to the point where the child agreed that the number in the two rows was the same. But before the experimenter went on to the next stage, Naughty Teddy would emerge from hiding, swoop over one row, and disarrange it. Once the one-to-one correspondence had been destroyed the child was invited to help put Naughty Teddy back in his box (an invitation that was usually accepted with glee) and the questioning was resumed: "Now, where were we? Ah yes, is the number in this row the same as the number in this row?" and so on. What happened was that many more children between the ages of four and six conserved number in the Naughty Teddy version of the task than in the traditional version (50 out of 80, compared with 13 out of 80).

Piaget's account of the reasons for failure cannot deal with this finding. His explanation makes use of several related arguments, putting the emphasis now here, now there. But at the heart of them all is the notion that children fail to conserve because they cannot sufficiently "decenter," that is, they are not flexible about shifting their point of view. Typically nonconservers are held to "center," or concentrate attention, on a particular state or feature, failing to take account either of transformations between states or of other features of the object. They center on the fact that one row of objects is longer than the other and fail to notice that the latter is more dense. In general, they are believed to center on the present moment and to make judgments on the basis of how things *now* appear, with no relation to how they were a moment ago.

It is quite possible to fit these arguments to the finding that children will sometimes change their judgments about the numbers of cars in two rows after the addition of enclosing garages. We have only to say that children who do so "center on fullness." However, there seems to be no way to fit them to the findings of the Naughty Teddy study (and these findings have already been replicated twice, by Julie Dockrell of Stirling University and by Irene Neilson of the Glasgow College of Technology). Nothing in Piaget's theoretical account of conservation suggests that it should matter who changes the arrangement of the objects.

But the Naughty Teddy results do fit very well with the idea that nonconserving children fail to answer the experimenter's question in the same way on the second occasion because, for them, it is not the same question. It seems different because it is not sufficiently detached, or disembedded, from the context of what the child believes the experimenter wants.

So disembedding will explain more of the findings than decentering will. But this does not establish that the decentering argument is false. It is possible that the child has difficulty with both decentering *and* disembedding. We must look at other evidence to see whether children are as limited in their ability to decenter as Piaget would have us believe.

In Piaget's view, inability to decenter is a feature of young minds that shows itself in a wide variety of ways. Some of these have already been considered. Another, perhaps the most fundamental, is the inability to appreciate the relativity of one's own point of view in space and time. A simple example of this is the inability to understand that one's own view of an object is not the same as that of someone looking at it from another side.

In a famous experiment, Piaget established that children presented with a three-dimensional model of a group of mountains have great difficulty choosing a picture of how the model would look to a doll viewing it from another position. For the most part, young children given this task choose the picture that shows exactly what they themselves see. It seems, then, that they are notably lacking in mental flexibility, bound by the egocentric illusion that what they see is the world as it really is. If this were true, it would certainly have far-reaching implications for the ability to think and reason.

Recent research has called this conclusion into question. My own thinking on the subject has been influenced by the work of Martin Hughes. Hughes placed before a group of children a configuration of two walls intersecting to form a cross. At the end of one of the walls he placed a wooden doll, representing a policeman. The children were then given another wooden doll, representing a boy, and were asked to "hide the boy so that the policeman can't see him." (The policeman was not tall enough to look over the walls.)

The arrangement made it easy to tell whether the children were able to escape from the domination of their own point of view, and the results were clear. Even three year olds were highly competent at the task. They showed no sign of a tendency to hide the doll from themselves, as would have been predicted from Piaget's theory, and they showed every sign of understanding what the policeman would be able to see from where he stood. Even when there were two policemen, placed so that the only effective hiding place was one where the boy doll was clearly visible to the child, about 90 percent of the responses from three- and four-year-old children were correct.

The policeman task differs in many ways from Piaget's mountain task, but one is particularly significant in light of what we now know. In the policeman task there is an interplay of motives and intentions that is entirely comprehensible, even to a child of three. For this reason the task makes *human sense* to the children: They understand instantly what it is all about. The verbal instructions are so well supported by the context that no difficulties of disembedding arise. As soon as the doll is handed over, the children's faces light up, they smile, they latch on.

The mountain experiment on the other hand does not make immediate human sense in this way. There is no interplay of motives and intentions, no intelligible context. The task is as disembedded as the one given the American Indian who was asked to translate into his native tongue the sentence, "The white man shot six bears today." The Indian was baffled. "How can I do that?" he asked. "No white man could shoot six bears in one day."

Now we can reconcile the disparity between children's skills as thinkers in everyday situations and their limitations when confronted with formal tasks. Most formal tasks are geared to minds that are capable of a high degree of disembedding of thought and language—minds that are able to dispense with the support of human sense—and these tasks make demands of a quite special kind.

When we first learn to think and to use language, it is within situations where we have purposes and intentions and where we can recognize and understand similar purposes and intentions in others. These humanly meaningful contexts sustain our thinking.

Precisely how they do this is of the greatest theoretical interest, but it is still mysterious. One thing is clear: When thought and language are functioning smoothly in real-life contexts, we are normally aware of the ends to which our activity is directed but not of the mental means that are needed to get there. We do not stop to think about our thinking or about the words we are using.

A formal task interrupts the flow of life. It demands deliberation, mental awareness, and control. It is by definition a thing to be considered out of context. We must set our minds to it. We must accept the premises, respect the constraints, direct our thought. This activity is difficult and, in a sense, unnatural. But that does not mean it should be avoided or abandoned—only that it will not happen spontaneously. We must recognize this fact so that we do not label our children "stupid" or "backward" if at first they find it hard.

The ability to take a problem out of context and consider it in its own right is the product of long ages of a particular kind of culture. It is closely linked to the development of literacy because written language, unlike speech, is by its very nature disembedded. Speech is transient, elusive, entangled in happenings. A written page, or a clay tablet, is physically separate and permanent: You can take it with you and go back to it. It is scarcely possible to learn to handle written language without becoming aware of it as a system and as a tool of the mind.

Disembedded intellectual skills underlie all our mathematics, all our science, all our philosophy. It may be that we value them too highly in comparison with other human skills and qualities, but we are not at all likely to renounce them. We have come to depend on them. And as schooling progresses, the emphasis on them becomes harder to evade or postpone. The student who can solve problems, as problems, divorced from human sense, is the student who will succeed in the educational system. The better a student is at it, the more awards he or she will receive, and the better that student's self-image will be. But large numbers of students never achieve even a moderate level of competence in these skills and leave school with a sense of failure.

Seen in the context of human history, universal compulsory schooling is a new social enterprise, and it is a difficult one. We should not be surprised or ashamed if we do not yet know how to manage it well. At the same time, if we are going to persist in it, there is urgent need for us to learn to manage it better. We must not forget how grave a responsibility we assume when we conscript children for these long, demanding years of service. And when the outcome is not all that we would wish, we must not resort to blaming this on the shortcomings of the children. Since we impose the demands, it is up to us to find effective ways of helping children to meet them.

Many children hate school because it is a hateful thing to be forced to do something at which you fail over and over again. The older children get, the more they are aware that they are failing and that they are being written off as stupid. No wonder many of our children become disheartened and bored.

What are we to do about it? There is no simple formula, but there are a number of guiding principles.

The first takes us back to the topic of decentering. Although research has shown that children are better at this than Piaget claims, it is true that human beings of any age can find it hard. As adults we often fail to understand the child's point of view. We fail to understand what perplexes a child and why. In *Cider with Rosie*, Laurie Lee gives an account of his own first day at school: "What's the matter, Love? Didn't he like it at school, then?"

"They never gave me the present."

"Present? What present?"

"They said they'd give me a present."

"Well, now, I'm sure they didn't."

"They did! They said: 'You're Laurie Lee, aren't you? Well, you just sit there for the present.' I sat there all day but I never got it. I ain't going back there again."

The obvious way to look at the episode is to say that the child didn't understand the adult. But if we are to get better at helping children, it is more profitable to say that the adult failed to make the imaginative leap needed to understand the child. The story carries a profoundly important moral for all teachers and parents: The better you know something yourself, the greater the risk of not noticing that children find it bewildering.

When Jess Reid of the University of Edinburgh studied children who were learning to read, she found that some did not have the least idea of what reading was. They could not say how the postman knew where to deliver a letter. They did not understand the relationship between the sounds of speech and the marks that we make on paper, or that these marks are a means of communication.

It would help greatly if children told teachers when they felt perplexed. Many do not. But if they are explicitly encouraged to ask questions, they can often do so effectively, and the act of asking helps children become conscious of their own uncertainty.

It is also important to recognize how greatly the *process* of learning to read may influence the growth of the mind. Because print is permanent, it offers special opportunities for reflective thought, but they may not be taken if the reading child is not given time to pause. Once children gain some fluency as readers, we can help them notice what they are doing as they extend their skills and begin to grapple with possibilities of meaning; for it is the thoughtful consideration of possibility—the choice of one interpretation among others—that brings awareness and control.

One final principle is implicit in all that has been said: If we want to help children to succeed at school and to enjoy it, it is not enough to avoid openly calling them failures. We must respect them as thinkers and learners—even when they find school difficult.

If we respect them and let them know it, then the experience of learning within a structured environment may become for many more of our children an opening of new worlds, not a closing of prison bars.

For further information:

Bruner, J. S. "The Ontogenesis of Speech Acts." *Journal of Child Language*, Vol. 2, 1975, pp. 1-19.

Donaldson, Margaret. *Children's Minds*. W. W. Norton, 1979.

Grieve, R., R. Hoogenraad, and D. Murray. "On the Child's Use of Lexis and Syntax in Understanding Locative Instructions." *Cognition*, Vol. 5, 1977, pp. 235-250.

Lempers, J. D., E. R. Flavell, and J. H. Flavell. "The Development in Very Young Children of Tacit Knowledge Concerning Visual Perception." *Genetic Psychology Monographs*, Vol. 95, 1977, pp. 3-53.

Macnamara, J. "Cognitive Basis of Language Learning in Infants." *Psychological Review*, Vol. 79, 1972, pp. 1-13.

Olson, D. R. "Culture, Technology and Intellect." *The Nature of Intelligence*, edited by L. B. Resnick. Halstead Press, 1976.

THE MIND
OF THE PUZZLER

ROBERT J. STERNBERG
AND JANET E. DAVIDSON

Robert J. Sternberg, associate professor of psychology at Yale, was cited last year by the American Psychological Association for his "major theoretical contributions to our understanding of human intelligence and mental abilities." He is the editor of *The Handbook of Human Intelligence*, to be published soon by Cambridge University Press.

Janet E. Davidson is a research associate in the Psychology Department at Yale. She specializes in intelligence and problem-solving.

Before departing from San Francisco on a flight to New York recently, a colleague of ours picked out some reading to test his wits. A professor of some accomplishment, he expected to make short work of the problems in *Games for the Superintelligent*, *More Games for the Superintelligent*, and *The Mensa Genius Quiz Book*. By the time he crossed the Rocky Mountains, however, he had realized that he was neither a genius nor, as *The Genius Quiz Book* puts it, "a secret superbrain who doesn't even know it." By the time he crossed the Mississippi River, he knew that he wasn't "superintelligent," either.

More often than not, the puzzles stumped him. How could two men play five games of checkers and each win the same number of games without any ties? He couldn't figure it out. How could you plant a total of 10 trees in five rows of four trees each? He drew several diagrams, and none of them worked. But he couldn't put the books down.

Our colleague wasn't alone in his frustration. Mental puzzles, whose appeal must be limited to the relatively intelligent, have nevertheless been a staple of the publishing industry for years. Martin Gardner's mathematical puzzles, from the monthly column he used to write for *Scientific American*, have been collected in 10 different books, with total sales of more than half a million copies. *Solve It*, *Games for the Superintelligent*, and *More Games for the Superintelligent*, all by James Fixx, have together sold nearly one million copies.

Puzzles can certainly be fun, and great ego boosters for those who eventually get the right answers. According to James Fixx, many people use mental puzzles to "strengthen their thought processes" and to "tune up their minds." Others use them to test or measure their own intelligence. In fact, *More Games* and *The Mensa Genius Quiz Book* actually contain what are supposed to be short IQ tests.

Many of the problems in these books require flashes of insight or "leaps of logic" on the part of the solver, rather than prior knowledge or laborious computation. We wondered just how people approach such puzzles—which are commonly called insight problems—and whether they provide a valid measure of a person's intelligence. To answer these questions, we examined the literature on problem-solving, and then conducted a mini-experiment to measure the relationship between performance on insight problems and scores on standard intelligence tests.

On the basis of our research, we identified three types of intellectual processes that, separately or together, seem to be required in solving most insight problems: the ability to select and "encode" information—that is, to understand what information is relevant to solving the problem, and how it is relevant; the ability to combine different and seemingly unrelated bits of useful information; and the ability to compare the problem under consideration with problems previously encountered. For example, in solving the problem of the checker players, faulty encoding would lead one to assume that the two men were playing each other. Correctly combining the facts that there were no ties and that each player won the same number of games should lead one to conclude that they couldn't be playing each other.

Similarly, to plant 10 trees in five rows of four trees each, one must get away from the idea of making the five rows parallel. People who are accustomed to thinking in geometric terms will usually imagine several other kinds of patterns, until they hit on the correct one:

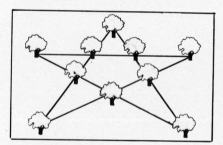

The literature on how people solve insight problems is meager, and includes almost no reports on research relating solution of these problems to intelligence. One of the few studies of this sort was done in 1965 by Norman Maier and Ronald Burke at the University of Michigan. Maier and Burke compared people's scores on a variety of aptitude tests with their skill at solving the "hat-rack problem." The problem calls on them to build a structure, sufficiently stable to support a man's overcoat, using only two long sticks and a C-clamp. The opening of the clamp is wide enough so that the two sticks can be inserted and held together securely when the clamp is tightened. Participants are placed in a small room and are asked to build a hat rack in the center of the room. The solution is shown below:

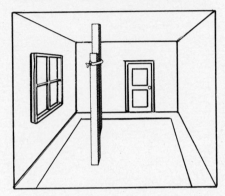

When the researchers compared people's ability to solve the hat-rack problem with their scores on the Scholastic Aptitude Test, the correlations were all trivial. In other words, whatever insight people needed to build the hat rack seemed to be unrelated to their scores on standardized intelligence tests. Burke and Maier concluded that the abilities needed to solve insight problems may be different from those required to solve problems of the kinds found on such tests. Their study is of limited value, however: They used only one problem, and scored the responses only in terms of "right" or "wrong."

We did find in the literature some theoretical basis for the lack of relationship between intelligence and performance on the hat-rack problem. Kjell Raaheim, a psychologist at the University of Bergen, in Norway, wrote in *Problem Solving and Intelligence* that "it is unreasonable to expect intelligence to be an important factor of success in solving tasks which are totally unfamiliar to the individual facing them." According to Raaheim, problems will best measure intelligence if they present a situation that is *intermediate* in its degree of familiarity to a problem-solver. Problems presenting situations that are either too familar or too unfamiliar will provide poorer measures of a person's intelligence.

In an ingenious set of experiments, Robert Weisberg and Joseph Alba, of Temple University, asked people to solve a set of insight problems. One was the familiar nine-dot problem, in which they were shown a three-by-three array of nine equally spaced dots and asked to connect the nine dots using four straight lines without lifting pencil from paper. The solution requires an approach similar to that used to plant the five rows of trees.

What is unique about Weisberg and Alba's study is that participants were actually given the insight they needed to solve the problem: They were told that it could be solved only by drawing the lines beyond the boundaries formed by the dots. Still, even after they were given the relevant insights, people in this study had considerable difficulty in solving the problem. Weisberg and Alba interpreted the results as suggesting that such problems may not really measure insight, but rather problem-specific prior knowledge. Our interpretation is a bit different. As we see it, subjects not only needed to know that they could draw the lines outside the boundaries; they also had to know how to combine what went outside the dots with what went inside. Performance on these insight problems therefore might not correlate with performance on intelligence-test problems.

Even though classic insight problems may not truly measure insight alone, we believed that problems could be found that do provide fairly accurate measures of insight, and that performance on such problems would be correlated with intelligence as it is typically measured by standardized tests.

To test this view, we compiled a set of 12 insight problems from a number of popular books. The problems vary in difficulty, in trickiness, and in the number of possible approaches that can be taken to reach a solution.

We recruited 30 people from the New Haven area by means of a newspaper advertisement that invited them to take part in a problem-solving experiment at Yale. Though not selected by scientific criteria, our small sample—19 men and 11 women—represented a fairly typical cross-section of urban residents, with a wide range of ages, occupations, and educational backgrounds. None were connected with Yale.

First, we gave them a standard IQ test (the Henmon-Nelson Test of Mental Ability), including questions of vocabulary, math, and reasoning. None of the problems were quite like our insight problems. A typical reasoning problem, for example, might require the person to solve an analogy such as: CAR is to GASOLINE as HUMAN is to (a. OIL b. ENERGY c. FOOD d. FUEL); or a number series such as: 3, 7, 12, 18, __? (a. 24 b. 25 c. 26 d. 27). The IQ test problems were multiple-choice, whereas the insight problems we used required people to generate their own answers.

The average IQ score of our sample on this test was 112, 12 points above the national average. (Elevated average IQs are typical in such experiments, since those who volunteer for studies on problem-solving are likely to be of above-average intelligence. People with very low IQs may not read newspapers, and probably wouldn't volunteer for experiments on problem-solving even if they do.)

Second, we gave our subjects a deductive-reasoning test on nonsense syllogisms, such as "All trees are fish. All fish are horses. Therefore, all trees are horses. Please indicate whether the conclusion is logically valid or not." (This one is.) Third, in a test of inductive reasoning, we presented our subjects with five sets of letters (for example, NOPQ, DEFL, ABCD, HIJK, UVWX) and asked them to choose the set that was based on a rule different from the rule used as a basis for the other four sets.

We included these two specific tests, as well as the more general IQ test, to judge the accuracy of a prediction we had made: If our problems genuinely measured insight, they should be more highly correlated with the inductive test, which requires one to go beyond the information given, than with the deductive test, which merely requires one to analyze the given information and draw the proper conclusion. Normal arithmetic or logic problems, for example, require primarily deductive rather than inductive reasoning skills.

Our subjects found the insight problems fun but sometimes frustrating, since the items varied considerably in difficulty. The easiest item, answered correctly by 73 percent of our sample, was this:

"Next week I am going to have

lunch with my friend, visit the new art gallery, go to the Social Security office, and have my teeth checked at the dentist's. My friend cannot meet me on Wednesday; the Social Security office is closed weekends; the art gallery is closed Tuesday, Thursday, and weekends; and the dentist has office hours only on Tuesday, Friday, and Saturday. What day can I do everything I have planned?" Reaching the answer (Friday) is easy because one can simply check off which days don't work.

The hardest item, answered correctly by only 7 percent of our subjects, was:

"A bottle of wine cost $10. The wine was worth $9 more than the bottle. How much was the bottle worth?" People probably had a hard time coming up with the answer (50 cents) because they misunderstood the word 'more.'

The average score on our insight problem test was 4.4 correct out of 12, or roughly 37 percent. The individual scores ranged from a low of one to a high of 10, with no difference between the average scores of the men and the women. The times people spent solving the problems ranged from 11 minutes to 47 minutes, with an average of 28 minutes.

When we examined the relationship between scores on the set of 12 insight problems and scores on the mental-ability tests, we found relatively high correlations between the insight-problem scores and the scores on the tests of IQ (.66 on a scale from zero to one, on which a correlation of zero means no relationship, and a correlation of one means a perfect relationship) and inductive reasoning (.63), and only a moderate correlation with the scores on the test of deductive reasoning (.34). (All of the correlations were statistically significant.) These correlations suggest that performance on insight problems does provide a good index of intelligence, and that such performance may be more closely related to inductive than to deductive reasoning.

We then looked at the relationship between the test scores and time spent on the insight problems, and found that people who spent the most time working on the problems tended to have a higher number of correct solutions, and higher IQ scores. (The correlation between time spent and

number of insight problems correctly solved was .62. The correlation between time spent and IQ was .75, which is remarkably high.) Why did smart people take longer on this task? Although we can only speculate, we suspect it is because they became more absorbed in the problems and more motivated to solve them. Our observations suggested that the less bright people either were too quick to choose the seemingly obvious but wrong answers on trick questions, or simply didn't know how to get started on the tougher problems and gave up more quickly.

When we looked at the correlations between the test scores on the insight problems and the scores on the standardized intelligence test, we found that the problems varied considerably in their validity as indicators of IQ. The problem of which day to schedule a lunch date with a friend had almost no correlation with IQ; the problem that proved to be the best predictor of IQ score was the following:

"Water lilies double in area every 24 hours. At the beginning of the summer there is one water lily on a lake. It takes 60 days for the lake to become covered with water lilies. On what day is the lake half covered?" To find the answer, people must realize that since the water lilies double in area every 24 hours, the lake will be half covered on the 59th day in order to be completely covered on the 60th.

What made some items better measures of IQ than others? We discovered two patterns among the "good" and "bad" indicators of IQ that we thought were striking, at least as preliminary hypotheses.

The best indicators of IQ seemed to be those problems that presented both relevant and irrelevant information: The key to success was the ability to distinguish necessary information from unnecessary. For example, people with high IQs tended to realize that "water lilies double in area every 24 hours" was an important clue to solving this problem. People with low IQs frequently ignored this information and tried to solve the problem by dividing the 60 days by two.

Our interpretation of performance on the problems supports the theory that the ability to detect and use clues embedded in the context of what one

reads plays an important role in solving verbal problems. When reading a text—whether it is a newspaper, a science book, or a verbal or arithmetic problem—much of the information may be irrelevant to one's needs; often the hard part is figuring out what is relevant, and how it is relevant.

The problems that proved to be poor indicators of IQ were the "trick" problems in which errors were due primarily to misreading the problem situation—fixing on the apparent question rather than on the actual question. Take the following problem: "A farmer has 17 sheep. All but nine break through a hole in the fence and wander away. How many are left?" People making errors generally failed to comprehend exactly what "all but nine" meant; many assumed that the nine had escaped and thus subtracted that number from 17 to get the number of sheep that remained behind.

If, as we have shown, insight problems do provide a good measure of intellectual ability—at least when they require one to make inductive leaps beyond the given data and when they require one to sift out relevant from irrelevant information—we must ask: Just what is insight? The reason that others have not found any common element in the various insights they have studied is that no one model works for all cases. We have identified three basic kinds of cognitive processes or insightful performance, one or more of which may be required to solve a given problem:

Selective Encoding, or processing of information. This kind of insight occurs when one perceives in a problem one or more facts that are not immediately obvious. Earlier, we referred to the importance of being able to sort out relevant from irrelevant information. This skill can provide the solver with a basis for selective encoding.

Consider the following problem: "If you have black socks and brown socks in your drawer, mixed in the ratio of 4 to 5, how many socks will you have to take out to make sure of having a pair of the same color?" Subjects who failed to realize that "mixed in the ratio of 4 to 5" was irrelevant information consistently came up with the wrong solution. (The correct answer: three.) In the hat-rack problem, noticing the relevance of the floor and ceiling as elements in the problem is also an example of selective encoding.

Selective Combination. This type of insight takes place when one sees a way of combining unrelated (or at least not obviously related) elements, as one must do in the following problem: "With a seven-minute hourglass and an 11-minute hourglass, what is the simplest way to time the boiling of an egg for 15 minutes?" Our subjects had all of the necessary facts, but they had to figure out how to combine the two timers to measure 15 minutes. In the hat-rack problem, figuring out how to combine the use of the floor, ceiling, C-clamp, and two sticks constitutes a similar insight of selective combination.

Selective Comparison. This kind of insight occurs when one discovers a nonobvious relationship between new and old information. It is here that analogy, metaphor, and models come into play. In the hat-rack problem, for example, one might think of how a pole lamp can be stabilized by wedging it between the floor and ceiling of a room, and how the same principle could be used in the construction of a hat rack.

Consider another type of selective comparison: If someone doesn't know a word on a vocabulary test, he can often figure out its definition by thinking of words he does know that have the same word stems. For example, if he doesn't know the word 'exsect,' he might be able to guess its meaning by thinking of a word that has the same prefix (such as 'extract,' where *ex* means out) and a word that has the same root (such as 'dissect,' where *sect* means cut). This information might help him realize that 'exsect' means 'to cut out.'

We emphasize the critical role of selection in each kind of information-processing. In Selective Encoding, one must choose elements to encode from the often numerous and irrelevant bits of information presented by the problem; the trick is to select the right elements. In Selective Combination, there may be many possible ways for the encoded elements to be combined or otherwise integrated; the trick is to select the right way of combining them. In Selective Comparison, new information must be related to one or more of many possible old pieces of information. There are any number of analogies or relations that might be drawn; the trick is to make the right comparison or comparisons. Thus, to the extent that there is a communality in the three kinds of insight, it appears to be in the importance of selection to each kind.

We believe that much of the confusion in the past and present literature on problem-solving stems from a failure to recognize the existence of and differences among these three kinds of insight, which together seem to account for the mental processes that have been labeled as insight, and which are involved in everything from solving problems in puzzle books to making major scientific breakthroughs.

Although we have focused on the importance of insight in problem-solving—and also in intelligence—insight alone is not enough to solve problems. Certain other essential ingredients exist, including:

Prior Knowledge. Even apparently simple problems often require a store of prior knowledge for their solution; complex problems can require a vast store of such knowledge. Consider the problem of the seven-minute and 11-minute hourglasses, and how to time a 15-minute egg. If people have used hourglass timers before, and can remember that they can turn them over at any point, the knowledge will certainly help.

Executive Processes. These are the processes used to plan, monitor, and evaluate one's performance in problem-solving. To start with, one must first study the problem carefully, in order to figure out exactly what question is being asked.

Another executive process involves monitoring one's solution process (keeping track of what one has done, is doing, and still needs to do) and then switching strategies if one isn't making progress. Sometimes it helps to try a new approach if an old one doesn't work.

Motivation. Really challenging problems often require a great deal of motivation on the part of the solver. Successful problem-solvers are often those who simply are willing to put in the necessary effort. Indeed, in our mini-study we found that the better problem-solvers were more persevering than the poorer ones.

Style. People approach problems with different cognitive styles. In particular, some tend to be more impulsive and others more reflective. It seems to us—although we have no hard experimental evidence to support our view—that the most successful problem-solvers are those who manage to combine both impulsive and reflective styles. We do not believe that most people follow just one style or the other. Rather, at certain points in the problem-solving process, people act on impulse; at other times, they act only after great reflection. The hard part is knowing which style will pay off at which point in solving problems.

Successful problem-solving involves a number of different abilities. For many problems, one kind of insight may provide a key to a quick solution. But we believe that most problems are like the apartment doors one finds in some of our larger cities: They have multiple locks requiring multiple keys. Without combining different kinds of insights, as well as prior knowledge, executive processes, motivation, and style, the problems remain locked doors, waiting for the clever solver to find the right set of keys.

Child Rearing and Child Development

Although child-rearing advice has changed over the ages, continuities can be identified. John Watson's early 1900 view that children should be reared strictly in order to correctly shape their behavior can be traced to John Locke's advice of the late 1600s. Similarly, post World War II advice to rear the child in a democratic and permissive atmosphere can be linked historically to Rousseau's 1700s concept of the child as being by nature, free of original sin, and full of natural curiosity. Today, child-rearing advice seems to have struck a middle road between Locke's "authoritarian" approach and Rousseau's "permissive" approach. Thus, parents are encouraged to provide their children with ample love, to cuddle their infants, to use reason as the major disciplinary technique, and to encourage verbal interaction. However, they are to do these things in an environment in which clearly spelled out rules are expected to be obeyed. Suggestion, persuasion, and explanation have become the preferred techniques of rule enforcement, rather than spanking or withdrawal of love.

Perhaps our modern day advice on child rearing merely reflects the ebb and flow of advice that has occurred over the ages. On the other hand, modern day child-rearing advice may reflect a growing awareness of effective child rearing based upon the accumulated knowledge gained from the scientific study of human development. Moreover, modern day child-rearing advice may reflect a growing aversion to the excessive violence, aggression, and alienation in contemporary American society. Finally, the decline in the size of the American family may have expanded our awareness of the needs of individual children. Extended families have become rare, with the typical nuclear family consisting of two adults and three or fewer children.

However, even the nuclear family is in a state of flux. Increasing numbers of children are being reared in single-parent families, due to a higher divorce rate and an increasing number of unmarried mothers. Changes in the traditional economic roles of women mean that more and more young children are receiving supplementary rearing, and an increasing number of children are receiving their primary caregiving from single-parent fathers.

Although the demands made of parents are more confusing and pressing than ever before, fewer parents seem to be prepared to assume responsibility for child rearing. Parenthood often is thrust upon an individual who has had minimal opportunity to acquire child-rearing expertise. Moreover, when inexperienced caregivers seek outside help, often they are confronted with conflicting advice with no standard against which to judge its validity.

To be sure, parenting is not an easy task in contemporary American society. At minimum, parents must be flexible and willing to try different approaches to child rearing, while constantly evaluating them against "expert" opinion and against their own common sense. Perhaps parents should take the same consumerism attitude toward child-rearing experts that they take toward manufacturers of other goods and services.

Looking Ahead: Challenge Questions

How do you view the notion that fathers can be as competent in child rearing as mothers? Do your opinions apply to infancy as well as childhood?

Increasing numbers of America's next generation of child rearers are reared in abusive and neglecting environments. What are the implications for American society if this social problem is not eliminated?

Behavior modification techniques reflect a direct approach to the management of child behavior. Do these techniques reflect a novel approach to child rearing, or are all techniques of child rearing forms of behavior modification?

America has been described as one of the most violent societies in the world. How does the media contribute to this image, or is it an image at all? If you were responsible for television programming for one of the major networks, what changes would you make in the types of programs shown in order to counter violence and sexism?

PARENT AND CHILD DEVELOPMENT

by Graham B. Spanier, Richard M. Lerner, and Judy A. Shea

The authors are, respectively, associate professor of human development, associate professor of child development, and doctoral student in human development and family studies, Pennsylvania State University, University Park.

THE history of evolution shows that human beings are social in nature. Over the course of time, we have found that it is more adaptive to live with other people than to live in isolation. Because of the need to rely on other humans for survival, one unique social group—the family —was invented. Over time, the family has become the most important institution for rearing and socializing children.

The importance of families for both individual and societal maintenance has been recognized for quite some time. However, it has been only recently that social scientists have come to understand that there are continuous bidirectional influences between families and others in the social environment. More importantly, such interactions are also occurring within the family. In essence, this means that not only are parents influencing their children's development—what they will do, what they will be, how they will act towards others—but children also affect their parents' development.

It is useful to remember that families exist within a larger world outside of the home. That is, all family members interact with other individuals such as neighbors, schoolmates, and co-workers. Families also come in contact with other organizations such as churches, PTA's, and the Boy Scouts. However, it is within the family that several values and attitudes important for future behavior develop.

How do different parenting styles relate to child behavior? One type of parent has been labeled the *authoritarian parent*. This type of parent shapes, controls, and evaluates the behaviors and attitudes of the child in accordance with an absolute standard of behavior. He or she favors punitive, forceful measures to curb "self-will" whenever the child's behaviors or beliefs conflict with what the parent thinks is correct. The parent's belief in respect for authority is combined with an orientation to have respect for work, preservation of order, and traditional social structure. The authoritarian parent does not encourage verbal give and take. Instead, he or she believes that a child should accept the word of the parent for what is correct conduct.

A second type of parent is labeled the *permissive parent*. This type of parent attempts to behave towards the child in a nonpunishing and accepting manner. The parent consults with the child about decisions regarding family "policy," and gives the child reasons for family rules. However, this parent largely allows the child to govern his or her own behavior. Reason, but not power, is used by this parent in his or her attempts to rear the child.

The third type of parent is labeled the *authoritative parent*. This type of parent tries to direct his or her child's activities through the use of a rational, issue-oriented style. Through explanations and reasoning, the parent attempts to elicit the desired behavior in the child. Such a parent encourages discussion of household rules because this allows him or her to share with the child the reasoning behind a policy. However, this parent exercises firm control over the child, but not to the extent that the child is overburdened with restrictions. Rather, the child's interests, needs, and abilities are taken into account. While keeping his or her own parental and adult rights in mind, the authoritative parent attempts to rear the child with rules that consider the rights and duties of both parents and children.

It appears that most parents, no matter what their orientation, want their children to show similar behaviors. These behaviors, which include friendliness, cooperation, and achievement, form a set of behaviors that describe a socially competent, responsible, and independent person. Authoritarian or permissive parents do not seem as successful as do authoritative ones in rearing children showing this generally desired set of behaviors. As compared to the other two parenting types, authoritative parents are more likely to have children who score higher on measures of purposive, independent, and dominant behaviors, and on measures of cooperation with adults and friendliness with other children.

Data from several studies suggest that the different parenting styles have contrasting roles in children's development. For example, with parents of young children, it was found that parents who explain their decisions also show more warmth. Conversely, restrictiveness in parents was related to their use of power, punishment, and physical means to prove their authority. Also, mothers who were accepting, supportive, caring, concerned, and loving, and who enforced established rules consistently, but sought the views of the child in a context of free and open discussion, had sons who were higher in self-esteem than did mothers who treated their sons harshly, gave little guidance, and enforced rules inconsistently. Similarly, girls who showed high levels of self-esteem, honesty, and altruism had warm, intimate interactions with their mothers and, when at least one parent was warm and accepting, both male and female children were likely to have high self-esteem.

Parental disciplinary strategies have also been studied. Parents who use *power assertive* discipline employ physical punishment, threats of punishment, and physical attempts to control their child's behavior. Parents who use *psychological* discipline may use one or both of the following techniques: love withdrawal, which involves the parent temporarily taking away love from the child because the child's actions have made the parent feel disappointed or ashamed; and induction, which involves parental use of rationality and explanation in attempts to influence the child's behavior.

The frequent use of power assertion by

a parent is associated with weak moral development in the child. Indeed, children of parents who use power assertion techniques frequently tend themselves to show high levels of aggressive behavior. Similarly, inconsistent parental discipline or parental conflict over discipline is associated with aggressive or delinquent behavior in children. However, inductive discipline combined with parental affection was associated with moral development. Similarly, in a study of fifth- and seventh-grade white, middle-class children and their parents, it was concluded that differences in the moral orientation of children (*e.g.*, in their consideration for others, feelings of fear or of guilt upon misbehaving) are at least in part due to different discipline and affection patterns of parents. Again, induction, or explanation of behaviors, and affection were associated with higher moral functioning.

Effects of infants on their parents

Just as mothers, fathers, and the family system shape the child, the child shapes them. Both parents and infants behave to maintain the other's behavior. For example, noises by the infant such as cooing and crying are exchanged with parental vocalizations. The looking behavior of an infant leads to more maternal talking than touching behavior, but maternal touching and talking appear to evoke equal levels of infant vocalization. Although this information indicates that parental behaviors may indeed depend on infant behavior, is the nature of the relationship reciprocal?

Research indicates that it is. One study reports finding no over-all differences between middle-class and working-class mothers in how *much* they talked in the presence of their infants; but there was a difference in how much they talked *to* their infants: middle-class mothers (78%) were more likely to respond to their infants' vocalizations than were working-class mothers (43%). Similarly, the sex of a child also influences how mothers are responded to. Female infants are more likely to respond to a maternal behavior than are male infants, although no difference exists between the sexes in total vocalizations.

If the infant is not merely reacting to parents' behaviors, he or she must be capable of starting a "conversation," keeping it going, and stopping it. Data indicate that infants do have such competencies. In the first few weeks of life, crying brings a parent closer to the baby and this increases the likelihood that the sight, smell, and feel of the infant could bring out other parenting behaviors. For example, in a study that illustrates how infant behaviors influence the infant-

mother pair, it was reported that, by a few weeks of age, infant crying behavior comes to follow a predictable cycle. Infants move from a state of quietness to soft whispering, then through gentle movements, kicking, thrashing, and finally intense crying. As the pattern become predictable to the mother, a response by the mother to one of the behaviors in the sequence might keep others from occurring. Kicking, for instance, might get the mother's attention, which in turn would keep the infant from crying.

Such interactions are not automatic, however. The mother or father will not respond to every infant cry. Infants can cry so much that the parenting styles are disturbed. Mothers report decrease in their feelings of attachment toward their three-month-old infants if crying and other demands for caregiving do not decrease, as they do in most infants. More over, one study suggests that differences between children who are easy to care for and those who are difficult to care for might exist because parents of the more difficult children have to use a lot more energy to care for them. Indeed, children who have the "easy" personality types, and also have good health and good bodies, are often found to be "invulnerable" to the known negative effects of poor parenting, even when this parenting is done by a psychotic parent. However, "invulnerable" children are often those who are associated with the parental practices labeled as authoritative. On the other hand, children who lack good health and show the characteristics of a "difficult" child are more often associated with parenting styles that are not as favorable. One reason for this relation may be that excessive crying by the child may require that parents use too much of their energy to meet these demands; and thus, there is less energy for caregiving or love.

Another team of researchers reports that the more an infant cried in any one quarter of the first year of life, the more the mother ignored the cry in the subsequent quarter. For some infants, their behavior forced their mothers to exceed their caregiving tolerance limits. After caregiving behavior failed to lead to a decrease in crying, the mother began to withdraw as the infant cried more; this led to increased crying and further maternal withdrawal.

The data indicate that infant-parent relationships are interactional, and that the infant is capable of starting and maintaining a relationship if the behavior does not exceed caregiver limits. These findings, in emphasizing the role of the child in family interaction, may give the impression that the parent is not important in

child socialization, but parents contribute too.

In one recent study, 36 mothers and their firstborn children (nine to 18 months old) were followed over a nine-month period. The mothers and children were studied at home, sometimes playing as they always did and sometimes performing tasks given to them by the experimenter. There was a strong correlation between children's intellectual, language, and social development and the quality of their mothers' care. For example, children who talked the most received the most verbal stimulation from their mothers, and children who most often handled toys and other objects had mothers who presented play materials to them often. Stimulating, responsive maternal behavior influenced the child's intellectual development. Nevertheless, such influences are not independent of the child's own contribution. It was also found that the child's social behaviors influenced the mothers' social behaviors.

There are other studies that indicate the importance of the parents' role in child functioning. The maternal characteristics most necessary for continuing interactions with an infant are the development of an awareness to the infant's capacity for attention, and an understanding of the infant's need to withdraw and ignore the parent after a period of attention. However, the infant's contribution is apparent again. Cycles of attention-nonattention were found in all long periods of parent-infant interaction. Nonattentive, looking-away behaviors may reflect the infant's need to maintain some control over the amount of stimulation received during a given period.

Not only do parents withdraw when infant behaviors are too intense, but they also change when the infants are too quiet. Extreme quietness and stillness in infants brings about various behaviors in parents designed to make the infant more active. Thus, parents may approach and communicate with the infant when there is too little stimulation from the infant, and they withdraw when there is too much stimulation from the infant. For instance, mothers may talk to and move sleepy infants in order to wake them up enough to eat, and then often must act to quiet the infant when later crying is too intense. Moreover, if an infant's behavior can not be changed by the mother, she may become disturbed.

Interactions with older children

Studies conducted with children at older ages also point to the role of the child in influencing parents' behavior. The age of the child influences the quality of the mother's verbal interaction. More so than was the case with the mothers of two-year-olds, mothers of three-year-olds use more complex explanations. Similarly, the child's age has been found to influence the play behavior both mothers and fathers show to the child. At older ages, the child's size, rather than age or reasoning abilities, influences the types of interaction within the family.

The sex of the child seems also to be associated with the type of parental behavior shown. In regard to some of the parental rearing practices discussed earlier, a study of fifth-grade children and their mothers found that boys receive more power assertion and love withdrawal, and less induction, than do girls. Similarly, parent-daughter pairs show higher levels of over-all and affectionate interaction than do parent-son pairs.

Other studies also highlight the somewhat different nature of parent-son vs. parent-daughter involvement. Although relatively few studies have assessed children's interactions with their fathers in comparison to interactions with their mothers, in a recent study 40 middle-class families were observed in their own homes. All families had infants 15 months of age. In general, mothers and fathers were more similar than dissimilar in the behaviors shown toward their child. However, there was a slight tendency for parents to prefer to interact with same-sex children. In addition, a parent was more active when alone with the child than when in the presence of his or her spouse. Similarly, infants directed more social behavior toward each parent when alone with him or her than when both mother and father were present.

A focus on one particular type of parent-child interaction—in families where child abuse occurs—will underscore the points cited above.

Child abuse is "any nonaccidental injury sustained by a child under 18 years of age resulting from acts of commission or omission by a parent, guardian, or care-taker."* Because of different beliefs by parents and different ideas about the correct way to discipline children, it is difficult to tell when appropriate physical punishment ends and abuse or neglect begins. It is even more difficult to know precisely how many children are abused in their families each year, although estimates are as high as 1,500,000 children. Most experts agree, however, that, whatever the exact number, the problem is serious.

Characteristics of the parents' own history and of the family situation are related to abuse. Parents who are child abusers were frequently themselves victims of abuse, neglect, and violence as children. Parents who are abusers are often impulsive, immature, self-centered, and hypersensitive. Abusing parents are often poorly educated. Mothers are most often the persons who abuse the child. Abuse more frequently occurs when the father is unemployed, or when the families' finances are strained. In addition, abuse is more common in families that move often.

Child abuse is correlated with social class. It is more likely in lower socioeconomic status families; more than half of abusive families have very low annual incomes. The American Humane Association reports that insufficient income has been cited as a factor in almost 50% of child abuse and neglect cases.

Another characteristic apparently related to the incidence of child abuse is family size. An observational study comparing abusive, neglectful, and normal families indicates that those patterns of family interaction found in abusive and neglectful families are especially likely in large families. The proportion of abusing families with four or more children is

*Robert L. Burgess, "Family Violence: Some Implications from Evolutionary Biology," paper presented at the annual meeting of the American Society of Criminology, Philadelphia, November, 1979.

twice that found in the general population.

However, abusing parents usually do not abuse all their children; one is usually selected to be the victim. There is evidence that characteristics of the child partially determine the probability that they will be abused. Infants who are premature, of low birth weight, who were born of caesarian sections or of unwanted pregnancies, or who have "difficult" personality styles are "at risk" for child abuse. Moreover, physically unattractive infants and older children are more likely to be the targets of abuse than are physically attractive children.

Some of the most recent research on child abuse details difference in patterns of parent-child interaction between abusive and non-abusive families. For example, one such study found group differences on three parent-child interaction factors: perceived communication between parent and child, the child's readiness to learn, and parental facilitating behavior. Others have found that abusive mothers spend significantly less time in auditory and tactile stimulation of their infants, were less age-appropriate in their stimulation strategies, and were less tolerant of activities initiated by their infants. Moreover, in a comparison of 87 abusive and 87 control families, group differences were found on a number of variables, including the child-centeredness of the home, social isolation, and patterns of parent-child interaction.

A key difference between abusive and non-abusive families is their contrasting patterns of parent-child interaction. However, this does not mean that we should only look to differences in parent behaviors. The data convincingly show that children play a large role in determining their own, as well as their parents', behaviors. Understanding of development must come from unraveling the bidirectional influences. Perhaps only then will education and intervention efficiently meet their goals.

A NEW LOOK AT LIFE WITH FATHER

Glenn Collins

Researchers have lately probed the father-infant relationship and found few significant differences in the way children relate to fathers and to mothers. Their studies may sharply alter our concepts of what parenting is all about.

For in the baby lies the future of the world:
Mother must hold the baby close so that the baby knows that it is his world;
Father must take him to the highest hill so that he can see what his world is like.
—MAYAN INDIAN PROVERB

The tiny white room on the ground floor of the John Enders Research Building is only a block away from the quiet green quadrangle of the Harvard Medical School. The plate on the door reads, "RESEARCH LABORA-TORY I," and the room is a jumble of television cameras, tape decks and video cables. There are, however, some unexpected items: boxes of Kimbies are stacked under a table; atop the table, a container of Wet Ones Moist Towelettes, and next to the Wet Ones, propped in a sturdy alumimum seat, a 96-day-old baby named Eddie. He is intently studying James, his father, standing before him. Two television cameras are capturing these moments on half-inch magnetic tape.

"Bet you're glad to see me!" says James, smiling. "Were you good with Mommy? You know, I missed you all day. . . ." As he talks to his son, he taps him, tickles him, and smiles, his eyebrows moving in a language of their own. Eddie arches forward in his jumpsuit, kicks his feet in their little red socks, coos and giggles. After exactly two minutes, James leaves the room. The cameras observe Eddie for another 30 seconds, and then they are turned off.

Although a pediatrician on the staff of the Child Development Unit of Children's Hospital Medical Center in Boston will later play back the tape, James and young Eddie aren't patients: They are participants in one aspect of current research on fathering. Investigators will play back the tape at one-seventh speed, and will conduct a microanalysis of the facial expressions of James and Eddie, recording their vocalizations and their body movements on matching graphs. This information will be used to create a saw-tooth chart that plots a father's typical interaction with a child; its signature is distinctive, different from the characteristic pattern of a mother's interaction.

□

Near Princeton, N.J., a father holds open the front door and waits with his wife and two children as a team of researchers hefts a videotape camera and assorted television equipment into his house. It is just about dinnertime, and the investigators, from the Infant Laboratory at the Educational Testing Service, ask the parents where they normally eat their evening meal.

"Tonight, in the dining room," says the father. The E.T.S. technicians start the camera running, and leave the house.

Tentatively, the parents call their children to dinner. The 3-year-old waves at the television eye. The 6-year-old sticks out his tongue. The father seems a bit unnerved. They start eating, and, before any of them might have expected, they forget about the technological presence in the dining room. After dinner, the E.T.S. researchers return for their equipment; later they analyze the behavior they view on the tape.

After studying 50 families, the E.T.S. investigators can generalize about what they have seen. Fathers talk more to their sons than they do to their daughters. Children talk less to fathers than to mothers, or to each other. And fathers, in their dinner behavior, tend to ask questions.

□

In a laboratory at the University of Wisconsin, a father sits in an easy chair four feet away from a television monitor. He is about to see something unpleasant, but he doesn't know it. Electrodes from an eight-channel polygraph recorder—a lie detector—have been attached to his index and middle fingers, and a rubber cuff has been inflated on his left bicep; his heart rate, skin conductance and blood pressure are being monitored. Soon the television screen glows with a six-minute videotape of a 5-month-old baby boy. The infant looks around gravely and makes a sound; then he squirms, and soon he begins to cry. Loudly. Insistently. Interminably. Even though the baby on the screen isn't his, the father feels ever more uncomfortable under the assault; he moves, tenses, his heart rate rises and his blood pressure soars. Later, after testing 148 subjects, the investigators are able to report that there is no physiological difference between the reaction of a father or a mother to the sight of a squalling baby. To both, it is equally distressing.

Research examining what fathers do and how they do it has been booming in recent years. Not all of it employs computer analyses and electronic bric-a-brac. Much of it involves nothing more complicated than placing a trained observer in a room with a father who is playing with, or talking about, his child.

The impact of all this father-watching is beginning to be felt in courts of law, in hospitals and in universities, which face the task of redirecting the training of a new generation of doctors, pediatricians, psychotherapists, health-care professionals and teachers. "Our whole society has had the notion that a biological bond between mother and child made fathers less able, less interested and less important than mothers in caring for children," says James A. Levine, a Wellesley College researcher. "Courts have based decisions on that notion, therapists have treated patients on the basis of it, and men and women have made life choices because of it."

In fact, 44 percent of the mothers of children under the age of 6 in this country are working, only 24 percent of existing families are traditional nuclear families, and the "two-paycheck" marriage is the norm for nearly half of all two-parent families in America. In the changing society reflected by these statistics, the new knowledge about fathering has important implications for how children will be raised and educated, and will help to shape the kind of nation we inhabit in the 1980's.

□

Fathers haven't always been a fashionable research subject for social scientists. "When I started out 17 years ago, there just wasn't much data," says Henry Biller, professor of psychology at the University of Rhode Island and a pioneering researcher in the field. "The recent increase in data collection on fathers is amazing. We have something of a revolution in thinking among those involved in early childhood development."

In past decades, researchers focused on the father as a role model, or studied him inferentially: by examining the impact of his *absence,* in families where the father had died, divorced or gone to war. Fathers have also long had a place in psychoanalytic theory, becoming important in the Oedipal stage, when the son competes with him for the mother.

Social-development theorists viewed the mother-infant relationship as unique, vastly more important than subsequent relationships; it was even termed the prototype for all close relationships. In 1958 and then again in 1969, John Bowlby, the British psychiatrist, published his elegant and influential theories of attachment, a word that is usually defined by behaviorists as the preference for, or desire to be close to, a specific person. "But the real synonym for 'attachment' is love," says Dr. Michael Lewis, a developmental psychologist at the Educational Testing Service. Bowlby, drawing on the animal-study work of ethologists and the parental-deprivation observations of cognitive psychologists, suggested that there was an evolutionary advantage to a unique bond between mother and infant; he reasoned that this bond was an imperative of the very growth and development of the species.

Subsequently, many researchers investigated the mother-child interaction, revealing the nature of the infant's early relationship with its caretaker. However, fathers weren't even present in most of the studies. "A major reason that fathers were ignored was that fathers were inaccessible," says E. Mavis Hetherington, a University of Virginia psychology professor who has studied family-related questions for 25 years. "To observe fathers you have to work at night and on the weekends, and not many researchers like to do that."

Studies of humans and of nonhuman primates began to suggest that infants had strong attachments to persons who had little to do with their caretaking and physical gratification; nor were these relationships necessarily derived from the child's bond with its mother. In a classic study, primatologist Harry Harlow demonstrated that the attachment process was not limited to a feeding context. Investigators also showed that the actual amount of time an infant and his mother spent together was a poor predictor of the success of their relationship. Consequently, a child's tie to its mother continues to be viewed as crucially important; however, its exclusivity and uniqueness have been challenged. The new research emphasizes the complexity of an infant's social world.

Researchers have now identified some of the ways in which fathers are important to children. Henry Biller sums up the findings: "The presence and availability of fathers to kids is critical to their knowledge of social reality, their ability to relate to male figures, to their self-concepts, their acceptance of their own sexuality, their feeling of security. Fathers are important in the first years of life, and important throughout a child's development." Frank A. Pedersen of the National Institute of Child Health and Human Development has also demonstrated that mothers can perform better in their parenting roles when fathers provide emotional support.

Researchers from a number of disciplines using ingenious new methods now suggest that the father-infant relationship is not what we thought it was: that, for example, there are few significant differences in the way children attach to fathers and to mothers; that fathers can be as protective, giving and stimulating as mothers; that men have at least the potential to be as good at taking care of children as women are; and that the characteristic interplay of father and infant, when scrutinized minutely, is distinctive in many fascinating ways. The new fathering research offers fresh insights about the "distant" father and about fathers' roles across disparate cultures; it reveals that fathers have been ignored in research and in medical practice in curious and interesting ways; and it offers a synthesis of the relationship between fathers, children, families and society.

James Herzog, M.D., a psychiatrist who teaches at Harvard, says this of the new findings: "We're in what I call the post-competency phase now. We don't need to prove that fathers 'can do it, too.' The question now is, what is the specific role of the male parent, and what is the difference between being a father and being a mother?"

□

In 1970 a Harvard Ph.D candidate named Milton Kotelchuck began a study of fathers that created a stir when it was presented in Philadelphia at the 1973 meeting of the Society for Research in Child Development. Kotelchuck, now director of health statistics and research for the Commonwealth of Massachusetts, had set up a classic "separation-protest" situation—a test of attachment—in studying the reactions of 144 infants when their fathers and mothers walked out of a play-

room and left them with a stranger. Previous studies had observed the effects of a mother's departure on her child; Kotelchuck was able to determine that infants were just as upset when a father left them.

In four other studies, Kotelchuck and his associates found few significant differences in the way the infants attached to fathers and to mothers. They demonstrated that, in fact, children have extended social worlds and can attach equally well to siblings, peers and other figures.

Michael E. Lamb, research scientist at the University of Michigan's Center for Human Growth and Development, has carried on his investigations—including the crying-baby experiment described earlier—at Michigan, the University of Wisconsin at Madison, and at Yale, and was the editor of an influential 1976 anthology, "The Role of the Father in Child Development." His first key study of attachment appeared in 1975; in it, 7- and 8-month-old boys and girls and their parents were viewed in the home setting. An observer dictated a detailed account of the behavior he saw into a tape recorder. That narrative was then analyzed by applying 10 measures of attachment and affiliation; whether the baby "Smiles," "Vocalizes," "Looks," "Laughs," "Approaches," "Is in proximity," "Reaches to," "Touches," "Seeks to be held" or "Fusses to." Lamb and his co-workers found that no preferences were evident for one parent over the other among these infants, at the age when they should, according to Bowlby's theory, be forming their first attachments.

Lamb and his colleagues reported that when mothers held their infants, it was primarily for things like changing, feeding or bathing; fathers mostly held their children to play with them, and initiated a greater number of physical and idiosyncratic games than mothers did. This paternal play tended to be boisterous and physically stimulating. Furthermore, boys were held longer than girls by their fathers; fathers start showing a preference for boys at one year of age and this preference increases thereafter.

Currently, Lamb and his associates are studying 100 families from the time of pregnancy until their children attain the age of 18 months. The sample includes families where there are working wives, also represented are a few fathers who are primarily responsible for infant care. In Sweden, for the past six months, they have been observing role-sharing fathers and both mothers and fathers who have primary responsibility for child care.

If Michael Lamb has tended to focus on the child in his work, Ross D. Parke, professor of psychology at the University of Illinois at Champaign-Urbana, has centered his research on fathers themselves. In a 1972 study that is a classic in the literature of fathering, Parke and his colleagues haunted a hospital maternity ward in Madison, Wis., and observed the behavior of both middle-class and lower-class parents of newborn babies. They found, most strikingly, that fathers and mothers differed little in how much they interacted with their children. Fathers touched, looked at, talked to, rocked and kissed their children as much as their mothers did. The study suggested that they were as protective, giving and stimulating as the mothers were —even when the fathers were alone with their babies.

In later work, Parke and his collaborators measured the amount of milk that was left over in a baby's bottle after feeding time; infants consumed virtually the same amount of milk whether fathers or mothers did the feeding. They found that fathers were equally competent in correctly reading subtle changes in infants' behavior and acting on them; fathers reacted to such infant distress signals as spitting up, sneezing and coughing just as quickly and appropriately as mothers did. Parke asserted that men had at least the potential to be as good at caretaking as women. However, fathers tended to leave child care to their wives when both parents were present.

In the last three years, Parke, Douglas Sawin of the University of Texas and their collaborators have conducted two major studies involving 120 families. They observed family interactions, and used high-speed electronic "event recorders" with 10-button keyboards and solid-state memories to tap out four-digit codes that recorded behaviors as they saw them. Although there are very few differences in *quality* between mothers' and fathers' interactions with their children, one observed disparity is that fathers are more likely to touch and vocalize to first-born sons than to daughters, or to later-born children.

□

Eddie and James, whose close encounter began this article, were participants in a continuing investigation of children's early learning abilities and communication patterns at the Child Development Unit of Children's Hospital Medical Center in Boston. Originally, father-infant and mother-infant pairs were videotaped periodically during the first six months of babies lives. The unit's newer work involves the father-mother-infant triad.

In Laboratory I, where young Eddie became something of an intramural television celebrity among social scientists, the research continues. Infants are placed in an alcove created by a blue-flowered curtain, and are taped with father or mother. These laboratory situations, though artificial, place the maximum communicative demand on the parent and child, the researchers say; they bring out the kinds of intense play situations that normally occur only during brief periods during an ordinary day.

Two trained observers play back the videotapes of the sessions and perform a "microbehavioral analysis" of the interaction of both the parent and the baby. The researchers assign numerical scores to rate such facial expressions as frowns, pouts and smiles; sounds like gurgles or coos; motions of hands and feet, and even eye movements. Ultimately, the observers note clusters of these behaviors and chart them during each second of elapsed time over the entire interaction.

Graphs of fathers' and mothers' behavior show distinctive patterns. In all of the families studied by the Child Development Unit, the chart of the mother's interaction is more modulated, enveloping, secure and controlled. The dialogue with the father is more playful, exciting and physical. Father displays more rapid shifts from the peaks of involvement to the valleys of minimal attention.

There are other characteristic differences: Mothers play more verbal games with infants, so-called "turn-taking" dialogues that are composed of bursts of talking or cooing that last four to eight seconds, and are interrupted by three- to four-second pauses. Fathers tend to play more physical games with infants; they touch their babies in rhythmic tapping patterns or circular motions.

To provide conceptual models for the way babies interact with adults, the Boston researchers have employed the theories of cybernetics, the discipline that studies the control and regulation of communication processes in animals and machines. Researchers have broken with the traditional lexicon of rat psychology, and talk about the "interlocking feedback of mutually regulated systems" and "homeostatic balances between attention and nonattention." The baby, in its reciprocal interaction with an adult, modifies its behavior in response to the feedback it is receiving. Infants, they say, seem to display periods of rapt attention followed by recovery intervals, in an internally regulated cycle that maintains the balance of the infant's heart, lung and other physiological systems.

"It's important to say that father doesn't offer some qualitatively better kind of stimulation; it's just different," says T. Berry Brazelton, M.D., director of the Child Development Unit, a pioneer in the study of family interactions. "Mother has more of a tendency to teach the baby about inner control, and about how to keep the homeostatic system going; she then builds her stimulation on top of that system in a very smooth, regulated sort of way. The father adds a different dimension, a sort of play dimension, an excitement dimension, teaching the baby about some of the ups and downs—and also teaching the baby another very important thing: how to get *back* in control."

There are also interesting similarities in infants' relationships with both parents, says Michael Yogman, M.D., the pediatrician who videotaped James and Eddie and who has specialized in the study of fathers at the Child Development Unit since 1974. "With both parents," he says, "we see that behavior is mutually regulated and reciprocal, that there is a meeting of behaviors."

Dr. Brazelton says that "there's no question that a father is essential to children's development. Our work shows that babies have this very rich characteristic model of reaction to at least three different people—to father, to mother and to strangers. It shows me that the baby is looking for richness, that he's looking for at least two different interactants to learn about the world." For Dr. Brazelton, to whom Mayan Indians told the saying that preceded this article, its poetry is exceedingly descriptive.

"It seems to me," says Dr. Brazelton, "that the baby very carefully sets separate tracks for each of the two parents—which, to me, means that the baby wants different kinds of people as parents for his own needs. Perhaps the baby is bringing out differences that are critical to him as well as to them."

The Boston researchers plan to explore the later development of the paternal and maternal dialogues with children. They also hope to refine their procedures to the point where they may be useful as a diagnostic tool for practitioners.

□

Fathers are being studied from other perspectives. Although psychiatric clinicians, those who see patients, had always noted that the father played an important role in the psychological development of children, as late as 1973 the psychoanalytic literature bemoaned the lack of theorizing about the father's role during the first two years of life.

Building on Margaret Mahler's ideas on the successive stages of an infant's "psychological birth," psychoanalyst Ernst Abelin and others focused on the father's role in helping infants separate from mothers.

Some behavioral psychologists can't take the efforts of the psychoanalytic theorists very seriously, since the data for such work are often derived from the study of a single patient who may be going through the process of becoming a father, or coping with difficulties of parenthood. "It's better to observe what's going on," says Alison Clarke-Stewart, a University of Chicago psychologist. "It's not distorted by retrospective recollection or the perceptions of the person who's being studied."

Psychoanalysts reply that the observational method is limited. "How people behave is highly determined by their fantasies, conflicts and unconscious processes," says Dr. Herzog. "These are the causes of the behavior that others observe. I have nothing against documenting this behavior, but we need to look at the inner life, too."

Part of that inner life is a well-documented clinical phenomenon, the so-called "womb-envy" —the envy of women's capacity to give birth—among some expectant fathers and even among male children. Perhaps a societal counterpart of this is the "couvade" phenomenon that anthropologists have noted in many cultures, where men undergo elaborate rites of passage paralleling their wives' pregnancies and birth-giving.

"We know that the time of pregnancy and becoming a father is extremely important to men, a crucial and stressful time," says Alan R. Gurwitt, M.D., a psychiatrist, analyst and associate clinical professor at the Yale Child Study Center. "Yet the astounding thing in this society is that the father has come to be a subject of ridicule—there is no end to the cartoon and the movie stereotypes portraying the expectant father, and fathers in general, as bumbling fools."

He says there is still a tendency to ignore fathers on the part of obstetricians, pediatricians, nurses and even child psychiatrists. "This failure to involve fathers even in the treatment of their children runs very deeply," says John Munder Ross, a Manhattan psychotherapist and clinical assistant professor at Downstate Medical Center, who is coediting an anthology of the new psychoanalytic views of fathering. "It may have to do with the relations of clinical workers to their own fathers. There seems to be an awful lot of stereotyping of fathers as 'absent and ineffectual,' or 'tyrannical and sadistic.' "

To the psychoanalysts, the process that is fathering continues. "The middle-aged father frequently finds himself in a painful situation," says Stanley Cath, M.D., a psychoanalyst and associate clincial professor at Tufts Medical School. "His adolescent children may be rebellious and challenging to him; he himself may be trying to separate from his own father, who may be aged or dying; and the grandfather himself may be looking for support" as he faces the debilitation of old age. "Of course, a man can be the father to his children, and also the father to his parents," says Dr. Cath. "We rediscover the father, and the definition of fathering, throughout our lifespan."

□

As a social phenomenon, the evolution of fathering in man and various primate precursors is a matter of sheer conjecture. Paleontology provides little data on social interaction. Some cultural historians have tried to make inferences from the study of recent "primitive" societies, by which they mean complex societies that have not received the blessings of technology.

Margaret Mead's famous 1930 study of the Manus people of New Guinea reported that, at the age of a year, children were given from the mother's care into the father's. He would play with the baby, feed it, bathe it, and take it to bed with him at night.

Fathers in the Thonga tribe in South Africa, observed during the last century, were ritually prevented from having almost anything to do with infants until the babies were 3 months old. However, fathers in the Lesu culture of Melanesia commonly took care of babies while their wives were busy cooking or gardening. And among the !Kung bushmen in northwestern Botswana today, fathers have a great deal of contact with children, holding and fondling even young infants.

In analyses of all known cultures, anthropologists have suggested that, in about two-thirds of societies, wives, and children accord the paterfamilias deference, that husbands exert authority over their wives and that most cultures trace descent through the father's line. In nonindustrial cultures, these analyses suggest, fathers generally play a small role in relating to young children. In other words, the similarities of men's roles outweigh the fascinating differences that may exist.

Male figures—though not necessarily fathers—are involved in child care in most cultures. Just how involved is another question. Applying a measurement called the Barry and Paxson Father-Infant Proximity Scale, researchers Mary Maxwell West and Melvin J. Konner at Harvard University found that social and cultural conditions are related to the level of involvement of fathers with their children, and suggest that there is the potential among males for caring for their young if other conditions encourage it. West and Konner found that fathers observed in cultures with monogamous nuclear families were generally involved parents. So were fathers in "gathering" societies—the form of society that existed during 98 percent of human history. They suggest that distant fathering is associated with warrior cultures ("hunting" societies) and with societies where men's agricultural or military activities take precedence.

Of course, the political and economic equivalents of warfare exist in modern industrial cultures, and it can be debated how much they affect males' involvement in fathering. There is conjecture that the tradition of the Roman pater-familias had some influence on current patterns, as well as the Christian concept of the Old Testament God. The few attempts at compiling histories of fathering show the Industrial Revolution to be a major disrupter of family life as it existed when many fathers were tradesmen or farmers working in the presence of their children.

The cross-cultural evidence shows clearly that the father has been many things in many societies; it suggests that, if the culture allows, fathering can be whatever fathers want to make of it.

□

Is there any answer to the question posed earlier by Dr. James Herzog: Is fathering the same as mothering? And, if not, is one parenting style superior to the other?

"You don't want to imply from these studies that people are interchangeable," says Alan Sroufe, a University of Minnesota child-development professor who is doing studies of attachment there. "Sure," he says, "an infant can attach to a woman or a man. But women have natural advantages in parenting. It's not just nursing—for example, mothers lactate as soon as a baby cries. But mothers also have the experience of carrying the baby for nine months, and if the business of attachment comes from sensitivity to being tuned into a baby, mothers have the advantage."

"But there is a crucial distinction to be made here," says Milton Kotelchuck. "Yes, pregnancy and lactation can make it easier for a mother to attach to a child. But the essential thing is that infants don't know that they

are supposed to relate more to the mother than to the father."

"It is my speculation—and I want to emphasize that word," says Michael Lamb, "that we will find that biological differences are very small, and that they are exaggerated and magnified by the rituals and the roles that societies build around those distinctions. But are these differences genetic? My answer is 'Yes, but'— where the but is more important that the yes.

"Aside from the question of genetics," he says, "there is good evidence to believe that mothers and fathers can be equally effective as parents. They just have different styles. Perhaps it's really not fathering or mothering—it's parenting."

□

One researcher attempting to synthesize the relationship between child, family and society is Michael Lewis, director and senior scientist at the Institute for the Study of Exceptional Children at the Infant Laboratory of the Educational Testing Service. (It was his investigators who conducted the videotaped observations of Princeton fathers at dinner.) Lewis holds that different people—mothers, fathers, peers, siblings, grandparents, uncles, aunts and other relatives—serve the child's needs in different cultures in different ways: "I am saying that a father's role is cultural and historic rather than biological and evolutionary."

"There's no good data on any of this," Lewis says, "but my impression is that, to an extent in the general culture, fathers are defining their functions in new ways—the 'new fathering' we hear about." He adds that "we haven't assessed the basic question of values here yet, and that's what we need to do. If the cultural matrix is changing, is it assisting the values of our culture?"

To an extent, society has legitimized the needs of parenting men. "In a sense, fathers have come out of the closet," says Mavis Hetherington. "They feel more comfortable about being parents, and are more actively fighting for their rights." Recent revolutionary changes in the way society views men are now treated by the media as commonplace: men's improved position in child-custody cases or men's right to single-parent adoptions in most states.

Nevertheless, it is James Levine's hunch that women are more aware of the issue of fatherhood than men are. "I think it is becoming more of a question for women as more of them are working outside the home. Women make demands on men to parent in a way that fits in with their new concepts of how they will live their lives," says Levine, a research associate at the Wellesley College Center for Research on Women who wrote an influential 1976 book on male parenting options, "Who Will Raise the Children?"

However, Levine says, "the biggest push for change is coming from the economic pressures—the necessity for both parents to work. I think the bottom line in all of this is the economic situation of women."

Michael Lamb believes that "it's a depressingly small number" of fathers who take on a large share of all that is involved in bringing up a child. He does not view the recent research about fathers' abilities as a new panacea. "But," he says, "I think we must realize that, in general, the average male won't be better than the average female as a caretaker. Yes, babies can attach to father. But that isn't to say that they won't be closest to the primary caretaker, which is usually mother."

Says Levine, "Where we really miss the boat is when we say the male role is changing, and cite as evidence the fact that men are changing diapers, bottle feeding, etcetera." The truly important part, Levine feels, involves a man's sense of emotional responsibility: "It's not just the taking *care* of kids, but it's who carries around that inner *sense* of caring, that extra dimension of emotional connection."

It is possible that there will be competition in parenting. "At this point," says Dr. Brazelton, "everyone is goading men on to do more, but the second that men get good at it, and really enjoy nurturing, it may cause problems that'll have to be faced. Fathers who are taking an equally nurturant role may threaten some mothers."

For Levine, looking ahead, the most interesting question is, "research for what?" It seems to him that the next step, theoretically and practically, is to give some guidance to medical and mental-health practitioners: "The most interesting area for research has to do with total family interaction, the family systems perspective."

Virtually all of the father-watchers are wary, however, of being prescriptive—of saying that fathers should parent in a specific, more "nurturant" way.

"The crucial impact of the new research," says Douglas Sawin, "should be that a father's role ought to be an optional choice—and that, with a little support and training and education, they can be primary parents —but only if they want to be. For they have the basic competence and warmth and nurturance abilities. Whether they implement them or not is their decision."

When Mommy Goes to Work...

What happens to her kids' emotional development... her husband's ego... her own self-esteem?

SALLY WENDKOS OLDS

Sally Olds has three daughters, aged 15, 18 and 20, and has worked part time or free lance in public relations and journalism ever since her youngest was a year old.

It used to be easy to diagnose the problems of children whose mothers worked outside the home—a group of youngsters that today totals more than 27 million in this country alone. Is Mary overly dependent and whiny? That's because she doesn't see enough of her Mommy. Does Billy do badly at school? Poor thing, he doesn't have the loving attention of a mother who could help him with his homework. Is Freddy stealing candy bars from the corner store? He wouldn't if he had Mom's guidance at home!

Such assumptions may seem logical, but they just don't hold up when scrutinized under the research microscope. As social scientists delve more deeply into the effects on children of their mothers' working, their findings are turning out to be quite different from long-accepted beliefs.

Let's take a moment for a brief history lesson. Twenty-five years ago, only 1.5 million mothers were in the labor force. Today, 14 million are. As late as 1940, only one female parent in ten worked outside the home. Today, four in ten do. Before 1969, most women with children between the ages of 6 and 17 spent their days at home. Today, the United States Department of Labor reports that a record nine million women with children 6 to 17 years old are working. In fact, nearly three million have little ones aged three to five, and over two and half million have babies under three!

With employment patterns shifting so dramatically, it's only logical that we reevaluate our long-held beliefs about child care and babies' needs in general—beliefs that for years have kept mothers tied to their babies' cribs for fear of sparking emotional and psychological traumas later on. Most of our baby-care gospel (example: "children need a loving mother at home") is based on studies of hospitalized youngsters conducted during the 1940's and 50's. Not surprisingly, researchers found that infants in understaffed institutions, who were cut off from familiar people and places and who were cared for by a bewildering succession of hospital nurses, eventually suffered severe emotional problems. Valid as these studies may be, they tell us nothing about babies who, though looked after by competent babysitters or day-care workers during the day, are reunited with their own loving parents come evening. Fortunately, studies of the last decade have sharpened and reinforced this distinction.

In 1973, for example, Harvard University pediatrician Dr. Mary C. Howell surveyed the voluminous literature on children of working mothers. After poring over nearly 300 studies involving thousands of youngsters, she concluded: "Almost every childhood behavior characteristic, and its opposite, can be found among the children of employed mothers. Put another way, there are almost no constant differences found between the children of employed and nonemployed mothers." To wit: Researchers found both groups equally likely to make friends easily or to have trouble getting along with their peers, to excel at their studies or to fail, to get into trouble or to exhibit model behavior, to be well adjusted and independent or to be emotionally tied to the apron strings, to love and feel loved by their parents or to reject them.

Just recently, Harvard psychologist Jerome Kagan and two researchers from the Tufts New England Medical Center, Phillip Zelazo and Richard Kearsley, zeroed in on the possible effects of day care on the emotional and developmental progress of infants whose mothers worked, as compared to children raised by their mothers at home. As the yardstick for his evaluation, Kagan used three characteristics considered "most desirable" by parents: intellectual growth, social development and ability to achieve a close relationship with the mother. His results? Provided the center was well staffed and well equipped, Kagan and his colleagues were unable to find *any* significant differences between the two groups of children.

Since a mother's working per se is no longer considered a crucial factor in a child's development, what factors *are* important? To find out, let's examine the problem from a different perspective. Instead of thinking in terms of working and stay-at-home mothers, we'll divide women according to whether or not they *enjoy* whatever it is they are doing, and here we can see the differences emerge.

Back in 1956, psychologist Jack Rouman traced the progress of 400 California school children and found that the emotional problems they suffered were related not to their mothers' employment status but, rather, to the state of their mothers' emotions. He concluded: "As long as the child is made to feel secure and happy, the mother's full-time employment away from the home does not become a serious problem."

Take Linda Farber, a Philadelphia city clerk who hates her job, is bitter at her ex-husband for leaving her, making it necessary for her to work, and who feels tied down by her six-year-old son, Greg. He, in turn, is wetting his bed again, gets stomachaches every morning before school and is withdrawing from other children. On the other hand, Marjorie Gorman would love to return to the personnel office where she worked before her kids were born, but her husband insists, "It's your duty to stay home with the children." Marjorie is bored and restless. Annie, her oldest daughter, has run away from home three times, has thrown a kitchen knife at her parents and is habitually truant.

Of course, these children's problems are not triggered simply by their mothers' attitudes about work. But maternal unhappiness and resentment is easily communicated to other members of the family, and can, indeed, influence the quality of home life.

Studies undertaken by University of Michigan psychologist Lois Wladis Hoffman bear this out. She found that employed women who enjoy their jobs are more affectionate with their children and less likely to lose their tempers than mothers who are disenchanted with their daily work. Furthermore, those who are content with their situations are more likely to have sons and daughters who think well of themselves, as measured on tests of self-esteem, than are resentful workers or unhappy homemakers. Following a 1974 review of 122 research papers on working mothers and their children, Dr. Hoffman concluded, "The dissatisfied mother, whether employed or not and whether lower class or middle class, is less likely to be an adequate mother." Norwegian psychologist Aase Gruda Skard agrees: "Children develop best and most harmoniously when the mother herself is happy and gay. For some women the best thing is to go out to work, for others it is best to stay in the home."

For Ellen Anthony, staying at home to care for her small baby was stifling. "I need to work," she insists. "Without some outside stimulation and a way to discharge pent-up energy, I become bored and aggressive. Now that I'm back at my public relations post, I don't overpower my daughter and husband so much and we're all happier." Carol Brunetti, on the other hand, left a good job as a department store buyer to devote full attention to her infant son. "I haven't missed my job for a minute," she says. "I love the flexibility of making my own hours. And whenever I want to go somewhere, I just take Jason along with me."

But Mom's attitude is not the only one that must be taken into consideration. No one will argue the fact that the happiness of both mother and children also depends on the father: How a husband feels about his wife's working is crucial to the emotional climate within the home. And his attitude is a distillation of many things—whether he considers himself a success or a failure at his own profession, what the basic marital relationship is like and how willing he is to assume a fair share of the management of the household and the children if his wife takes a job.

Obviously, the woman whose husband approves of her working is lucky: Balancing job and family is never easy, but when a wife has to do the juggling herself, as well as contend with a husband's opposition, it's twice as difficult.

Happily, many a man who was originally opposed to his wife's working has discovered that he likes spending more time getting to know his children, that money problems have lessened and that he and his wife have more to talk about now that she's also exposed to new people and situations.

Although many psychoanalysts continue to stress the need for an exclusive relationship between mother and baby, recent research has shown that such relationships are probably the exception rather than the rule, even in families where the female parent does not go out to work. For one thing, most fathers today are vital figures in their children's lives. A 1974 study by Milton Kotelchuck of Harvard University found that one- and two-year-olds are just as attached to their fathers as to their mothers. And for another, the typical baby in our society is cared for by several other people in addition to its parents.

According to anthropologist Margaret Mead, who has examined child-rearing patterns in societies around the world, the notion that a baby must not be separated from its mother is absurd. Babies are most likely to develop into well-adjusted human beings, she says, when they are cared for "by many warm, friendly people"—as long as most of the loved ones maintain a stable place in the infants' lives.

There's the rub. For many working mothers, finding these "warm, friendly people" to care for their children on a long-term basis is often a frustrating and expensive proposition. Experts agree that the following scenarios are probably the most stable (and, in turn, most successful), especially for babies and toddlers:

• A father who is able to dovetail his work schedule with his wife's so that their child can be looked after by one parent or the other.
• A grandmother, other relative, friend or neighbor who cares for a child in his or her own home.
• Family day care—an arrangement similar to the one above but between people who have not previously met, often arranged by a public agency.
• A full-time babysitter who comes to the house five days a week and may perform housekeeping chores, too.
• A well-run, well-staffed day-care center.

But once the parents have made the decision that Mommy should work, what about the kids? How will *they* take to their mother's new role—and if they don't, what can you do to make them understand?

Most likely, children will have mixed feelings about Mommy's new job. David, nine, whose mother is the only working mother on the block, sometimes asks her, "Why can't you be home when I get home from school like Mark's mother? She always gives us milk and cookies." But the day David's class visited the dress factory where his mother works, he proudly explained her role in designing the clothes they saw being produced.

One woman met her child's resentment head-on. After ten-year-old Lisa had asked for the umpteenth time, "Oh, why do you have to work, anyway?" her mother stopped what she was doing, sat down with her daughter and explained just how important her job was to her. She let Lisa know that she understood the child's annoyance but she made it clear—without getting angry—how unhappy, bored and restless she would be staying home.

A group of 11-year-olds told an investigator that they loved the responsibility of using their own keys to let themselves in and out and they relished the privilege of having the house to themselves for a few hours after school.

What can both parents do to help children more readily accept their mother's employment? Child-care experts suggest that you:

• Plan your schedules so that at least one parent is with the baby for half his or her waking hours during the first three years of life.
• Institute new child-care arrangements a week or so before you start a job, so that your child has a chance to get used to the new set-up.
• Don't take a full-time job for the first time or make a big change in child-care arrangements when your baby is between six months and a year old, or between one-and-a-half and two-and-a-half. Try to wait a couple of months after any major upheaval—such as a move to a new home, a long illness or the break-up of a marriage.
• Keep in close touch with whoever is caring for your child and consider her or him a partner in nurturing.
• Plan "child time" into your schedule when your youngsters can depend on having some uninterrupted time with you. It need not be long, but it should be regular.
• Let your children know how much they mean to you, and that they mean more to you than your job.

"The mother who obtains satisfaction from her work, who has adequate arrangements so that her dual role does not involve undue strain, and who does not feel so guilty that she overcompensates, is likely to do quite well and, under certain conditions, better than the nonworking mother," insists Dr. Hoffman.

In other words, it's not a matter of "whether" or "where"—but of "how" the woman who works balances the seemingly conflicting elements in her life. As one magazine editor explains, "I feel I have the best of both worlds—I love my family and I love my work, and every day in every way I feel a little better about being me."

Suffer the children

Child abuse: one of the world's most horrifying social problems.

Gary Turbak

RON MADDUX killed Melisha Gibson. Because she had wet her bed, Maddux forced the four-year-old to walk for hours between the kitchen and her bedroom. Occasionally, he made her drink a spoonful of hot sauce. Each time she vomited. Once, he promised her a glass of water if she'd down another gulp of the sauce, but when she complied, he drank the water instead. In the evening, he began hitting her with a stick as she walked. After she was finally allowed to sleep, he awakened her and put her in a cold shower because she had again wet the bed. Before morning, Melisha died in her sleep.

Was Ron Maddux some crazed stranger who had spirited Melisha away from her loving parents? No, he was her stepfather, and her mother was not unaware of what was happening.

The abuse of children—most often by parents—has become a social ill of major proportions. "If you had a disease that affected so many children annually," says Dr. Douglas Besharov, director of the U.S. National Center on Child Abuse and Neglect, "you'd have an epidemic." Dr. Vincent Fontana of the New York Foundling Hospital Center for Parent and Child Development believes child abuse "may be one of the most common causes of death in children." In the U.S.A., 2,000 youngsters are abused to death each year. Only cancer, accidents, congenital abnormalities, and pneumonia take more young lives there. West German parents batter 1,000 of their progeny to death each year; England is not far behind, with 700. In Canada, about 100 children die every year as a result of ill treatment. Statistics are lacking for most other nations, but there's no reason to believe their children are any safer. Only recently has any country taken a hard look at the cruelty being inflicted upon its children.

In 1961, a U.S. doctor, C. Henry Kempe, coined the term "battered child syndrome" to explain the repeated fractures, burns, cuts, and bruises suffered by thousands of U.S. children. Only through doctors willing to testify in such cases can a path be blazed through the taboos against interfering with the rights of parents.

Taking the wraps off child abuse has unveiled a nightmare. Babies are dunked in boiling water. Youngsters are locked in boxes or closets for years. Bed-wetters are chained to their beds. Infants with soggy diapers are set on hot steam radiators. Little fingers are held in open flames and forced onto hot burners. Lighted cigarettes are pressed against tender young skin. Children are beaten with fists, electric cords, auto fan belts, pool cues, baseball bats, and chair legs. And they are stabbed, shot, shocked, drowned, and have plastic bags tied over their heads. Usually, parents are responsible.

Surprisingly, these abusive mothers and fathers are not psychotics on the rampage; 90 percent of them fall into the broad classification of "normal." They are the people next door, the couple sitting next to you in church. They are—potentially—any parents.

Perhaps the factor most often leading a parent to abuse his child is the abuse he himself suffered as a youngster. Parents nearly always rear their children the way they were raised, and if their history includes abuse, they pass it on to the next generation. One study in England discovered a family with five generations of abuse, including six deaths, three batterings, ten cases of cruelty or starvation, and 11 children left unsupervised. Only seven offspring were not obviously mistreated.

West German sociologists have uncovered other reasons for parental abuse of children: the child thwarts the plans parents may have for their own lives; the youngster doesn't live up to their expectations; the parent feels threatened by the child and comes to regard the child as a rival; the child resembles an unliked relative; he or she is of the wrong sex; the child is the result of one parent's former marriage and is resented by the new spouse; or the youngster is deformed or retarded and thus thought to bring disgrace to the family.

Although child abuse ignores political boundaries, race, income, and social, educational, ethnic, and class distinctions, a profile of the potentially abusive parent has emerged. He is immature. He feels isolated and distrustful of others. He often lacks self-control and has a poor

Reprinted from THE ROTARIAN for June 1979.

self-image. He exhibits a low tolerance for day-to-day frustrations. Most abuse, says U.S. physician Dr. Claude Frazier, "is a result of the inability of rather ordinary people to cope with life's stresses."

And so, for reasons perhaps deeply buried in their psyches, these parents lash out at their children. The ill treatment may come in several forms. Physical abuse is the most common and is limited only by the cruel ingenuity of the adult. Emotional abuse, such as the ignoring, rejecting, berating, or abandoning of a child, is more subtle; this kind of treatment can permanently scar the child's developing personality. Sexual abuse is greatly underdiagnosed but is known to be perpetrated frequently, particularly against young girls. Finally, parents may neglect to properly feed and clothe a youngster, or they may withhold needed medical help.

What is being done about this glaring social evil? Programs vary from well-developed to non-existent. West Germany now has a government-sponsored 24-hour abuse hotline and information center located in Hamburg. Poland uses its system of "protective courts" to separate abused or neglected children from their parents; about 1,000 sentences a year are passed there curtailing or suspending parental rights.

Some Australian states provide a 24-hour reporting center, and offer extensive protection to those who register complaints. France's Association for Defense of Child Abuse Victims and England's National Children's Bureau are two of the many organizations working on the problem in those nations. The Israeli justice system employs a "youth examiner" to ferret out the truth in suspected incidents of abuse and neglect; the examiner supplants the police in many cases and is allowed to testify in court on the child's behalf.

The U.S. National Center for the Prevention and Treatment of Child Abuse and Neglect in Denver, Colorado, provides residences where troubled families may live as a unit while they work together on the problem. Other Denver programs include therapy for parents, a round-the-clock crisis nursery, and a therapeutic play school for abused children. Many similar organizations and programs are functioning in other U.S. cities.

One of the biggest roadblocks to effective prevention or treatment is in finding the families who need it. A few governments legally require doctors, nurses, and teachers to report suspected cases; but in most countries, reporting is purely voluntary. France has recently begun pushing for more citizen participation in locating abused children. The magazine Paris-Match urges its readers to report abuse, assuring them they will remain anonymous. It suggests this procedure: If you suspect that harm has been done to a child, talk to him and try to determine the source of his injuries; report suspected abuse or neglect to a social worker or teacher; or summon a policeman when you spot an abused child in a public place.

Recognizing the signs of abuse is not always easy. The U.S. Department of Health, Education, and Welfare says that abused children—in addition to their obvious injuries—may seem unduly afraid of parents, fear contact with all adults, have normal injuries that are improperly treated, display poor general care, exhibit extremes of behavior, have unexplained learning problems, go to school early and stay late, and be improperly clothed. Such symptoms should be reported to authorities—by anyone who observes them.

Like their children, abusive parents often follow a behavioral pattern. They may remain isolated or mix

Healing the damaged child

"THE RIGHT to affection, love, and understanding. . . . The right to be brought up in a spirit of peace. . . ." These are two of the 10 rights cited in the United Nations Declaration of the Rights of the Child, the humanitarian document which this year, on its 10th anniversary, inspired the International Year of the Child. But many children will never attain these rights unless concerned adults, like ourselves, help to change their circumstances.

How do we do this? How do we invade the sanctum of the family, the basic, and the hardest to penetrate of all social units, surrounded as it is by a wall of respectability, regardless of its internal conditions? Public exposure of abusive parents is disgracing, embarrassing to accuser and accused. Yet, when a child's safety—perhaps his life—is in question, how do we NOT respond? What CAN we do?

For one thing, we can become advocates of the rights of children. As advocates, we can be on the lookout for abused children, and we can report their condition to local authorities or child welfare agencies. We can make sure that counseling is available for abusive parents. And we can offer our services as teachers, surrogate parents and grandparents—and friends—to children who have known the terrors of brutality.

"The hearts of small children are delicate organs," wrote U.S. novelist Carson McCullers in "The Member of the Wedding." "A cruel beginning in this world can twist them into curious shapes. The heart of such a child may fester and swell until it is a misery to carry within the body. . . ."

The International Year of the Child[*]—the first year of Rotary's 3-H program—is the time to reach out to our damaged children—through awareness, through advocacy, through active evidence of love.   —THE EDITORS

*A/E Editor's note: The United Nations proclaimed 1979 the International Year of the Child to recognize the human rights of children.

poorly with neighbors. They may offer inconsistent explanations for what could reasonably be normal childhood injuries in their youngsters. They may refuse professional help for their children. Usually, they are overly critical of and rarely exhibit pride in their children. They keep their children confined at home for long periods. They make unrealistic demands.

It should be the responsibility of every individual to report suspicious circumstances to proper officials. To report a case of abuse when, in fact, none exists may cause hard feelings and resentment; but failure to report an actual case will result in a child's suffering needlessly, sometimes even in his death.

Child abuse is certainly not new. Roman fathers were allowed to kill their unwanted children. Various other cultures have also practiced infanticide, and corporal punishment is a disciplinary tactic in many societies. It is still shocking, though, to realize that—in the words of U.S. psychologist David Bakan—"children are being tortured daily in their homes by the very people who gave them life.

"It may well be," says Bakan, "that a long time ago in the cave when it was cold and there was not enough food, the father—irritated by the sound of his crying child—picked up the baby and hurled it against the wall. But we are no longer in the cave."

For some children, unfortunately, a modern habitat makes little difference.

Rotarians and other concerned citizens in your community can help, however, by discovering these mistreated youngsters and offering them—and their parents—the kind of social assistance that has proven effective elsewhere.

The battering of helpless children is a sick—and sickening—social practice. Saving the life, the health, the sanity, of just one child is reason enough for any adult to take a stand whenever he can give assistance. Fear, indifference, the desire to "mind our own business," should not be allowed to interfere with the natural, humane desire to help whenever we hear the screams of children or see their battle scars. Where the children suffer—and no one defends them—the society suffers even more.

The Children of Divorce

I remember it was near my birthday when I was going to be 6 that Dad said at lunch he was leaving. I tried to say, "No, Dad, don't do it," but I couldn't get my voice out. I was too much shocked. All the fun things we had done flashed right out of my head and all the bad things came in, like when he had to go to the hospital with his bad back and when he got mad at me. The bad thoughts just stuck there. My life sort of changed at that moment. Like I used to be always happy and suddenly I was sad.

—An 8-year-old girl

On the surface, the children of divorce don't seem any different from kids whose families are still intact. They wear the same tattered jeans, smile with the same metallic braces, spend mindless hours listening to The Who. But they are different—for divorce, though no longer a stigma, is nonetheless a wrenching series of crises that sets these children apart. While much attention has been devoted to the plight of the single mother, and more recently to the travails of the single father, professionals finally are addressing themselves in a systematic and intelligent way to the dilemma of children of divorce. And the results are startling. Says Albert Solnit, director of the Yale Child Study Center in New Haven, Conn.: "Divorce is one of the most serious and complex mental-health crises facing children of the '80s."

The problem is formidable in numbers alone. There are currently 12 million children under the age of 18 whose parents are divorced—and all in all, around 1 million children a year suffer through the dissolution of their families. The sheer magnitude of this marital falling-out has impelled sociologists, psychologists, family-court judges and educators to explore just how gravely the children are affected. In spite of the comforting old saw that children are flexible enough to learn to "cope" and "bounce back," the evidence suggests that the impact of divorce and the resulting period of adjustment can be both painful and damaging. "The trauma of divorce is second only to death," says child psychologist Lee Salk. "Children sense a deep loss and feel they are suddenly vulnerable to forces beyond their control."

Counseling groups have sprung up in schools, in the courts and in private practice to help children through the transition from two parents to one. New attention is also being focused on the unanticipated problems of step-families (p. 190), now referred to in sociological jargon as "reconstituted" or "blended" families.

Scary Stereotypes: The innocent victims of divorce have always been a popular subject. In 1927, Clara Bow and Gary Cooper starred in the movie "Children of Divorce," a melodrama in which the grown-up offspring descend into debauchery and, finally, suicide. The contemporary treatment of the subject deals less with the scary stereotypes and more with the realistic heartbreak of both parents and child. In the climactic custody battle for a 6-year-old boy in the film "Kramer Vs. Kramer," there are no "good guys" or "bad guys," no winners—only losers. The children of divorce have also become a staple of prime-time television serials and a market for specialized books. The ranks of current fiction and nonfiction for children now boast no fewer than 46 titles dealing with family breakups, including a read-aloud picture book written for pre-schoolers called "Mommy and Daddy Are Divorced."

The country's institutions are finding themselves forced to address the problem in new ways. Schools, traditionally reluctant to get involved in a child's life outside the classroom, are now beginning at least to take notice of the special needs of children from divorced families. Many boys take out their frustration and anger in school, becoming bullies or disrupting the classroom. Girls, on the other hand, are apt to become withdrawn and silent. The burden has fallen on teachers to help these students because divorcing parents are often not up to dealing with their children's stress. "When a mother can't get out of bed in the morning or remember to put make-up on, she can't go to a PTA meeting or listen to kids' problems," explains Mary Hirschfeld, a Beverly Hills divorce lawyer-turned-family counselor.

Courts are also struggling with the new complexities of child custody. Whereas 100 years ago children invariably remained with the father after divorce, traditional custody later shifted to the mother, unless she was proved seriously unfit. Now, with more and more parents negotiating for joint custody, with fathers fighting for sole custody and with distressing numbers of parents resisting any custody, family courts are backlogged with long and painful battles. The children are caught brutally in the middle.

Such strain and pressure is spawning a whole new specialization in divorce among family counselors. Research has shown that the brunt of the shock can be lessened, for example, if the children are told about the divorce in a realistic way, if they are reassured about keeping in contact with both parents and if their daily routines are disturbed as little as possible. Professionals also encourage children to air their problems instead of bottling them up. In Lexington, Mass., 30 teen-agers in a self-help group called Divorced Kids Group meet weekly under the supervision of a high-school guidance counselor to sort out their complex feelings and give one another support. "Sometimes I feel I've got the worst deal. My family is so screwed up,"says one 17-year-old girl. "Then I come here and someone has far more problems."

Though divorce is not easy on any child, some come through it with few scars. Called "the survivors" by family professionals, such children can become more self-reliant and relaxed with the removal of marital stress. "They get along well with both parents," says Nancy Weston, director of the Divorcing Family Clinic in Santa Monica, Calif. "They have a great time with each of them."

Ultimate Impact: For most of divorce's children, however, the prognosis is uncertain. It is estimated that 45 per cent of all children born in any given year will live with only one of their parents at some time before they are 18. No one is sure what the ultimate impact will be. "Traditionally, the family has been the transmitter of social values," observes Arthur Norton, chief of the Marriage and Family branch of the Census Bureau. "Will instability in the family make social institutions unstable? The jury is still out."

In a way, I thought I'd made it happen. I thought maybe I'd acted mean to my mother and my sister and I was being punished by God. So I tried to be really good by not waking Mom before schooltime and getting my own breakfast and maybe God would change His mind.

5. CHILD REARING AND CHILD DEVELOPMENT

But it's been three years now, and I'm used to it all. Sometimes, when I make a wish with an eyelash, though, I still wish for Dad to come home.

—A 9-year-old girl

Pervasive as divorce may be, few children are prepared for it to happen in their families. A child's world suddenly collapses, and one expert estimates that for 80 per cent of the children, there is no warning at all. Even when the tidings come gently, the reaction is almost universal: shock, followed by depression, denial, anger, low self-esteem and, among preteens, the feeling that they are somehow responsible for the divorce. "The child learns the rules of human relationships in the immediate household," says Donald A. Bloch, director of the Ackerman Institute for Family Therapy in New York. "When the child sees that world splitting up, he feels his world is shattered. His learned rules no longer make sense or are true."

A child's response to divorce varies according to age. Toddlers between the ages of 2 and 4, for example, often regress in their development to a more dependent level, demanding to be fed instead of feeding themselves, reverting to diapers. In this age group, when sexual interest runs high, the removal of the parent of the opposite sex is thought by some psychiatrists and psychologists to be particularly detrimental to the child's sexual development. At the same time, children this age often wish parents of the same sex out of the competition, and when the parent actually leaves, the child is convinced he or she has caused it.

Children between the ages of 6 and 8 also take on the responsibility for the split-up, but they have the additional fears of abandonment and often of starvation. "They are old enough to realize what is going on, but they don't have adequate skills to deal with it," explains John Tedesco, chief psychologist at the Des Moines Child Guidance Center in Iowa. Many experts agree that this is the most critical age for children of divorce—and it is the one with the largest number of children affected.

Some children react by trying to gain control over what they feel to be chaos. One little boy, who used to delight in derailing his toy trains, began carefully running the cars over the tracks day after day. Others, especially boys whose fathers have left, try to become the missing parent, assuming responsibilities that are not appropriate for their young age. One 7-year-old in East Hampton, N.Y., worked himself into exhaustion by staying up all night to protect his mother and sister from burglars. In a study of 26 children of divorce between the ages of 5½ and 7 in Marin County, Calif., social worker Judith Wallerstein was struck by their pervasive sense of sadness. Unlike toddlers who could fantasize that their families were still intact, these slightly older children could not, and they tended to dream up fanciful reasons for the divorce. "They only knew each other two days before getting married and they should have known each other at least nine," one 7-year-old explained to Wallerstein.

Father Figure: Between the ages of 8 to 12, the children's most distinguishing emotion is anger directed at whatever parent is thought to be the initiator of the divorce. A 9-year-old girl accused her mother of kicking her father out of the house. "She's acting like a college kid," the girl told Wallerstein in disgust. "At age 31—dancing and dating and having to be with her friends." The anger can erupt in classrooms and alienate friends just when they are most needed. At the same time, children at this age often form a very close relationship with one friend, or with a teacher or another adult, transferring emotions from the noncustodial parent. But other effects may come to the surface later, cautions Hilary Anderson who founded CHILD (Children Helped in Litigated Divorce) in Chicago. "Often a girl will look for a father figure in people she dates. She looks for someone to take care of her. She gives up."

Teen-agers have a different set of problems. Unlike younger children, they feel little sense of blame for the separation of their parents, but they are saddled with what Tedesco calls the "loyalty dilemma." "Mom doesn't want me to like Dad, and vice versa," says 14-year-old Hilary Brodley of Chicago, eighteen months after her parents' separation. "She tells me bad stories. He tells me others. I'm always in the middle."

The sex of the child also plays a part in the impact of divorce. According to University of Virginia psychologist E. Mavis Hetherington, who recently completed a study on 72 divorced middle-class families, boys are the harder hit. More is expected of them, she explains, and they receive far less support from their mothers, teachers and peers as a result. The boy may then begin a destructive circle of bullying other children, then crying when they hit back. As a consequence of alienating boys his own age, the child turns to younger boys or to little girls, learning feminine rather than masculine play patterns. A little girl, on the other hand, vents her sadness by crying—literally—for attention. "When she whines, she is usually helped," says Hetherington.

Cutting through all age and sex distinctions is an obsessive desire to reunite the parents. One 2½-year-old in Chicago spent fretful hours trying to place his father's hand in his mother's hand. A 9-year-old New York girl spent all winter without a jacket on, trying to get sick enough so her parents would have to care for her—together. "All I did was get a lot of colds," she says ruefully. Even though her parents have been separated for four years, a 13-year-old girl in Virginia is adamant that they not get a divorce. "Once all the papers are signed, I wouldn't have a chance," she says. "Now I have hope."

You never feel permanent anymore. I feel like an animal with a mind. You have to spend so much time with each person. You go from place to place. And I don't feel at home at Dad's. I feel very strange when his girlfriend is around. I think of it as being her fault.

—A 15-year-old girl

Adjusting to postdivorce life between two homes and two parents, often in reduced circumstances, is complicated and confusing. The costs of litigation and maintaining two households can reduce the family's income enormously, and a recent Census Bureau report found that only 25 per cent of divorced, separated or single mothers receive child support. One financially pressed divorcee in Los Angeles had to move her three children across town into her parents' one-bedroom house. In that single move, her oldest child lost not only his father and his home, but also his school and his friends. After constantly getting into fights at his new school and failing at his schoolwork, he entered therapy just in time. "The child was suicidal because he had swallowed all the guilt and couldn't handle all the change," explained Los Angeles counselor Jim Larson.

Children involved in custody battles are the most torn. Easily swayed by appeals from either parent, children are often duped into switching allegiances. One 13-year-old California girl was told to choose which parent she wanted to live with. She chose her mother because she had been promised her own phone. But the phone never materialized. "Christmas came and there was no phone," says the girl who is now in a counseling group. "She bribed me. Dumb. So I went back to Dad. Then we all started fighting. I was switching back and forth. The court finally said I was totally confused."

To avoid the no-win pain of custody fights, more and more parents are turning to joint custody, sharing equal responsibility in caring for the children. Eight states now have joint custody provisions. Ordinarily, this means that the children shuttle between their parents' homes. In Houston, Texas, Heath Ruggles, 6, and his older brother Tracy, 9, spend one night with their mother, the next with their father and stepmother, and alternate weekends. The four-year-old experiment seems to be working—almost. Heath's nursery school report card last year found him exemplary in all ways except for one confusion: he wasn't sure where he lived. Chuck and Joan Mathison of Long Beach, Calif., came up with an imaginative solution to this problem: they move and the children stay. They spend alternate years living with their two children Todd, 10, and Lisa, 11, in their old house, relinquishing one night a week and weekends to the off-year parent. Psychologists and the courts are divided about the wisdom of joint custody. "One group of psychologists tells us the best course is to shuttle the child back and forth between the parents on an equal basis," says Marvin Freeman, recently retired supervising judge at the Los Angeles Family Law Court. "The others think they should stay put in one home. At least they both agree that the kids should have their own bed wherever they go." The arrangement also leads to problems when the two parents disagree over a matter such as schooling or medical treatment: at times the courts have to break these deadlocks.

Embittered parents who don't think the courts will give them a fair shake sometimes resort to kidnapping their own children. About 25,000 children a year are snatched or hidden from one parent by the other. Children's Rights, Inc. (CRI), a Washington-based clearinghouse for information on parental kidnapping, estimates that if snatched children aren't found within six months, they probably won't be found for years. Parents on the run move frequently and often don't enroll the children in school for fear of being traced. "Child-snatching still amazes me," says Rae Gummel, CRI co-director. "It's like a bad soap opera."

Each man my mother went out with I considered my next stepfather. And with every one I'd try to be that much more caring so that he'd like me and we'd get off to a good start. I finally realized she was just having fun and didn't want to get married again right now. So I bagged the whole thing. I was exhausted trying to be a son to each one. Her boyfriends became just people.
—A 15-year-old boy

The return to the dating game is invariably a chaotic time for both parent and child. Both men and women feel compelled to join a social whirl to re-establish their attractiveness, leading to a temporary neglect of the children. The children can feel abandoned as a result—but may store up their resentment. "It can burst out later," says Chicago divorce attorney Burton Zoub. "Years later they'll say, 'You never came to see me during that time'."

Parental dating often poses a threat to the children who see the new partner as replacing the departed parent. The children tend to feel as if they're being disloyal—and may be jealous over the newcomer's place in their parent's affections. But over a period of time, children can enjoy—and adjust to—their parent's friends if they feel included in the relationship. "I'd be furious with you if you had a secret lover we didn't know about," one 9-year-old girl told her mother. "But Larry is a friend to all of us."

Juggling sexual activity and parenting also poses a challenge, both to divorced parents and their curious offspring. One divorced mother in Washington worked it out by trading her sons off every other weekend with another divorced woman, leaving one house child-free. But on the whole, children seem far less disturbed by their parents' sexual activity than the parents do. "I caught one guy sneaking out of the house at 5 a.m.," said one 12-year-old boy in disgust. "Why didn't he want to have breakfast with me? It was tacky." Indeed, many children hope for even the appearance of a normal family. Eleven-year-old Eddie Coleman in New York City is happy his father's girlfriend has moved in. "Before, all we had was a grownup, a boy and a little black cat in this big house," says Eddie. "It feels nice to have a family."

No matter how hard I try to erase the idea, I really want to get married. Even with my parents and all my grandparents divorced, I believe in commitment. In fact, I want a huge wedding with bridesmaids, a partner for my whole life and a family. It's a

challenge and the optimism I have is funny to me. But if I'm lucky, I'll have that sense of continuity.
—A 23-year-old woman

The verdict is still out on how this generation of divorced children will fare in their own marital lives. Hetherington, an acknowledged expert in the field, is pessimistic after her work with divorced families. She predicts three out of four children of divorce will repeat the pattern. Wallerstein is more optimistic because the children she sees still believe a mother, father and children living under the same roof is the norm—and a worthwhile goal.

Muddling Through: How long is the period of adjustment for children of divorce? That also varies with the age of the child and the stability of the child's life following separation. Hetherington concludes that the impact dwindles away a year or two after the separation. "All of the family members tend to get worse before they get better," she says. "An important message to understand is that, even though the situation seems to be deteriorating, it improves very suddenly." The adjustment takes longer, according to Wallerstein. In the study she co-authored with psychologist Joan Kelly, she found that five years after the separation, a third of the children seemed to be resilient; an equal number seemed to be muddling through, coping as they could, and the rest were bruised, looking back to life before the divorce with intense longing.

Some institutions and professionals are now trying to ease the painful passage through divorce for the children. A training program for teachers on how best to cope with divorced parents and their children is being offered through the McLean Institute for School Consultation in Belmont, Mass. Many schools, such as the public schools in East Hampton, N.Y., have instituted programs to spot troubled children early. Utilizing dolls, clay and drawing to reach the children, the East Hampton program has proved very beneficial. "Jake," a second-grader, refused to believe his father had left home even though the father had moved to California. "He withdrew by becoming a machine in 'Star Wars' rather than Jake at home," says counselor Polly Haessler. Finally Jake admitted to himself that his father was indeed gone when he built a house out of blocks, put in mother and father dolls, then took the father doll out.

Best Interest? Courts are turning more and more to outside professionals for help in deciding custody and visitation cases. Instead of the old bitter adversary proceeding where lawyers fought for their clients regardless of the best interest of the child, some states are either referring such cases to conciliation courts, where the families can work out a compromise with an impartial third party, or appointing a guardian to represent the child. In contested custody cases in Wisconsin, the court is required by law to appoint an attorney for the child. The lawyer interviews teachers, clergy, neighbors and friends for guidance as to which living arrangement is best for the child. The attorney's fee is paid by the parents if they are able, or by the community.

In Los Angeles, where the conciliation court successfully mediates 55 per cent of the cases, the court employs five therapists for custody evaluations as well as a staff of custody investigators—social workers with master's degrees—who do family studies to determine the child's best interest. "They solve more problems than all the lawyers and judges put together," says Judge Freeman.

Kidnapping one's own children may well be on its way to being a Federal offense. States now vary widely on child-snatching laws. While 39 states have enacted the Uniform Child Custody Jurisdiction Act, the remaining eleven are potential havens for parental kidnappers. The Parental Kidnapping Prevention Act, now in Senate hearings, would honor and enforce custody and visitation decrees of other states, and make it a Federal misdemeanor to restrain or conceal a child in violation of a custody or visitation decree. Some think the cure may be worse than the disease. Criminalization "may increase the potential for violent confrontation and emotional trauma, if not physical danger to the child," FBI executive assistant director Lee Colwell warned in Senate hearings last week.

Mock Trial: Counseling programs are also helping to mend familial fences and build support systems for children who withdraw into emotional isolation. In Hennepin County, Minn., the Department of Court Services offers a free program called The Divorce Experience for families about to be dissolved. The first meeting explains the court system and divorce laws to parents, the next two explain the process to the children, having them take part in a mock trial. In Rolling Meadows, Ill., a peer-group counseling program for divorced kids uses such exercises as falling backward off a 6-foot-high "Trust Log" into the hands of the group and scaling a 14-foot-wall using nothing but each other for help. The program has been so successful that social worker Toby Landesman experimented with a mother-daughter group. "A lot of kids think they had something to do with the divorce, so we build bridges back home," says Landesman.

The brunt of divorce can be eased from the beginning if the children are properly told and reassured about their futures. Child psychologist Lee Salk advises parents to tell the child about their plans together if possible and not to hide their own distress. "The most important thing parents can do is to tell the child that even though they are divorcing each other, they are not divorcing the child," says Salk, himself the divorced father of two. Richard A. Gardner, a New Jersey psychiatrist and the author of five books on divorce, suggests that the children be told the real reasons for the split-up. "Just telling the child that 'We don't love each other anymore,' is a cop-out," says Gardner. "Tell them the real reasons, like, 'Your father drinks too much,' or 'I've met someone else I care about more.' But no matter what deficiencies are presented to the child, the parent must present the other parent's assets as well."

Though divorce is upsetting to everyone involved, it is equally disturbing, perhaps worse, for children to live in an embattled household. And there are some who profess that divorce can be positive for children. "All crises provoke tension and behavioral difficulty, but they can also be learning and growing experiences," says sociologist Lenore Weitzman, director of the California Divorce Law Research Project. "No one knows how much disruption it causes for unhappy families to remain intact. No one's done that study."

No Role Models: For better or worse, divorce continues to split families at an alarming rate. The number of children involved in divorce has tripled in the last twenty years. And though parents, children and professionals are struggling to deal with such new domestic realities as single-parent families, there are no longstanding precedents, no established role models to draw from. Divorce and its aftermath can be a labyrinth of confusion and conflict, some of which may never be resolved. To divorce lecturer and author Rabbi Earl Grollman of Temple Beth El in Belmont, Mass., divorce can be even more traumatic then death. "The big difference is, death has closure, it's over," says Grollman, who performs divorce ceremonies for families. "With divorce, it's never over."

LINDA BIRD FRANCKE with DIANE SHERMAN in Washington, PAMELA ELLIS SIMONS in Chicago, PAMELA ABRAMSON in San Francisco, MARSHA ZABARSKY in Boston, JANET HUCK in Los Angeles and LISA WHITMAN in New York

After Remarriage

There are four of hers and three of his and one of theirs. His ex-wife has remarried and gained two of her new husband's. Her ex-husband has also remarried into a ready-made family, adding two more stepsons and stepdaughters. And there are four sets of grandparents, not to mention assorted aunts, uncles and cousins. On the "geneogram" at the Stepfamily Foundation, Inc., in New York, the family structure looks like the organization chart of a multinational corporation. But to counselor Jeannette Lofas, president of the foundation, this is the norm. "There are only 22 characters in this cast," laughs Lofas. "This is going to be an easy one to work out."

The nation's swelling step-population now includes some 12 million stepparents and 6.5 million stepchildren under 18. And though people like to think that such blended families live in rewedded bliss, the bliss can be short-lived. The impact of remarriage on a family, regardless of how high the expectations, is second only to the crisis of divorce. Because there are no guidelines for acceptable step-family behavior, at least one expert attributes the higher rate of divorce in second marriages—40 per cent as against 33 per cent in first marriages—to the strain of trying to work it all out. Says Andrew Cherlin, assistant professor of Social Relations at Johns Hopkins University: "It takes a real emotional toll to try to cope with the problems that people in first marriages take for granted."

Brunt: The problems that arise in remarriage are all the more devastating because, for the most part, they are unexpected. The children's secret and often subconscious longing to reunite their real parents is shattered and they are faced with a new parent they neither want nor have room for emotionally. The unsuspecting stepparent can bear the brunt of anger the children have stored up toward the parent they feel deserted them. "We had a terrific time until Sam's mother and I were married," says a New York attorney. "Then slam. Sam all but pretended I was invisible."

Children entering a step-family can feel twice defeated, once for having been unable to prevent the divorce, and again for not being able to prevent the remarriage. Children often form especially strong bonds with a single parent. The arrival of a new partner, particularly for the father, weakens these bonds and the children feel abandoned yet again. "There is a tendency for the new wife to take priority over a man's time, his children, his money," says anthropologist Paul Bohannan, who conducted a survey on stepfathers for the National Institute of Mental Health. "She says the kids can't come for the weekend and he goes along with it."

Juggling different rules and values while still trying to please both sets of parents also places an exhausting burden on the children. "What always happens is that if I get into trouble at school or if my grades are bad," says 14-year-old Janey Harris, who lives in Marin County, Calif., "I'll go through the whole hassle with Mom and stepfather. Then I'll think it's all over and I have to go through it again with Dad. I get tired of it." Children can also feel torn by a divided sense of loyalty. "If we go to Disneyland or something like that with our real dad," says Alex Grishaver, 12, "we don't tell our stepfather because we don't want him to feel bad for not taking us to places like that."

To add to the confusion, children of remarriage often inherit an instant set of new stepsisters and stepbrothers, relationships they are not prepared for. "Not only do the kids not get the pay-

(continued on following page)

(continued from preceding page)

offs in the remarriage that the parents get, but they pay a price," says Dena Whitebook, director of counseling at the American Institute of Family Relations in Los Angeles. "The long-hoped-for brother turns out to be a pig and they find themselves sharing a bathroom with a stranger." At the other extreme, some older step-siblings hit it off too well and start relationships of their own, a tricky dilemma that even the experts find confusing. At a seminar attended by 70 marriage counselors last year the participants were asked to vote on whether step-siblings should be allowed to date. The audience refused to declare either way.

'Super Mom': To help step-families through the maze of both expected and unexpected problems, workshops, discussion groups and candid how-to books are becoming part of the family therapy network. In her book, "Instant Parent," stepmother Suzy Kalter confesses she ended up with an ulcer and a failing marriage until she stopped trying to be "Super Mom." The nearly disastrous experience of New York stepmother Jeannette Lofas, whose four stepdaughters stopped talking to her after she married their father eight years ago, led her to co-author the book "Living in Step" and to found the Stepfamily Foundation, Inc., in 1975. Lofas has worked with 120 step-families and lost only two to divorce. "The usual problem is that the adults have different parenting styles, resulting in the total nonstructuring of the family," says Lofas, whose relationship with her stepdaughters is now strong. "There are not clear-cut chores. No one knows where they fit."

Despite the problems that stepfamilies face, five out of six divorced men and three out of four women remarry within three years. At the Stepfamily Foundation of California, Inc., psychologist Emily Visher and her husband, John, a psychiatrist, are cautiously optimistic about the prospects of these remarriages. "Children have seen the disruption of adult relationships either through death or divorce and now they have the opportunity of seeing a couple working together in a positive way," says Visher, co-author with her husband of the book "Stepfamilies." "That can give them faith in their own future." The way to the future may be rough. "In remarriage there is no honeymoon," says John Visher, himself a stepfather of twenty years' standing. "There is instant pandemonium rather than the gradual progression of first-family marriages. Remarriage does not mean that you'll live happily ever after."

LINDA BIRD FRANCKE with
MICHAEL REESE in San Francisco

What Is TV Doing To America?

In its 43 years, television has been praised as a miracle and damned as a distorter of reality. Now, new evidence is emerging about the medium and how it affects the people who watch it.

Soon after 28-year-old David Radnis watched the movie "The Deer Hunter" on TV in his Chicago-area home, he was dead—one of at least 29 viewers in the U.S. who shot themselves imitating the show's Russian-roulette scene.

When Hoang Bao Trinh fled from Vietnam to Silver Spring, Md., he spent months baby-sitting his grandchildren in front of the TV set. Soon the whole family was speaking English, much of it learned by imitating speech heard on the televised programs.

Such cases reflect TV's increasingly pervasive influence on America, both for good and bad. In a country where television has become a major—and in some cases primary—force determining how people work, relax and behave, the consequences are staggering. Recent studies show that the lives of Americans, from their selection of food to their choice of political leaders, are deeply affected by TV, and that influence is growing.

In an age when millions of inexperienced young people are growing up in front of the tube without close guidance of elders, many Americans worry that the nation could be ruined by a generation that gets its moral values from "Flamingo Road," its cultural standards from "Laverne & Shirley" and its sense of family relationships from "Dallas."

Most broadcasters, with support from some researchers, maintain that TV is unfairly blamed for merely conveying what the public demands and argue that the medium's power is exaggerated. They contend that most people treat television simply as one of many sources of information, and that most homes have basically been unaltered since the first modern home-TV set was marketed in 1939.

Others in the industry are worried that what author and actor Steve Allen calls the "amoral force" of TV and other popular media is helping to weaken old values. "It's horrendous," says Allen. "That our nation, our society, our culture is in some state of moral and ethical collapse is absolutely undeniable. In about 50 years, you could create what we already have a good percentage of—people who think it's perfectly OK to grab what they want, to do what they want, and the only bad thing is getting caught."

Linking the Tube and Violence

A report released in May by the National Institute of Mental Health says that "violence on television does lead to aggressive behavior by children and teenagers who watch the programs." In one five-year study of 732 children, "several kinds of aggression—conflicts with parents, fighting and delinquency—were all positively correlated with the total amount of television viewing." Defenders of TV have long held that there is no clear link between viewing and violence.

The findings covered a wide range of topics. In one survey, more than half the parents thought their children learned more about sex from TV than from any other source except the parents themselves. TV also was cited for fostering bad habits by glamorizing highly advertised junk foods and frequent use of alcohol.

The federally sponsored study noted that almost all Americans watch TV, many for hours each day. Some of the most avid watchers are the very young and very old, women and minorities. Heavy viewers are usually less educated.

"Television can no longer be considered as a casual part of daily life, as an electronic toy," the report stated. "Research findings have long since destroyed the illusion that television is merely innocuous entertainment."

TV is also partly blamed for a sharp slide in traditional learning. Since television became nearly universal in the early 1960s, average scores for high-school students taking the Scholastic Aptitude Test, the broadest measure of academic ability, have plunged from 478 to 424 on the verbal exam and from 502 to 466 in mathematics.

A panel of educators appointed to study the decline noted that by age 16 most children had spent 10,000 to 15,000 hours watching television—more time than they have spent in school. The panel's conclusion: "Is television a cause of the SAT-score decline? Yes, we think it is. . . . Television has become surrogate parent, substitute teacher."

As TV's children graduated in the 1960s and '70s, an Adult Performance Level test found that "20 percent of the American population was functionally incompetent, that is, could not perform the basic kinds of reading, writing or computing tasks—such as calculating the change on a small purchase, addressing an envelope, reading a want ad or filling out a job application." The result, says Paul Copperman, president of the Institute of Reading Development in San Francisco, is that "society may be compelled to support an increasing percentage of dysfunctional or only marginally functional citizens."

TV Has Brought Americans Together

Even the severest critics admit that television has achieved unprecedented results in making the public aware of a huge variety of developments—from war in Lebanon and the Falkland Islands to the plight of migrant workers.

Veteran broadcaster Eric Sevareid argues that television has had an enormously positive influence on America in three main areas: It has brought families together more, it has counteracted the country's tendency toward fragmentation, and it has stayed independent of government.

Says Sevareid: "On balance, TV is better for us than bad for us. When Gutenberg printed the Bible, people thought that invention would put bad ideas in people's heads. They thought the typewriter would destroy the muse, that movies would destroy legitimate theater, that radio would destroy newspapers and that TV would destroy everything. But it doesn't happen that way."

A main virtue of TV, according to scholars, is that the medium is a powerful force for freedom—a far better source of information and motivation than the party apparatus that used to dominate politics in many sections of the country.

Television's broadening of perspectives also is credited with boosting worthwhile causes and diminishing the ethnic, religious and geographic prejudices that have plagued American history. Cited as a key example are the "freedom marches" that caught the attention of TV viewers in the early 1960s. Laws were then passed guaranteeing civil rights that blacks had sought for more than a century.

Many educators add that television has given Americans a wealth of experience and knowledge that isn't being measured by today's school tests. The National Education Association, the nation's biggest teachers' organization, has called for cultivation of "electronic literacy" and has distributed guides to help teachers solidify what students learn from programs like "Holocaust" and "Shogun."

Millions of young Americans have been led through the alphabet and rudiments of algebra by the educational series "Sesame Street" and "Electric Company" of the Children's Television Workshop. One study suggested that children who watch a lot of TV in their early years tend to read more widely later on than children who were lighter viewers when they were young.

The medium also provides an invaluable window on the world for invalids and the elderly. Steve Allen recalls a series of visits he made to hospitals where Vietnam veterans were being treated: "What was helping to pull them through the day was television. The television set does provide company for lonely people, a voice in the house."

Broadcasters point out that, no matter what sociologists think, the public likes what it is getting on television. The A.C. Nielsen Company, an audience-measuring firm, announced that, despite a decline in network viewing, America's 80 million television households averaged a record level of 6 hours and 44 minutes a day in front of the tube in 1981—up 9 minutes from 1980. That's three times the average rate of increase during the 1970s.

Observes one network executive: "It's all there, good and bad. All you have to do is change the dial."

How the Brain Reacts to TV

Until recently, there was little research on how the human brain absorbs information from TV. Many scholars long have been convinced that viewers retain less from television than from reading, but evidence was scarce.

Now, a research project by Jacob Jacoby, a Purdue University psychologist, has found that more than 90 percent of 2,700 people tested misunderstood even such simple fare as commercials or the detective series "Barnaby Jones." Only minutes after watching, the typical viewer missed 23 to 36 percent of the questions about what he or she had seen.

One explanation is that TV's compelling pictures stimulate primarily the right half of the brain, which specializes in

emotional responses, rather than the left hemisphere, where thinking and analysis are performed. By connecting viewers to instruments that measure brain waves, researcher Herbert Krugman found periods of right-brain activity outnumbering left-brain activity by a ratio of 2 to 1.

Another difficulty is the rapid linear movement of TV images, which gives viewers little chance to pause and reflect on what they have seen. Scientists say this torrent of images also has a numbing effect, as measured electronically by the high proportion of alpha brain waves, normally associated with daydreaming or falling asleep.

The result is shortened attention spans—a phenomenon increasingly lamented by teachers trying to hold the interest of students accustomed to TV. To measure attention spans, psychophysiologist Thomas Mulholland of the Edith Nourse Rogers Memorial Veterans Hospital in Bedford, Mass., attached 40 young viewers to an instrument that shut off the TV set whenever the children's brains produced mainly alpha waves. Although the children were told to concentrate, only a few could keep the set on for more than 30 seconds.

Other researchers have found unrealistic career expectations among young people who watch a lot of TV. According to "Television and Behavior," the new federal report: "Heavy viewers want high-status jobs but do not intend to spend many years in school. For girls, there is even more potential for conflict between aspirations and plans; the girls who are heavy viewers usually want to get married, have children and stay at home to take care of them, but at the same time they plan to remain in school and have exciting careers."

Frustration of these expectations, according to social scientists, can spill over into communities, helping to fuel destructive outbursts, ranging from disruption of schools to ghetto riots. Once civil disturbances are telecast, they may spread through imitation, as they did from Washington, D.C., to dozens of other cities in 1968.

Fictional shows can have a similar effect. An airplane bomb threat on "Doomsday Flight" was followed by a rash of similar occurrences across the nation.

"Facts" Are Not Always as They Seem

Another concern is the growing number of Americans who rank television as their main source of news and information—more than two thirds, according to the Roper Poll.

Some complain that "facts" on TV are not always what they seem. A new form of program, the "docudrama," is cited as a potential source of confusion. Mixing established facts and conjecture, a docudrama often is accepted as totally accurate. One such program, "King," was criticized by associates of the Rev. Martin Luther King, Jr., for allegedly misrepresenting

Who Watches TV the Most?
Weekly TV Usage

Older women (ages 55 and over)	36 hr., 33 min.
Older men	33 hr., 15 min.
Younger women (ages 18-55)	31 hr., 49 min.
Younger men	28 hr., 3 min.
Teenagers	22 hr., 59 min.
Children (ages 2-11)	25 hr , 10 min.

USN&WR—Basic data: A. C. Nielsen Company

the personality of the late civil-rights leader.

In his objections to video coverage of budget cutting and poverty, President Reagan joined a long list of politicians who charge that their efforts have been distorted by TV's need for dramatic pictures, rather than factual analysis. The late Chicago Mayor Richard Daley complained that "protesters" against various causes often would show up outside his office door, unknown to him inside, wanting not to present their grievances to him but to get coverage by TV crews whom they had notified in advance.

Television also is blamed for making viewers impatient by distorting their notions of what to expect from life. "TV teaches that all problems can be resolved quickly—within 30 minutes on a sitcom, 30 seconds in a commercial," says Neil Postman, a communications professor at New York University. When that doesn't happen in real life, he adds, "many people become frustrated or depressed."

Author Ben Stein, a speech writer during the Nixon administration, says the fictional creations of TV have tended to make Americans contemptuous and suspicious of their leaders. In his book, *The View From Sunset Boulevard: America as Brought to You by the People Who Make Television*, Stein notes that most "heavies" in TV shows are conservative authority figures such as high-ranking officials and business executives. And a recent study by the Media Institute in Washington, D.C., concludes that two thirds of business leaders in entertainment series are portrayed as foolish, greedy or immoral, and half their actions as illegal.

Helping to Reshape Democracy

Scholars have grown increasingly troubled by some of the effects of TV on democratic government.

More than two decades ago, Richard Nixon's sweat during a televised debate with John F. Kennedy weighed heavily against the Republican candidate for President, and apparently became a factor in his defeat. Since then, other TV debates during political campaigns also have been judged as much for cosmetics as for content, and are regarded as having contributed to winning or losing.

Even in the midst of ballot counting, TV's effects are far-reaching. In 1980, networks declared Ronald Reagan the projected winner soon after polls in Eastern states closed but before balloting ended in the West. Experts say some prospective voters never went to the polls in the West, believing their choices would make no difference.

A lesser-known issue that worries many political scientists is the frequent satirizing of public officials by entertainers such as Johnny Carson and Mark Russell.

According to some scholars, widely viewed TV skits poking fun at former President Jerry Ford's occasional clumsiness may have contributed to his defeat in 1976 by popularizing the notion that Ford was too awkward to lead the nation. Subsequent Presidents—Jimmy Carter and

Ronald Reagan—also have been the objects of ridicule on TV—not a laughing matter if, as some believe, the satire prejudices a candidate's chance for election. Humorous commentary on politics in this country dates back to colonial times, but the immediacy and pervasiveness of television have given such satire added potency. "Now, one or two comics can start nationwide waves of derision that are almost impossible to overcome," says Robert Orben, a humor consultant to many politicians.

Worries About Morality

Concern also is growing about the sexual content of programs flooding cable systems and videocassette machines now installed in more than one third of American homes.

Until recently, X-rated shows made up a heavy majority of the sales of prerecorded videotapes for exhibition on home sets. Among the three-dozen pay-cable networks, at least three—the *Playboy* channel, Eros and Private Screenings—include explicit sexual material. Depending on which channel they select, viewers can find everything from partial nudity to simulated intercourse.

Mainstream-movie channels, such as Home Box Office and Showtime Entertainment, also owe some of their success to occasional airings of unedited theatrical films intended for adults only. Such films often contain obscene language, gore and degrees of undress that would never make it past the in-house censors of conventional TV.

All this has prompted a backlash by communities trying to limit what can be brought into homes via cable. In Manhattan, officials have tried to deny use of the "public access" channel to amateur producers who air programs with footage of people who were persuaded to undress or even engage in sex acts in front of the camera.

Peggy Charren, president of Action for Children's Television, urged Congress to head off a wave of local censorship by requiring cable systems to offer free lock boxes—devices that keep children from watching certain channels.

Others have suggested antiobscenity statutes similar to the rules governing over-the-air television. Many constitutional experts believe, however, that cable will continue to be protected by the First Amendment in the same manner as theatrical movies, books and magazines—especially in light of a recent U.S. district-court ruling that Utah's ban on "indecent" cable programs was unconstitutionally vague.

Some scholars also are concerned about another aspect of moral values that may have been distorted by TV. Lois DeBakey, communications professor and head of a nationwide literacy movement, lists the television industry among "profit-hungry pleasure peddlers" who have created a national tendency to exalt entertainment above crucial needs such as health and education. Noting that highly televised sports stars are paid an average of $250,000 a year and teachers only $20,000, DeBakey asks: "Do we honestly

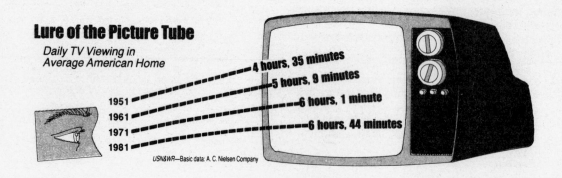

Lure of the Picture Tube

Daily TV Viewing in Average American Home

1951 — 4 hours, 35 minutes
1961 — 5 hours, 9 minutes
1971 — 6 hours, 1 minute
1981 — 6 hours, 44 minutes

USN&WR—Basic data: A. C. Nielsen Company

expect to motivate young people to take school seriously when the highest monetary and social rewards are reserved for occupations in which education is often unnecessary?"

Bigger Role for Special Interests?

Many business and political leaders are troubled by recent developments in video communications, including a movement toward deregulation of TV.

In conventional broadcasting, stations have always been licensed by the Federal Communications Commission to use a scarce public commodity, the airwaves. As a result, they are bound by laws and policies that strictly limit obscenity and prohibit any company from owning more than seven stations, as well as by the fairness and equal-time doctrines requiring free time for opposing views and candidates when controversial opinions are aired.

None of those rules applies, however, to the new outlets of cable, videocassettes and pay TV. Moreover, a drive is under way, backed by the Reagan administration, to repeal those rules for all broadcasters and leave ownership and program content up to what FCC Chairman Mark S. Fowler calls the new "competitive pressures of the marketplace." Fowler's proposals have drawn fire from critics, who call the deregulation movement an invitation for companies and organizations with the most money to control what people see on TV.

Already, various ideological groups are rushing to buy their way onto the tube. By raising as much as 70 million dollars a year from viewers and using the money to purchase air time, conservative evangelists such as Jerry Falwell and Pat Robertson have virtually drowned out the broadcasting voices of the major denominations. Falwell's TV operation launched the Moral Majority, cornerstone of a religious right wing that was active in the conservative shift of the last elections. A Falwell ally, Texas-based TV preacher James Robison, has aired two hour-long specials—"Wake Up, America" and "Attack on the Family"—in more than 50 cities. This spring, producer Norman Lear's liberal group, "People for the American Way," countered with "I Love Liberty," a 3-million-dollar extravaganza.

Local stations have taken the lead in what they call "issue-oriented advertising," commercials espousing political views. Participation so far has mostly been by big firms, such as Mobil Oil, attacking what they regard as excessive government regulation.

Backers of "message programing" maintain that rules of fairness and equal time are no longer needed because the many cable channels, independent stations and networks using relay satellites offer affordable soapboxes to almost anybody.

Opponents, however, say that is wishful thinking, because reaching a large portion of the national audience is too expensive except for a few rich organizations and individuals.

Do Viewers Respond Too Quickly?

Fresh criticism is being leveled at the potential for abuse in two-way cable systems spreading across the country.

These systems allow viewers with home computers or push-button consoles to communicate with central computers in requesting data, ordering merchandise, conducting banking transactions and responding to opinion polls.

Because computers can build dossiers from viewers' responses, civil libertarians fear violations of privacy by businesses or government agencies.

"Two-way systems are hitched to computers that scan each household every 6 seconds, recording all manner of information," explains Les Brown, editor of *Channels of Communication* magazine. "They know what we watch, what we buy through television, how we vote in public-opinion polls."

More than 90,000 homes now have two-way systems, and rapid expansion into a fully "wired society" is expected eventually. Already, there are TV alarm systems tied to police stations and customers' homes that can turn on TV sets and record when people enter or leave a home. Although these processes are now aimed solely at detecting intruders, the possibility of other uses is alarming to some observers.

Brown says he discovered one unsettling ramification of the cable age when he was discussing the issue of privacy in two-way-cable systems during an interview on the Cable News Network. Suddenly, the interviewer called for an instant plebiscite on Brown's concern, and an undetermined number of noontime viewers on the Columbus, Ohio, QUBE system pushed response buttons on their sets.

Eighty-five percent rejected Brown's suggestion that there was anything to worry about.

Knowing that daytime audiences are frequently dominated by preschoolers who may not understand what they are doing but who are capable of pushing the response button, Brown comments: "What's frightening to contemplate is that such polls are routinely conducted on every kind of important national issue, and their results cited as public opinion.

"You will never hear a cable newscaster say, 'QUBE took a poll today, and here's what some 4-year-olds think about the sale of AWACS to Saudi Arabia.' But some poor congressman may think he hears the voice of his constituents" in those results.

Despite the uncertainties, there is widespread hope that the new video age will benefit from the industry's past mistakes and triumphs and do the country far more good than harm.

As Benjamin Barber, a Rutgers University professor of political science, observes: "It is difficult to imagine the Kennedy generation, the '60s, Watergate, the Woodstock generation or even the Moral Majority in the absence of national television."

Now, he adds, those concepts "belong to history, for we stand—prepared or not—on the threshold of a new television age that promises to revolutionize our habits as viewers, as consumers and ultimately as citizens."

JAMES MANN

HOW I STOPPED NAGGING AND STARTED TEACHING MY CHILDREN TO BEHAVE

Paul S. Graubard

An embattled psychologist turned househusband tells how he learned to use his professional skills to run his home, train his children—and save his sanity.

I had always felt that taking care of a house would be a breeze. Becoming a homemaker on a full-time basis would give me more time with my children, and still leave room for all the personal projects I had been putting off. My job was getting routine, and I was sick of commuting. I wanted a change.

My wife, Joy, was delighted when I suggested switching roles. During the 18 years I had worked, she said, she had probably cleaned the toilet 3,000 times, mopped the kitchen floor at least twice that often, and fixed over 15,000 meals. Our children were beginning to grow up—Amy was 16, Risa was 17, Michael was six and in school now also, and even little David was two. Joy had long wanted to go back to teaching elementary school and to have more time for playing her flute. She was more than happy to turn the house over to me.

It seemed an ideal arrangement. I felt I was a good father, and this would really give me a chance to show what I could do. I am a child psychologist and a college professor; it would be easy enough to give up my practice for a while, and I could take off a year or more from teaching. This new arrangement would give me time to write a children's play I had in mind, to perfect my French cooking, to practice the guitar.

Disillusionment set in early—the first morning, to be exact. I wasn't used to changing diapers, writing notes to the teacher, looking for lost sneakers, cooking breakfast and matching up socks—all at once. No matter what I asked the children to do, their sleepy voices would answer, "In a minute." A minute had never seemed like much, but try to get a school-bus driver to wait that long! Michael was always the last one out. He usually made it, but sometimes he didn't and I would have to drive him to school, muttering words he never heard in "Dick and Jane."

The first evening I cooked my secret chicken recipe and brought it to the table. My first surprise came when I found that the children assigned to set the table hadn't done their jobs. My wife smiled understandingly and told me it had happened before and would happen again. Then the children told me frankly that they preferred Kentucky Fried Chicken to mine.

The evenings that followed were not much better. Instead of sitting down with a martini and the newspaper at five o'clock, I was in the kitchen. I peeled and chopped and basted—and snapped at the kids. Joy sat in the den with a mountain of schoolwork. She hardly noticed what we ate.

During the next few weeks there were mornings when I found myself thinking about having a drink instead of a cup of coffee. The only bright spot in my daily routine was that brief period every afternoon when David took a nap. Once, when he refused to sleep, I was tempted to put some—just a little—gin in his orange juice. Fortunately, a neighbor dropped by just in time.

The house, as well as my mental stability, seemed to be coming apart at the seams. Dust, clutter and dog hairs filled the family room, toys and clothing inched their way up the stairs, dishes overflowed in the sink. How, I asked myself, could one person hope to accomplish all that had to be done in the course of a normal day? And if that wasn't bad enough, the children's behavior was. Not only did I have to nag them into doing what little they did around the house, but most of the time they didn't even seem to be listening to me. I never knew whether they would follow orders or not. Would they take the bicycle out of the driveway before it was run over or after? Would they walk the dog in time to prevent an accident? Would they stop fighting before or after I lost my temper?

When I wasn't settling fights, I was tying shoes. I scrubbed hands and faces, did the laundry, set the table, washed dishes and everything else I thought four children required. As slow a learner as I was, I soon realized there was a relationship between my lack of free time and my children's lack of responsibility around the house. By the time I came to this, however, they'd not only strengthened their existing bad habits but had picked up some new ones.

I pleaded with them. It didn't help. I hollered at them. They hollered back. I called family meetings, explained my position over and over again, and ended up talking to myself. Their passive-resistance campaign, wherein they did what they had to do, but ever so slowly, was giving me indigestion. My self-image as a father was in bad shape.

The household had functioned well when my wife was in charge of things. I began to realize the price of that pleasant state. Joy had often said that she'd never had a minute to herself—I now knew what she was talking about. Frankly, I didn't want to put in that much time or energy; taking care of the family was my first priority, but I wanted a life of my own, too. When I figured out that for the rest of the year I would be doing three loads of wash every Tuesday and Thursday morning, I knew I had to do something—fast.

At that point, I started looking for all the help I could get. The most help came from my wife, but she found, as I had found out before her, that with the pressures of a job and commuting there was precious little time left over. Prepared foods, disposable diapers and Dr. Spock were helpful, too, but I was still overwhelmed.

I finally ended up using what I knew best—psychology. In my practice as a child psychologist, I'd worked with hundreds of families and thousands of children. My specialty had been behavior modification. I'd used it to help children overcome social and academic difficulties and to help families learn to work together.

It is a well-known adage that the shoemaker's children often go without shoes. I had not been applying skills to my own children's development. Now, faced with my own survival needs, I began to apply behavior-modification techniques at home.

Dr. B.F. Skinner of Harvard University is usually credited with inventing behavior modification. The real credit should go to Grandma. She started the method when she formulated her famous law: "First finish your spinach. Then you may have your ice cream." I began using it whenever I could.

To apply Grandma's Law, I had to be specific about what I wanted. I started out by making a list of the most important problems. The first list read: toilet train David, get Michael off to school on time, get Michael and Amy to clean up after themselves, have Amy come home on time in the evening, help Risa and Amy stop squabbling, and get everyone to do a share of the chores.

Once I was satisfied that achieving those goals would be to the children's benefit as well as my own, I had to find a way of motivating them, of making them want to reach the goals. I thought of it—as Grandma might have—as a *when-then* proposition. *When* I saw the desired behavior (or even anything that came close to it), *then* I would reinforce it. "Reward improvement" became my motto.

Reinforcers, in psychologist's terms, are simply rewards that work. Reinforcers increase the number of times a given behavior occurs. You have to observe the child closely in order to know when and what to reinforce, and which reinforcer is appropriate to use. For example, some of my children would have given almost anything to go on a fishing trip with me. The others couldn't have cared less. Only the child, through his or her behavior, can tell you whether the reward works. If it doesn't, it obviously isn't a reinforcer.

Behavior modification sounds simple, and in many respects it is. But to repeat: Behavior that is reinforced will be strengthened; behavior that is not reinforced will be weakened. That is the essence of the method. Reward a child for the good things he does, and those good things are likely to be repeated. Conversely, if you do *not* reinforce good behavior, it is not likely to be repeated.

I discovered (actually my wife pointed it out to me) that I had fallen into a trap. I had been rewarding my children's misbehavior by paying so much attention to it, and I was taking the good things for granted. Everyone likes to be praised or rewarded when he or she does a good job, and children are no exception. In the beginning, I used some material rewards to help us get back on the track; after a while I found my own interest and encouragement to be the greatest reinforcers of all.

I used the following three-step method:

1. *Specify* what you want to change; for example, dawdling over homework or coming home late.

2. *Make a change.* See if you can solve the problem before it gets out of hand. For example, I found serving dinner earlier cut down on the squabbling. Make up a *when-then* sentence; *When* Amy comes home on time, *then* she can use the car. *When* David uses the potty, *then* he can go swimming.

3. *Evaluate.* Check off on a calendar every day in which the desired behavior occurs. Both you and the child will be encouraged by the progress. If there is no progress, you had better think up another approach.

Here are some examples of how I used this method:

Toilet training. When David's movements were becoming regular, I used the when-then proposition. When you use the potty, I told him, then we can go swimming. I read to him while he was on the potty. When he got off, I didn't say anything, but I stopped reading the book. When he got back on, I resumed reading. Maybe it was the book, maybe it was the promise of the beach or maybe he was just ready, but it took him only two days to master toilet training.

Getting up in the morning. It was harder getting Michael to the bus stop on time. I knew he loved to watch TV, so I told him he could watch a program after supper if he earned a ticket. He could earn his ticket by being *at* the bus stop by 8:10, which would give him, and me, five minutes to spare. I also told him I would wake him up once and once only.

The first day Michael didn't make it to the bus stop until 8:14. That night he tried to stay up late anyway. No ticket, no late TV, I told him. Tears welled up in his eyes, and he begged for another chance. I held firm and repeated the deal to him.

On the second day the same thing happened. The third day he asked if he could watch a late program if he earned his ticket. I assured him he could. It was the easiest morning I had with him. I kept the system going for another two weeks, and I let him know how proud I was of him whenever I could. When I felt he could manage on his own, I dropped the ticket system.

Clean up, curfew (and finding someone to clean the house). After Amy's cheerleading stage, which consisted of her leaping through the house and shouting oaths to spur her team on, she entered her sloppy and defiant stage.

The condition of the kitchen was hard on the eye after her snacks of garlic powder and assorted concoctions on Ritz crackers. She also had trouble meeting her curfew, and I was getting tired of hearing how "everybody else's father" let their daughters stay out later than I did.

Fortunately, about that time Amy received her driver's permit. So I made a deal with her. For starters she had to be in by 9:30 on school nights. She also had to clean up any messes she made in the kitchen. I told her that when she met those conditions, she could borrow the car on Saturday or Sunday afternoons. She agreed.

I also told her she had to pay for her own gas. When she said she had no money, I offered her a job in the house doing the heavy cleaning at standard wages. She accepted.

Amy followed the rules and got her rewards.

I also had trouble teaching Michael to clean up. Somehow, he always "forgot." He was young, he said, and God hadn't finished with him yet, so how could I expect him to be perfect?

Michael was a baseball fanatic. I made a deal with him. When he kept the kitchen neat for three days in a row, then I would take him to the Batting Cage, which featured a machine that pitched real hardballs right over the plate. It was a place he very much wanted to go.

I checked off whether he kept the kitchen neat. Every time he did what he was supposed to, I thanked him. I also set a good example, because by this time I had learned that children will do what you do and not what you say should be done.

Michael's memory improved 100 percent. The third day I took him to the Batting Cage. I then required him to keep the kitchen clean for a week in exchange for another trip there. By this time cleaning up after himself was becoming a habit. I continued taking him to the

Batting Cage every week or so because he liked it so much, and I told him I appreciated how much he'd changed.

Squabbling. My daughters seemed to bicker constantly, and it didn't help when I added to the din by yelling at them to stop.

We had recently eaten in a Chinese restaurant and the children had thoroughly enjoyed it. I told them we would return to the restaurant on the condition that they reduce their bickering. I said I was going to keep a record of every fight, which we finally defined as any discussion that could be heard two rooms away. They could argue as much as they wanted to in the cellar, but only there. When they decreased their arguments in the house to fewer than five a week, we could have Chinese food again.

Every time they argued in the house, no matter who started it I checked it off on the calendar. The first day I counted 12 arguments, the majority of which concerned who was wearing whose clothes.

They exchanged clothes so frequently they could no longer remember which item of apparel was whose. They also lent each other's clothes to friends. Together we sorted out the clothes and worked out the rule: no borrowing, no lending. Risa and Amy agreed to try it out for a month. The arguments dramatically decreased, and within three weeks they met their goal.

Pitch in. After a while, when I was beginning to get the children's attention fairly regularly, I decided it was time to become a little more organized. I listed all the household chores. The children took turns picking their favorite jobs, and the rest were placed on an alternating system so that everyone ended up taking turns cleaning pots or mopping the floor.

To the greatest extent possible I used Grandma's Law. Spurred on by a desire to watch "The Wonderful World of Disney" and "Animal Kingdom," Michael really became efficient at dishwashing and sweeping. Risa became a whiz at finishing her homework so she could use the phone, and even David picked up his toys more readily so he wouldn't miss out on our nightly wrestling match. The allowances were given out *after* Saturday chores, and I did the little ones' laundry only if it had been put in the hamper. The big ones had to do their own. I also discovered that routines are to children what a foundation is to a house. Once they were on a solid basis—knew what was expected of them—things held up very well.

Modifying my own behavior. At the beginning I needed a lot of help. Not only was I tired and overworked, I was resentful. I'd wanted to write plays, not grocery lists. I'd wanted to cook gourmet dinners, not hamburgers and rice with ketchup. I had to begin ridding myself of my own bad habits.

I knew that behavior modification would work with the children, but I also had to motivate myself. I used rewards here, too. *When* David kept dry for seven days, *then* I would exchange baby-sitting duties with a neighbor and spend an afternoon out. When Amy learned to clean up after herself in the kitchen, then I would spend a few hours working on my writing. I also tried to use reinforcers—skiing, swimming, telling stories—that I as well as the children would enjoy.

One day, when I lapsed back into a nagging and threatening stage, I kept track of the number of times I nagged them; there were 18 in a ten-hour period. The deal I made with myself was that *when* I had fewer than five a day I would go fishing by myself on a Sunday.

I told everyone in the family what I was doing and asked them for their help. I told them that when I reached my goal, then I would make them their favorite meal—spaghetti with French fries on the side. I asked everyone to praise me when I settled disagreements reasonably.

Habits are hard to break, our own as well as our children's, and most of us need all the help and support we can get. More eyes, or in this case ears, helped me become more aware of myself. If I did a good job, the children told me so, and that made me feel good.

Questions from friends. Some friends voiced concern over my use of behavior modification. They were concerned that I was "bribing" my children. I did not feel that way at all. Rewarding is not bribing. The children earned every reward they got, and they worked hard. Complaining and becoming indignant usually didn't help me correct a situation. Reinforcement did.

The year comes to an end. During the course of the year we all had to learn to give and take a little, and that took time and work. I certainly ended up appreciating the job my wife had done in the house, and she appreciated what it was like to work full time and commute. And we all began feeling good about life in the household. Behavior modification allowed me to get my work done as well as to be with and to take care of my family. It also gave me an alternative to nagging and punishing. More important, the approach helped the children develop self-confidence, independence and skills.

As the year ended, Joy and I admitted to each other that we both found our career shifts disquieting. Missing work and adult company was only part of the picture for me. I felt economically dependent. Joy felt displaced. At the beginning especially her feelings were hurt when the children came to me to heal a wound or comfort them. She also found that the pressures of a full-time job kept her away from the music she liked so much.

I didn't want to go back to work full time. I enjoyed being with the children. Besides, I flattered myself that they needed me at home more than a full-time job would allow. Joy didn't want to spend all her days away from home although she liked some time out of the house.

So now we both work part time and share household responsibilities. I have a small private practice, consult and write. Joy works as a free-lance musician and teacher in a day-care center. There are certain problems that go along with this arrangement. Sometimes we have too much work and sometimes not enough. Sometimes we have enough money and sometimes we don't. But, overall, we feel it is a good arrangement, for the children as well as us. Each of us can now share more fully in their day-to-day lives, which pleases the children as much as it does us. And isn't that what family life is all about?

Development During Adolescence and Early Adulthood

In 1904 G. Stanley Hall published his extensive work, *Adolescence: Its Psychology and Its Relation to Physiology, Anthropology, Sociology, Sex, Crime, Religion, and Education.* In this work, Hall advanced his "ontogeny recapitulates phylogeny" theory of development. Hall believed that the development of the individual organism (ontogeny) repeated the various phases of the evolution of the species (phylogeny). The adolescent repeated the 18th century's idealism marked by revolt against authority, passion and emotionality, and commitment to goals. In short, Hall envisioned adolescence as a period of "storm and stress." Whereas Hall's recapitulation theory no longer is regarded as having scientific merit, his characterization of adolescence as a time of turmoil and rebelliousness has persisted.

To be sure, adolescence is a time of marked physical, social, emotional, and cognitive change. Secondary sex characteristics appear accompanied by rapid changes in height, weight, and body proportion. Social development involves reduced dependence on the family and greater dependence on peers. Cognitive achievements include abstract reasoning, hypothesis testing, and inductive and deductive reasoning. The adolescent's thinking becomes liberated from the concreteness of the child's reasoning. The pressures of peer group, school, and family may produce conformity, or may lead to rebellion or withdrawal directed against friends, parents, or society at large.

Other researchers argue that much of the storm and stress of adolescence is a myth, created from an overemphasis on adolescent fads and rebelliousness and an underemphasis on obedience, conformity, and cooperation. Overemphasis on the "negative" aspects of adolescent behavior may create a set of expectations that the adolescent strives to achieve. In any event, adolescence is a major transitional period in human development. It is a time for casting off the dependence of childhood and for assuming the independence and responsibilities of adulthood. Adolescence also leads to separation from the family, a topic that has received surprisingly little attention from developmentalists.

Whereas the onset of adolescence is demarcated by the emergence of secondary sex characteristics and the achievement of reproductive maturity, the onset of adulthood is more difficult to distinguish, particularly in modern technological societies. In some cultures a ritualistic ceremony marks the transition to adulthood—a transition that occurs quickly, smoothly, and relatively problem free. In our culture the transition is vague indeed. Does one choose the age at which the adolescent achieves the right to vote, the privilege of driving a car, or perhaps the right to sign one's own informed consent form in order to participate in behavioral research? In any event, the status of adulthood usually is granted shortly after the teen years.

Developmentalists are finally addressing themselves to the study of problems of "middle" and "old" age, but they have shown far less interest in the early years of adulthood. Yet, during early adulthood many individuals experience significant changes in their lives. Marriage, parenthood, divorce, single parenting, employment, the effects of sexist or racist policies, each may have powerful influences on ego development, self-concept, and personality. Some individuals seem to "grow stronger" when confronted by such changes in daily life whereas others have difficulty coping.

Looking Ahead: Challenge Questions

How might our society help to make the transition from childhood to adulthood less problematic for teenagers?

How would you define adolescence? Adulthood? To what extent would your definition apply universally?

Do you agree that adolescence is a time of "storm and stress"? If you were participating in a survey of adolescents' attitudes about their current family relationships, would your answers support the "storm and stress" view?

How stable is personality? What steps can be taken to provide support systems for young adults who are caught up in transitional life crises? Why do you suppose there is so much resistance to prevention programs?

Adolescents and Sex

James E. Elias

James E. Elias is assistant professor of sociology at California State University at Northridge. He has directed several research studies and is the author of numerous publications in the field of human sexuality.

Probably more misinformation exists about adolescent sexuality than about any other sexually related topic. Questions about adolescent sexuality can be grouped into three categories: (1) Is a "sexual revolution" occurring among adolescents? (2) What influences do erotic stimuli and pornography exert in the life of the adolescent? (3) What is the relationship between sex education and adolescent attitudes and behavior patterns?

I would like to relate some of the findings of four different studies that explored the above questions. All were conducted during the past four years at the Institute for Sex Research at Indiana University.

The Sexual Revolution

Perhaps the most important finding was that increased premarital coitus among our adolescent population indicative of a sexual revolution is *not* supported by the data. An analysis of the etiology of this belief may provide some answers and bring the situation into proper perspective. In determining whether a sexual revolution is occurring among adolescents, three "levels" must be considered: the *media level,* where products, programs, and performances project the image of a sensate and sexually oriented society; the *attitudinal level,* which includes the feelings and opinions expressed by adolescents; and the *behavioral level,* which includes activities adolescents actually engage in.

The revolution obviously exists in the media, which bombard the public with sexual stimuli. If young people responded to these stimuli, and if the promises of sexual success were pursued, then a real sexual revolution would be taking place. The trend toward sexual explicitness that has occurred in the media has been rapid, exposing the population to a candidness that in the past was only implied. Parents are shocked by many media presentations, yet they are the prime consumers of this material, not their children. Thus, a "schizophrenia" between the *normative* system and actual practices is evident.

Adolescents have become more permissive in their attitudes toward sexual behavior and openly discuss sexuality and sexual relationships as a natural part of everyday life. Parents are often startled by such openness because, in their childhood, sex was taboo as a discussion topic. Therefore, frank curiosity, questions about nonmarital intercourse, or even the mention of a word like *homosexuality* at the dinner table give parents the idea that their children have completely escaped their grasp and gone astray. Parents fail to realize that the frankness of dialogue is not automatically accompanied by a corresponding frankness in behavior.

It is in this sphere that possible ambiguity between parental and adolescent attitudes is most evident. The past generation engaged in nonmarital and extramarital intercourse more than they apparently admitted. In other words, their professed attitudes were more conservative than their behaviors. The present generation illustrates the reverse: attitudes are more liberal than behavior. Unfortunately, parents tend to equate attitudinal positions with behavior.

In terms of actual sexual behavior, adolescents have not changed radically from their parents. The frequency of nonmarital coitus has been increasing for females. Kinsey reported a 20 to 25 percent nonvirginity rate for college females. A more recent study at the Institute for Sex Research shows that this rate has risen to 33 percent. This increase has occurred over a twenty-five-year period and certainly cannot be called "revolutionary." The fear that the availability of oral contraceptives might encourage adolescent promiscuity is unfounded. It appears that the use of oral contraceptives has not had a significant effect in this age group. In addition, among adolescents the availability or nonavailability of oral contraceptives is not the chief factor in their decision to have intercourse.

For males there has been little change in the frequency of nonmarital coitus—remaining around the 60 percent level for the college population. There is a definite increase in petting, including petting to orgasm, which may be a substitute for coital behavior. However, a high nonmarital coital frequency, indicative of a promiscuous society, is not in evidence. Those engaging in nonmarital intercourse are doing so more often and enjoying it more than their elders did, without attendant guilt feelings. Therefore, the idea of a sexual revolution is encouraged and perpetuated by the mass media, *not* by research data.

Erotic Stimuli

It seems most strange that our society chooses to restrict, repress, and condemn any material that tends to arouse sexual feelings. Those members of the middle class most critical of erotic materials are among its chief consumers. These conflicting behaviors, creating disparate public and private norms, are reflected in the inconsistent enforcement of "community standards." No agreement on the evaluation of erotica exists.

My studies of the place erotica occupies in adolescent sexual development show some interesting results. One study consisted of depth interviews with adolescents from varying social classes. Respondents were questioned about what material they would consider "unacceptable." The range of

> "Kinsey reported a 20 to 25 percent nonvirginity rate for college females. A more recent study at the Institute for Sex Research shows that this rate has risen to 33 percent. This increase has occurred over a twenty-five-year period and certainly cannot be called 'revolutionary.' "

responses was considerable. The most frequent response from males reveals that they do not view erotic materials as objectionable. (Erotic materials include nudist books, sex action graphics, and stag or "blue films" showing explicit sexual activity.) In their definitions of unacceptability, the social class and sex differences of the respondents are evident. Higher social classes equate acceptability with "tastefulness" or aesthetic values. A more rigid standard exists among females, who seem to find even the marginal materials unacceptable.

In determining what is "erotic," material often has been assessed in terms of "significant others"—individuals or groups that include peers, parents, teachers, and the community. Values differ according to generation, sex, and socioeconomic levels. Males, breaking away from home ties earlier than females, seek their peers for support, and this group becomes the norm-interpreting agency for many of them. Their definitions of erotica are seldom similar to those of their parents with the possible exception of upper and upper-middle class males. It is significant that *none* of the males saw their definitions as similar to those of their teachers or the community.

Females, on the other hand, strongly identify with the family value system, and over two-thirds of the respondents indicated definitions similar to those of their families. The other one-third of the females see their definitions as similar to those of their peers.

Any discussion of exposure to erotica must deal with the types available: general material of a sexual nature, such as *Playboy*; marginal erotica; erotica; and hard-core erotica.

> "Those engaging in nonmarital intercourse are doing so more often and enjoying it more than their elders did, without attendant guilt feelings. Therefore, the idea of a sexual revolution is encouraged and perpetuated by the mass media, not by research data."

General sexual materials contain no exposed sex organs or explicit sexual activity. *Marginal erotica* includes pictures, magazines, and books that show sex organs but not sexual activity. Also belonging in this category are live performances of the striptease variety that do not involve sexual activity. *Erotica* includes those types of material that depict sexual activity—coitus, fellatio, or cunnilingus. Live performances that involve masturbation or "fondling" of the sex organs belong here. *Hard-core erotica* is a category reserved for "blue films" and live performances where sexual acts, particularly coitus, are explicitly depicted. (None of the adolescent sample had ever seen a live show of this type.)

Nearly all adolescents had been exposed to *Playboy*, the most popular magazine of its kind on the current market. *Playboy* allows "fantasy to replace fact" in the depiction of female nudes. (Males in higher socioeconomic groups tend to show a greater interest in the articles than in the pictures.)

Interest in marginal erotica occurs primarily in the male sector of the adolescent subculture. Nearly all males in this group have been exposed to this type of material because products are widely distributed and openly displayed. Since most "nudist" magazines are male oriented, females have a low exposure. Erotica, on the other hand, is not as easily available and must be sought out or found in private rather than in public displays. Widest exposure to this type of material occurs among middle-, lower-middle-, and lower-class males. Decks of cards depicting sexual behavior, cartoon books, and photographs are not uncommon in this sector of the young male's world, where sexual arousal and peer acceptance are all-important.

Most frequently, a male's first exposure occurs when a member of his peer group shares the erotica in his possession. The progression seems to be from pictures showing nude females to those depicting heterosexual activity. Adolescents profess great interest in these materials, and curiosity about sexuality seems to be strong among members of this subculture. They report that their first encounter with erotica occurs early—around age seven or eight. The majority voice a positive reaction to the materials.

Females show a curiosity toward erotic material, but they label the material "bad" or "nasty." Their exposure seems limited more to marginal erotic materials, probably because most material is directed toward the male market. Their reactions range from embarrassment to "It makes me feel dirty inside," and these responses probably reflect their tendency to adhere to family standards.

Erotica appears to serve several purposes for the adolescent male: arousal, and in some cases, subsequent masturbation; sex education, especially when there has been no other source; and peer-group status through the ownership of the medium of information. Many of the males interviewed indicated that the value of the materials was enhanced when they discovered that possession brought not only peer group acceptance but increased status.

Sex Education

Sex education (education about human sexuality) begins as a matter of course very early and continues throughout the life-span of the individual. Much of this education is indirect. In addition, parents frequently turn aside questions that a child asks or offer no explanation for the negative sanctioning of interest in the sexual. Formal sex education should start as early as the child begins school because he has already asked questions and, for the most part, they remain unanswered or answered by poor analogies or with reprimands that are psychologically harmful.

As the child reaches puberty, he looks to his peers for interpretations, and peer-group norms persist. Direct questions (often pretending prior knowledge) about human sexuality are common, especially among males. In contrast to the direct sexual approach taken by males, young adolescent females seem heavily oriented toward the romantic aspect of love. The sexual information shared by adolescents seems to consist of "pooled ignorance." The individual with "the answers," whether accurate or not, gains status in the eyes of his peers, and the quality of his information frequently goes unchallenged.

My study of high school students and their sources of sex

6. ADOLESCENCE AND EARLY ADULTHOOD

education reinforces the findings of past research: *the peer group is the major source of sex information.* The source that provided a "great deal of information" was, for males, other males of the same age, and for females, other females of the same age. The second major source of sexual information is peers of the opposite sex. Teachers, who in the past have provided little, if any, instruction in this area, have emerged as another source of information—for adolescents who have taken a course in sex education and for those who have not.

The parental role in sex education appears to be lacking except in the mother-daughter relationship. Sixty-five percent of the females reported that their mothers had discussed sex with them. Discussions often centered around menstruation and the "negative" aspects of premarital sexual intercourse. The father served as a source of information in only 2 percent of the cases, and 33 percent of the females reported that neither parent had talked with them.

Parents evidently do not provide an equivalent kind of instruction for males. Sixty-four percent of the males reported that neither parent had discussed sex with them, and 26 percent indicated that they had discussed sex with their fathers. Only 10 percent answered positively to a mother-son discussion. Interestingly enough, males indicated that neither parent was the first source of information on any of the nine topics included in the study. For females the mother is the first source of information regarding menstruation, contraception, pregnancy, and menopause. However, in areas such as sexual intercourse, male erection, masturbation, prostitution, and homosexuality, peers provide the first source of information.

In summary, the sources of learning about human sexuality are various, the most frequent being the peer group. Much of the information is learned at ages earlier than previously expected, and the "innocence of youth" is largely a myth.

Attitudes Toward Sex Education

From a short series of questions asked in the post-test situation concerning sex education in the schools, it is clear that adolescents have a positive attitude toward it. Over 90 percent of the students who had taken such a course indicated that they felt sex education should be taught in the schools. Religious teachings are often cited as being in conflict with the teachings of sex education. However, 95 percent of the students in a predominantly Catholic community, after having taken part in the program, did not find sex education in disagreement with their religious beliefs.

Another prevailing view is that sex education in school conflicts with that given at home. Over 90 percent of the students who had taken the sex education course disagreed. The course offered in this particular school system did not assume an overt "moral" stance with regard to sexual matters, and this may explain why students reported little conflict among school, home, and church. Since the home and the church are not major sources of sex information, the conflict issue appears to be a myth.

The sex education course seemed to effect significant changes in adolescent attitudes. Students declared that they would handle sex education with their own children differently than they themselves had experienced it. What to look for in a mate and "how far to go" on a date are great concerns of the adolescent, and the benefit of a sex education course helped provide a frame of reference where otherwise only vague peer-group norms would apply. Mate selection seems especially important for those who will not seek education beyond high school and will probably marry soon after graduation.

As currently presented in the educational system, sex education offers "too little too late," and in many instances the best it can do is present accurate information to correct the misinformation students have acquired. Sexual learning begins long before the advent of formal education and informal sources remain the primary vehicle of information.

What Do We Know About Teenagers as Mothers?

By Mark W. Roosa, Hiram E. Fitzgerald, and Nancy A. Carlson

Dr. Roosa is Acting Director, Center for Family Studies, Arizona State University, Tempe. Dr. Fitzgerald is Professor in the Department of Psychology, Michigan State University, East Lansing. Dr. Carlson is former Associate Professor in the department of family and child ecology, Michigan State University, East Lansing.

The study described herein was supported, in part, by a grant from the William T. Grant Foundation.

In recent years, because of the historically high rate of childbearing among teenagers, the subject of pregnant teenagers and teenage mothers has received much attention. Numerous studies have been made; hearings have been held at various levels of government; and special projects for teenage mothers have been started in many communities throughout the United States. With this amount of attention focused upon the phenomenon, one might wonder whether there is anything more to add to our knowledge of teenagers as mothers. Unfortunately there is.

Upon reviewing research on teenage mothers, one becomes aware of a number of flaws in research design—flaws which are characteristic of much of the research in this area. First, apparently very few researchers use a comparison group in the study of teenage mothers. Instead, the teenage mothers alone as a group are compared to an established standard. For instance, teenage mothers complete a survey about knowledge of child development, the results are reported, and it is suggested that gaps in the teenagers' knowledge hold severe consequences for the development of their children. We are not told how a group of nonteenage mothers from the same population would score on the survey instrument.

When a comparison group *is* used, as is common in medical studies of teenage pregnancy, data for a local sample of teenagers often are compared to data for a national sample of older women. This procedure confuses differences due to local conditions (such as socioeconomic status or quality or availability of health care facilities) with differences due to maternal age.

Second, most nonmedical studies of teenage mothers rely solely or primarily upon subjective methods for gathering data. Teenage mothers may be observed casually while they interact with their children in their homes or elsewhere; without the benefit of an observation schedule or even a delineation of behavioral categories, records are made of significant events that occurred during the visit. In other studies, teenage mothers are interviewed in a free-flowing, open-ended format, often without the benefit of an interview guide or a systematic method of recording the exchange. The use of subjective methods, especially without multiple observers or respondents, places a burden upon the researcher to be objective and to avoid bias. When such methods are used without a comparison group the possibility that the results may be biased and/or misleading is increased considerably.

Third, studies of teenage mothers often use nonrepresentative samples, commonly low-income, urban, Black teenage mothers from a city in the eastern United States. Though teenage pregnancy probably is not a randomly distributed phenomenon, there is still a need to study the phenomenon as it occurs in a number of populations within the United States. Only by comparing the results obtained from a variety of samples can we begin to differentiate those aspects of teenage motherhood that are related to maternal age from those that are related to other factors.

Finally, research into teenage pregnancy typically has been narrowly focused. Most studies in this area can be classified as either medical, sociological, psychological, or educational. However, teenage pregnancy and motherhood are complex phenomena and must be studied with designs that are multivariate. The poorly educated teenage mother does not exist independent of her prenatal care, her economic status, her psychological well-being, or her sociological status in the world. These are all aspects of the same individual and to look at only one aspect of that individual is to obscure the complexity of real world events.

For the reasons mentioned above, the validity of many studies of teenage mothers must be questioned. It is not very reassuring to think of the large number of programs that are serving teenage mothers with such an inadequate research base.

The Mother-Infant Project

Medical studies focus upon perinatal and neonatal risk factors in teenage pregnancy. However, seldom have these studies examined the long-term effects of teenage childbearing upon the children involved. In those studies that have followed the development of the children of teenagers, the results are consistent: children born to teenage mothers score lower on I.Q. tests, do less well in school, and are labeled as having behavioral problems more often than do children of older mothers (1–5). (In at least two of these studies, the data were gathered in the 1950's.) Unfortunately, there is little in these longitudinal studies to suggest possible causes for the developmental problems that children of teenage mothers experience.

The Mother-Infant Project (MIP) at Michigan State University compared the childbearing and initial child-rearing experiences of teenage and older mothers. By a comparison of the two groups of mothers and children, we sought to determine possible reasons for the developmental differences earlier studies had found.

Although the quality of past research on teenage parenting practices and attitudes has been relatively poor, the results have been consistent. In all cases, teenage parents are reported to have poor care-giving skills. Earlier studies have reported problems with the attitudes of teenage mothers toward their children and with the quality of their sensitivity and responsivity to their children's needs. If these findings are valid, it is reasonable to expect that children of teenage mothers will be reared in less than optimal environments. A mother's attitude toward parenting in general or toward her child in particular has been shown to be related to the way the mother interacts with the child and to the child's later developmental status. The quality of the home environment and the quantity and type of toys and play materials that are available to the child (both too much and too little may be inappropriate) also have been shown to be related to later development. Parental social-economic class has been shown to have a strong effect upon many aspects of a child's development and to be strongly related to later developmental status. Finally, the mother-child interactional unit, which actually cannot be separated from the other elements discussed above, appears to have been a strong role as a mediator of other influences on child development. Because of the contrast between what is known or suspected about teenage parenting behavior and what is thought to be necessary for normal or enhanced development of children, the Institute for Family and Child Study at Michigan State University undertook a comparative study of teenage parenting.

The Mother-Infant Project followed 67 first-time mothers in urban and rural areas of central Michigan from the last months of their pregnancies through the third month postpartum. The mothers were interviewed in their homes; the medical records of their deliveries were reviewed; their infants were given behavioral and neurological tests shortly after birth; the mothers and their infants were observed with detailed recording instruments once a month for three months; the household settings provided for the children were recorded; and the mothers completed scales that rated their infants' temperaments and their own attitudes toward their infants.

Results

A comparison of those mothers below 20 years of age (n = 17) with those over 20 (n = 50) revealed a number of differences and a surprising number of similarities. The teenage mothers had significantly less education than the older mothers, and the teenagers' households had less than half the income of the older mothers. About half of the teenagers (compared with over 90% of the older mothers) maintained a relationship with the child's father after the birth; half of the teenagers continued to live with their parents or other relatives. The teenage mothers generally sought prenatal medical care a month or more later than the older mothers did and were much less likely to take part in prenatal classes (Lamaze, LeLeche). However, the teenage mothers had easier deliveries than did the older mothers.

As had been reported in numerous other studies, the teenage mothers in this study tended to have slightly shorter pregnancies and to have slightly smaller infants than those of the older mothers though the differences were not significant. However, there were no differences between the Apgar Scores of the two groups of infants nor between the behavioral or neurological scores of the two groups. In contrast to the reports of other researchers, no differences were found between the attitudes of the two groups of mothers. No differences were found between the temperament ratings of the two groups of infants either.

The homes of teenage mothers were more crowded than those of older mothers and were less likely to offer a quiet place where the infant could be put to escape from noise and playful adults during naps. Teenagers also provided their infants with fewer toys with moving parts and/or noise makers (such as mobiles or rattles) than did older mothers. The differences in the home environments were strongly related to the education/income differences between the two groups.

There were numerous similarities in the way the two groups of mothers handled, played with, and responded to their infants. However, the older mothers spent more time talking to their infants—especially when the mother and infant were looking at each other—than did the younger mothers. The older mothers also responded more quickly and more often to their infants' cries or other distress signals than did the younger mothers. This finding supports the contention of earlier researchers that teenage mothers are less sensitive than older mothers are to an infant's signals. There were no significant differences between the behaviors of the two groups of infants.

Thus, although it appears that there were numerous differences between the background characteristics (primarily income and education), the home environments, and the caretaking patterns of teenage mothers and older mothers, there were also positive findings. Consistent with current theories of child development, any of the reported differences could be used to support causal inferences about the developmental problems of the children of teenage mothers reported by earlier researchers. However, the general results of our study support a much more positive view of teenage mothers than currently appears in the literature. None of the suspected differences in maternal attitudes, neonatal status, or infant temperament were found; presumably, therefore, these variables can be removed from consideration as causes of the cited developmental differences. Furthermore, since the deliveries of teenagers were easier than those of older mothers, there is no reason to speculate that the delivery experiences of teenagers negatively influence maternal attitudes or are related, directly or indirectly, to the cited developmental differences. On the contrary, the easier deliveries may play a role in enhancing the young mothers' attitudes toward their infants and parenting in general.

Further analysis of the data suggest that any negative effects of adolescent childbearing upon child development are not due to the mother's age alone. Rather, negative consequences may be due to the "side effects" of early childbearing. Teenage mothers tend to drop out of school and as a consequence have a low level of education, limited job opportunities, and reduced earning power. A married teenager's husband often shares these limitations. Thus, teenage parents have fewer material and educational resources to invest in their child's development. Moreover, the newly acquired role of parent places limitations upon the ability of these teenagers to achieve whatever vocational, educational, or economic goals they may have held

prior to assuming the responsibilities of parenthood.

The role of education in improved caretaking is probably an important one. The more educated mothers in this study appeared to be much more aware than the teenage mothers were of their infants' needs and of what to expect from the child as the child grew. This increased awareness presumably was due both to the direct results of extended education and to the knowledge of resources for finding information on child development.

Many of the differences between the results of the Mother-Infant Project and those of previous studies may be due to the methods we used. In contrast to previous studies, the data in the present study, as much as possible, are based upon objective information; on direct, detailed observations of the ways mothers handled their babies. Furthermore, all information about teenage mothers was compared directly with similar information about mothers 20 to 30 years of age. Previous studies too often have relied upon subjective, clinical judgments without the benefit of comparison groups.

Conclusions

The Mother-Infant Project has suggested some specific causal mechanisms for possible developmental differences between the children of teenage and older mothers. Income and education were implicated as the major sources of differences between teenagers and older mothers, with their influence distributed by way of neonatal status, maternal attitudes, home environments, and mother-infant interaction. If future studies support the

findings of this study, the identification of the specific causal mechanisms will be an important consideration in the development of intervention programs to work with teenage mothers and their infants or in the revision of existing programs to give them new direction.

Furthermore, if the independent contributions of income/education and maternal age to infant development are as reported above, there are direct implications for programs concerned with adolescent parenting. Programs designed to prevent adolescent pregnancy would need to publicize the impact of early parenthood on income/education and the impact of income/education on child development. Programs that work with young mothers could well use the strengths of young mothers (their apparent energy and enthusiasm and love for their children) to overcome some of the educational and informational weaknesses discussed above.

References
1. Oppel, W.C. and Royston, A.B. "Teenage Births: Some Social, Psychological, and Physical Sequelae." *American Journal of Public Health,* 1971, *61*(4).
2. Hardy, J.B., Welcher, D.W., Stanley, J., and Dallas, J.R. "Long-Range Outcome of Adolescent Pregnancy." *Clinical Obstetrics and Gynecology,* 1978, *21*(4).
3. Vandenberg, B. Reported in C.S. Chilman *Adolescent Sexuality in Changing American Society: Social and Psychological Perspectives.* Washington, D.C.: U.S. Government Printing Office, 1980.
4. Broman, S.H., "Longterm Development of Children Born to Teenagers," in K.G. Scott, T. Field, and E. Robertson, (Eds.), *Teenage Parents and Their Offspring.* New York: Grune and Stratton, 1981.
5. Belmont, L., Cohen, P., Dryfoos, J., Stein, Z., and Zayac, S., "Maternal Age and Children's Intelligence," in K.G. Scott, T. Field, and E. Robertson (Eds.), *Teenage Parents and Their Offspring.* New York: Grune and Stratton, 1981.

THE SIBLING BOND
A Lifelong Love/Hate Dialectic

VIRGINIA ADAMS

The link between brothers and sisters is in some ways the most unusual of family relationships. It is the longest lasting, often continuing for 70 or 80 years or more, and the most egalitarian. It is also the least studied. Researchers have been more interested in the relationship between parents and offspring than in sibling interaction. Even when psychologists have focused on the children in a family, they have paid attention chiefly to the effects of birth order on personality and intelligence, or to the role young siblings play in early development when they act as caretakers for still younger brothers and sisters. From the nature of most studies, one might almost deduce that sibling relationships end with childhood.

Over the past few years, however, a growing number of researchers have begun to ask questions about brothers and sisters in adulthood. Do siblings drift apart when they leave home, or do they stay in touch? If they maintain a real relationship, what is it like, and how long is it likely to last?

Some answers have already appeared in print or been reported at professional meetings. Others will be published over the next few months in three book-length studies now in preparation. Most of the new work falls under one of three headings: *fervent sibling loyalty* (never before systematically studied) that arises only under certain family conditions and is so extreme as to produce unexpectedly negative effects in some cases; *sibling rivalry* that can persist into adulthood and even into old age; and *sibling solidarity*, a sense of closeness that leads some siblings to turn to each other for understanding.

Overall, the latest research makes it clear that siblings can exert an important mutual influence, for good or ill, throughout the life span; this is sometimes so even when they are geographically separated. Some psychologists expect sibling relationships to become even more significant as the divorce rate increases, the number of one-parent families grows, and family size declines.

Research confirms what common sense suggests: that the degree and nature of sibling interaction varies greatly, not only from one set of siblings to another but within the same pair at different times in their lives. Some brothers and sisters become and remain best friends; others heartily detest each other.

The most interesting fact, although it is not often noted by researchers or acknowledged by siblings, is that love and hate may exist side by side, in very uneasy equilibrium. One writer speaks of "the delicate balance of competition and camaraderie among all sisters." Her words would seem to apply equally well to brothers. Whether the balance can be maintained, or whether it tips dramatically to one side or the other, depends partly on parental behavior and attitudes and partly on certain critical experiences in the lives of siblings themselves.

Fervent Sibling Loyalty

Among the most innovative of the psychologists now studying adult brothers and sisters are Stephen Bank, adjunct associate professor at Wesleyan University, and Michael D. Kahn, associate professor at the University of Hartford. In a seven-year period they have audiotaped more than 100 interviews with siblings in pairs or in larger groups, and in the course of their work as psychotherapists they have studied many other siblings. Bank and Kahn will describe some of their findings in *Sibling Relationships: Their Nature and Significance Across the Lifespan*, a book edited by Michael E. Lamb and Brian Sutton-Smith that will be published next summer. They will give a more detailed account of their work in their own book, *The Sibling Bond*, due out next February.

Bank and Kahn are particularly interested in "Hansels and Gretels," siblings as intensely loyal as the fairy-tale children whose loving concern for each other saved them from the wicked witch when their father and stepmother turned them out into the forest to starve. The two psychologists have observed the Hansel and Gretel phenomenon in numerous sibling groups, and they are at pains to distinguish it from sibling solidarity, the kind of cohesiveness that leads adult siblings to offer each other a modest degree of support in time of trouble. In an ordinary relationship, one sister might invite another in the throes of divorce to come and visit for a weekend. An extremely loyal sister, Bank said, might take a sibling into her home indefinitely, acting as "a kind of parent to someone who has been wounded."

Extreme loyalty, Bank says, "involves an irrational and somewhat blind process of putting one's sibling first and foremost," with a willingness to make enormous sacrifices. Pointing out that loyalty comes from the French word *loi* ("law"), he notes that intense loyalty is an unwritten contract providing that "we will stick together."

One of two brothers in their 20s told Bank, "If I ever got in any trouble, I wouldn't go to my wife—I wouldn't go to a friend—I wouldn't go to my boss; I'd go to my brother." One of four brothers aged 36 to 45 said of the other three, "If I knew they needed it, I'd give any one of these guys my last buck, despite my obligations to my wife and children."

The adult Hansels and Gretels that Bank and Kahn studied tried to be together as often as they could and were unhappy when necessity kept them apart. The two young brothers, students at the same university, shared a fantasy that they would not let even marriage part them. They talked about buying a joint homestead, "where their wives and children would blend with them into a big, happy household."

Some of the extremely loyal siblings were bound together by a private code—a special way of exchanging glances, for example, or a word or phrase that meant nothing to outsiders. "The four brothers," Bank said, "repeatedly broke into raucous laughter after one had made what seemed to the interviewer a perfectly neutral comment. They sarcastically 'apologized' for the 'silly' behavior of their brother as if to say, 'This is our sense of humor; *you'll* never understand it, since you didn't grow up with us.' "

How do such intense attachments develop? The critical factor is a kind of family collapse as the children are growing up, with the parents becoming actually or psychologically unavailable. In each of the families studied, the parents were hostile, weak, or absent, and the external circumstances of the children's lives were threatening. "Confronted with a hostile environment," Bank said, "they clung together as the only steady and constant people in one another's lives." The parents of the two college-age brothers died within two years of each other, when the boys were nine and 11 and then 11 and 13, and both boys were seriously abused by a psychotic foster mother. The mother of the four middle-aged brothers died when they were teenagers, and their father was emotionally exhausted, sometimes abusive, and unable to form a close relationship with his

children. The family was in a slum in which physical danger was a constant.

Parents who want their children to become and remain fervently loyal to each other do not understand the paradox that Bank underscores: "The *deep* bond between siblings will not develop if parents are real good parents; with good parents, you'll get caring, and solidarity, but not intense loyalty, because there's not much need for it."

Bank's assertion that intense sibling loyalty presupposes a kind of parental abandonment draws indirect support from a number of studies. One of these was done in 1965 by Albert I. Rabin, a Michigan State University psychologist, who compared kibbutz children in Israel with children raised in traditional families there. He found much less sibling jealousy in the kibbutz children, whose parents were with them only two hours a day, than in youngsters whose parents were available to them around the clock.

Even more persuasive evidence comes from the classic study by Anna Freud of six unrelated children orphaned by the Nazis before they were a year old. Kept together in the Terezin concentration camp and, after the war, in a succession of hostels, they had no chance to form consistent relationships with caring adults. When they were about three, they were flown to England and looked after in a special nursery for months to help them make the transition to a more normal life. For a long time, they appeared almost incapable of jealousy.

"It was evident," Anna Freud wrote, "that they cared greatly for each other and not at all for anybody or anything else. They had no other wish than to be together and became upset when they were separated. . . . There was no occasion to urge the children to 'take turns'; they did it spontaneously. . . . They were extremely considerate of each other's feelings. . . . When one of them received a present from a shopkeeper, they demanded the same for each other child, even in their absence. On walks they were concerned for each other's safety in traffic, looked after children who lagged behind, helped each other over ditches, turned aside branches for each other to clear the passage in the woods, and carried each other's coats. In the nursery they picked up each other's toys. . . . At mealtimes handing food

to the neighbor was of greater importance than eating oneself."

Among many examples of the children's mutual concern, this one is typical: "John, daydreaming while walking, nearly bumps into a passing child [who does not belong to the group]. Paul shouts at the passerby: '*Blöder Ochs; meine John; blöder Ochs Du*' ('Stupid fool; that's my John; you stupid fool)."

There can, of course, be too much of even such a good thing as loyalty. If parents thought more about it, they might worry a bit less about signs of rivalry and a bit more about excessively close ties. They might look up the story of Dorothy Wordsworth, sister of the poet, who gave her life entirely to her brother William, renouncing any independent existence of her own. They might also remember the reclusive Collyer brothers, who gave their lives to each other—and cannot have had much joy from the sacrifice. In the less extreme cases that Bank and Kahn studied, intense loyalty often imposed "the burden of an obligatory responsibility to one another." Sometimes it stifled friendships with outsiders whom siblings did not happen to like. Often it conflicted with loyalty to spouse and children.

Some very loyal brothers had difficulty admitting wives to their group at all and would submit their choice of spouse to their brothers for approval as if to a review board. At times the system worked well. The first wife admitted to the four-brother group mentioned earlier was a physical-education major who proved eminently suited to life among these macho brothers. "She had grown up with brothers," Bank said. "She knew how to handle brothers. She adapted by becoming 'one of the boys,' accepting their male humor and participating in sports with them. They, in return, adopted her almost as a sister. It was the perfect fit." In other cases, though, wives were made to feel "as if they were on the outside of a very exclusive club."

There were times when extreme loyalty made difficulties for the siblings themselves. The younger of the two college-age brothers felt he was a nobody who existed only as an extension of his brother. Despite the warmth the two felt for each other, Bank said, he decided to get away by himself for a few years so he could discover his own identity. When loyalty was one-way rather than reciprocal, with one sibling doing most of the giving, recipients often felt resentful—despite their gratitude—at being subjected to a kind of domination, while perpetual givers often found themselves shunting aside their own legitimate interests. "If you keep helping and helping, that is in a sense neurotic," said Bank.

But he emphasized that he "would not want to be quoted as calling these people only neurotic." Many siblings reported that their loyalty brought them advantages: never feeling entirely alone, learning skills from each other, having a chance to practice parenthood.

Loyal siblings can be deeply sensitive to each other's needs. According to Bank, "They show some of the qualities of a good psychotherapist; they know when to shut up and when to push." And, he went on, "I don't want to put down the absolute altruism we've seen in these very loyal siblings, because there is such a thing." Citing Jane Goodall's observation that when parent chimpanzees die, a "sibling" takes over as caretaker, Bank suggested that somewhat analogous behavior, having important survival value, may occur in human beings.

Rivalry in Adulthood

Bank and Kahn believe that the degree of rivalry between siblings has been vastly exaggerated and that what looks like rivalry often masks other feelings, for instance, dependency, or simply a need for some kind of intense relationship with a brother or sister. Most psychologists, however, argue that some degree of sibling rivalry is almost inevitable in childhood, and there is plenty of research evidence to support that view. Many people assume that this early rivalry dissipates in adulthood, but on that point the evidence is far from conclusive. Last September two psychologists, both associate professors of education at the University of Cincinnati, made a strong case for the persistence of rivalry into adulthood in a paper presented to the American Psychological Association. Helgola G. Ross and Joel I. Milgram (the brother of psychologist

Stanley Milgram) recruited 65 subjects aged 25 to 93 from a Midwestern university community, two senior citizen centers in town, and a Methodist retirement home in the suburbs.

Most of the data came from interviews that were tape-recorded, transcribed, and content-analyzed so that recurrent topics could be noted. In group interviews, all the subjects met in age groups (20s, 30s, 40s, 50s, or 60s) of four to six people. Individual follow-up interviews were conducted with 10 of the subjects so that rivalry could be explored in depth.

Seventy-one percent of the subjects reported that they had sometimes felt rivalrous toward brothers or sisters. Of those, 36 percent claimed that they had been able to overcome the feelings in adolescence or adulthood, but 45 percent admitted that the feelings were still alive.

Of subjects who admitted to experiencing rivalry at some time, 40 percent said it had begun in childhood, 33 percent believed it had not surfaced until adolescence, and 22 percent said they could not remember feeling it at all until adulthood.

About half of the subjects said that adults had initiated their rivalrous feelings when they were children. Parents were most often cited, although grandparents came in for their share of blame, and so, at times, did teachers.

The key stimulus for rivalry was favoritism. Some parents openly compared siblings, asking a child to match standards of behavior, skill, or personal characteristics achieved by a favored brother or sister. In other cases the comparison was covert; the child observed the parents' preferential treatment of one or more favored brothers or sisters.

Roughly 50 percent of all rivalry was said by the subjects to have been initiated by siblings, in half of these cases by brothers, in a third by sisters, in a tenth by the subjects themselves.

When competition began in childhood, Ross and Milgram said in their paper, it appeared to be "a vying for the parents' attention, recognition, and love, but also a more general juggling for power and position among the siblings." Sometimes the precipitating factor was the experience of being cared for by an older sibling. (According to Brenda K. Bryant, a psychologist at the University of

California at Davis who has studied siblings as caretakers, sibling babysitters are perceived by their charges as rougher disciplinarians than parents. Young babysitters, Bryant suggests, seem to pattern themselves after the comic strip character Lucy, "whose approach to caretaking with peers such as Charlie Brown is to resort to the sweet reason of the mailed fist.")

Ross and Milgram found that a pattern of rivalry sometimes took shape when a young sibling accepted an older one as mentor and then discovered that the mentor was less disposed to praise the younger person's accomplishments than to depreciate them.

The two experimenters emphasized that inequalities in levels of accomplishment were not by themselves sufficient to generate rivalry. Siblings did not necessarily believe that more is better unless parents thought so.

Some subjects indicated that rivalry could actually be fun. Others said it served to motivate them. "If siblings have the ability to live up to high standards, comparative expectations are not necessarily debilitating," said Ross and Milgram. Many subjects told them that when they managed to find their own areas of expertise, competitiveness gave way to pride in the former rival's successes.

More often than not, however, rivalry was destructive. Some subjects felt deeply hurt. "Many siblings felt excluded from valued sibling or family interactions and the sense of wholeness they can provide," Ross and Milgram said. "Some dissociated themselves psychologically and geographically from particular siblings or the family on a semi-permanent basis; two broke relations completely."

If competition was hurtful, what kept it going? Most often, parental favoritism continuing into adulthood. Also mentioned frequently was provocatively competitive behavior by the siblings themselves.

At times, the difficulty was family gossip that made too much of differences between brothers and sisters, assigning constricting roles or labels. Yet another problem was that siblings rarely talked about their rivalry. Successful siblings often did not even know that their achievements were causing envy, and siblings who felt inferior did not want to say so. "Admitting sibling rivalry may be experienced as equivalent to admitting maladjustment," Ross and Milgram believe. Besides, "To reveal feelings of rivalry to a brother or sister who is perceived as having the upper hand increases one's vulnerability in an already unsafe situation."

Psychologists often observe that even intense feelings of rivalry can coexist with feelings of affection and solidarity. One of the most telling examples is the case of William James, the philosopher-psychologist, and his brother Henry, the novelist. Henry's perceptive biographer, Leon Edel, gives a fascinating account of what he calls their "long-buried struggle for power," which began from the moment of Henry's birth and did not end until William's death.

Whatever praise William voiced over the years for Henry's writing was overbalanced by barbed criticism, especially of Henry's complex literary style. The older brother called Henry "a curiosity of literature." In a letter to the younger man he once wrote, "for gleams and innuendos and felicitous verbal insinuations you are unapproachable" and exhorted him to "say it *out*, for God's sake, and have done with it." William was not quite at ease with his own sharp words, though, and he urged Henry not to answer "these absurd remarks."

On that occasion, Henry complied, but to another critical letter he wrote, "I'm always sorry when I hear of your reading anything of mine, and always hope you won't—you seem to me so constitutionally unable to 'enjoy' it." Yet he did not appear resentful. Inscribing a gift copy of his novel *The Golden Bowl* to his brother, he called himself William's "incoherent, admiring, affectionate Brother."

Henry never knew of William's unkindest remarks about him. They were written in 1905, when William's election to the Academy of Arts and Letters followed Henry's by three months. Petulantly, William declined the offer. He was led to that course, he explained in a letter to the academy secretary, "by the fact that my younger and shallower and vainer brother is already in the Academy and that if I were there too, the other families represented might think the James influence too rank and strong."

As Edel points out, William was being both untruthful with himself and inconsistent: "He had not considered that there was a redundancy of Jameses when he and Henry had been elected to the Institute [of Arts and Letters, the Academy's parent body] in 1898. He was having this afterthought only now, when Henry had been elected before him to the new body." Indeed, William's conscience was again not quite clear about his own behavior; his letter acknowledged that he was being "sour."

The relationship of the brothers was more complex than these quotations suggest. When William was dying, Henry wrote to a close friend, "At the prospect of losing my wonderful beloved brother out of the world in which, from as far back as in dimmest childhood, I have so yearningly always counted on him, I feel nothing but. . .weakness. . .and even terror."

To someone else, Henry confided that "William's extinction changes the face of life for me." Yet the change was perhaps not wholly unwelcome. Henry "had always found himself strong in William's absence," Edel writes. "Now he had full familial authority; his nephews deferred to him; his brother's wife now became [in effect] wife to him, ministering to his wants, caring for him as she had cared for the ailing husband and brother. Henry had ascended to what had seemed, for 60 years, an inaccessible throne."

Sibling Solidarity

Even rivalrous brother-sister relationships may show a good deal of the quality known as sibling solidarity, or cohesiveness. One of the most important investigators of this quality is Victor G. Cicirelli, a professor of developmental and aging psychology at Purdue University. The burden of Cicirelli's 12 years of sibling research is that brothers and sisters remain important to each other into old age, often becoming more important in time.

In a study published last year in the *Journal of Marriage and the Family*, Cicirelli compared the feelings of 100 college women toward their parents and toward their brothers and sisters and found that his subjects felt significantly closer to siblings than to fathers. For the most part, they also felt closer to siblings than to mothers; that difference was not significant.

For a study of siblings in midlife, Cicirelli visited 140 Midwesterners, most of them aged 30 to 60, and interviewed them about their relationships with their 336 siblings. His results, as yet unpublished, show little conflict between brothers and sisters.

More than two-thirds of the subjects (68 percent, to be exact) described their relationships with siblings as close or very close; only 5 percent said they did not feel at all close. Sisters felt closer than brothers or cross-sex pairs. In general, cohesiveness increased slightly with age.

Asked how well they got along with brothers and sisters, 78 percent said well or very well; 4 percent said not very well or poorly. As to the degree of satisfaction the relationship brought, 68 percent called it considerable or very great, while 12 percent reported little or no satisfaction.

Other questions brought fewer positive responses. Asked how much interest they thought their siblings had in their—the subjects'—activities, 59 percent said they perceived the interest as very great or moderate, but 21 percent saw little or none. Well under half—41 percent—said they felt free to discuss personal or intimate matters with a sibling; 36 percent said they rarely or never did so. Only 8 percent usually or frequently talked over important decisions with a sibling; 73 percent rarely or never did so.

Cicirelli found little overt conflict: 93 percent maintained that they never or only rarely felt competitive; 89 percent asserted that their siblings were never or only rarely bossy; and 88 percent said they never argued with siblings, or did so only once in a while. Speculating on the far higher percentage of people admitting to rivalry in the Ross-Milgram study, Cicirelli suggested that the small-group interview method those psychologists used "might be more likely to stimulate self-disclosure about rivalry than traditional interview methods."

Cicirelli has administered questionnaires to 300 men and women over 60 in order to learn about sibling relationships in later life. Some 17 percent of his elderly subjects saw the sibling with whom they were in closest touch at least once a week, while 33 percent saw that sibling a minimum of once a month. There was some drop in the frequency of visits with increasing age, but the diminished contact did not seem to lessen closeness.

Overall, 53 percent used the words "extremely close" to describe their relationship, and another 30 percent characterized it as "close." The 83 percent for the two responses combined is striking, compared with the 68 percent reported above for the middle-aged. Cicirelli believes that as older people witness the aging and death of parents and see the effects of the years on themselves and their siblings, their sense of belonging is threatened. Strengthening ties with those who remain, he theorizes, may be partly an attempt "to preserve the attachment to the family system of childhood."

Even so, when Cicirelli asked his elderly subjects which family member they turned to for emotional support and practical assistance, he found that most relied mainly on their children. Only about 7 percent said a sibling was a major source of psychological support.

In a very different kind of study, Cicirelli administered a projective measure, the Gerontological Apperception Test (GAT), to 64 men and women aged 65 to 88 to elicit deep attitudes and feelings of a kind that are not likely to emerge in interviews. The GAT is made up of 14 pictures depicting ambiguous situations such as an older woman on a park bench observing a young couple. Subjects are asked to make up a story about each picture, telling "what the people are thinking and feeling and how it will come out."

From his analysis of responses, Cicirelli learned that sisters had a greater impact on the feelings and concerns of siblings than did brothers. He also discovered that sisters had different effects on sisters than they did on brothers. More often than not, the stories told by female subjects who had one or more sisters showed concern about keeping up their social skills and relationships with people outside the family, helping others in the community, and being able to handle criticism from younger people. Cicirelli interpreted that to mean that "sisters appear to stimulate and challenge the elderly woman to maintain her social activities, skills, and roles."

The stories told by male subjects with sisters tended to be happier in tone than the stories of men with brothers, and they revealed less worry about money, jobs, family relationships, and criticism from the young. "The more sisters the elderly man has, the happier he is," Cicirelli concluded. "Sisters seem to provide the elderly male with a basic feeling of emotional security."

Solidarity may be of major significance to some siblings, but to others it counts for nothing; it may not even develop. Michael Kahn says that if siblings have "low emotional access" to each other—if there are no important interactions early in life because the siblings are many years apart in age, or for other reasons—they cannot become truly important to each other.

Nor are they likely to be close as adults when sibling incest has occurred in the early years. "Feelings of guilt, shame, and anxiety linger on," Kahn says, and sisters, more deeply affected by incest than brothers, experience profound feelings of betrayal, sometimes even if they were willing participants in the experience. "They don't trust their brothers, ever. Sometimes they don't want to be in the same room with them."

Bank also observes that siblings may avoid each other as adults if there are unresolved conflicts left over from childhood because the parents were "conflictophobes," people who forbade sibling quarrels. "If you've been taught that it's dangerous to fight with your sibling, you may freeze around him when you're adults and sit in the same room hating his guts."

Both Bank and Kahn stress the lasting harm of "frozen misunderstandings" developed in childhood. These are distorted perceptions of a sibling that brothers and sisters may carry uncorrected into their adult relationship. A sister whose brother often hit her when they were children may infer, and believe for the rest of her life, that he did it because he was hateful. But it may be that hitting was the only way he could make the physical contact for which he was emotionally starved. And even if a child's image of a sibling was correct in youth, it may need later revision. "We change, but we may transact our relationship as if there had been no change," Bank says.

Adult Turning Points: Satisfactions and Stresses

Circumstances create a great diversity of adult sibling relationships, from hatred to detachment to love. "I have always experienced her as a vicious individual," a 28-year-old woman said of her sister in the course of a study by Elizabeth Fishel, author of *Sisters*. Helene S. Arnstein, author of *Brothers and Sisters, Sisters and Brothers*, quotes a sister who said of her brother: "If we weren't siblings I'd never see David again, because I don't care for the kind of person he has become."

History is filled with examples of more satisfying sibling relationships than that. Freud and his brother, Alexander, enjoyed each other's company all their lives. In his 1957 book on his father, *Glory Reflected*, Freud's son Martin wrote, "My father and Alexander could not have been more different in their outlook on life, but they were always good friends." Alexander often went along on holiday trips with Freud and his wife and children, and was Freud's frequent companion on climbing expeditions. The brothers had a particularly good time swimming together during an Adriatic holiday in 1895. "Uncle Alexander and father were seldom out of the water," wrote Martin. "When, as sometimes happened, they refused to come ashore even for lunch, a waiter would wade or swim out to them balancing a tray with refreshments and even cigars and matches."

In her autobiography *Blackberry Winter*, Margaret Mead tells of her lifelong warm relationship with her sister Elizabeth. "Her perceptions . . . have nourished me through the years. Her understanding of what has gone on in schools has provided depth and life to my own observations on American education. And her paintings have made every place I have lived my home."

Thinking of the women in her mother's family, Mead was struck by the way in which, generation after generation, pairs of sisters became good friends. "In this," she said, "they exemplify one of the basic characteristics of American kinship relations. Sisters, while they are growing up, tend to be very rivalrous, and as young mothers they are given to continual rivalrous comparisons of their several children. But once the children grow older, sisters draw closer together and often, in old age, they become each other's chosen and most happy companions."

If sibling relationships sometimes grow closer as siblings age, they may also founder at certain of life's turning points. Bank and Kahn say that siblings are best studied when under stress, because that is when the frequently submerged dynamics of their relationship are most likely to come to the surface, exposing the true nature, the real strength or fragility, of the bond. It is also at such moments that the "delicate balance" of a sibling relationship may tip decisively.

One turning point that can disrupt a previously close tie comes with a sibling's discovery that a brother or sister is getting a divorce, drinking too much, or going into psychotherapy. Under such circumstances, presumably untroubled siblings are often afraid that they will develop the same difficulty. Their reaction may be to make themselves feel better by offering the troubled sibling hostile advice on "how he could improve himself," Bank says. The mechanism, he explains, is projective identification: "The reason I don't like you is that I see in you what I know all too well I have inside me."

Of course, when a sibling goes into therapy, it does not inevitably damage a relationship. The outcome may be quite the opposite. "Under carefully arranged conditions, siblings can learn to cooperate with each other to resolve important conflicts in family relationships," Kahn and Bank write in a case report to be published in the journal *Family Process*. Called "In Pursuit of Sisterhood," the paper tells of Maureen, a 29-year-old nurse who entered treatment out of a kind of general unhappiness. Among other things, she hated the fact that her family had never taken her seriously.

Eventually the therapist called a series of "sibling rallies," meetings of the four sisters. The three older women told Maureen that she had never let them know how she felt. They all agreed that none of them was as close to the others as they wanted to think they were. Over a period of weeks, the four managed to thaw some of the

"frozen misunderstandings" from their common past and to become a cohesive group; for the first time, Maureen considered herself the equal of her sisters. After a while, Kahn and Bank said, the group confronted their mother and father and "successfully parried their parents' attempts to avoid discussing feelings." The ultimate result: "Faced with a unified sibling group, the parents were forced to redress old grievances by being helpful and accepting."

Physical illness is another situation that sheds light on sibling relationships. One illness that has been studied by many psychiatrists and medical sociologists is end-stage renal disease, in which doctors may be considering a kidney transplant.

Genetically, the best donors are brothers and sisters, because they provide the closest tissue match, reducing the danger that the patient's body will reject the transplanted organ. Yet siblings volunteer to donate a kidney less often than do parents. In a study of more than 300 relatives of transplant patients, Roberta G. Simmons, a sociologist at the University of Minnesota, found that 52 percent of the patients' sisters and 54 percent of their brothers did not volunteer. In contrast, only 14 percent of the patients' parents and only 33 percent of their children failed to volunteer.

Norman B. Levy and Jorge Steinberg, New York psychiatrists who have interviewed many pairs of kidney donors and recipients, have described a patient who got a kidney from her mother and told a researcher, "My sister was better matched, but she got pregnant." The two psychiatrists believe that the pregnancy very likely came about "accidentally on purpose" because the sister did not really want to donate.

Another case Levy and Steinberg described illustrates the apparent power of the emotions siblings feel for each other. The family wanted the needed kidney to be given by the patient's sister, who was not on good terms with the family, because they imagined that the gift would bring family harmony. The patient let herself be persuaded to accept her sister as donor, but she told the psychiatrists that she was afraid her sister would somehow find a way to make her pay for the gift. The prospective donor was no more

enthusiastic. "After I give her the damned kidney, I never want to see her again," she said. In short, Levy said, "They hated each other," and he and Steinberg predicted—correctly—that the patient's body would soon reject the hated sister's kidney.

The dependency, illness, and death of parents provide other possible turning points in the relationship of brothers and sisters. Cicirelli finds that siblings' negative feelings toward each other often emerge as an elderly parent becomes increasingly dependent. "Why should I look after my father?" a sibling thinks. "Let my brother do it."

On the other hand, there are siblings who compete to do the most for a dependent parent. "A common observation for those of us who deal with families of aged people," writes Martin A. Berezin, a psychoanalyst, "is the irrational, hostile attitude that siblings express to each other as they quarrel about what should be the proper care for an aged parent. Each accuses the other of negligence, lack of sympathy, or avoidance of responsibility. They challenge each other with questions of who telephoned or visited how many times." In such cases, according to Barbara Silverstone, a social worker, each sibling claims to have the parent's welfare uppermost, "but the underlying motive is winning out in a family contest."

Many researchers say that sibling bonds often weaken or disintegrate entirely when the last parent dies. "The wounds that are given and received during a parent's illness and dependency," Silverstone says, are often "only the final blows ending a relationship which has been distant or seething for years." A brother or sister who sacrificed too much for a parent may resent those who did too little. Or, Silverstone suggests, "Siblings may resent the martyred caretaker who stood between them and their dying mother, making it impossible for them to share her final days."

In some instances, Bank and Kahn say, a parent's death "can set off fratricidal feelings and struggles as siblings jockey for positions of leadership within the adult sibling group." Yet there are times when a parent's illness brings siblings together. One sister said to Silverstone of her brother, "I never realized what a great person he'd turned into until I spent all that time at home when Mother was sick. We're real friends now." Generally speaking, Bank believes, previously bad sibling relationships get worse after the parents' death; good ones improve.

An Inescapable Bond

Bank and Kahn call the sibling relationship "a lifelong process, highly influential throughout the life cycle." Even when brothers and sisters drift apart as they enter careers and begin to raise families, they are likely to renew their relationship eventually. "It is extremely rare for siblings to lose touch with one another," Cicirelli says. As the British sociologist Graham Allan puts it, it is "permissible to forget about a neighbor or other associate, but less appropriate to 'drop' a sister or brother."

Throughout life, siblings are likely to serve each other as models, spurs to achievement, and yardsticks by which to measure accomplishments. In the best of circumstances, they become sources of practical help, nonjudgmental advice, and true intimacy. Indeed, Cicirelli remarks, "The nature of the sibling relationship is such that intimacy between siblings is immediately restored even after long absences."

"One of the main theses of our book," Kahn says, "is that siblings are becoming more and more dependent upon one another in contemporary families because of the attrition in family size. If you have only one sibling, that one becomes enormously important." The decreased availability of parents in one-parent homes and in households where both mother and father work also makes siblings count for more with each other. The rising divorce rate, too, intensifies adult sibling relationships by making them more significant than a husband or wife in an ephemeral marriage.

Bank and Kahn also predict that the rising divorce rate will lead to increased sibling conflict, "with adolescent and adult siblings taking sides with each parent in a kind of proxy war." But with or without divorce, conflict occurs between many—some would say most—brothers and sisters.

"One can conceive of rivalry as a feeling which is always latent, appearing strongly in certain circumstances while closeness is elicited in others," Cicirelli said recently. "Possibly there is a balance between the functional and dysfunctional aspects of the sibling relation which is manifested in solidarity versus rivalry. There may be a love-hate dialectical process throughout the life span that leads to new levels of maturity or immaturity in sibling relationships."

Some siblings are well aware of their ambivalence. "My mixed feelings toward my sister, my irradicable love-hate mix, have been almost the longest-standing puzzle of my life," a woman of 30 told Elizabeth Fishel.

Even siblings who prefer not to confront their ambivalence probably do not wholly escape its effects. Whatever its nature in particular cases—warm or cool—the sibling relationship remains alive in some sense. Mental images of each other, vivid or half forgotten, can influence brothers and sisters even when they are oceans apart and not consciously preoccupied with each other. "It's a relationship for life," Bank says. "It's forever."

'Too Weary to Go On'

Why are so many children committing suicide,
and what can be done to prevent it?

JOHN LANGONE

While her parents were attending a neighborhood party and her sister was playing the piano in the living room, Vivienne Loomis, of Melrose, Massachusetts, went downstairs to the basement one December night and hanged herself. She was 14 years old. On the kitchen table her family found this poem:

> When you are
> Too weary
> To go on
> And life strikes
> Such a finalizing chord,
> You have a choice.
> You can either
> Take a bow
> And leave.
> Or carry the tune
> Appreciating the crescendo
> As exactly that.

Vivienne Loomis was an attractive ninth-grader with a gift for writing. Her family loved her, she was well liked by her friends and teachers, and no one doubted that her intelligence and ability would carry her far in life. Her suicide bewildered them all.

The story of Vivienne's death—and of her life—will soon be familiar to many Americans; it is documented and analyzed in a new book, *Vivienne: The Life and Suicide of an Adolescent Girl* (Little, Brown, $12.95). Her story is far from unusual. In the United States today, suicide among youth has become epidemic.

The overall suicide rate has remained about the same for the past 30 years, but the proportion of young people taking their lives is greater than ever before. Among 15- to 24-year-olds, suicide is the third leading cause of death, after homicide and accidents. In 1978, for example, nearly 2,000 young people between the ages of 10 and 19, the over-

whelming majority of them males, killed themselves—twice as many as in 1968. In the 20- to 24-year-old age group, 3,500 committed suicide, up from 1,500 ten years earlier. In each of the past ten years, as many as 200 children aged 14 and under—a few as young as 5—have killed themselves. Suicide among children aged 5 through 14 has now moved from the ninth to the eighth leading cause of death.

Beyond these statistics, and beyond what are probably the even more numerous unreported suicides disguised as accidents, are countless cases of young people who attempt to take their lives but fail. "Suicide attempts outnumber actual suicides among young people by fifty to one," says Dr. Calvin Frederick, of the National Institute of Mental Health. Dr. Cynthia Pfeffer, a psychiatrist at Cornell, agrees: "The number of children who threaten and attempt suicide has increased. Studies in the nineteen-sixties indicated that no more than ten per cent of the children sent to outpatient clinics showed suicidal behavior. In a recent study I did, thirty-three per cent of the children had suicidal ideas."

Most people cannot comprehend the mental state that leads to suicide, especially the suicide of a child. Why would he take his life, and why is the number of suicides among children rising? The answers are not absolute. They depend, as do virtually all questions in the nebulous science of human behavior, on causes that are difficult to pin down. Emotional development, environment, and genetics are possible factors. Psychosis, parental rejection, divorce, a history of suicide in the family, revenge on a parent, unemployment, pressure to grow up too fast and too soon, and, in a very young child, the wish to rejoin a dead brother or sister or a pet—all have been cited as reasons. Just as adults are often "crying out for attention" when they make even halfhearted attempts at suicide, so are many children, says Dr. Michael Jellinek, chief of child psychia-

try at Massachusetts General Hospital. "The kid may be saying, 'I can't tell you how I feel, so I'll hurt myself.' "

One who did express feelings—indeed, gave warning signals—was Vivienne Loomis, whose story should help parents, teachers, and psychologists in dealing with the emotional problems of other children. The first half of *Vivienne* consists of her poetry, essays, letters, and diary entries; the second half is a commentary, written by John Mack, a professor of psychiatry at Harvard Medical School, and Holly Hickler, an English teacher at the Cambridge School of Weston, in Massachusetts. Interspersed among passages of more or less typical confessions and frustrations of a sensitive young girl are entries containing suggestions of suicidal intent, some of them painfully explicit (see box, A/E p. 216). Yet neither close friends, to whom Vivienne confided these notions, nor parents nor teachers treated the signals seriously—if they recognized them at all.

Vivienne, who had an older sister and brother, was above average in intelligence and seemed like a typical adolescent schoolgirl. Her parents were Unitarians who lived in a Roman Catholic neighborhood—liberals among political conservatives. The father, a minister, was a decent and fair-minded man, but indecisive; the mother was energetic, strong-willed, and ambitious for creative achievement. Vivienne's introspective personality and her obvious talent for writing set her apart from her schoolmates and sometimes made her an object of derision. This paralleled the discomfort of her parents—described by her brother as "always a little bit different"—in the town. But what was most telling of all was Vivienne's excruciating need to shoulder the griefs and burdens of her family, writes psychiatrist Mack: "Two related aspects of her development—emotional injury in her earliest human relationships and the intense capacity for empathy with the pain of others—

would leave her exquisitely vulnerable to loss and disappointment, and, ultimately, to depression and suicide."

It is obvious that depression—and its dark angels, isolation, helplessness, hopelessness—can ultimately lead to thoughts of suicide. But most people experience these emotions from time to time and learn to control them. The difficult thing is to find ways of helping young people deal with frustration and depression that even adults at times cannot manage.

Psychotherapist Margery Fridstein works on Chicago's North Shore, an affluent area dubbed the "suicide belt" (in one recent 17-month period, 28 teenagers took their own lives). She thinks that television dramas with swift, superficial, and happy endings are a disservice to children. "Kids don't like to read books—they'd rather watch television and see the story end quickly—and so they don't know how to deal with long-term frustration. They don't have the built-in patience, when something bad happens all of a sudden, to tolerate it." Because pills or a rope or even a gun is readily available, says Fridstein, "it is much easier to do this dramatic thing."

Fridstein also suggests that parents often expect too much of their children. "The parents put pressure on the child to either reproduce what they themselves have done, or do much bet-

ter. And the child may say, 'I can't, I can't, I'm going to give up.'" Says Charles Irwin, a pediatrician and the director of the Adolescent Medical Unit at the University of California in San Francisco, "A lot of families expect that the minute youngsters become thirteen or fourteen, they should be capable of making it on their own. In reality, teenagers probably need as much support at that point in their lives as toddlers need, although of a different sort."

Yet the *absence* of parental pressure can confuse children, too. Says Patricia Couto, executive director of the Crisis Intervention Center in Nashville, "In some ways there was more pressure on kids years ago. They were expected to go to school, grow intellectually, and be, say, a doctor or lawyer—and they got a lot of guidance. Now the expectations are still there but the guidance is not. We tell the kids they must make their own decisions. It's a tremendous conflict, and I don't think teen-agers are prepared to make decisions from all the choices they are given."

Couto has had direct experience with confused children, for Nashville, the nation's country music capital, has become something of a suicide center as well. Says Couto, "This place is Music City, and the teen-agers come in with their backpacks and guitars, and they think that they're going to walk right into the RCA Building and someone is

going to hear them and they'll be a big hit. Well, the fact is they can't even get in the door, and in two days every cent they have is gone. A lot of them, boys and girls, wind up as prostitutes, and when they call us they say, 'I haven't eaten in three days, I have no place to stay.'" Most of these get help; for others, the answer is tragedy. Last year alone, Nashville recorded 57 suicides; 22 of them were youngsters, one of whom was only eleven years old.

Florida, too, has become a kind of last resort for the young. The overall suicide rate there is 17.7 per 100,000, well above the national average of 12.5 per 100,000. In part, that toll can be explained by the state's large population of old people, who are often poor and lonely and prone to suicide. But the rate among those between the ages of 15 and 24 has grown alarmingly. Psychologist William Young, executive director of the Sarasota Guidance Clinic, attributes this rush toward self-destruction partly to Florida's rapid population growth. Hordes of transients arrive there every year, seeking serenity. "Many people sell their houses up north and expect things to be different here," says Young. "They've left their friends and families, and they're lonely—and maybe angry because they do not find quite what they expected. Sometimes they bring their adolescents with them, and they're displaced down

'How Can You Kill Nothing?'

Excerpts from *Vivienne:*

Do you think you could squeeze in some time to write me? ... There's a rumor in my mind that says you don't much care for me any more. My problem is that I believe it whether it's true or not ... I don't think I've ever been so lonely in my life!!! ... Sorry to be so gloomy.
Letter to a teacher, July 2, 1972

*You reach for a smile
But there is no one there
To reflect it.
You are utterly and absolutely
Alone.*

*Will there never be a hand
To grasp at yours within the mirror?
Will there never be an arm
To hold you tight amidst the terror?*
Diary entry, (undated) 1973

I am worthless. I am of no use to anyone, and no one is of any use to me. What good to kill myself? How can you kill nothing? A person who has committed suicide has had at least something to end ... Why live? Why die? ... To keep on living an empty life takes patience from an empty person ...
Diary entry, April 11, 1973

I have spent the past half hour in the back bathroom trying to strangle myself, and sending a prayer. The prayer was

not strong enough. I never could pray. You can tell when a prayer doesn't get through ... But I have been able to practice how to strangle [myself]. I know that I will need the knowledge some day soon. There are two effects to clutching your throat. One is life and one is death. Life comes in the form of a whitened face and a sensation of tingling through your whole body ... Death comes as an increasingly darkening face and unstrained thin breathing ... In the mirror I had the privilege to see for myself what my dead face will look like...
Diary entry, July 9, 1973

*Life is lost in dried flowers;
Brittle and faded stars
Have lost their riches
The winds have scattered.*
Diary entry, written in the last three weeks of her life

here, too, without friends, having to start all over." Most people who call Young's clinic are suicidal. "Many of these people have not been able to change gears and cope with losses," he says. "They're depressed."

What is perhaps most puzzling to psychologists is the increase in the suicide rate among very young children. Conventional wisdom holds that innocent, unworldly childhood is somehow invulnerable to depression; apart from occasional temper tantrums and moments of sadness, children are not supposed to withdraw, to mourn, to feel hopeless. But psychologists point out that although young children may not show the same symptoms of depression as adolescents or adults, they can indeed suffer deeply.

Some experts think that certain forms of depression may be hereditary. Other researchers have shown that parents can transfer their moods to their children. Cynthia Pfeffer has found that mothers of suicidal children are more often depressed than mothers of those who are not. Her study seems to reinforce the findings of Anna Freud; in her *Psychoanalytic Study of the Child*, published in 1951, she wrote that "depressive moods of the mother during the first two years after birth create in the child a tendency to depression."

Loneliness and hopelessness, which can lead to thoughts of suicide, are quite common in pre-adolescents. Says Dr. Marianne Felice, of the University of California at San Diego, "They say, 'I'm bad, nobody loves me.' Often these kids are not good at anything, and every youngster needs to feel successful in something—swimming, having friends,

being the best hopscotcher, having Mother's love."

Sadness, combined with the promise of happiness in the hereafter, can also lead to suicide attempts. As one nine-year-old boy who tried to hang himself explained, "I want to go to heaven because God will be my friend. I don't have any friends here." A five-year-old boy told a psychiatrist he wanted to die so that he could "speak with Jesus" and see his grandmother again.

Although a small child may talk about suicide, it is not usually to adults that he reveals such thoughts. This is also true of adolescents. Says Patricia Couto, "They're different from adults. They're not usually candid when they telephone us. They'll say they're calling about a friend they're concerned about. But you can usually tell from the tone of voice whether that's true. And when you finally ask them if they're talking about themselves, they might say yes, and they'll be relieved." But, she adds, adolescents do confide in their friends. "That's the biggest difficulty we face in dealing with teen-age suicides. They'll give their signals to their friends, and swear them to secrecy. Their code is, You don't tell an adult. The friends really try to help, but it's beyond their ability. We have to break down that code, and teach the kids that if someone tells you he's planning to kill himself, it's serious and he may do it."

How to stop them in time? First, parents must always be alert to self-destructive signals, however vague they may be, from children. Among the signals: indirect comments about how they

might as well be dead; the giving away of treasured personal possessions; marked personality changes. Once any of these signals has been noticed, the thing to do is talk things over calmly and openly. Direct questions are best, say the experts. If the parents cannot cope with an adolescent's depression, they should suggest that the child talk to someone at a crisis intervention center, or to a counselor, a doctor, or a clergyman. If the child refuses, the parent should seek advice about what to do next from one of these sources.

"What we see in the typical suicidal person," says William Young, "is someone who has considered only one way out of his problems. We have to try to help him understand that there are many solutions besides suicide."

But getting teen-agers to grasp the alternatives is not easy. Says Couto, "There's virtually no way to convince a teen-ager that things aren't always going to be so bleak. As you get older you realize that. But with teens, no matter how you go about it, you have difficulty getting through because their pain is so intense."

No one got through in time to save Vivienne Loomis. Her surrender to death, as the authors of her story point out, is a grim reminder of the mercurial state of the adolescent mind. "Vivienne," they write, "recorded a despair that others her age have felt. The lesson she teaches us at fourteen is impressive. All children are under our care. No matter where encountered, each child belongs to each of us."

THE MANY ME'S OF THE SELF-MONITOR

Is there a "true self" apart from the social roles we play?
Perhaps not for people identified in studies as high
self-monitors, who are keenly aware of the impression they are
making and constantly fine-tuning their performance.

MARK SNYDER

Mark Snyder is professor of psychology at the University of Minnesota in Minneapolis, where he teaches a graduate-level course called "The Self." In addition to his research on self-monitoring, he is studying stereotypes and the effect of stereotypes on social relationships.

"The image of myself which I try to create in my own mind in order that I may love myself is very different from the image which I try to create in the minds of others in order that they may love me."

—W. H. Auden

The concept of the self is one of the oldest and most enduring in psychological considerations of human nature. We generally assume that people are fairly consistent and stable beings: that a person who is generous in one situation is also likely to be generous in other situations, that one who is honest is honest most of the time, that a person who takes a liberal stance today will favor the liberal viewpoint tomorrow.

It's not always so: each of us, it appears, may have not one but many selves. Moreover, much as we might like to believe that the self is an integral feature of personal identity, it appears that, to a greater extent, the self is a product of the individual's relationships with other people. Conventional wisdom to the contrary, there may be striking gaps and contradictions—as Auden suggests—between the public appearances and private realities of the self.

Psychologists refer to the strategies and techniques that people use to control the impressions they convey to others as "impression management." One of my own research interests has been to understand why some individuals are better at impression management than others. For it is clear that some people are particularly sensitive to the ways they express and present themselves in social situations—at parties, job interviews, professional meetings, in confrontations of all kinds where one might choose to create and maintain an appearance, with or without a specific purpose in mind. Indeed, I have found that such people have developed the ability to carefully monitor their own performances and to skillfully adjust their performances when signals from others tell them that they are not having the desired effect. I call such persons "high self-monitoring individuals," and I have developed a 25-item measure—the Self-Monitoring Scale—that has proved its ability to distinguish high self-monitoring individuals from low self-monitoring individuals. (See box on page 219.) Unlike the high self-monitoring individuals, low self-monitoring individuals are not so concerned about taking in such information; instead, they tend to express what they feel, rather than mold and tailor their behavior to fit the situation.

My work on self-monitoring and impression management grew out of a long-standing fascination with explorations of reality and illusion in literature and in the theater. I was struck by the contrast between the way things often appear to be and the reality that lurks beneath the surface—on the stage, in novels, and in people's actual lives. I wanted to know how this world of appearances in social relationships was built and maintained, as well as what its effects were on the individual personality. But I was also interested in exploring the older, more philosophical question of whether, beneath the various images of self that people project to others, there is a "real me." If we are all actors in many social situations, do we then retain in any sense an essential self, or are we really a variety of selves?

Skilled Impression Managers

There are striking and important differences in the extent to which people can and do control their self-presentation in social situations: some people engage in impression management more often—and with greater skill—than others. Professional actors, as well as many trial lawyers, are among the best at it. So are successful salespeople, confidence artists, and politicians. The onetime mayor of New York, Fiorello LaGuardia, was particularly skilled at adopting the expressive mannerisms of a variety of ethnic groups. In fact, he was so good at it that in watching silent films of his campaign speeches, it is easy to guess whose vote he was soliciting.

Of course, such highly skilled performances are the exception rather than the rule. And people differ in the extent to which they can and do exercise control over their self-presentations. It is the high self-monitoring individuals among us who are particularly talented in this regard. When asked to describe high self-monitoring individuals, their friends say that they are good at learning which behavior is appropriate in social situations, have good self-control of their emotional expression, and can effectively use this ability to create the impression they want. They are particularly skilled at intentionally expressing and accurately communicating a wide variety of emotions both vocally and facially. As studies by Richard Lippa of California State University at Fullerton have shown, they are usually such polished actors that they can effectively adopt the mannerisms of a reserved, withdrawn, and introverted individual and then do an abrupt about-face and portray, just as convincingly, a friendly, outgoing, and extraverted personality.

High self-monitoring individuals are also quite likely to seek out information about appropriate patterns of self-presentation. They invest considerable effort in attempting to "read"

and understand others. In an experiment I conducted with Tom Monson (then one of my graduate students), various cues were given to students involved in group discussions as to what was socially appropriate behavior in the situation. For example, some of them thought that their taped discussions would be played back to fellow students; in those circumstances, I assumed they would want their opinions to appear as autonomous as possible. Others believed that their discussions were completely private; there, I assumed they would be most concerned with maintaining harmony and agree-

ment in the group. High self-monitoring individuals were keenly attentive to these differences; they conformed with the group when conformity was the most appropriate behavior and did not conform when they knew that the norms of the larger student audience would favor autonomy in the face of social pressure. Low self-monitoring individuals were virtually unaffected by the differences in social setting: presumably, their self-presentations were more accurate reflections of their personal attitudes and dispositions. Thus, as we might have guessed, people who are most

MONITOR YOUR SELF

On the scale I have developed to measure self-monitoring, actors are usually high scorers, as are many obese people, who tend to be very sensitive about the way they appear to others. For much the same reason, politicians and trial lawyers would almost certainly be high scorers. Recent immigrants eager to assimilate, black freshmen in a predominantly white college, and military personnel stationed abroad are also likely to score high on the scale.

The Self-Monitoring Scale measures how concerned people are with the impression they are making on others, as well as their ability to control and modify their behavior to fit the situation. I believe that it defines a distinct domain of personality that is quite different from the traits probed by other standard scales.

Several studies show that skill at

self-monitoring is not associated with exceptional intelligence or with a particular social class. Nor is it related, among other things, to being highly anxious or extremely self-conscious, to being an extravert, or to having a strong need for approval. They may be somewhat power-oriented or Machiavellian, but high self-monitoring individuals do not necessarily have high scores on the

"Mach" scale, a measure of Machiavellianism developed by Richard Christie of Columbia University. (Two items from the scale: "The best way to handle people is to tell them what they want" and "Anyone who completely trusts anyone else is asking for trouble.") The steely-eyed Machiavellians are more manipulative, detached, and amoral than high self-monitoring individuals.

The Self-Monitoring Scale describes a unique trait and has proved to be both statistically valid and reliable, in tests on various samples.

At left is a 10-item abbreviated version of the Self-Monitoring Scale that will give readers some idea of whether they are low or high self-monitoring individuals. If you would like to test your self-monitoring tendencies, follow the instructions and then consult the scoring key. —M.S.

These statements concern personal reactions to a number of different situations. No two statements are exactly alike, so consider each statement carefully before answering. If a statement is true, or mostly true, as applied to you, circle the T. If a statement is false, or not usually true, as applied to you, circle the F.

1. I find it hard to imitate the behavior of other people.   T F
2. I guess I put on a show to impress or entertain people.   T F
3. I would probably make a good actor.   T F
4. I sometimes appear to others to be experiencing deeper emotions than I actually am.   T F
5. In a group of people I am rarely the center of attention.   T F
6. In different situations and with different people, I often act like very different persons.   T F
7. I can only argue for ideas I already believe.   T F
8. In order to get along and be liked, I tend to be what people expect me to be rather than anything else.   T F
9. I may deceive people by being friendly when I really dislike them.   T F
10. I'm not always the person I appear to be.   T F

SCORING: Give yourself one point for each of questions 1, 5 and 7 that you answered F. Give yourself one point for each of the remaining questions that you answered T. Add up your points. If you are a good judge of yourself and scored 7 or above, you are probably a high self-monitoring individual; 3 or below, you are probably a low self-monitoring individual.

skilled in the arts of impression management are also most likely to practice it.

Although high self-monitoring individuals are well skilled in the arts of impression management, we should not automatically assume that they necessarily use these skills for deceptive or manipulative purposes. Indeed, in their relationships with friends and acquaintances, high self-monitoring individuals are eager to use their self-monitoring abilities to promote smooth social interactions.

We can find some clues to this motive in the way high self-monitoring individuals tend to react to, and cope with, unfamiliar and unstructured social settings. In a study done at the University of Wisconsin, psychologists William Ickes and Richard Barnes arranged for pairs of strangers to spend time together in a waiting room, ostensibly to wait for an experiment to begin. The researchers then recorded the verbal and nonverbal behavior of each pair over a five-minute period, using video and audio tapes. All possible pairings of same-sex undergraduates at high, moderate, and low levels of self-monitoring were represented. Researchers scrutinized the tapes for evidence of the impact of self-monitoring on spontaneous encounters between strangers.

In these meetings, as in so many other aspects of their lives, high self-monitoring individuals suffered little or no shyness. Soon after meeting the other person, they took an active and controlling role in the conversation. They were inclined to talk first and to initiate subsequent conversational sequences. They also felt, and were seen by their partners to have, a greater need to talk. Their partners also viewed them as having been the more directive member of the pair. It was as if high self-monitoring individuals were particularly concerned about managing their behavior in order to create, encourage, and maintain a smooth flow of conversation. Perhaps this quality may help self-monitoring people to emerge as leaders in groups, organizations, and institutions.

Detecting Impression Management In Others

High self-monitoring individuals are

WILLIAM JAMES ON THE ROLES WE PLAY

A man has as many social selves as there are individuals who recognize him and carry an image of him in their mind . . . . But as the individuals who carry the images form naturally into classes, we may practically say that he has as many different social selves as there are distinct *groups* of persons about whose opinions he cares. He generally shows a different side of himself to each of these different groups. Many a youth who is demure enough before his parents and teachers swears and swaggers like a pirate among his 'tough' young friends. We do not show ourselves to our children as to our club companions, to our masters and employers as to our intimate friends. From this there results what practically is a division of the man into several selves; and this may be a discordant splitting, as where one is afraid to let one set of his acquaintances know him as he is elsewhere; or it may be a perfectly harmonious division of labor, as where one tender to his children is stern to the soldiers or prisoners under his command."

—William James
The Principles of Psychology, 1890

also adept at detecting impression management in others. To demonstrate this finely tuned ability, three communications researchers at the University of Minnesota made use of videotaped excerpts from the television program "To Tell the Truth." On this program, one of the three guest contestants (all male in the excerpts chosen for the study) is the "real Mr. X." The other two who claim to be the real Mr. X are, of course, lying. Participants in the study watched each excerpt and then tried to identify the real Mr. X. High self-monitoring individuals were much more accurate than their low self-monitoring counterparts in correctly identifying the real Mr. X. and in seeing through the deception of the other two contestants.

Not only are high self-monitoring individuals able to see beyond the masks of deception successfully but they are also keenly attentive to the actions of other people as clues to their underlying intentions. E. E. Jones and Roy Baumeister of Princeton University had college students watch a videotaped discussion between two men who either agreed or disagreed with each other. The observers were aware that one man (the target person) had been instructed either to gain the affection or to win the respect of the other. Low self-moni-

toring observers tended to accept behavior at face value. They found themselves attracted to the agreeable person, whether or not he was attempting to ingratiate himself with his discussion partner. In contrast, high self-monitoring observers were acutely sensitive to the motivational context within which the target person operated. They liked the target better if he was disagreeable when trying to ingratiate himself. But when he sought respect, they were more attracted to him if he chose to be agreeable. Jones and Baumeister suggest that high self-monitoring observers regarded agreeableness as too blatant a ploy in gaining affection and autonomy as an equally obvious route to respect. Perhaps the high self-monitoring individuals felt that they themselves would have acted with greater subtlety and finesse.

Even more intriguing is Jones's and Baumeister's speculation—and I share their view—that high self-monitoring individuals prefer to live in a stable, predictable social environment populated by people whose actions consistently and accurately reflect their true attitudes and feelings. In such a world, the consistency and predictability of the actions of others would be of great benefit to those who tailor and manage their own self-presentation in social situations. From this perspective, it becomes quite understandable that high self-monitoring individuals may be especially fond of those who avoid strategic posturing. Furthermore, they actually may prefer as friends those comparatively low in self-monitoring.

How can we know when strangers and casual acquaintances are engaged in self-monitoring? Are there some channels of expression and communication that are more revealing than others about a person's true, inner "self," even when he or she is practicing impression management?

Both scientific and everyday observers of human behavior have suggested that nonverbal behavior—facial expressions, tone of voice, and body movements—reveals meaningful information about a person's attitudes, feelings, and motives. Often, people who engage in self-monitoring for deceptive purposes are less skilled at controlling their body's expressive movements. Accordingly, the body may be a more revealing source of information than the face for detecting those who engage in self-monitoring and impression management.

More than one experiment shows how nonverbal behavior can betray the true attitude of those attempting impression management. Shirley Weitz of the New School for Social Research reasoned that on college campuses where there are strong normative pressures supporting a tolerant and liberal value system, all students would avoid saying anything that would indicate racial prejudice—whether or not their private attitudes supported such behavior. In fact, she found that among "liberal" white males at Harvard University, the most prejudiced students (as determined by behavioral measures of actual attempts to avoid interaction with blacks) bent over backwards to *verbally* express liking and friendship for a black in a simulated interracial encounter. However, their *nonverbal* behaviors gave them away. Although the prejudiced students made every effort to say kind and favorable things, they continued to do so in a cool and distant tone of voice. It was as if they knew the words but not the music: they knew *what* to say, but not *how* to say it.

Another way that prejudice can be revealed is in the physical distance people maintain between themselves and the target of their prejudice. To demonstrate this phenomenon, psychologist Stephen Morin arranged for college students to be interviewed about their attitudes toward homosexuality. Half the interviewers wore "Gay and Proud" buttons and mentioned their association with the Association of Gay Psychologists. The rest wore no buttons and simply mentioned that they were graduate students working on theses. Without the students' knowledge, the distance they placed their chairs from the interviewer was measured while the interviews were going on. The measure of social distance proved to be highly revealing. When the student and the interviewer were of the same sex, students tended to establish almost a foot more distance between themselves and the apparently gay interviewers. They placed their chairs an average of 32 inches away from apparently gay interviewers, but only 22 inches away from apparently nongay interviewers. Interestingly, most of the students expressed tolerant, and at times favorable, attitudes toward gay people in general. However, the distances they chose to put between themselves and the interviewers they thought gay betrayed underlying negative attitudes.

Impression Managers' Dilemmas

The well-developed skills of high self-monitoring individuals ought to give them the flexibility to cope quickly and effectively with a diversity of social roles. They can choose with skill and grace the self-presentation appropriate to each of a wide variety of social situations. But what happens when the impression manager must effectively present a true and honest image to other people?

Consider the case of a woman on trial for a crime that she did not commit. Her task on the witness stand is to carefully present herself so that everything she does and says communicates to the jurors clearly and unambiguously her true innocence, so that they will vote for her acquittal. Chances are good, however, that members of the jury are somewhat skeptical of the defendant's claims of innocence. After all, they might reason to themselves, the district attorney would not have brought this case to trial were the state's case against her not a convincing one.

The defendant must carefully manage her verbal and nonverbal behaviors so as to ensure that even a skeptical jury forms a true impression of her innocence. In particular, she must avoid the pitfalls of an image that suggests that "she doth protest her innocence too much and therefore must be guilty." To the extent that our defendant skillfully practices the art of impression management, she will succeed in presenting herself to the jurors as the honest person that she truly is.

It often can take as much work to present a truthful image as to present a deceptive one. In fact, in this case, just being honest may not be enough when facing skeptical jurors who may bend over backwards to interpret any and all of the defendant's behavior—nervousness, for example—as a sign of guilt.

The message from research on impression management is a clear one. Some people are quite flexible in their self-presentation. What effects do these shifts in public appearance have on the more private realities of self-concept? In some circumstances, we are persuaded by our own appearances: we become the persons we appear to be. This phenomenon is particularly likely to occur when the image we present wins the approval and favor of those around us.

In an experiment conducted at Duke University by psychologists E. E. Jones, Kenneth Gergen, and Keith Davis, participants who had been instructed to win the approval of an interviewer presented very flattering images of themselves. Half the participants (chosen at random) then received favorable reactions from their interviewers; the rest did not. All the participants later were asked to estimate how accurately and honestly their self-descriptions had mirrored their true personalities.

Those who had won the favor of their interviewers considered their self-presentations to have been the most honest of all. One interpretation of this finding is that those people were operating with rather pragmatic definitions of self-concept: that which produced the most positive results was considered to be an accurate reflection of the inner self.

The reactions of other people can make it all the more likely that we become what we claim to be. Other people may accept our self-presentations at face value; they may then treat us as if we really were the way we pretend to be. For example, if I act as if I like Chris, chances are Chris will like me. Chris will probably treat me in a variety of friendly ways. As a result of Chris's friendliness, I may come to like Chris, even though I did not in the first place. The result, in this case, may be beneficial to both parties. In other circumstances, however, the skilled impression manager may pay an emotional price.

High self-monitoring orientation may be purchased at the cost of having one's actions reflect and communicate very little about one's private attitudes, feelings, and dispositions. In fact, as I have seen time and again in my research with my former graduate students Beth Tanke and Bill Swann, correspondence between private attitudes and public behavior is often minimal for high self-monitoring individuals. Evidently, the words and deeds of high self-monitoring individuals may reveal precious little information about their true inner feelings and attitudes.

Yet, it is almost a canon of modern psychology that a person's ability to reveal a "true self" to intimates is essential to emotional health. Sidney Jourard, one of the first psychologists to hold that view, believed that only through self-disclosure could we achieve self-discovery and self-knowledge: "Through my self-disclosure, I let others know my soul. They can know it, really know it, only as I make it known. In fact, I am beginning to suspect that I can't even know *my*

own soul except as I disclose it. I suspect that I will know myself "for real" at the exact moment that I have succeeded in making it known through my disclosure to another person."

Only low self-monitoring individuals may be willing or able to live their lives according to Jourard's prescriptions. By contrast, high self-monitoring individuals seem to embody Erving Goffman's view of human nature. For him, the world of appearances appears to be all, and the "soul" is illusory. Goffman defines social interactions as a theatrical performance in which each individual acts out a "line." A line is a set of carefully chosen verbal and nonverbal acts that express one's self. Each of us, in Goffman's view, seems to be merely the sum of our various performances.

What does this imply for the sense of self and identity associated with low and high self-monitoring individuals?

I believe that high self-monitoring individuals and low self-monitoring individuals have very different ideas about what constitutes a self and that their notions are quite well-suited to how they live. High self-monitoring individuals regard themselves as rather flexible and adaptive people who tailor their social behavior shrewdly and pragmatically to fit appropriate conditions. They believe that a person is whoever he appears to be in any particular situation: "I am me, the me I am right now." This self-image fits well with the way high self-monitoring individuals present themselves to the world. It allows them to act in ways that are consistent with how they believe they should act.

By contrast, low self-monitoring individuals have a firmer, more single-minded idea of what a self should be. They value and strive for congruence between "who they are" and "what they do" and regard their actions as faithful reflections of how they feel and think. For them, a self is a single identity that must not be compromised for other people or in certain situations. Indeed, this view of the self parallels the low self-monitoring individual's consistent and stable self-presentation.

What is important in understanding oneself and others, then, is not the elusive question of whether there is a quintessential self, but rather, understanding how different people define those attributes of their behavior and experience that they regard as "me." Theory and research on self-monitoring have attempted to chart the processes by which beliefs about the self are actively translated into patterns of social behavior that reflect self-conceptions. From this perspective, the processes of self-monitoring are the processes of self—a system of operating rules that translate self-knowledge into social behavior.

For further information, read:

Gergen, Kenneth. *The Concept of Self*, Holt, Rinehart & Winston, 1971, paper, $4.50.

Goffman, Erving. *The Presentation of Self in Everyday Life*, Doubleday (reprint of 1959 edition), paper, $2.50.

Snyder, Mark. "Self-Monitoring Processes," in *Advances in Experimental Social Psychology, Vol. 12*, Leonard Berkowitz, ed., Academic Press, 1979, $24.

Snyder, Mark. "Cognitive, Behavioral, and Interpersonal Consequences of Self-Monitoring," in *Advances in the Study of Communication and Affect, Vol. 5: Perception of Emotion in Self and Others*, Plenum, 1979, $24.50.

Snyder, Mark. "Self-Monitoring of Expressive Behavior," *Journal of Personality and Social Psychology*, 30(1974): 526-537.

SINGLE PARENT FATHERS:

A New Study

Harry Finkelstein Keshet and Kristine M. Rosenthal

Harry Finkelstein Keshet, Ph.D., and Kristine M. Rosenthal, Ed.D., are co-directors of the Parenting Study at Brandeis University. Dr. Keshet, a divorced father with joint custody of his son, is an instructor in the Parenting Program at Wheelock College, Boston, and clinical director of the Divorce Resource and Mediation Center, Inc., Cambridge, Mass. Dr. Rosenthal, a single parent of three children, is an assistant professor at Brandeis University.

This article is about single-parent fathers who are rearing their young children after marital separation. It discusses what fathers do for and with their children and how being a single parent affects their lifestyles and work responsibilities.

The article is based on interviews, conducted by trained male interviewers, with 49 separated or divorced fathers who live in the Boston area and have formal or informal custody of their children.[1] At the time of the interviews, each father's youngest child was between the ages of three and seven and there were no more than three children in any of the families. Each father had been separated from his wife for at least one year.[2]

Over half of the fathers in the sample (53 percent) were legally divorced; the remainder were separated informally. Most of the men had been married and living with their spouses for a minimum of five years.

The majority of fathers were highly educated; barely a fourth had had less than a full college education and nearly half had either completed or were in the process of completing graduate or professional training. More than half of the fathers were in professional or semi-professional occupations, 20 percent were in business or administration and 20 percent had blue-collar jobs or worked as craftsmen. Another six percent of the sample were students;

two percent were unemployed.

Seventy-six percent of the fathers worked full-time or longer at their occupations; the others worked half time or less. A majority of the fathers earned relatively high incomes: 15 percent earned over $25,000, 25 percent earned between $15,000 and $25,000 and 30 percent earned between $10,000 and $15,000.

We felt that residential stability and housing were important factors in childrearing. Therefore, we were interested in the types of housing arrangements the men had made. Over half of the fathers (54 percent) occupied houses which they owned, while the others lived in apartments or rented homes. Most of the men showed a high rate of residential stability—50 percent had lived in the same dwelling for two years or longer and 12 percent had lived in the same place for more than a year.

Half the men lived alone with their children, 35 percent shared housing with other adults and the remaining 15 percent lived with their lovers. Only a few men in the sample lived with extended families.

Almost all of the fathers reported that their children were attending day care centers or schools or were cared for by hired babysitters when the fathers were working.

Until recently, little research on the role of the father in marriage or after marital separation has been reported. Men have been studied as workers and professionals but not as fathers and husbands. For a married man in modern society, the qualities of being a "good husband" have been similar to those of being a "good father." The good father-husband is an economic provider. He forms a relationship and bond with his wife but not necessarily with his child for the relational tie between child and father has not been deemed essential.

There is a very strong cultural bias that women, biologically, psychologically and temperamentally, are best suited for child care and that mothering rather than parenting is the primary ingredient in child development.[3] This reflects the traditional view that male and female roles are based on traits that are essentially different and complementary. Women bear and rear children, and men support and provide for their wives and children. Men are not expected to be active in childrearing in or outside of marriage.

When a marriage ends in divorce, a father not only separates from his wife but is likely to be separated from his children as well. As E. E. LeMasters said: "The father's parental role in the U.S. is particularly tied to the success or failure of the pair bond between himself and his wife."[4]

The failure of his marriage is also likely to mean the loss of child custody for fathers. Most men do not seek custody of their children and those who do may experience sex role bias on the part of the judiciary. In 1971, for example, it was reported that mothers received custody of their children in over 90 percent of the custody decisions in United States Courts.[5]

Information available on the number of single-parent fathers indicates that more men are now being awarded custody of their children and that the men in our study are part of a small but growing number of fathers who are rearing their children after marital separation. Census data show that from 1960 to 1974 the number of male-headed families, with children and no spouse present, increased from 296,000 in 1960[6] to 836,000 in 1974.[7] The number of families headed by males with children under six and no spouse present also increased, from 87,000 in 1960[8] to 188,200 in 1970.[9]

In our study, we were particularly interested in the following four aspects of parenting: entertainment of children outside of the home, homemaking activities, child guidance and nurturance and child- and parent-oriented services. We also asked the fathers if they felt they had been prepared to carry out these activities and whether they received any help from other adults in conducting them.

Entertainment

Our earlier research had shown that fathers of young children in nuclear families and in separated families often entertain their children. In this study, all the fathers reported that they frequently relied on structured recreational activities for their children. A majority of fathers said they took their children swimming and to playgrounds, museums, restaurants and, less frequently, to child-oriented shows and movies. Finding activities for children seemed to be a major part of their roles as recently-separated fathers. One father reported:

"At first, I had to entertain them . . . bowling, movies, swimming, trips to relatives. I often would do reading and roughhousing with them also . . . I thought it was my responsibility to provide some structured activities."

"I went to every park, museum, playground, movie, zoo and what-have-you imaginable . . . I was constantly looking for things to do," another said.

Recreation and entertainment are "doing" activities and as such they are consistent with the parenting activities and male socialization role found within the nuclear family experience. Separated and divorced fathers often played with their children and felt prepared to perform this aspect of the single-parent role. Although most fathers reported that they received little help with their recreational parenting activities, they also said that when they became involved with women their women friends often accompanied them and their children on recreational ventures. It seems that the recreational aspects of parenting served as a comfortable way for them—and other adults—to interact with their children.

Homemaking

Homemaking seemed to us to be an essential part of the single-parent role. We asked the men about meal preparation and general household management.

Over 90 percent of the fathers reported that they frequently performed the homemaking functions of housecleaning, preparing meals and food shopping and, with the exception of housecleaning, most men felt that they had been prepared to perform these homemaking activities when they separated from their spouses. Most of the fathers also said that they did not receive significant help in homemaking, except in food preparation. Here, nearly half the fathers reported getting some assistance from other adults who shared their dwellings.

Child Guidance and Nurturance

The guidance and nurturance aspect of parenting was defined as direct father-child interaction, with the men giving care or direction to their young. We asked questions concerning discipline and the setting of limits; mealtime, bedtime and bathing routines; dealing with children's feelings; and shopping with children for clothing.

The most frequently reported guidance and nurturing activities were discipline, serving meals, bathing children and dealing with children's feelings and emotional upsets. More than 95 percent of the men reported that they frequently performed these activities on a regular basis. In contrast, less than half of the men said they bought clothing for their children.

The need to provide guidance and nurturance seemed to be more of a problem for the fathers than their entertainment and homemaking roles. Most fathers felt prepared to discipline or bathe their children but were less prepared for dealing with their emotional upsets. As one father explained:

"I felt unprepared for dealing with the children's emotional needs and being open to what they were feeling. I was very inadequate in that I couldn't deal with my own feelings very well. I was afraid, I didn't know how to listen or respond to them."

"Dealing with feelings openly or

expressing them, especially negative feelings, like grief or anger . . . those were the areas where I felt totally handicapped," a second said.

The socialization of males in our society does not prepare them to be nurturant and sex role definitions of childrearing in the nuclear family are likely to emphasize emotional responsiveness as a feminine trait and therefore a part of the mother's role. Boys learn instrumental skills that prepare them to be workers and family providers and they are neither expected nor encouraged to develop emotional skills which may interfere with their achievement.[10]

The more successfully a man has been socialized in instrumental behavior, the more likely he is to lack effective interpersonal skills. For example, a positive and significant relationship between a father's high achievement motivations and his feelings of inadequacy in the father role, and a negative orientation toward preschool children, has been reported by Veroff and Feld.[11] The authors also suggest that consideration of the emotional needs of young children may be incongruent with what fathers have previously learned about good masculine performance.

Our sample of fathers expressed difficulty in relating to their children's emotional needs, yet they attempted to respond to the requirements of their new roles, sometimes with the help of others. They received the most assistance in those areas where they felt least prepared. For example, 44 percent reported receiving help from others in dealing with children's feelings.

Services for Children and Parents

Being a single parent required acting as the child's sole agent in relationship to agencies and professionals. Nearly 75 percent of the men reported calling for babysitters themselves and over 90 percent were actively involved in all the other common child-oriented activities, such as taking a child to a doctor or dentist and talking with their children's teacher and the parents of their friends. Most of the men (80 percent) felt prepared to perform these functions after separation. The calling of babysitters was performed with a lower level of confidence—nearly half

(45 percent) felt unprepared to do this. A majority of the men reported performing these activities with no help from others.

All in all, however, it appears that the fathers in our sample were very active in all the aspects of parenting that we explored. They were most prepared for performing the recreational, homemaking and child-oriented service aspects of parenting, and least prepared for the child nurturance aspects. They received help from other adults in large measure for nurturant activities and certain homemaking activities, while help was not frequently reported for recreational and child-oriented service activities.

Time as Role Salience

More than half of the fathers (53 percent) reported spending half or more of their time at home interacting with their children. Others spent some time doing so and only four percent said that they spent very little time with their children.

We had expected that at least in the families in which the fathers lived with other people, the children would spend a significant amount of time interacting with other adults. However, we found that only nine percent of the fathers said that their children spent half or more of their time with other adults and 43 percent reported that their children spent very little or no time with other adults.

This finding that the father was the adult in the home with whom the children most frequently spent their time is also supported by data on the kinds of childrearing help fathers received from their lovers or dates. Women lovers rarely took or were permitted to take a major child care role with the father's children. Most frequently they accompanied fathers and children in out-of-home recreational activities.

These findings suggest that the single-parent role was a highly salient one and that fathers even protected their children from the influence of other adults.

Compared to the hours spent with other adults, children spent a much greater part of their time with peers: 45 percent of the fathers reported that their children spent half or more of their time playing with other children; 37 percent reported that they

spent some time doing so and only 18 percent reported that they spent very little or no time playing with peers.

In summary, fathers and children's peers were those most involved with the children in terms of time. Other non-related adults, even when they were available, spent less time with the father's children. The new time relationship with their children was described by one father this way:

"Spending time alone with the children came as a change after separation . . . They were alone with me all the time . . . It was the first time I'd been with them alone. I was putting them to bed, getting them dressed, getting their meals . . . I began to see I could do it."

Another explained: "One of the big problems was how being a full-time parent would influence my time. How I could put this whole thing together in terms of spending a lot of time with them; at the same time, having time to do other things. I didn't know how it would work out."

Role Strains

Three-quarters of the men we talked to said that they felt closer to their children as a result of their change in marital status and new parenting role. Their relationship to the children was more direct, no longer being filtered through the conflicts of an ailing marriage. Yet being a single parent had its own set of difficulties. Many fathers expressed serious concerns with the time strains they experienced after the marital breakdown.

Like most men, the fathers in our sample seemed to fit their time structures into the demands of the workplace, school or other organization in which they participated. As single parents, the needs of their children had priority over the requirements of external organizations, especially when the children were ill or had school vacations. At such times, fathers had to take time off from work or arrange for others to care for their children. Role strain often resulted from conflicts between their child care responsibilities and social needs and work responsibilities.

Work and Child Care

As noted previously, the majority of men in our sample were in demanding

professional and semi-professional occupations. In order to ascertain how they perceived the management of child care and work responsibilities, we listed a set of work-related behaviors and asked the men how they felt their child care obligations limited their work activities.

Job mobility was the area cited as being most limited. Fathers reported their work life was hampered in terms of working hours (63 percent), work priorities (62 percent), earnings (55 percent) and job transfer (52 percent). Within the work setting itself, limitations were noted in the areas of type of work (66 percent), promotions (38 percent), relations with co-workers (28 percent) and supervisors (20 percent).

Single parenting clearly limited earnings, hours and work relations. Work identity, a cornerstone of male self-definition, was challenged by an emerging parenting identity. One father said:

"Taking care of her (his daughter) was a real conflict with work. I was trying to build my business, but had to stop to pick her up at 3:00. It was rough starting something new, not making much money and limiting my working hours . . . Often, what I gave her was given grudgingly because I was feeling terribly limited by the schedule and by the tremendous pressures I was feeling."

In an open-ended question, we asked fathers to indicate the kind of services they felt would help make parenting and work more compatible. Over half (55 percent) said that time flexibility at work would help alleviate the constraints of these often conflicting responsibilities. One father for whom this was already a viable arrangement said:

"The advantages of where I work is that my hours are flexible. There is no problem in going home in the late afternoon to be with the kids . . . I make up the time by coming to work at 7:30 a.m. and every other weekend. Sometimes I bring my kids back to work if there is some great necessity, but I don't want this to happen often."

Fathers were also aware of the need for both long-range and immediate services for themselves and their children. Many felt that their parenting roles had not been accorded social legitimacy. Their employers, co-workers and peers often lacked appreciation or understanding of their needs as single parents and offered them little support. The single-parent father's dilemma has been stated clearly: "Economic efficiency is given so much priority in our society that it is difficult to imagine an American father neglecting his job or refusing a promotion out of deference to the needs of his children . . ."[12]

Social Life and Parenting

Our findings indicated that a major limitation for single-parent fathers was the decrease in the amount of time spent alone with other adults. Over half of the fathers studied said that they were involved with a woman as a sexual partner. The majority of these women (61 percent) were either divorced or separated and almost half of them had children from a previous marriage. The majority of the fathers reported that their lovers were helpful with the children.

The most frequently reported role for women friends (62 percent) was companionship with fathers and children in recreational activities away from home. A more active and direct child care role at the father's home was not frequently reported. For example, only 31 percent said that their lovers watched their children at home when the father was present and only 15 percent stated that their lovers cared for children alone for substantial periods of time. This suggests that the single-parent fathers in our sample were somewhat reluctant and guarded in allowing their women friends to share substantially in caring for their children.

When questioned about any conflict with lovers concerning a father's relationship to children, over half (56 percent) indicated that this was an issue because of the limitations placed on their social life by child care obligations. Eighty-five percent of the men said that their social life would be different were the children not present. The areas in which fathers felt their lives to be limited by parenting responsibilities were: social life, mentioned by 63 percent of the fathers; sports, noted by 17 percent; and home activities, referred to by 15 percent.

Being a Single Father

Our analysis showed that being a single parent required a major shift in lifestyle and priorities for most men. The bond between parent and child became a new focal point for self-definition and set the criteria for organizing the more traditional spheres of male functioning at work and in social life. The men in our study limited work and social activities to meet the needs of their children and, in doing so, they felt they had developed a closer relationship with them.

The experience of marital separation had brought the men into the sphere of what is commonly considered the woman's world—of being responsible for children's growth and satisfying children's needs. The men responded by restructuring their daily lives in order to care directly for their dependent children. As a result, fathers felt more positive about themselves as parents and as individuals. A majority of the men reported that being a single parent had helped them to grow emotionally. They felt they had become more responsive to their children and more conscious of their needs, a responsiveness they reported as reaching out to other adults as well.

---

[1] The interviews were part of a larger study, partially supported by a grant from the Rockefeller Foundation.

[2] The criteria used in the selection of the sample of families (the age of the youngest child, the limit on the number of children in each family and the minimum period of separation of parents) circumscribed the range of time of separation experienced among those interviewed. The mean number of years of separation was 2.6. Half (51 percent) of the fathers in the sample had been separated for no more than two years; over a third (36 percent) had been separated for three to four years, and the remainder, for over four years.

[3] John Bowlby, *Maternal Care and Mental Health*, Geneva, World Health Organization, 1951.

[4] E.E. LeMasters, *Parents in Modern America*, Homewood, Illinois, Dorsey Press, 1971.

[5] Robert R. Bell, *Marriage and Family Interaction*, Homewood, Illinois, Dorsey Press, 1971.

[6] U.S. Department of Commerce, Bureau of the Census, *Family Characteristics, 1960 Census*.

[7] U.S. Department of Commerce, Bureau of the Census, *Current Population Reports*, Ser. P-20, no. 271, 1974.

[8] U.S. Department of Commerce, Bureau of the Census, *Family Characteristics, 1960 Census*.

[9] U.S. Department of Commerce, Bureau of the Census, *Family Characteristics, 1970 Census*.

[10] Lenard Benson, *Fathering, A Sociological Perspective*, New York, Random House, 1968.

[11] Joseph Veroff and Sheila Feld, *Marriage and Work in America*, New York, Van Nostrand Reinhold, 1970.

[12] E.E. LeMasters, op. cit.

DOES PERSONALITY REALLY CHANGE AFTER 20?

ZICK RUBIN

Zick Rubin, who says he hasn't changed much in recent years, is Louis and Frances Salvage Professor of Social Psychology at Brandeis University and a contributing editor of *Psychology Today*. He is the coauthor (with the late Elton B. McNeil) of *The Psychology of Being Human*, Third Edition, an introductory psychology textbook that has been published by Harper & Row.

In most of us," William James wrote in 1887, "by the age of 30, the character has set like plaster, and will never soften again." Though our bodies may be bent by the years and our opinions changed by the times, there is a basic core of self—a personality—that remains basically unchanged.

This doctrine of personality stability has been accepted psychological dogma for most of the past century. The dogma holds that the plaster of character sets by one's early 20s, if not even sooner than that.

Within the past decade, however, this traditional view has come to have an almost archaic flavor. The rallying cry of the 1970s has been people's virtually limitless capacity for change—not only in childhood but through the span of life. Examples of apparent transformation are highly publicized: Jerry Rubin enters the 1970s as a screaming, war-painted Yippie and emerges as a sedate Wall Street analyst wearing a suit and tie. Richard Alpert, an ambitious assistant professor of psychology at Harvard, tunes into drugs, heads for India, and returns as Baba Ram Dass, a long-bearded mystic in a flowing white robe who teaches people to "be here now." And Richard Raskind, a successful ophthalmol-

ogist, goes into the hospital and comes out as Renée Richards, a tall, well-muscled athlete on the women's tennis circuit.

Even for those of us who hold on to our original appearance (more or less) and gender, "change" and "growth" are now the bywords. The theme was seized upon by scores of organizations formed to help people change, from Weight Watchers to est. It was captured—and advanced—by Gail Sheehy's phenomenally successful book *Passages*, which emphasized people's continuing openness to change throughout the course of adulthood. At the same time, serious work in psychology was coming along —building on earlier theories of Carl Jung and Erik Erikson—to buttress the belief that adults keep on developing. Yale's Daniel Levinson, who provided much of Sheehy's intellectual inspiration, described, in *The Seasons of a Man's Life*, an adult life structure that is marked by periods of self-examination and transition. Psychiatrist Roger Gould, in *Transformations*, wrote of reshapings of the self during the early and middle adult years, "away from stagnation and claustrophobic suffocation toward vitality and an expanded sense of inner freedom."

The view that personality keeps changing throughout life has picked up so many adherents recently that it has practically become the new dogma. Quantitative studies have been offered to document the possibility of personality change in adulthood, whether as a consequence of getting married, changing jobs, or seeing one's children leave home. In a new volume entitled *Constancy and Change in Human Development*, two of the day's most influential behavioral scientists, sociologist Orville G. Brim, Jr., and psychologist Jerome Kagan, challenge the defenders of personality

stability to back up their doctrine with hard evidence. "The burden of proof," Brim and Kagan write, "is being shifted to the larger group, who adhere to the traditional doctrine of constancy, from the minority who suggest that it is a premise requiring evaluation."

And now we get to the newest act in the battle of the dogmas. Those who uphold the doctrine of personality stability have accepted the challenge. In the past few years they have assembled the strongest evidence yet available for the truth of their position— evidence suggesting that on several central dimensions of personality, including the ones that make up our basic social and emotional style, we are in fact astoundingly stable throughout the course of adult life.

The 'Litter-ature' on Personality

Until recently there was little firm evidence for the stability of personality, despite the idea's intuitive appeal. Instead, most studies showed little predictability from earlier to later times of life—or even, for that matter, from one situation to another within the same time period—thus suggesting an essential lack of consistency in people's personalities. Indeed, many researchers began to question whether it made sense to speak of "personality" at all.

But whereas the lack of predictability was welcomed by advocates of the doctrine of change through the life span, the defenders of stability have another explanation for it: most of the studies are lousy. Referring derisively to the "litter-ature" on personality, Berkeley psychologist Jack Block estimates that "perhaps 90 percent of the studies are methodologically inadequate, without conceptual implication, and even foolish."

Block is right. Studies of personality have been marked by an abundance of untested measures (anyone can make up a new "scale" in an afternoon), small samples, and scatter-gun strategies ("Let's throw it into the computer and get some correlations"). Careful longitudinal studies, in which the same people are followed over the years, have been scarce. The conclusion that people are not predictable, then, may be a reflection not of human nature but of the haphazard methods used to study it.

Block's own research, in contrast, has amply demonstrated that people *are* predictable. Over the past 20 years Block has been analyzing extensive personality reports on several hundred Berkeley and Oakland residents that were first obtained in the 1930s, when the subjects were in junior high school. Researchers at Berkeley's Institute of Human Development followed up on the students when the subjects were in their late teens, again when they were in their mid-30s, and again in the late 1960s, when the subjects were all in their mid-40s.

The data archive is immense, including everything from attitude checklists filled out by the subjects to transcripts of interviews with the subjects, their parents, teachers, and spouses, with different sets of material gathered at each of the four time periods.

To reduce all the data to manageable proportions, Block began by assembling separate files of the information collected for each subject at each time period. Clinical psychologists were assigned to immerse themselves in individual dossiers and then to make a summary rating of the subject's personality by sorting a set of statements (for instance, "Has social poise and presence," and "Is self-defeating") into piles that indicated how representative the statement was of the subject. The assessments by the different raters (usually three for each dossier) were found to agree with one another to a significant degree, and they were averaged to form an overall description of the subject at that age. To avoid potential bias, the materials for each subject were carefully segregated by age level; all comments that

referred to the person at an earlier age were removed from the file. No psychologist rated the materials for the same subject at more than one time period.

Using this painstaking methodology, Block found a striking pattern of stability. In his most recent report, published earlier this year, he reported that on virtually every one of the 90 rating scales employed, there was a statistically significant correlation between subjects' ratings when they were in junior high school and their ratings 30 to 35 years later, when they were in their 40s. The most self-defeating adolescents were the most self-defeating adults; cheerful teenagers were cheerful 40-year-olds; those whose moods fluctuated when they were in junior high school were still experiencing mood swings in midlife.

'Still Stable After All These Years'

Even more striking evidence for the stability of personality, extending the time frame beyond middle age to late adulthood, comes from the work of Paul T. Costa, Jr., and Robert R. McCrae, both psychologists at the Gerontology Research Center of the National Institute on Aging in Baltimore. Costa and McCrae have tracked people's scores over time on standardized self-report personality scales, including the Sixteen Personality Factor Questionnaire and the Guilford-Zimmerman Temperament Survey, on which people are asked to decide whether or not each of several hundred statements describes them accurately. (Three sample items: "I would prefer to have an office of my own, not sharing it with another person." "Often I get angry with people too quickly." "Some people seem to ignore or avoid me, although I don't know why.")

Costa and McCrae combined subjects' responses on individual items to produce scale scores for each subject on such overall dimensions as extraversion and neuroticism, as well as on more specific traits, such as gregariousness, assertiveness, anxiety, and depression. By correlating over time the scores of subjects tested on two or three occasions—separated by six, 10, or 12 years—they obtained estimates of personality stability. The Baltimore

researchers have analyzed data from two large longitudinal studies, the Normative Aging Study conducted by the Veterans Administration in Boston and the Baltimore Longitudinal Study of Aging. In the Boston study, more than 400 men, ranging in age from 25 to 82, filled out a test battery in the mid-1960s and then completed a similar battery 10 years later, in the mid-1970s. In the Baltimore study, more than 200 men between the ages of 20 and 76 completed test batteries three times, separated by six-year intervals. Less extensive analyses, still unpublished, of the test scores of women in the Baltimore study point to a similar pattern of stability.

In both studies, Costa and McCrae found extremely high correlations, which indicated that the ordering of subjects on a particular dimension on one occasion was being maintained to a large degree a decade or more later. Contrary to what might have been predicted, young and middle-aged subjects turned out to be just as unchanging as old subjects were.

"The assertive 19-year-old is the assertive 40-year-old is the assertive 80-year-old," declares Costa, extrapolating from his and McCrae's results, which covered shorter time spans. For the title of a persuasive new paper reporting their results, Costa and McCrae rewrote a Paul Simon song title, proclaiming that their subjects were "Still Stable After All These Years."

Other recent studies have added to the accumulating evidence for personality stability throughout the life span. Gloria Leon and her coworkers at the University of Minnesota analyzed the scores on the Minnesota Multiphasic Personality Inventory (MMPI) of 71 men who were tested in 1947, when they were about 50 years old, and again in 1977, when they were close to 80. They found significant correlations on all 13 of the MMPI scales, with the highest correlation over the 30-year period on the scale of "Social Introversion." Costa and McCrae, too, found the highest degrees of stability, ranging from .70 to .84, on measures of introversion-extraversion, which assess gregariousness, warmth, and assertiveness. And Paul Mussen and his colleagues at Berkeley, analyzing interviewers' ratings of 53 women who were seen at ages 30 and 70, found significant correlations on such aspects of introversion-extraversion as talkativeness, excitability, and cheerfulness.

Although character may be most fixed in the domain of introversion-extraversion, Costa and McCrae found almost as much constancy in the domain of "neuroticism," which includes such specific traits as depression, anxiety, hostility, and impulsiveness. Neurotics are likely to be complainers throughout life. They may complain about different things as they get older—for example, worries about love in early adulthood, a "midlife crisis" at about age 40, health problems in late adulthood—but they are still complaining. The less neurotic person reacts to the same events with greater equanimity. Although there is less extensive evidence for its stability, Costa and McCrae also believe that there is an enduring trait of "openness to experience," including such facets as openness to feelings, ideas, and values.

Another recent longitudinal study of personality, conducted by University of Minnesota sociologist Jeylan Mortimer and her coworkers, looked at the self-ratings of 368 University of Michigan men who were tested in 1962–63, when they were freshmen, in 1966–67, when they were seniors, and in 1976, when they were about 30. At each point the subjects rated themselves on various characteristics, such as relaxed, strong, warm, and different. The ratings were later collapsed into overall scores for well-being, competence, sociability, and unconventionality. On each of these dimensions, Mortimer found a pattern of persistence rather than one of change. Mortimer's analysis of the data also suggested that life experiences such as the nature of one's work had an impact on personality. But the clearest message of her research is, in her own words, "very high stability."

Is *Everybody* Changing?

The high correlations between assessments made over time indicate that people in a given group keep the same rank order on the traits being measured, even as they traverse long stretches of life. But maybe *everyone* changes as he or she gets older. If, for example, everyone turns inward to

about the same extent in the latter part of life, the correlations—representing people's *relative* standing—on measures of introversion could still be very high, thus painting a misleading picture of stability. And, indeed, psychologist Bernice Neugarten concluded as recently as five years ago that there was a general tendency for people to become more introverted in the second half of life. Even that conclusion has been called into question, however. The recent longitudinal studies have found only slight increases in introversion as people get older, changes so small that Costa and McCrae consider them to be of little practical significance.

Specifically, longitudinal studies have shown slight drops over the course of adulthood in people's levels of excitement seeking, activity, hostility, and impulsiveness. The Baltimore researchers find no such changes in average levels of gregariousness, warmth, assertiveness, depression, or anxiety. Costa summarizes the pattern of changes as "a mellowing—but the person isn't so mellowed that you can't recognize him." Even as this mellowing occurs, moreover, people's relative ordering remains much the same—on the average, everyone drops the same few standard points. Thus, an "impulsive" 25-year-old may be a bit less impulsive by the time he or she is 70 but is still likely to be more impulsive than his or her agemates.

The new evidence of personality stability has been far too strong for the advocates of change to discount. Even in the heart of changeland, in Brim and Kagan's *Constancy and Change in Human Development*, psychologists Howard Moss and Elizabeth Susman review the research and conclude that there is strong evidence for the continuity of personality.

People Who Get Stuck

The new evidence has not put the controversy over personality stability and change to rest, however. If anything, it has sharpened it. Although he praises the new research, Orville Brim is not convinced by it that adults are fundamentally unchanging. He points out that the high correlations signify strong associations between measures, but not total constancy. For example, a .70 correlation between

scores obtained at two different times means that half of the variation (.70 squared, or .49) between people's later scores can be predicted from their earlier scores. The apostles of stability focus on this predictability, which is all the more striking because of the imperfect reliability of the measures employed. But the prophets of change, like Brim, prefer to dwell on the half of the variability that cannot be predicted, which they take as evidence of change.

Thus, Costa and McCrae look at the evidence they have assembled, marvel at the stability that it indicates, and call upon researchers to explain it: to what extent may the persistence of traits bespeak inherited biological predispositions, enduring influences from early childhood, or patterns of social roles and expectations that people get locked into? And at what age does the plaster of character in fact begin to set? Brim looks at the same evidence, acknowledges the degree of stability that it indicates, and then calls upon researchers to explain why some people in the sample are changing. "When you focus on stability," he says, "you're looking at the dregs—the people who have gotten stuck. You want to look at how a person grows and changes, not at how a person stays the same."

Brim, who is a president of the Foundation for Child Development in New York, also emphasizes that only certain aspects of personality—most clearly, aspects of social and emotional style, such as introversion-extraversion, depression, and anxiety—have been shown to be relatively stable. Brim himself is more interested in other parts of personality, such as people's self-esteem, sense of control over their lives, and ultimate values. These are the elements of character that Brim believes undergo the most important changes over the course of life. "Properties like gregariousness don't interest me," he admits; he does not view such traits as central to the fulfillment of human possibilities.

If Brim is not interested in some of the personality testers' results, Daniel Levinson is even less interested. In his view, paper-and-pencil measures like those used by Costa and McCrae are trivial, reflecting, at best, peripheral aspects of life. (Indeed, critics suggest that such research indicates only that people are stable in the way they fill out personality scales.) Levinson sees the whole enterprise of "rigorous" studies of personality stability as another instance of psychologists' rushing in to measure whatever they have measures for before they have clarified the important issues. "I think most psychologists and sociologists don't have the faintest idea what adulthood is about," he says.

Levinson's own work at the Yale School of Medicine (see "Growing Up with the Dream," *Psychology Today*, January 1978) has centered on the adult's evolving life structure—the way in which a person's social circumstances, including work and family ties, and inner feelings and aspirations fit together in an overall picture. Through intensive interviews of a small sample of men in the middle years of life—he is now conducting a parallel study of women—Levinson has come to view adult development as marked by an alternating sequence of relatively stable "structure-building" periods and periods of transition. He has paid special attention to the transition that occurs at about the age of 40. Although this midlife transition may be either smooth or abrupt, the person who emerges from it is always different from the one who entered it.

The midlife transition provides an important opportunity for personal growth. For example, not until we are past 40, Levinson believes, can we take a "universal" view of ourselves and the world rising above the limited perspective of our own background to appreciate the fullest meaning of life. "I don't think anyone can write tragedy—real tragedy—before the age of 40," Levinson declares.

Disagreement Over Methods

As a student of biography, Levinson does not hesitate to take a biographical view of the controversy at hand. "To Paul Costa," he suggests in an understanding tone, "the most important underlying issue is probably the specific issue of personality stability or change. I think the question of *development* is really not important to him personally. But he's barely getting to 40, so he has time." Levinson himself began his research on adult development when he was 46, as part of a way of understanding the changes

he had undergone in the previous decade. He is now 60.

Costa, for his part, thinks that Levinson's clinical approach to research, based on probing interviews with small numbers of people, lacks the rigor needed to establish anything conclusively. "It's only 40 people, for crying out loud!" he exclaims. And Costa doesn't view his own age (he is 38) or that of his colleague McCrae (who is 32) as relevant to the questions under discussion.

Jack Block, who is also a hard-headed quantitative researcher— and, for the record, is fully 57 years old—shares Costa's view of Levinson's method. "The interviews pass through the mind of Dan Levinson and a few other people," Block grumbles, "and he writes it down." Block regards Levinson as a good psychologist who should be putting forth his work as speculation, and not as research.

As this byplay suggests, some of the disagreement between the upholders of stability and the champions of change is methodological. Those who argue for the persistence of traits tend to offer rigorous personality-test evidence, while those who emphasize the potential for change often offer more qualitative, clinical descriptions. The psychometricians scoff at the clinical reports as unreliable, while the clinicians dismiss the psychometric data as trivial. This summary oversimplifies the situation, though, because some of the strongest believers in change, like Brim, put a premium on statistical, rather than clinical, evidence.

When pressed, people on both sides of the debate agree that personality is characterized by *both* stability and change. But they argue about the probabilities assigned to different outcomes. Thus, Costa maintains that "the assertive 19-year-old is the assertive 40-year-old is the assertive 80-year-old. . .*unless something happens to change it*." The events that would be likely to change deeply ingrained patterns would have to be pretty dramatic ones. As an example, Costa says that he would not be surprised to see big personality changes in the Americans who were held hostage in Iran.

From Brim's standpoint, in contrast, people's personalities—and especially their feelings of mastery, con-

trol, and self-esteem—will keep changing through the course of life. . . *unless they get stuck*. As an example, he notes that a coal miner who spends 10 hours a day for 50 years down the shaft may have little opportunity for psychological growth. Brim believes that psychologists should try to help people get out of such ruts of stability. And he urges researchers to look more closely at the ways in which life events—not only the predictable ones, such as getting married or retiring, but also the unpredictable ones, such as being fired or experiencing a religious conversion—may alter adult personality.

At bottom, it seems, the debate is not so much methodological as ideological, reflecting fundamental differences of opinion about what is most important in the human experience. Costa and McCrae emphasize the value of personality constancy over time as a central ingredient of a stable sense of identity. "If personality were not stable," they write, "our ability to make wise choices about our future lives would be severely limited." We must know what we are like—and what we will continue to be like—if we are to make intelligent choices, whether of careers, spouses, or friends. Costa and McCrae view the maintenance of a stable personality in the face of the vicissitudes of life as a vital human accomplishment.

Brim, however, views the potential for growth as the hallmark of humanity. "The person is a dynamic organism," he says, "constantly striving to master its environment and to become something more than it is." He adds, with a sense of purpose in his voice, "I see psychology in the service of liberation, not constraint."

Indeed, Brim suspects that we are now in the midst of "a revolution in human development," from a traditional pattern of continuity toward greater discontinuity throughout the life span. Medical technology (plastic surgery and sex-change surgery, for example), techniques of behavior modification, and the social supports for change provided by thousands of groups "from TA to TM, from AA to Zen" are all part of this revolution. Most important, people are trying, perhaps for the first time in history, to change *themselves*.

Some social critics, prominent

among them Christopher Lasch in *The Culture of Narcissism*, have decried the emphasis on self-improvement as a manifestation of the "Me" generation's excessive preoccupation with self. In Brim's view, these critics miss the point. "Most of the concern with oneself going on in this country," he declares, "is not people being selfish, but rather trying to be better, trying to be something more than they are now." If Brim is right in his reading of contemporary culture, future studies of personality that track people through the 1970s and into the 1980s may well show less stability and more change than the existing studies have shown.

The Tension in Each of Us

In the last analysis, the tension between stability and change is found not only in academic debates but also in each of us. As Brim and Kagan write, "There is, on the one hand, a powerful drive to maintain the sense of one's identity, a sense of continuity that allays fears of changing too fast or of being changed against one's will by outside forces. . . . On the other hand, each person is, by nature, a purposeful, striving organism with a desire to be more than he or she is now. From making simple new year's resolutions to undergoing transsexual operations, everyone is trying to become something that he or she is not, but hopes to be."

A full picture of adult personality development would inevitably reflect this tension between sameness and transformation. Some aspects of personality, such as a tendency to be reclusive or outgoing, calm or anxious, may typically be more stable than other aspects, such as a sense of mastery over the environment. Nevertheless, it must be recognized that each of us reflects, over time, both stability and change. As a result, observers can look at a person as he or she goes through a particular stretch of life and see either stability or change or—if the observer looks closely enough—both.

For example, most people would look at Richard Alpert, the hard-driving psychology professor of the early 1960s, and Ram Dass, the bearded, free-flowing guru of the 1970s, and see that totally different persons are here now. But Harvard psychologist David McClelland, who knew Alpert well, spent time with the Indian holy man and said to himself, "It's the same old Dick!"—still as charming, as concerned with inner experience, and as power-oriented as ever. And Jerry Rubin can view his own transformation from Yippie to Wall Streeter in a way that recognizes the underlying continuity: "Finding out who I really was was done in typical Jerry Rubin way. I tried everything, jumped around like crazy with boundless energy and curiosity." If we look closely enough, even Richard Raskind and Renée Richards will be found to have a great deal in common.

Whether a person stays much the same or makes sharp breaks with the past may depend in large measure on his or her own ideas about what is possible and about what is valuable. Psychological research on adult development can itself have a major impact on these ideas by calling attention to what is "normal" and by suggesting what is desirable. Now that researchers have established beyond reasonable doubt that there is often considerable stability in adult personality, they may be able to move on to a clearer understanding of how we can grow and change, even as we remain the same people we always were. It may be, for example, that if we are to make significant changes in ourselves, without losing our sense of identity, it is necessary for some aspects of our personality to remain stable. "I'm different now," we can say, "but it's still me."

As Jack Block puts it, in his characteristically judicious style: "Amidst change and transformation, there is an essential coherence to personality development."

For further information read:

Block, Jack, "Some Enduring and Consequential Structures of Personality" in A.I. Rabin et al. eds., *Further Explorations in Personality*, Wiley-Interscience, 1981, $24.50.

Brim, Orville G., Jr., and Jerome Kagan, eds., *Constancy and Change in Human Development*, Harvard University Press, 1980, $27.50.

Costa, Paul T., Jr., and Robert R. McCrae, "Still Stable After All These Years: Personality as a Key to Some Issues in Adulthood and Old Age," in Paul B. Baltes and Orville G. Brim, Jr., eds., *Life-span Development and Behavior* Vol. 3, Academic Press, 1980, $35.

Levinson, Daniel J., et al., *The Seasons of a Man's Life*, Alfred A. Knopf, 1978, $10.95; paper; Ballantine Books, 1979, $5.95.

THE JAPANESE BRAIN

Atuhiro Sibatani

Atuhiro Sibatani is a developmental biologist in the Molecular and Cellular Biology Unit of the Commonwealth Scientific and Industrial Research Organization in Sydney, Australia.

The idea that the Japanese live in harmony with their surroundings, turning everyday rituals into art forms, has been ascribed sometimes to genetic inheritance, sometimes to cultural conditioning. But in recent years a clever new technique designed to study speech and hearing defects has yielded one of the most tantalizing —and controversial—theories to date: that Japanese brains function differently from other people's not because of inheritance or conditioning but because of the peculiarities of the Japanese language. If this provocative hypothesis proves to be correct, we may have to revise some of our venerable convictions, for it may turn out that the language we learn alters the physical operation of our brains.

The startling assertion that language shapes the neurophysiological pathways of the brain is the thesis of a dry academic tome that, amazingly, became a best seller in Japan when it appeared in 1978. Written by Tadanobu Tsunoda, *The Japanese Brain: Brain Function and East-West Culture* has yet to be translated into English, but information about its contents has crossed the oceans and is provoking a good deal of discussion in Western circles. What Tsunoda has found, he claims, is that the language one learns as a child influences the way in which the brain's right and left hemispheres develop their special talents.

That the brain's hemispheres specialize in different tasks has been recognized since the 19th century. Neurologists studying men injured by strokes or battle wounds found that damage to the brain's left side often interfered with speech. Since then, scientists have demonstrated hemispheric specialization with techniques such as dichotic listening tests, which present different words simultaneously to both right and left ears to determine which ear "excels" at which tasks.

For most right-handed people, the left hemisphere appears to be the main seat of language, as well as of precise manual manipulations, mathematics, and other analytic functions. The right hemisphere is superior in dealing with spatial concepts, recognition of faces, musical patterns, environmental sounds, and perhaps intuitive and artistic processes. For left-handed people, it is harder to generalize about the brain's organization (see box, pages 234-235).

These are observations made by Western scientists working with Caucasian subjects. Tsunoda's research with Japanese patients, on the other hand, seems to have revealed fundamental differences in the way that Caucasian and Japanese brains divide up the labor of processing sensory data.

A specialist in hearing difficulties at Tokyo Medical and Dental University, Tsunoda was studying patients whose speech was damaged, testing the possibility that he might somehow transfer language processing to the undamaged part of the brain. In the course of his research, Tsunoda devised a unique dichotic listening test designed to be independent of the subject's conscious awareness. The test required subjects to tap simple, regular patterns on a Morse code key. Tones keyed by the tapping process were then fed back to each ear through earphones. One ear received the sound directly; the other ear received the signal delayed by two-tenths of a second. Tsunoda gradually increased the loudness of the delayed signal until it interfered with the subject's key-tapping performance. The purpose was to ascertain whether one ear—and its associated brain hemisphere—predominated in registering this interference.

In addition to the time delay, Tsunoda also supplied each ear with different kinds of sounds—not only pure tones but also such sounds as spoken words, animal noises, Japanese and Western musical instruments, and ocean waves.

One of Tsunoda's findings is that in the brains of right-handed Westerners, Koreans, Chinese, and Ben-

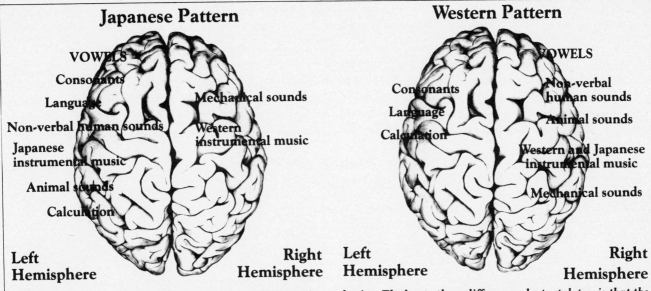

Japanese Pattern

VOWELS
Consonants
Language
Non-verbal human sounds
Japanese instrumental music
Animal sounds
Calculation

Mechanical sounds
Western instrumental music

Left Hemisphere   Right Hemisphere

Tadanobu Tsunoda, a specialist in hearing difficulties, believes that the two halves of the Japanese brain divide up the labor of processing sounds in a way that differs from Western

Western Pattern

VOWELS
Consonants
Language
Calculation

Non-verbal human sounds
Animal sounds
Western and Japanese instrumental music
Mechanical sounds

Left Hemisphere   Right Hemisphere

brains. The key to those differences, he postulates, is that the Japanese deal with all vowels in the left hemisphere, while Westerners handle isolated vowels in the right hemisphere.

M. E. Challinor

galis, vowel sounds usually get processed in one side of the brain if they occur in isolation, but in the other half if the vowels occur in a spoken context, that is, if they are surrounded by consonants. But right-handed Japanese and Polynesians, Tsunoda discovered, usually process all vowels in the left or dominant half, whether they occur in a spoken context or not.

Mechanical sounds—bells, whistles, and helicopter noises—are among the few sounds that Japanese and Polynesians handle in the right hemisphere as do other ethnic groups. Western instrumental music is also processed in the right hemisphere. By contrast, Japanese subjects handle Japanese music in the left hemisphere, possibly because Japanese music attempts to mimic the human voice.

The Japanese and Polynesians also tend to depend on their left brains for processing nonverbal human utterances that express emotions—sounds such as laughter, crying, or sighing—along with natural sounds such as cricket chirps, cow calls, bird songs, and ocean waves. By contrast, those who speak European languages handle all these sounds in their right hemispheres.

Tsunoda suggests that the Japanese may utilize the left hemisphere more heavily because the Japanese and the Polynesian languages are particularly rich in vowels. One can make up complex sentences in Japanese using vowels only: *"Ue o ui, oi o ooi, ai o ou, aiueo"* means "A love-hungry man who worries about hunger hides his old age and chases love." Polynesians also use lots of vowels, as in the cry of distress, *"Oiaue!"* leading some experts to suggest that the Japanese race has Polynesian roots.

A fundamental discovery of Tsunoda is that the Japanese, in contrast to Westerners, process far more sounds in only one hemisphere. Furthermore, if a

sound normally processed in the left hemisphere, whether voices or insect chirps, is buried amidst other background noises, the entire load of processing all the sounds is switched to the left. This switching process, characteristic of all human brains, is not surprising since a first priority of the brain is language.

Curiously enough, certain odors, including perfumes, alcohol, and tobacco smoke, also seem to trigger this switching ability. Because Tsunoda associates the effects of these chemicals with emotional reactions, he infers that the Japanese process emotion in the dominant hemisphere, apparently opposite to Westerners.

Tsunoda is convinced that the switching stimulus is not inherited, but is acquired by every child through the use of the language that he or she speaks. Japanese people brought up in the United States, for example, have the characteristic Caucasian brain lateralization. That is, they process consonants on the left and vowels on the right. Conversely, Americans brought up in Japan and fluent in the language acquire typically Japanese brains. Tsunoda shows that the response of the natively blind, and hence illiterate, Japanese is exactly the same as that of the literate members of the population. From this he concludes that the emergence of the Japanese brain is not triggered simply by learning to read and write Japanese but rather by listening to the language and speaking it.

Tsunoda's results have been heralded by some as beautiful and clear-cut; others have adopted a wait-and-see attitude, since his results have so far not been replicated. Still, brain researchers are intrigued with

233

Tsunoda's hypothesis that language affects the way the brain's two halves process language.

However, Western scientists are frankly skeptical about some of Tsunoda's sweeping speculations. He conjectures, for example, that in the Japanese brain, logical thinking and emotional responses are not partitioned into separate hemispheres as they seem to be in the West, but are tucked into one and the same verbal hemisphere. This may cause the Japanese to depend more on intuitive and emotional reactions than on logical trains of thought.

Nor do the Japanese distinguish analytic problems and natural sensations in the clear-cut way that Westerners do, according to Tsunoda. The Japanese seem to have a psychological need to live immersed in natural sounds such as bird and insect songs, animal cries, snow thudding off tree branches, ocean waves beating against the shore, and winds whistling through forest pines. That harmony of nature and environment is evident in all aspects of Japanese life, from their calligraphy to the tea ceremony to Noh drama and Ikebana flower arranging. In Japanese landscape and architecture, physical objects melt into the character of space rather than oppose it. For example, the Japanese use few partitions, rooms combine into sweeping space, and the garden may recess into the house so that dwellers can be outdoors while sitting indoors. Tsunoda believes that this blurring of physical barriers and natural elements may help explain the deep sense of harmony within the group that results in the social cohesion of the Japanese nation.

The negative aspect, however, is that the Japanese may be overtaxing the left hemisphere, particularly when forced to learn a variety of foreign languages. After speaking other languages for a few days or months at a time, the Japanese brain seems to switch sounds normally processed on the right to the opposite hemisphere. This undoubtedly places a tremendous burden on the over-utilized verbal hemisphere.

One of the most intriguing spin-offs of Tsunoda's work may be its implications for sociobiology, the science that studies the genetic predisposition of social behavior. Tsunoda argues that some differences in brain function are conditioned by the mother tongue, rather than by genetic factors of ethnic origin. If Tsunoda is right, the patterns of each individual's perceptions, cognitions, mental acts, and social behavior can be dramatically affected during early childhood by one of the most human of activities—language. The debate over strict genetic determinism, so heated on this side of the ocean, has not thus far troubled the Japanese. Whether or not this indifference results from the "inscrutable" nature of the Japanese brain may constitute another absorbing chapter for those interested in Japan's role in modern society.

The sinister hand

Among certain African tribes, children who showed a preference for their left hand were "cured" by having that hand immersed in boiling water and deliberately scalded, ensuring that they would use their right hand while learning important skills. In many other parts of the world, until a generation ago, schoolteachers regularly forced pupils to write with their right hands, regardless of the children's inclinations.

Nevertheless, some people—roughly 10 to 15 percent of the world's population—persisted in remaining left-handed. Recent studies indicate that the trait is inherited, but a century ago no one knew that for sure. In 1865 the French neurosurgeon Paul Broca became fascinated with these people. An early explorer of the human brain, Broca had just discovered that in right-handers, certain speech centers were found only in the left cerebral hemisphere. Among left-handers, he reasoned, the reverse must be true: Their speech center must be in the right hemisphere. Knowing that the left hemisphere controls the right side of the body and vice versa, some scientists pushed this logic even further. They declared that the location of organs such as the heart must be reversed in the bodies of left-handers. Although anatomists soon proved them wrong, Broca's view of left-handedness as a mirror image of right-handedness was dominant for nearly a century.

In the past two decades, however, it has become clear that left-handers vary enormously in the way they process information. While a minority of them do use their right hemisphere for language, as Broca predicted, roughly 60 percent of left-handers process speech in their left hemispheres, just as right-handers do, and another group appears to use both sides; such dual processing makes people less likely to lose their ability to speak if they ever suffer a brain injury or a stroke.

These variations proved so intriguing to brain scientists—especially to those studying the differing specialties of the two cerebral hemispheres—that left-handed people rapidly became their favorite experimental subjects.

The mushrooming studies of left-handers in the past few years have shown that left-handers are less strongly lateralized than right-handers, that is, they show less difference between the two sides of their brain. Thus, while right-handers typically choose their right eye when conditions demand the use of a single eye, among left-handers the chances of being "left-eyed" are only 50-50. Even the right-handed relatives of left-handers are more likely to recover from loss of speech following damage to the left side of their brain than are people whose relatives are all right-handers; this implies a genetic tendency toward weaker laterali-

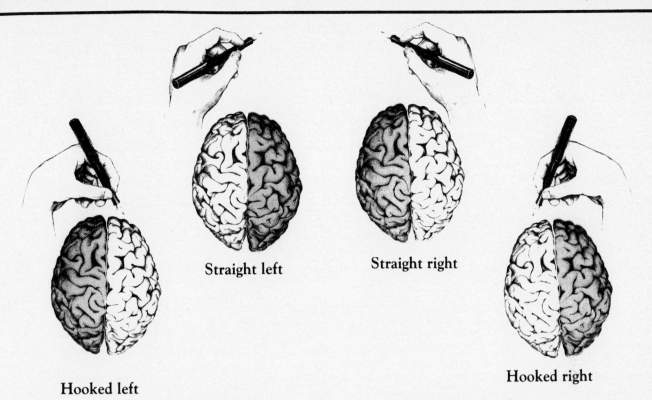

Straight left

Straight right

Hooked left

Hooked right

Scientists are trying to determine if hand and writing posture indicate which brain hemisphere is used for language. Initial results show that left-handers who use the hooked position for writing process language on the left side of their brains, as do the majority of right-handers who use the straight hand position. But left-handers who use a straight hand posture seem to process language in the right hemisphere, as do the small minority of right-handers who use a hooked position.

zation among relatives of left-handers.

But what are the advantages or handicaps of weaker lateralization? This is what researchers are now trying to find out.

In the past, left-handers were all lumped together and accused of being clumsy, retarded, stammerers, stubborn, criminal, neurotic, or homosexual.

"They squint, they stammer, they shuffle and shamble, they flounder about like seals out of water. Awkward in the house, and clumsy in their games, they are fumblers and bunglers at whatever they do," wrote the British psychologist Cyril Burt in 1937. He was particularly scathing about left-handed girls who "often possess a strong, self-willed, and almost masculine disposition: by many little tell-tale symptoms, besides the clumsy management of their hands—by their careless dress, their ungainly walk, their tomboy tricks and mannerisms—they mutely display a private scorn for the canons of feminine grace and elegance."

Today, having shown that none of the above is true, brain scientists are studying left-handers to see whether their particular patterns of brain organization lead to any special talents. Some are looking for clues that might explain why so many artists, including Michelangelo, Leonardo da Vinci, Picasso, and Escher, have been left-handed. Conceivably, since the right hemisphere is superior for imagery and visual abilities, there is some advantage to using the hand that is controlled by the same hemisphere—namely, the left hand—for drawing or painting. This would avoid having to send signals through the corpus callosum which links the two hemispheres.

One recent study has shown that left-handers who process language in both hemispheres do better than other groups on tests of tonal pitch recognition. This talent presumably arises because information regarding pitch is duplicated in the two halves of the brain. Another study has found that a higher than normal percentage of musicians are ambidextrous. Researchers have been unable to show whether this is cause or effect; it is an open question whether or not people who are less lateralized tend to be more gifted musically, or whether playing music develops both hands—or possibly both sides of the brain.

Scientists eventually hope to discover how various patterns of brain organization determine specialized ways of dealing with the world—from spatial, verbal, and mathematical abilities to musical or artistic gifts—not just among those who are left-handed, but among all people. —*Maya Pines*

Washington-based free-lance writer and author of The Brain Changers: Scientists and the New Mind Control.

Development During Middle and Late Adulthood

There are two extreme points of view concerning the latter part of the life span. The first point of view, "disengagement," argues that the physical and intellectual deficits associated with aging are inevitable and should be accepted at face value by the aged. The second point of view, "activity," acknowledges the decline in abilities associated with aging, but also notes that the aged can maintain satisfying and productive lives if they desire.

Extreme views in any guise suffer from the problem of homgeneity. The problem of homogeneity involves stereotyping all individuals within a category or class as having the same needs and capabilities. Whether one's reference group is racial, ethnic, cultural, or age-related, stereotyping usually leads to counter-productive, discriminatory social policy that alienates the reference group from "mainstream" society.

Evidence compiled during the past decade clearly illustrates the fallacy of extremist views of middle and late adulthood. Development during the later years of life is not a unitary phenomenon. For example, although there are common physical changes associated with aging, there also are wide individual differences in the rates of change as well as the degree to which changes are expressed. Moreover, not all physical changes associated with aging are negative. Reactions to stress also vary. Much has been written about the negative aspects of stress. The positive aspects of stress have received less attention, yet some individuals seem to welcome stress inasmuch as it provides them opportunities for decision making and maintenance of a sense of control over the events of their life. Although the nature of the problems that must be negotiated at various age periods may differ, individual differences in how problems are resolved are as much a part of later development as they are of early development.

Erik Erikson was among the first to draw serious attention to the conflicts associated with each of the age periods in the life cycle, including adulthood and aging. Subsequent investigators have drawn attention to the major problems of middle age—that period of development which marks the transition to maturity and old age. Popular accounts of the pervasiveness of the "mid-life crisis" have been tempered by more empirical studies which suggest that the mid-life crisis may be a real phenomenon indeed, but real only for a minority of individuals. Nevertheless, far less is known about development during the adult years than is known about the years of infancy, childhood, and adolescence.

Behavioral gerontology remains a specialization within human development that is absent from most graduate programs in developmental psychology. On the other hand, efforts to encourage training and research in this area are increasing, perhaps in response to the rapid increase in the proportion of the population represented by the aged. One can only hope that during the current decade significant advances will be made in our knowledge of the later years of development.

Looking Ahead: Challenge Questions

How does contemporary American society view the aged? What events may be changing our attitudes toward this period of development?

What are the crises and conflicts that are characteristic of middle- and late-adulthood? How are they different from crises of earlier age periods of development? How are they the same?

What are the physical changes of aging? How do they influence intellectual functioning? Emotional functioning?

What are your views on the American way of death? Have you experienced the death of an older person in your family? Would you like your own death to be handled similarly?

SHE & HE

Melvin Konner

Melvin Konner, a Harvard biological anthropologist, is chairman of anthropology at Emory University.

nke Ehrhardt, Patricia Goldman, Sarah Blaffer Hrdy, Corinne Hutt, Julianne Imperato-McGinley, Carol Nagy Jacklin, Annelise Korner, Eleanor Emmons Maccoby, Alice Rossi, Beatrice Blyth Whiting. These are the names of some distinguished women scientists who devote their lives to the study of brain, hormones, or behavior, human and animal. They range from the world famous to the merely well known. Each, within her discipline, has a reputation for tough-mindedness. All have in common that they have given considerable attention (most of them many years) to the question of whether the sex differences in behavior each has observed—in the field, in the clinic, and in the laboratory—have a basis that is in part biological.

Without exception, they have answered this question in the affirmative. One cannot imagine that they did so without difficulty. Each has suffered, personally and professionally, from the ubiquitous discrimination against women that is common outside the academy and within it. Each has worked with some man who envisioned her—in his heart of hearts—barefoot, meek, pregnant, and in the kitchen. Each has sacrificed more than the average brilliant man to get in a position to work on a problem that troubles her intellectually, and the payment of that sort of price makes the truth more compelling. Nevertheless, each is wise enough to know that over the long course of time, the very sorts of oppression she has experienced are bulwarked and bastioned by theories of "natural" gender differences.

These women are doing a balancing act of formidable proportions. They continue to struggle, in private and in public, for equal rights and equal treatment for people of both sexes; at the same time, they uncover and report evidence that the sexes are irremediably different—that after sexism is wholly stripped away, after differences in training have gone the way of the whalebone corset, there will still be *something* different, something that is grounded in biology.

Like many stories in modern behavioral science, this one begins with Margaret Mead. She was one of the greatest of all social scientists. In a world in which all odds were against it, she established a concept of human differences as more flexible, more malleable, more buffeted by the winds of life experience—as delivered by our very different cultures—than anybody had then thought possible. And this concept has stood the test of time.

No question so engaged her interest as that of the role of gender in behavior. In trip after stubborn trip to the South Seas, she gathered information impossible to come by otherwise. Among headhunters and fishermen, medicine men and exotic dancers, in steamy jungles, on mountaintops, on vivid white beaches, in bamboo huts, in meeting houses on stilts high above water, in shaky-looking seagoing bark canoes, she took out her ubiquitous notebook and recorded the behavior and beliefs of men and women who had never heard of American sex roles. By 1949, when *Male and Female* was published, she had done so in seven remote societies.

In all her cultures there was homicidal violence, and in all, that violence occurred at the hands of men. Tchambuli men may have been effeminate in relation to certain American conventions, but they were still very devoted to taking victims—and, more traditionally, hunting heads. Mundugumor men were unthreatened by having their women provide for them. But that was because it freed them to plot and fight.

This may be traced in a like manner through all the world's thousands of different cultures. In every culture there is at least some homicide, in the context of war or ritual or in the context of daily life, and in every culture men are mainly responsible for it. There are, of course, individual exceptions, but there is no society in the ethnographic or historical record in which men do nearly as much baby and child care as women. This is not to say anything, yet, about capacity; it is merely a statement of plain, observable fact. Men are more violent than women, and women are more nurturant, at least toward infants and children, than men.

Even in dreams the distinction holds. In a study of dreams in 75 tribal societies around the world, men were more likely to dream of coitus, wife, weapon, animal, red, while women were more likely to dream of husband, mother, father, child, cry.

Of course, this is ethnographic fact, and that raises some eyebrows. Although cross-cultural surveys are quantitative in nature, they are based on individual studies consisting mainly of mere description. As such, they are the victims of "hard science" snobbery. That snobbery is most ill-founded. Ethnology is in its earliest phase as a science. Just as "mere" description of the look of a newly delineated brain region or a type of liver cancer as they appear under the microscope is a first step on a new path in science, so, equally, is the description of a society—description using the human eye, ear, and mind without computers.

evertheless, we recognize quantification as necessary, and, at least until recently, such quantification was more usual in the work of psychologists than of anthropologists. For many years now, psychologists in the Western world have studied gender differences, and they have done so with an exactitude very difficult to match in the tropical jungle. Eleanor Maccoby, an elder stateswoman of American psychology, and Carol Jacklin, a young scientist trained in part by Maccoby, have, after years of work on the problem, written a major book, *The Psychology of Sex Differences*. It not only summarizes their own work but, more important, systematically re-

views and tabulates hundreds of carefully described and annotated studies by other investigators. They review studies of sex differences on scores of different dimensions—tactile sensitivity, vision, discrimination learning, social memory, general intellectual abilities, achievement striving, self-esteem, crying, fear and timidity, helping behavior, competition, conformity and imitation, to name only a few.

For most of these dimensions it may be emphatically stated that there is no consistent pattern of gender difference. For almost all there are at least some studies that find a gender difference in either direction—usually both—and many studies that find no difference. Indeed, the main thrust of the book is to demolish cliché after cliché about the difference between boys and girls, men and women. There is no evidence that girls and women are more social, more suggestible, have lower self-esteem or less achievement motivation than boys and men, or that boys and men are more analytic. In the realms of tactile sensitivity and fear and timidity there is weak evidence of a gender difference —girls show more of these. There is also weak evidence that girls are more compliant than boys and less involved in assertions of dominance. In the realm of cognitive abilities, there is good evidence for superiority of girls and women in verbal ability and of boys and men in spatial and quantitative ability.

But the strongest case for gender difference is made in the realm of aggressive behavior. Out of 94 comparisons in 67 different quantitative studies, 57 comparisons showed statistically significant sex differences. Fifty-two of the 57 studies that showed differences showed boys to be more aggressive than girls.

Maccoby and Jacklin do not report on studies of nurturance per se, but in an earlier book, published in 1966, Maccoby summarized 52 studies in a category called "nurturance and affiliation"; in 45 studies, girls and women showed more of it than boys and men, while in only two did males score higher, with five showing no difference.

hile it is difficult to get accurate information in nonindustrial cultures on such measures as verbal and spatial ability, a number of excellent studies have been done on child behavior, using techniques of measurement and analysis that live up to a high standard of rigor. Beatrice Whiting has been a leader in this field, originating techniques of study and sending students out to remote corners of the Earth (as well as making field trips herself) to bring back accurate knowledge about behavior. She is one of the most quantitatively oriented of anthropologists and may be said to have built an edifice of exactitude on the foundation that was laid by Margaret Mead. She has been at it for about 40 years.

In a series of investigations that came to be known as the Six Cultures study, Whiting, together with John Whiting and other colleagues, studied children's behavior through direct, detailed observations, in standard settings, distributed throughout the day. These observations were made by teams in a New England town called Orchard Town—its identity is still a mystery—and in five farming and herding villages throughout the world. In Mexico, Kenya, India, Japan, and the Philippines, as well as in New England, hundreds of hours of observations were made.

In all six cultures, boys differed from girls in the direction of greater egoism and/or greater aggressiveness, usually both. The difference varies greatly from culture to culture, presumably in response to different degrees of inculcation of gender role. Even more interesting, the girls in one culture may be more aggressive than the boys in another. But the direction of the difference within any culture is always the same. In other words, studies of children who are not fully socialized to their cultures underscore gender differences in the areas of aggressiveness and nurturance.

It may be argued that the children in Whiting's studies had nevertheless been trained; they ranged in age from three to 12. Furthermore, all of the six cultures may well be sexist.

till, we can go younger. Annelise Korner has spent many years studying newborn infants, and one of her central interests has been sex differences. She, as well as other investigators, has found that at birth boys show more muscle strength—greater head lift in the prone position, for example—while girls show greater skin sensitivity, more reflex smiles, more taste sensitivity, more searching movements with their mouths, and faster response to a flash of light.

But before we resort to this indirect accounting, it behooves us to consider another category of evidence: the sort of evidence that comes from studies of hormones, behavior, and the brain.

The idea that humoral factors secreted by reproductive organs influence gender differences in behavior is very old; castration has long been used in attempts to reduce aggressiveness in animals and men, and systematic experimental work demonstrating that this works has been available since 1849. The question is no longer whether hormones secreted by the testes promote or enable aggressive behavior, but *how*, and also: What else goes on in a like manner?

The principal male gonadal hormone in mammals is testosterone. It belongs to a chemical class known as steroids. The steroid class includes the two principal female reproductive hormones: estradiol—the key estrogen in humans—and progesterone, the gestation-promoting substance secreted in massive quantities by the placenta, and in lesser quantities, in the nonpregnant woman, by the ovaries. Estradiol and progesterone, together with the pituitary hormones that regulate them, participate in the determination of the monthly cycle. Although nothing so fabulous as that exists in males, there is much in common between testosterone's mode of action and that of the two female sex steroids.

The brain is the main regulatory organ of behavior, and behavior is that organ's major output; for a molecule to affect behavior it must generally first affect the brain, or at least the peripheral nerves. Sex steroids are no exception. Giving a rat a systemic injection of estradiol (radioactively labeled for tracing) will produce a high concentration of this hormone in certain brain cells—specifically, in their nuclei—within two hours. Twenty-two hours after that there will be a correspondingly massive increase in the tendency of the rat—if female—to respond to stimulation with sexual posturing. What happens in those 22 hours will tell a tale that may very well change the way we look at cell biology, but the tale cannot be told without at least a few more years of research.

Meanwhile, we know, as children like to say, *for sure*, that sex steroid hormones affect behavior, and we know they get around quite well in the brain. Using radioactive labeling, it has been very easy to show not only that they pass from blood to brain, but they concentrate selectively in certain brain regions. That is, concentrations occur in brain regions that play an important role in courtship, sex, maternal behavior, and violence—just the behaviors in which the sexes most differ and the ones most subject to influence by testosterone, estradiol, and progesterone.

Although the way the system works is scarcely understood, there are clues. For instance, injection of testosterone lowers the threshold for firing of nerve fibers in the pathway that leads to the hypothalamus, and as such in all likelihood mediates an excitatory influence on sexual and aggressive behavior. This finding gives substance to the action of testosterone on behavior. It is one thing to say that this hormone probably influences sex and aggression by acting on the brain; it is quite another to find a major nerve bundle deep in the brain, likely to be involved in sex and aggression, that can fire more easily when testosterone acts on it than when it does not. A key link in the story has been formed.

But we don't even need to reach so deeply into the brain. Peripheral nerves have now been shown in several experiments to concentrate these hormones. In songbirds in which the male of the pair is the singer, testosterone is concentrated in the motor nerves to the syrinx—the bird's voice box—and this is almost certainly part of the reason testosterone promotes song, which is a male courtship pattern. In female rats, injection of estradiol increase the size of the region of sensitivity of the nerve to the pelvic region, even when that nerve is detached from the brain; this is presumably part of the mechanism that makes the female susceptible—some of the time, anyway—to male advances.

Such is the view of the physiologist, which is, not surprisingly, pretty unrelenting. What is a bit surprising is that someone like Alice Rossi has accepted it. Rossi is a family sociologist. After years of distinction in her field, she became dissatisfied with 19th-century sociologist Emile Durkheim's dictum that only social facts can explain social facts and began to take seriously the notion that at least some social facts might be explained by biological ones. She has become adept in reading the biological literature, and when she reviews it for her sociologist colleagues, she does not attempt to conceal from them her belief that some of the observed gender difference in social behavior—for example, in parenting—is attributable to causes in endocrinology.

In reviewing the well-known sex difference in nurturing behavior—obvious particularly within the family, and in all cultures—Rossi has accepted the possibility that it may have its roots partly in hormonal differences. She has defended this viewpoint in several recent articles, in the scholarly as well as semipopular literature.

From a hormonal perspective, nurturance has not been as well studied as aggressiveness, in some ways the antithesis of nurturance. In many studies of humans and other animals, testosterone at least clearly enables and perhaps directly increases aggressiveness. While no one with any experience in this field thinks that there is a simple relationship between testosterone and aggression, most people now accept that some such relationship does exist.

To take an example, although repeated studies of aggression and testosterone in prison inmates have produced a confused picture, one intriguing discovery stands out: Among male prison inmates, in one very good study, the higher the adult testosterone level, the earlier the age of the first arrest. That is, the men who had the highest levels had been arrested youngest, in early adolescence. In another study, the level of testosterone in male juvenile delinquents was correlated with their level of observed aggressive behavior.

This finding brings us to one of the most central facts about the gonadal hormones: They rise very dramatically at adolescence. From very low levels during early and middle childhood, testosterone (especially but not exclusively in males) and estradiol and progesterone (both especially but not exclusively in females) all rise to adult levels over the course of a few years, and the female monthly cycle is instituted. Few studies have measured hormones and behavior in the same individuals, but it is likely that adolescent behavior—and its gender differentiation—is influenced by these massive hormonal changes. Gender differences in fat, muscle mass, and the pitch of the voice, all of which contribute to gender-specific behavior, are determined in large part by the teenage boy's rise in testosterone.

ne could conceivably leave the picture here, stress the similarity between the sexes in neurobehavioral plan, and suggest that evolution made a single beast with a single twist: an infusion of different hormones, coming from the gonads, just at the moment of reproductive maturity, just when we would expect the genders to begin to be really different.

The difficulty with this neat picture is that we have overwhelming evidence that the sexes differ in their behavior long before puberty, when previously we had thought that there were not enough circulating sex steroids to make the difference.

There is increasing evidence that the accounting may lie deep in the brain. In 1973 it was shown for the first time that male and female brains differed structurally. In the most forward portion of the hypothalamus, male and female rats differed in the density of synaptic connections among local neurons. Furthermore, castration of males just after birth would leave them with the female brain pattern, and injection of testosterone into females—likewise just after birth—would give them the male pattern.

To say that this study by Geoffrey Raisman and Pauline Field "rocked the neuroscience community" seems an extreme statement, yet I believe it to be accurate. There are several reasons. For one thing, it was the first demonstration that the brains of the sexes differ, in any animal. For another, the difference was in a region where it should have been—a region concerned with the brain's regulation of the very gonadal hormones we have been looking at. But most impressive of all, to those who knew the field, was the demonstration that sex hormones, circulating *at birth*, could change the brain. One of the most interesting experiments of the kind produced "pseudo-hermaphrodite" monkeys by administering male gonadal hormones to female fetuses before birth. As they grew, these females showed neither the characteristic low female level of aggressive play nor the characteristic high male level but something roughly in between.

or these reasons, investigators had, before 1973, already begun to talk about a change in the brain by male sex hormones around the time of birth; to put it crudely, a masculinization of the brain. But the involvement of the brain was only speculative until the report of Raisman and Field, which then gave the phrase its first genuine meaning.

That, as it now appears, was only the beginning of the story. A few years later, Dominique Toran-Allerand did a tissue-culture experiment—with brain slices in petri dishes—in which she watched the process in action. She made thin slices of the hypothalamus of newborn mice—of both sexes—and kept them alive long enough to treat them with gonadal steroid hormones, including testosterone. Her brief paper, published in *Brain Research*, shows the stunning results in photomicrographs. The cells in the slices treated with testosterone show more and faster growing neural processes than with the testosterone-free solution. In effect, she was able to watch as testosterone changed the newborn brain. Her work did not imply that the faster, more florid growth made the testosterone-treated hypothalamus *better*—only different.

For these and a variety of other reasons, the community of scientists working in this field concluded that the basic plan of the mammalian organism is female and stays that way unless told to be otherwise by masculine hormones. That this was not a necessary arrangement was shown by the sexual differentiation of birds, in which the opposite seems to be true; the basic plan is male, and the female course of development is the result of female hormones. But the mammal story was becoming clear: The genetic signal for masculinity, from

the Y chromosome, did its work on a female structural plan, through masculine hormones.

It is only natural to doubt whether such generalizations are applicable to that most puzzling of all mammals, the one that does research on its own nature. My own doubts in the matter—formidable at the time—were largely dispelled by the investigations of Anke Ehrhardt and her colleagues, first at the Johns Hopkins School of Medicine, later at the Columbia College of Physicians and Surgeons. Ehrhardt has spent years studying the condition and clinical treatment of certain unfortunate "experiments in nature"—anomalies of sexual and psychosexual development. In one such set of anomalies, known as the adrenogenital syndrome, a genetic defect produces abnormally large quantities of the sex steroid testosterone. For girls with the syndrome, masculine levels of the hormone are floating around in the blood throughout gestation, until the time of birth. Shortly after birth the condition can be corrected, so that it is presumably only in the prenatal period that the hormone can have its effects.

At age 10 these girls are psychologically different from their sisters and from unrelated controls. They are described by themselves and by their mothers as doing less doll play, being more "tomboyish," and expressing less desire to marry and have children when they grow up. Whatever value judgment we choose to place on these phenomena—I am inclined, for the moment, to place none—they seem to be real. They have been repeated by different investigators with different samples and even with different syndromes that amount, hormonally, to much the same thing. Taken together with the increasing animal evidence, these findings suggested to Ehrhardt and her colleagues—and to many others as well—that humans too could experience psychosexual differentiation, affecting both behavior and the brain, as a result of masculinizing hormones acting near or before birth.

his possibility received stunning confirmation in a series of discoveries made by endocrinologist Julianne Imperato-McGinley of the New York Hospital-Cornell Medical Center. These had to do principally with the analysis of a new syndrome of abnormal sexual differentiation that defied all previous rules. It was confined to three intermarrying rural villages in the southwestern Dominican Republic and, over a period of four generations, afflicted 38 known individuals from 23 interrelated families. It is clearly genetic but has arisen only recently due to mutation and intermarriage.

Nineteen of the subjects appeared at birth to be unambiguously female and were viewed and reared that way. At puberty they first failed to develop breasts and then underwent a completely masculine pubertal transformation, including growth of a phallus, descent of the testes, deepening of the voice, and the development of a muscular masculine physique. Physically and psychologically they became men.

The physiological analysis undertaken by Imperato-McGinley and her colleagues revealed that these individuals are genetically male—they have one X and one Y chromosome—but lack a single enzyme of male sex-hormone synthesis, due to a defective gene. The enzyme, 5-alpha-reductase, changes testosterone into another male sex hormone, dihydrotestosterone. Although they lack dihydrotestosterone almost completely, they have normal levels of testosterone itself. Evidently these two hormones are respectively responsible for the promotion of male external sex characteristics at birth and at puberty. The lack of "dihydro" makes for a female-looking newborn and prepubertal child. The presence of testosterone makes for a more or less normal masculine puberty.

But for present purposes, the most extraordinary thing about these people is that they become men of their culture in every sense of the word. After 12 or more years of rearing as girls, they are able to completely transform themselves into almost typical examples of the masculine gender—with family, sexual, vocational, and avocational roles. Of the 18 subjects for which data were available, 17 made this transformation completely, the other retaining a female role and gender identity. The 17 did not make the transformation with ease. Imperato-McGinley reports that it cost some of them years of confusion and psychological anguish. But they made it, without special training or therapeutic intervention. Imperato-McGinley and her colleagues reason that the testosterone circulating during the course of growth in these men has a masculinizing effect on their brains.

What are we to make of these extraordinary facts? For the immediate future, at least as far as I am concerned, nothing. It is simply too soon. Given present knowledge, for instance, it is not beyond the realm of possibility that the observed differences between the brains of the two genders serve only physiological functions. The brains must be different to exert different control over different reproductive systems, having nothing at all to do with behavioral subtleties. But I think this unlikely. If not now, then in the very near future, it will be extremely difficult for an informed, objective observer to discard the hypothesis that the genders differ in their degree of violent behavior for reasons that are in part physiological. [See Currents, p. 14, of first evidence of differences in human brains.]

If the community of scientists whose work and knowledge are relevant should come to agreement on this point, then it seems to me that one policy implication is plausible: Serious disarmament may ultimately necessitate an increase of women in government. Some women are as violent as almost any man. But speaking of averages there is little doubt that we would all be safer if the world's weapon systems were controlled by average women instead of by average men.

I think it appropriate to end where we began, contemplating the women who have helped unearth these facts. Visualize them in their offices and laboratories, trying to sort out what it all means; how do they handle the dissonance their findings must engender? I suspect that they do it by making a reconciliation—not a compromise—but a complex difficult reconciliation between the idea of human difference and the ideal of human equality. It is one that we must all make soon.

Late motherhood: Race against Mother Nature?

ELISE VIDER

Elise Vider, a free-lance writer from West Hartford, previously has written for Better Health, *and regularly for* Connecticut *magazine and the* Hartford Advocate.

Having a baby is no longer an automatic part of a young woman's life.

Medical and sociological changes of recent years have so increased the options for today's young women that the decision of when--and in rare cases whether--to have a baby can be tormenting.

The women born in the immediate post-war baby boom entered their child-bearing years in the late 1960s, a time of social and political upheaval that challenged many of the assumptions of the previous generation. Many women of this new generation chose to pursue careers, often as an alternative to the tradition of marriage and having a family. Many have had more than one marriage; many have not married at all or married much later than their mothers. Add to that the effects of newly developed birth control measures and the changed moral climate that made them acceptable.

The result? A dramatically reduced birth rate in the 1970s. Births for every 1,000 people in Connecticut hovered between 11 and 12 during the late 1970s, compared to its peak of nearly 24 in 1957. Hospitals, including the Hospital of St. Raphael, reduced their numbers of maternity beds. Some hospitals even closed entire wings because of the drop in births. Having babies was simply not a priority for many young women.

Racing the biological clock

But as that generation of baby boom women enters its 30s, a sense of growing urgency about having children has entered the minds of many. No longer do the reproductive years span a seemingly endless horizon. Many women have become acutely aware of the ticking of a biological time clock that limits the number of years they can have children. Many doctors, counselors and other experts have observed anxiety among women in their 30s and early 40s who have not had children. These women, the experts say, feel pressured to have a baby before it's too late to take their turn grabbing what one physician has called "the brass ring."

Not surprisingly, the number of births is once again on the rise, although not nearly at 1950s and '60s levels. Still, the sudden spurt of births has prompted many to refer to "the baby boomlet." Many of these new mothers are markedly older than their own mothers. The U.S. Department of Health and Human Services recently reported that the birth rate for women ages 25 to 29 now equals that for those ages 20 to 24, and that first births are up sharply among women in their early 30s. The National Center of Health Statistics reports that from 1975 to 1978, there was a 37 percent increase in women ages 30 to 34 who had their first child and that for women ages 35 to 39, the increase was 22 percent.

Mothers ages 35...and older

In Connecticut, about five percent of all live births were to mothers ages 35 and older in 1977 and 1978, the last years for which figures are available. That percentage is now starting to increase, a state statistician said. The figure hit its all time high in the mid-1950s when women tended to have more children and therefore continued to bear them later in life. In 1977, over 1,500 Connecticut babies were born to women ages 35 to 39 and 134--or about 10 percent of those whose birth order is known--were first babies. Women ages 40 to 44 had 262 babies, about 9 percent as first babies. Ten babies were born to mothers 45 to 49, one of which was a first baby.

The spate of middle-agers as first time mothers is still too new for experts to determine all the implications. Still, there are medical, sociological and psychological factors that are receiving closer scrutiny. Articles abound and several books have been published on the subject. A recent, three-year study by the Wellesley College Center for Research on Women reported that the decision to have children, the pregnancies, perceptions of childbirth and performance as parents were significantly different for older mothers. Psychologists who did the study reported to the NEW YORK TIMES that when they started their research in 1976, their definition of a "late timing" parent was a 30-year-old. Surprisingly, by the time they finished interviewing in 1979, the boundaries had shifted so dramatically that they ended up focusing on an age range of 37 to 44.

Late motherhood: how risky?

Medical considerations--the health and well-being of mother and child--are the most pressing concern about older mothers. Obstetricians classify first-time mothers aged 35 and older as "elderly primaparas" and as high risk patients. By the late 30s and early 40s, it is agreed, the potential for a problem pregnancy and delivery, difficulty conceiving, maternal mortality rates and the danger of chromosomal abnormalities all increase.

Doctors stress that medical advances make it easier and safer than ever before for women to bear children later in life. Dr. Brian Rigney, chairman of obstetrics and gynecology at St. Raphael's, said the oldest first-time mother in his practice was a 43-year-old who had "beautiful twins" with no problems.

The authors of UP AGAINST THE CLOCK, a 1979 book on deferred childbrith, contacted numerous physicians and health professionals to assess the risks for older mothers and their babies. Their finding: "All in all, the news is good. There is growing consensus among health professionals that the medical risks to both the older mother and her baby have been exaggerated and that healthy women of any child-bearing age who have access to fine medical care can look forward to a normal pregnancy and a healthy baby. These optimistic conclusions, however, should not be taken to mean that there are no drawbacks, from a medical standpoint, of postponing children."

Perhaps the biggest risk for older mothers is the increased probability of bearing a child with a birth defect caused by chromosomal abnormality, particularly Down's Syndrome or mongolism. Dr. Rigney reported that up to age 30, the chances of a mother bearing a child with Down's Syndrome are less than one in a thousand. At age 35, the odds increase to one in 100 to 120. And by age 45 or older, the odds are one in 45. The probabilities are the same, he added, regardless of whether the woman has had previous children.

The reason for the dramatically increased risks of chromosomal abnormalities, it is believed, is the age of the mother's egg cells. Unlike men, who produce new sperm, women are born with lifetime supplies of oocytes, or immature egg cells. As women age, these cells can be affected by exposure to medications, pollutants, infections and radiation so that, by mid-life, the chances are higher of an oocyte producing an egg with an abnormal number of chromosomes. When the number of chromosomes in the fetus varies from the normal 46, the result can be a serious birth defect, including Down's Syndrome.

Some recent research also indicates some risk among older fathers. Men over age 55 seem more likely than their younger counterparts to contribute a sperm with an incorrect chromosome count. Twenty-three chromosomes from father and 23 from mother provide the normal 46 count in the fertilized egg or fetus.

It is now possible to screen for chromosomal abnormalities through the process of amniocentesis, in which the doctor inserts a hollow needle into the abdomen of a pregnant woman and withdraws a small amount of the amniotic fluid that surrounds the fetus. By examining the fluid, doctors can determine if the fetus has any serious chromosomal birth defect.

Usual practice at St. Raphael's on this sensitive subject is to make expectant mothers in their late 30s aware that such screening is possible and to perform amniocentesis if the patient wishes, according to Dr. Rigney. But, he added, "If a couple does not want an abortion, there is very little sense in the test." Only a small percentage of hospital patients choose amniocentesis, he said.

If a patient opts for amniocentesis, it is crucial that it be handled by a doctor and laboratory well acquainted with the delicate procedure because of its inherent risks. Amniocentesis carries a one in 200 chance of damage to the fetus or loss of pregnancy, said Dr. Rigney. In some cases, the extracted cells do not grow in the laboratory, necessitating a repeat of the entire procedure, he added.

Age and fertility

Older women have more difficulty conceiving in the first place, doctors say, because fertility drops in the late 30s as satisfactory and regular ovulation begins to fail. The existence of fibroid tumors, which are benign growths in or around the uterus, and endometriosis, in which cells of the uterine lining adhere to the tubes and ovaries, are more likely in older women and both are linked to infertility. For women who choose to defer childbearing until middle age, difficulties in conceiving can be particularly upsetting because of the deadline pressure. And, unfortunately, doctors still have no reliable way to gauge fertility of a patient before she attempts pregnancy.

"If you were to ask at age 26 if you were going to be fertile at age 36, you couldn't possibly be told," said Dr. Rigney. Patients with a history of irregular menstrual periods or abdominal inflammation can be infertile at any age. Fertility is simply less likely with progressive age, he said.

Medical problems such as increased frequency of diabetes and high blood pressure among older women can make pregnancy and delivery difficult. Hypertension, in particular, is linked to toxemia in newborns, a condition that can cause an infant to be stillborn. Vaginal deliveries are sometimes more difficult and, said Dr. Rigney, "It is fair to say that there is an increase in Cesarean sections with the age of the mother." Chances of miscarriage increase after age 40, Dr. Rigney also said. Maternal mortality rates rise with the age of the mother, increasing tenfold between ages 20 and 45, he added.

Despite all the potential problems, there is agreement that medical advances, especially the sophisticated monitoring during pregnancy with devices such as ultrasound, which provides a picture of the developing fetus, amniocentesis, fetal monitoring and other modern tests, make it more likely than ever that a healthy woman in her 30s or early 40s will have a normal pregnancy and healthy baby.

And, who knows for sure what will

happen in the future? For an increasing number of life-threatening problems, medical and sometimes even surgical treatment is becoming possible for babies not yet born. The latest and most exciting treatment for specialists is actual direct treatment of the fetus while still in the mother's womb. An unborn baby girl in California was recently saved from probable death by giving her mother large doses of a vitamin called biotin in the final trimester of pregnancy.

Is there a "best" time?

Nor is biological age the only factor in determining the optimal age for having babies. When social and emotional considerations are taken into account, the benefits of later parenthood increase. A girl of 16--and sometimes even younger--is biologically capable of having a child, Dr. Rigney pointed out, but to do so usually has emotional repercussions from the interrupted adolescence. "Ideally, the age for motherhood is a combination of both biological and emotional maturity. And that's probably going to be in the mid 20s," said Dr. Rigney. The actual average age of first-time mothers at St. Raphael's, by Dr. Rigney's observation, is in the late-teens to early-20s.

When it comes to the quality of parenting, the emotional maturity and stability of many older women are no small consideration. Many experts feel that older adults make better parents because they are often more mature and capable and because, having waited so long, they are exceptionally enthusiastic. The marital stability of older couples "whose relationship has withstood the test of time" is another bonus, according to Dr. Ronald Angoff, a St. Raphael's pediatrician who specializes in child development.

Most of the older parents he sees in his practice are couples who have been married awhile and pursued separate careers, intentionally deferring childbirth. For these couples, the decision to have children does not come lightly.

"What it means to have children and give up the independence you've had before and the ability to do what you want to do, when you want to do it, to have a newborn infant who is totally dependent on you, I think, takes a degree of maturity," said Dr. Angoff.

Some older mothers tend to better educate themselves about pregnancy and childbirth and are "good consumers. And consumerism is healthy in medicine as in anything else," said Dr. Angoff. As a result, the "potential for these infants to do better and

develop better is there." But the flip side of that is that older parents can be excessively anxious and preoccupied with the fear that something is wrong with the child. Overall, he said, it is important to note that "the trend is relatively new. We don't really know how these kids will turn out."

The Wellesley study of older mothers reported a number of advantages. Generally, the older mothers were more financially secure and many, having already had careers, were more settled and secure about having experienced professional success. The women in the study reported less resentment than their younger counterparts about having to sacrifice for their children. One participant was quoted as saying, "I've had 20 years now of going out to the opera and how many more do you have to see?"

For many women in their 30s, however, who have not reached a decision about whether to have children, the dilemma can be fraught with agony and anguish. The fear of a change of heart after it's too late is a strong factor. Still, warned Dr. Angoff, for the woman who reasons that she is in her late 30s and had better have a child although she doesn't feel ready, "That's the wrong reason to have a baby."

Stress Can Be Good For You

Susan Seliger

Every weeknight in New York, thousands of people remain hunched over their desks until well past the dinner hour. They leave the office with stuffed briefcases, unwind with a couple of drinks and a late meal, and finish their day's labors with a few hours of reading in bed. In the morning, they crowd into buses, trains, and cars and inch their way back to the office. Noontime finds them waiting on line to get into overpriced, understaffed restaurants. And when the sun sets on the city, once again those thousands of desk lamps will shine on in almost empty offices.

Stress? Of course.

A sure prescription for an early grave? Nonsense.

It's not that stress can't be harmful. It's been linked to every disease from asthma to heart disease to ulcers. But a number of recent studies have turned upside down the prevailing wisdom about who is most at risk. More important, these studies have found that stress is not always harmful, that it is in fact a crucial, often productive part of life—in short, that stress can actually be good for you. A person who feels in control of his life can channel the stressful energy that accompanies both the drive to achieve and city living and can make himself healthier than those who avoid cities, conflict, and competition altogether. And this new research raises serious questions about the multi-million-dollar anti-stress industry, with its 72-million annual tranquilizer prescriptions and its hundreds of stress clinics and counseling businesses—most often aimed at exactly the wrong people.

ACCORDING TO THE LATEST RESEARCH, THE ABILITY to control stress is within each person's power. It is the perception of and attitude about both self and environment that most influence whether a person will be hurt by stress. What researchers are finding is that bad stress is triggered not by the pressures of decision-making but rather by the feeling that one's decisions are useless, that life is overwhelming and beyond personal control.

Those people making the decisions, the high-powered, high-pressure executives that many have believed are most vulnerable, turn out, therefore, not to be. And it is not that they are genetically more fit to cope that accounts for their rise to the top. It is their attitude. Yet, the notion that they are

at risk has been perpetuated by those selling stress services to employers who are all too willing to spend money for stress counseling for their top people. Unfortunately, it's the underlings these managers supervise who are at far greater risk, people the employers pay little attention to.

"An executive who makes a lot of decisions is better off than his secretary," says Dr. Kenneth Greenspan, director of the Center for Stress Related Disorders, at Columbia-Presbyterian Medical Center. "Secretaries—along with assembly-line workers—are at a great deal of risk from stress because all their decisions are predetermined: when they start work, when they stop, what they do. They fear that they can be easily replaced; they see themselves as victims. And that produces bad stress."

When she came to New York from the Midwest to be a nurse, Joanna Sedgwick* never imagined she would experience stress. She thought stress only affected higher-level people, like doctors. Sedgwick moved into an apartment on the Upper West Side and soon found a job. She also found bedpans, bureaucracy, and belittling treatment by doctors. By the end of a workday, she invariably had a migraine.

Seeking relief, Sedgwick went to the Center for Stress Related Disorders. The biofeedback treatment she was given eased her pain, but it didn't stop the migraines from coming on. With encouragement from Dr. Greenspan, she came to realize that what was wrong with her were her feelings about her work.

"I got no respect; I couldn't make any decisions. Doctors looked down their noses at me and the other nurses," Sedgwick recalls. She ended up returning to school and became a research nurse. One year later, she was appointed head administrative nurse. She gets respect; her headaches are gone.

"I'm under a lot more stress now than I was as an ordinary nurse, and I work harder, But it's different," Sedgwick says. "I decide about treatment; I supervise other nurses. I no longer feel as if everyone is running my life. And I don't get those migraines anymore."

Nor does Joe Carter get his workday headaches anymore, or the dizziness and anxiety he felt as he headed home at night. Joe works for a utility company, managing about 60 people and answering to several bosses. Unlike most of the middle

---

* *The patients' names have been changed.*

managers around him, he has no college education, and that disparity worried him. Whenever some minor thing went wrong at work—and there were often emergencies that made him work more than 24 hours straight—he used to worry that he'd lose his job. His supervisors were much quicker to point out his mistakes than to pat him on the back.

And no relaxation awaited him when he got home at night. His wife always seemed to have some chore for him to do, and he found himself constantly worrying about earning enough money to put his teenage children through college.

Finally, Carter decided to undergo biofeedback and relaxation training at the Center for Stress Related Disorders, and that led to a more important decision: to talk to his bosses about their assessment of his work. He found that they regarded him as a more valuable employee than he had thought. His symptoms began to fade. Soon he found his confidence had increased enough to allow him to feel comfortable telling his wife he wanted to spend time at home just relaxing with her. If not as dramatic as Joanna Sedgwick's, Carter's recovery proved the same point: An increase in his self-confidence led to an increase in his sense of control over his life and eliminated the chronic stress he was undergoing.

Dr. Greenspan himself could be considered a stress case. Having squeezed three interviews into the morning, he rushes to the deli around the corner and wolfs down a sandwich so that he can race back to the center, see more patients, and then buzz over to another wing of the hospital to check on his latest research project. He talks fast; he walks fast. By most objective standards, he is under a great deal of stress. "But it isn't *bad* stress," insists Greenspan. "I love what I'm doing, and I know how and when to ease up. That makes all the difference."

So DOES SUCCESS. IN 1974, THE METROPOLITAN LIFE Insurance Company examined 1,078 men who held one of the three top executive positions in Fortune 500 companies and found that their mortality rate was 37 percent lower than that of other white males of a comparable age.

The explanation may come in a study of 259 executives at Illinois Bell conducted by Suzanne Kobasa, Ph.D., a psychologist at the University of Chicago. She found that certain people seemed to be particularly able to handle stress—their health was not affected no matter how intense their job pressures or how ominous their family medical history. Based on her research, Kobasa concluded that if people felt a sense of purpose, viewed change as a challenge and not a threat, and believed that they were in control of their lives, they were not adversely affected by stress.

Executive women—presumably under a great deal of stress to make it in the corporate world—must feel some of this sense of control. Recent studies show no signs that their push into the upper ranks is causing them bad health. Metropolitan Life's 1979 study of 2,352 women listed in *Who's Who* showed their annual death rate to be 29 percent lower than that of their contemporaries. Indeed, the groups of women who have the highest rates of heart disease are secretaries and saleswomen—"women in jobs with little security, status, or control," explains Suzanne Haynes, Ph.D.

Another myth is that city life is bad for mental health. Back in 1954, Dr. Leo Srole, now professor emeritus of social sciences at Columbia University's Center for Gerontology, did a study of Manhattan residents that seemed to confirm that "stressful" living conditions in the city were driving people crazy. Dr. Srole reported that 23.4 percent of his white midtown Manhattan sample were suffering some kind of "emotional impairment" that interfered with their daily lives. That percentage seemed high until 1975, when Dr. Srole matched it with the findings of a similar Cornell University sample of a rural county in Nova Scotia. His conclusion was startling: New Yorkers had a "significantly lower" incidence of mental impairment than did the rural folk. According to Dr. Srole, one reason may be that "cities have resources for satisfaction that rural communities don't have."

These findings are reinforced by a 1978 report by the President's Commission on Mental Health that found that "rural communities tend to be characterized by a higher-than-average rate of psychiatric disorder, particularly depression . . . by restricted opportunities for developing adequate coping mechanisms for facing stress . . . by an acceptance of conditions as being beyond individual control."

RESEARCHERS HAVE COME TO BELIEVE THAT THERE are actually three kinds of stress: normal stress; distress, or bad stress, which is normal stress that has become chronic; and eustress, or good stress. Each of these kinds of stress is basically a three-stage series of reactions within the body that enable it to adapt to change. Since life is constant change, such reactions are obviously important; without them the body cannot survive. These reactions are most extreme (and thus easiest to monitor) under acute stress, a form of normal stress that one feels when threatened—a car swerving toward you; a child about to put his hand into a fire; the sound of footsteps behind you on a dark, lonely street.

The first stage of any stress reaction is alarm. The endocrine glands release hormones, including adrenaline; the heartbeat speeds up, as does breathing; oxygen-rich blood is directed away from the skin to the brain and the skeletal muscles for fast action. Pupils dilate to take in more information; hormones enter the blood to increase its coagulating ability in case of injury; and digestion slows so that more of the body's energy can be devoted to fighting or fleeing. The surge of energy, concentration, and power that comes with the stress alarm enables people to perform in a crisis—sometimes beyond their normal physical capacities.

Once the alarm stage of stress has passed, the body enters the second stage, one of recuperation in which it repairs any damage caused by the demands of the fight-or-flight response. This is the stage where one can say "Whew!" The third stage is a return to the body's normal state of relaxed alertness.

A diagram of this process would look something like this:

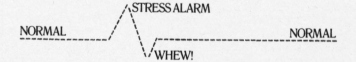

These large sawtooth jags of acute (or normal) short-term stress are part of regular living and are necessary for it. "A certain amount of stress is needed to tune you up for action and keep you on your toes," writes Dr. Hans Selye, the granddaddy of stress research.

Bad stress is normal or acute stress that becomes chronic, continuing for weeks and months so that the body never gets much time to say "Whew!" and recuperate. This kind of stress means trouble.

A normal, healthy life pattern might look like this on the stress diagram:

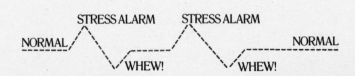

On the other hand, chronic stress might look like this:

One person who found herself in a chronic-stress cycle was Leslie Friedman, who ran a personnel department in a bank, overseeing the careers of about twenty employees. Friedman worked more than 50 hours a week, and when she went home at night, she had a second job: helping her husband with his business. Friedman didn't think her bosses appreciated her efforts, and by noon each day she'd have a splitting headache and a backache too. But at the end of the evening, although she was dead tired, she couldn't fall asleep. In the morning, she would drag herself out of bed and begin the punishing cycle all over again.

Friedman was able to break out. She discovered that her boss didn't expect her to do all that she was doing and that that was the reason she didn't get the appreciation she thought she deserved. So she quit and found another job, where her skills at managing people were put to good use. She also convinced her husband that he had to hire an assistant. Going home doesn't mean going on to a second job anymore, and, although Friedman still works very long hours, she says that the challenge of the new job seems to be energizing rather than enervating her.

Chronic stress can inflict real bodily harm. First, it can lower resistance to disease. According to Dr. Paul J. Rosch, an internist and president of the American Institute of Stress, in Yonkers, "interferon, a non-specific polypeptide which is one of the basic defenses against virus infections and is now being investigated in the treatment of cancer, is also suppressed under some conditions of emotional stress." If acute stress is occasional, the body's immune system can bounce back. If it is prolonged, the immune system is thrown out of whack.

Second, repeated and unremitting episodes of acute stress mean repeated release of adrenaline. If the problem prompts no physical exertion to use up the adrenaline—and most stresses in modern life are of a mental rather than a physical nature—then excess adrenaline will remain in the system and can play a part in the buildup of cholesterol in the arteries that can lead to heart disease.

There are early, recognizable signs that can allow a person to avoid entering a cycle of long-term, chronic stress. In addition, people can actually increase their capacity to cope with potentially stressful events.

"Knowing the danger signals can help you operate successfully at much higher levels of stress," says Dr. Sidney Lecker, director of Corporate Stress Control Services, in Manhattan. Once you become aware of the symptoms, there are definite steps you can take (see box on page 250) so that, as Dr. Lecker puts it, "you can go back into the thick of things and operate on the ragged edge of disaster—safely."

T HE FLIP SIDE OF THE STRESS COIN IS EUSTRESS. IT comes from successfully rising to a challenge, feeling confidence and a sense of control over one's destiny. Dr. Rosch believes that people who thrive on stress might die without it. "I take care of patients who are recuperating from heart attacks," he says. "Now, the ideal prescription for one guy is to lie on a beach in the Bahamas, but for another kind of patient that same prescription would be lethal.

"I'm convinced that good stress is healthy," continues Rosch, who began his stress research three decades ago with Selye. "Look at symphony conductors. They undergo physical exertion, deadlines, traveling, dealing with prima donnas in the orchestra. But, on the other hand, they have pride of accomplishment, the approbation of their peers, the plaudits of the audience.

"Look at the life and health records of conductors and you'll see it's outstanding. They live forever. Look at them." Waving his arms enthusiastically, he checks off their names: "Stokowski, Fiedler, Toscanini." He pauses. "The real secret to a long and healthy life is to enjoy what you're doing and be good at it. It's not to avoid stress."

One of the leading popular advocates of the theory that good stress may have the power to heal is Norman Cousins, the former editor of *Saturday Review*. Cousins says that laughter is one of those forms of good stress—and, as he wrote in *The New England Journal of Medicine* and in his book *Anatomy of an Illness*, he's convinced it saved his life.

Laughter? Yes, laughter. It might seem to be just another form of physical exertion, making the body respond much as it does under any kind of acute stress: The oxygen supply to the brain increases; the heartbeat speeds up, rushing oxygen-rich blood to the muscles; the pupils dilate; and so on. But recent brain research indicates that something far more powerful is at work on a biochemical level: Endorphins, the body's natural painkillers, are also being released. What the researchers do not yet know is whether endorphins, which may actually reverse some of the damage of the distress reaction, are secreted in equal amounts under all kinds of stress or in greater quantities during eustress.

"We're just on the frontier of discovering the nature of the biochemical reactions of stress, such as the release of endorphins," says Dr. Lorenz Ng, former chief of the Pain Studies Program at the National Institute on Drug Abuse, in Bethesda, Maryland, and medical director of the Washington Pain Center. "It's the newest thing in stress research, and it may lead us to understand the differences between good and bad stress," says Ng.

Dr. Rosch believes that the biochemical effects of eustress may actually reverse the course of various diseases, including cancer. He's written on this subject in a chapter of *Cancer, Stress and Death* for the "Sloan-Kettering Institute Cancer Series." "Cancer and other diseases set in when the immune system weakens," Rosch says. "There is evidence that on the cell walls of lymphocytes responsible for mediating the immune response there are receptor sites for ACTH, which is the prime hormone released under stress, endorphins, met-enkephalin, and other brain hormones. This implies that the brain can talk directly to the immune system and that the immune system talks back. The intriguing possibility is that people may be able to tune in to that conversation—and even influence it, just as they can be trained to influence other systems, like pulse rate and skin temperature, through biofeedback. People may have the ability to cure themselves."

A CTUALLY, THE IDEA OF STRESS'S BEING HEALTHY HAS been around for a long time. In *Stress Without Distress*, published in 1974, Selye explained that this was possible, but no one in the stress field paid much attention. They were too busy making a living convincing people that stress was affecting their health. They wanted people to continue popping down their daily anti-stress pill and to spend $1,500 per week at anti-stress clinics. "Stress has become so popular that a variety of entrepreneurs and charlatans have capitalized on it," says Rosch.

The medical profession is also campaigning against stress, acknowledges Rosch. For example, Dr. Theodore Cooper, while dean of the Cornell University Medical College, headed a three-year program called "The Consequences of Stress: The Medical and Social Implications of Prescribing Tranquilizers." The program's message went by closed-circuit television lectures to nearly 20,000 physicians in 26 cities and to 100,000 more physicians through similar tape recordings. The financier for all this was Hoffmann-LaRoche, Inc., makers of Valium, which is the biggest-selling tranquilizer in the world.

Yet, there is still great dispute in the medical community over the usefulness of tranquilizers for dealing with stress. Many doctors are convinced that they can do more harm than good. "Avoidance of stress has led to abuse of tranquilizers," says Dr. Nelson Hendler, the head of Mensana, a pain clinic in Baltimore, and a psychiatric consultant at Johns Hopkins Hospital's Pain Treatment Center. Valium doesn't help stress, insists Hendler. It inhibits the release of serotonin, which stimulates sleep naturally. And it may interfere with stage-three sleep—perhaps the most restful stage in the sleep cycle, in which REM (rapid eye movement) sleep occurs—and stage-four sleep, which is the deepest.

"One in three people who goes to a doctor about stress gets a prescription for a tranquilizer," Hendler says. "Most people should not fill it."

The anti-stress brigade has also been joined by hundreds of companies that provide counseling on stress, alcoholism, and other problems. Millions of workers are now eligible for such benefits. For instance, Isidore Lefkowitz Elgort, an advertising agency in New York, pays for employees to attend T.M. sessions to help them handle stress.

Many of these efforts may indeed be useful. However, a good number are misguided—aimed at the people under the least stress, the executives, instead of at their underlings. Other anti-stress efforts seem to cause more problems than they cure.

"Most organizations buy one-shot educational packages—a lecture on stress," says James Manuso, Ph.D., creator of the in-house biofeedback stress-counseling center at Equitable Life in New York. "Someone goes in there and tells the employees how much stress they're under, scares the hell out of them, and then leaves. That just *adds* to the stress."

Even Dr. Roy Menninger, president of the Menninger Foundation, in Topeka, Kansas, which charges New York corporation executives up to $2,300 each to learn, among other things, how to handle stress, believes the view that "stress is bad" has gone too far. Dr. Lecker is more emphatic: "Stress is essential for meeting challenges. If you didn't have stress, you'd be dead."

How to Convert Bad Stress Into Good

THERE ARE CERTAIN PHYSICAL signals that provide a warning that the body's habitual response to stress is becoming destructive. People can learn to recognize these signals and to change their characteristic responses to daily tensions. They thus can endure higher levels of stress and perhaps even profit from them.

The telltale signals:

□ Cold hands, especially if one is colder than the other.

□ Indigestion, diarrhea, too frequent urination.

□ Being susceptible to every cold or virus that goes around (which could mean that the physical strains of distress are weakening the immune system).

□ Muscle spasms or a soreness and tightness in the jaw, back of the neck, shoulders, or lower back.

□ Shortness of breath.

□ Headaches, tiredness, sleeping too much or too little.

□ Becoming suddenly accident-prone.

When someone recognizes any of these signals, he should stop what he is doing—if only for two or three minutes—take several deep breaths, and try to relax. If the tension also shows itself through tapping toes or drumming fingers, he should stand up and do a few jumping jacks or take a brisk walk around the office or the block, trying to look at everything as if for the first time.

The most important key to defusing distress is to become conscious of that inner voice each person has. Human beings are constantly assessing themselves and their environment and reporting silently to themselves: "This looks threatening; I don't think I can handle it. I certainly can't handle it without a cigarette. . . ."

Many people are not conscious of this internal commentator, but if a person learns to listen to the way he talks to himself, he may find that he is usually not being as encouraging as he could be—that he is actually making matters worse for himself.

Instead of standing on the line at the bank checking his watch and listening to his inner voice computing how long it has taken "those incompetent tellers" to handle each transaction, worrying about how late he will be to his appointment, and wondering why he didn't get cash for the weekend yesterday, he should make his inner voice be soothing: "I don't like waiting on this line, but there is nothing I can do about it now, so I might as well relax. Look how tense everyone else is getting. It's actually kind of funny."

Another trick is to stop thinking about the time. It may be slipping by, but counting the seconds only fritters away energy and activates the stress response. Dr. Meyer Friedman and Dr. Ray H. Rosenman, the authors of *Type A Behavior and Your Heart,* found that time consciousness, or "hurry sickness," was a key personality trait of the heart-attack-prone Type A personality. One stress researcher says she found that simply removing her wristwatch for several weeks greatly reduced the time pressures she felt.

To convert bad stress to good, remember the following:

Before an event expected to be stressful, visualize what may take place. Such a rehearsal will make the actual event seem familiar, helping one to relax and handle the situation with confidence.

During a tense situation, such as taking a test or meeting a tight deadline, talk nicely to oneself, don't harp on poor preparation or performance. Instead, one should make one's inner voice offer praise for what one did accomplish, and reassurance that the situation isn't so bad after all.

Afterward, luxuriate in the relief of the burden's being lifted. Even if things didn't go so well, avoid puritanical self-criticism. This refreshing interlude can help strengthen the system to better resist the wear and tear of future distress.

"Any bad stress can be turned around," insists Dr. Kenneth Greenspan, "if you take steps that make you feel that you are controlling your life and it isn't controlling you." —S.S.

Coping with the Seasons of Life

A British study of the varieties of human experience

John Nicholson

John Nicholson is the author of "Seven Ages" (Fontana Paperbacks). This article is excerpted from the social science weekly "New Society" of London.

There are two very different views about the importance age plays in people's lives. There is the Shakespearean tradition, encapsulated in the "Seven Ages of Man" speech in *As You Like It*, which suggests that our lives fall into distinct phases and that people change as they get older, generally for the worse. Other writers take the view that we are "as old as we feel." André Gide remarked at the age of seventy-three, "If I did not keep telling myself my age over and over again, I am sure I should hardly be aware of it." Which view is right? In an attempt to answer this question, some 600 men, women, and children between the ages of five and eighty were interviewed last winter in the Colchester Study of Aging. The aim of this survey was to build up by objective means a subjective picture of the human lifecycle.

A few years ago you got the "key to the door" at twenty-one. But only one in eight of the adults we interviewed gave twenty-one as the age at which they considered they became adult. Most men judged that they became adult sometime between eighteen and twenty-one, while women gave more varied answers, with a significant proportion of them designating the mid-to-late-twenties.

What are young adults like? Though some functions—notably the performance of our hearts and circulatory systems—reach a peak slightly earlier, the years between twenty and twenty-five represent the pinnacle of our biological development. Physically and intellectually, we have never before been so good and never will be again.

On the negative side we found young adults to be self-centered and still naïve in their views on what life is all about. In psychological terms many of them were still in the throes of the identity crisis that had begun to disturb them in adolescence. Particularly among the unmarried, there seemed to be an internal conflict between wanting to establish a position which commands respect and not wanting to get into a rut. They were afraid of slipping into the habits of their boss, for example, by taking a briefcase home in the evening. And yet many were anxious to carve out a niche for themselves and enjoy the status and economic advantages of their jobs.

On the positive side they enjoyed the feeling of "no longer being a kid." Some—particularly the married—expressed pleasure in mapping out the future. Others complained that they were required to make once-and-for-all decisions, that their options were closing, and that they were anxious about their ability to cope with the future.

For some young adults the feeling of emotional insecurity far outweighs the self-confidence which comes from standing on their own two feet. Psychiatrists consider that many early marriages are "take-care-of-me contracts," entered into in a spirit of panic rather than out of conviction that one has found the ideal partner for life.

This is only one of the dangers presented by the freedom of young adulthood. For some people freedom becomes an obsession, to be guarded at all costs. As one example of this, many young adults we spoke to in Colchester were strongly opposed to the idea of having children, mainly because of the restrictions they felt it would impose on their sense of freedom.

People tend to look back on their early twenties with pleasure. When we asked our sample what age they would most like to be if they had the choice, the twenties proved to be a popular decade. Those who favored it did so because that was when life had been most enjoyable.

Perhaps the most striking feature of young adulthood is its exclusiveness with regard to age. At no other period of life do we spend less time in the company of people older or younger than ourselves; and it may well be that never again are we so sensitive to the difference of even a year.

People who reach young adulthood without having had any sexual experience are now in a minority (though barely). Since most adolescents say that they are opposed to casual sex, and seem to feel quite strongly that sex ought to occur only in the context of an established loving relationship, it may well be that many of today's teenagers have at least one such relationship before young adulthood.

In some respects, the intimate relationships young adults try to form are similar to earlier relationships with their parents and friends. They may well have loved their parents and felt deeply committed to best friends. The new dimension is being in love, and the problem which has taxed young adults since time began is how to distinguish between being in love and liking, depending on, or being infatuated.

"One of the pleasures of middle age is to find out that one was right, and that one was much righter than one knew at, say, seventeen or twenty-three." Or so said the poet Ezra Pound.

People in their forties are sandwiched between two demanding and often—in their eyes — unreasonable generations, both of which rely on them for psychological and practical support. At no other stage in their lives do so many people depend on them, and that realization causes people in their forties to brood darkly on the cyclical nature of life and the passing of time. They also ask themselves more mundane questions like: Should a woman/man of my age really be wearing slit-skirts/jeans? So although the forties may not precisely be middle age, they are an age-conscious decade.

Our appearance does begin to change in the forties. The full effects of these changes are not yet apparent, but we are beginning to look different. The balance between physical improvement and physical degeneration wavers during the thirties, then tips toward degeneration.

During our survey in Colchester we asked people in their forties what was the worst thing about life now compared with ten years ago. Their main complaints were the feeling of being so much older and worries about their appearance and health. But they were not aware of any significant change in their sex life. Most of those we interviewed disagreed strongly with the suggestion that sexual relationships are more important to young people.

7. MIDDLE AND LATE ADULTHOOD

The people we talked to seemed to be more concerned about physical than mental decline, and they were right, because in this period of our lives there is little cause for alarm. Any fears about declining mental faculties are more likely to be imaginary than real.

Our survey asked if any age since adolescence had seemed particularly difficult, and we were astonished to find that none of the people in the forty-to-forty-five age group described their present age in these terms. Our results clearly support those who deny existence of a midlife crisis, and we must conclude that if there is such a thing as the male menopause, it affects only a small group.

Unless we decide to tear up our roots and start again, we have to alter the emphasis in our personal relationships from sexuality to sociability, particularly in marriage. It is in the forties that husbands and wives start sizing each other up and wondering how they will adjust to living as a couple again without the shared responsibility of parenthood to bind them. Most couples of this age realize that an enormous emotional vacuum is about to open up, and it is interesting to see how they prepare to deal with it. In Colchester, we found that more women had jobs in the thirty-five-to-forty-nine age bracket than in any other.

The importance of women's jobs rose steadily from one age group to the next. It overtook money as a priority at forty, and by the end of the fifties ranked almost equal with friends. The fact that this was the only change in life-priorities shown by either sex between twenty-nine and fifty-nine clearly establishes this as one of the most significant changes in the forties.

How do men prepare themselves for the future? Although we didn't find that the majority of men in their forties in Colchester were becoming more interested in hobbies, some clearly were prepared to run the gamut of their wives' and children's sneers and were developing new interests to take their minds off worries and prepare for retirement.

Psychologists describe the qualities we need to develop in the forties as mental flexibility and the ability to broaden our emotional investment to include new people, activities, and roles. One person in ten of those in their early forties in Colchester said they found it more difficult than ten years ago to adapt to change or to accept new ideas, whereas three times this number said they found it less difficult.

When the Colchester survey asked its participants to list the things they worried about, we found that concern about children among people of thirty-six to forty-five was the largest single worry of either sex at any age. Nine out of ten of the women we interviewed, whose eldest child was between sixteen and nineteen, said they were worried about their child's future. The men in our survey were much less likely than their wives to worry about their children. Their most frequent worry was money.

People in their forties wonder whether permissiveness hasn't gone too far, and increasingly find themselves identifying with their own parents and defending their values rather than rebelling against them. So as middle age approaches, there seems to be a clear shift in our loyalties and attitudes, which is part of a growing awareness that we are about to join the older generation.

Perhaps the most uncertain feature of life is its length. The uncertainty makes it inevitable that thoughts about death should color the final stage of our lives. But the prospect of dying does not seem to destroy our ability to make the best of whatever age we happen to be. An old woman in Colchester said, "Some people thought I was doing too much and I ought to slow down a bit. I said, 'I've retired from work, I didn't retire from life'."

Researchers have constructed a table of events old people find most stressful. The death of a spouse comes at the top of this list, followed by being put into an institution, the death of a close relative, major personal injury or disease, losing a job, and divorce. Being widowed seems to affect men more severely than women. A recent British study found that the death rate among men and women during the year after they are widowed is ten times higher than among people of the same age who are still married.

As we approach the end of our lives we become less interested in the outside world and more concerned with ourselves. The psychological task that becomes increasingly important is to come to terms with ourselves, to find some justification for our lives, and to reconcile ourselves to the fact that it is going to end. Paradoxically, the person who believes that his or her life has been most worthwhile seems to have the fewest qualms about the prospect of its coming to an end.

What is the recipe for a successful old age? Some people say that unless old people keep themselves active and engaged, they will become a misery to themselves and a burden on others. Others take the view that an old person who continues to devote his energy to worldly matters cannot possibly have time to solve the psychological problems of old age. We now know that there is no single pattern which can be recommended as the recipe for a successful old age.

Perhaps the most useful characteristics we can possess at this stage of our lives are flexibility and acceptance. Changes need to be made, and the unpalatable fact of our own mortality has to be accepted. There is some evidence that we can predict in advance how easily an individual will come to terms with the final realities on the basis of how well he or she has made adjustments earlier in life. For example, people who had problems resolving the intimacy-versus-isolation crisis in their twenties, and who found it difficult to maintain an intimate relationship at age thirty, seem to have difficulty coping with the psychosocial crisis that comes with old age.

Younger people often complain about the way the old ramble on about the past. But research shows that the tendency some old people have to review the events of their lives can actually be therapeutic. It increases their chances of facing death with equanimity.

Some of the strongest fears of death expressed in our interviews came from people in their teens and twenties. Among the old, advancing age seems to produce a greater interest in death, but certainly no greater fear. One old woman said, "I feel that from the day you're born your life is mapped out for you. As for death, well, whatever way that comes, I can't stop it, so it doesn't worry me." An eighty-year-old said, "Dying doesn't worry me. The only thing I do worry about is if I go unexpectedly and leave a muddle for everyone to clear up."

Two major conclusions can be drawn from our Colchester Study of Aging. First: We ought to bury the notion of universal, age-related life crises. Many people never experience any discernible psychological crisis. And when crises do occur they tend to be caused by events which just happen to fall at roughly the same point in most people's lives, rather than because a person has reached a certain age.

Second: Age has remarkably little effect at any stage in life on how we think of ourselves or on how we view the world. As as eighty-year-old Colchester woman said, "I don't put things into blocks. If you just think, 'Well, I'm only one day older than I was,' you don't really feel very much different."

The Aging Body

After twenty, the decades take their toll. You may get wiser, but your memory dims. Your body parts grow, shrink, disappear. It's a process you can only watch with wonder, so you'd do well to know the wonders to watch for.

John Tierney

John Tierney is a staff writer for Science 82 *magazine.*

There are many gruesome things to be said about a man's body as it creeps past the age of thirty. But first a word about the President's hairline:

"It's a hairline you normally see only on a child or a eunuch," says Dr. Norman Orentreich, the inventor of the hair transplant, who has studied men's scalps for three decades and still has a hard time accounting for Ronald Reagan's hairline. Men typically lose hair around the temples. It's an effect of androgen, a hormone produced in the testicles after puberty, and it seems to happen to all men, even those who otherwise keep a thick head of hair all their lives. Yet here is Ronald Reagan with a straight line of hair above his forehead. "He's not wearing a hairpiece," Orentreich says, "and he hasn't been castrated, so I'd have to assume that he happens to have some sort of rare hereditary variation."

This is a comforting fact. Ronald Reagan's scalp is further proof of what gerontologists have come to realize in the past two decades—that the only absolute rule about the aging process is that it eventually stops. The individual variations are enormous at every age and in every part of the body.

THE CATALOG OF DECAY

that follows is merely a list of the average ravages, most of which will hit you sooner or later but some of which you may escape. The victim is a hypothetical American man—one, say, who works in an office, gets a little exercise, has no serious vices, and doesn't dabble in such exotica as macrobiotic diets or megavitamins. At thirty he's not a bad specimen. A little plumper than he used to be, a little slower, a little balder, yet smarter than ever. Still, his body has just passed its peak. It has started dying a little every day, losing about one percent of its functional capacity every year. Cells are disappearing, tissues are stiffening, chemical reactions are slowing down. By seventy his body temperature will be two degrees lower. He will stand an inch or so shorter and have longer ears.

No one understands why. The most appealing theory for why we disintegrate as we get older was offered in an eighteenth-century treatise called *Hermippus Redivivus, Or, The Sage's Triumph over Old Age and the Grave, Wherein, a Method Is Laid Down for Prolonging the Vigour of Man, Including a Commentary upon an Ancient Inscription, in Which This Great Secret Is Revealed, Supported by Numerous Authorities.* A man aged, according to this theory, because he lost vital particles every time he exhaled. The Great Secret— how to find a new source of particles—was revealed by the discovery of a tomb whose occupant had lived to 115. The fellow managed to live so long, according to the tomb's inscription, WITH THE AID OF THE BREATH OF YOUNG WOMEN. Today's physicians advise jogging.

"Exercise will make you feel fitter, but there's no good evidence that it will make you live longer," says Dr. Jordan Tobin of the National Institute on Aging. The same goes for practically every other prescription. Because scientists don't know what causes cells to break down with age, they can't say that anything causes longevity. They can only note that certain types of men age better—those who have long-lived parents, a satisfying job, and plenty of money. Married men tend to outlive bachelors, with one notable exception: if you look at a chart comparing the average life expectancy of men according to their occupations, it turns out that the best job may well be pope (or at least cardinal). Of course, worrying about statistics like these will only hasten the aging process. So your best strategy may simply be to relax, hope that you have the right genes, and accept peacefully the indignities as they occur. You might also consider taking afternoon naps. They don't seem to have hurt Mr. Reagan.

7. MIDDLE AND LATE ADULTHOOD

30 In most ways, he is at his peak—the tallest, strongest, maybe the smartest he's ever been. And yet he can see the first lines on his forehead, he can't hear quite as well as he could, his skull's circumference has even started swelling. And his degeneration has just begun.

40 He's an eighth of an inch shorter than he was ten years ago, and each hair follicle has thinned two microns, but not everything's shrinking: his waist and chest are ballooning. All over, he's begun to feel the weight of time's passage: his stamina is greatly diminished.

50 His eyes have begun to fail him, particularly at close range. He notices quirky changes: his speaking voice has risen from a C to an E-flat, his thumbnails are growing more slowly, and his erections have dipped below the horizontal mark. His waist is as big as it will get.

60 By now he has shrunk a full three quarters of an inch, he has trouble telling certain colors apart, trouble distinguishing between tones, trouble making distinctions among the different foods he tastes. His lungs take in just about half what they could thirty years ago.

70 His heart is pumping less blood, his hearing is worse, vision weakening still; yet if he's made it this far, say the statistics, he'll live another eleven years. And if he has the right attitude, he will look back with awe at the wonders that have made him what he has become.

Weight

He loses a bit of his body each day, yet the body just gets bigger. The reason is fat. He's not burning up enough food—both because he's not as active as he used to be and because his basal metabolism (the rate at which the resting body converts food into energy) is slowing down about 3 percent every decade. So while muscle and other tissue is dying, accumulated fat is taking up more of his body. That's the case until middle age, after which his weight levels off and then slowly declines: he starts losing more tissue than he gains in fat.

Age 20: 165 pounds, 15% of it fat
Age 30: 175 pounds
Age 40: 182 pounds
Age 50: 184 pounds
Age 60: 184 pounds
Age 70: 178 pounds, 30% of it fat

Nails

Aged nails grow more slowly, which makes for easy grooming but weathered nails. Measured in millimeters per week, his thumbnail grows:

Age 20: 0.94 millimeters
Age 30: 0.83 millimeters
Age 40: 0.80 millimeters
Age 50: 0.77 millimeters
Age 60: 0.71 millimeters
Age 70: 0.60 millimeters

Stamina

The weakening of our man's heart, lungs, and muscles means that there's less oxygen coming in and that the heart is slower in dispersing it through the bloodstream to the muscles. A healthy seventy-year-old man can still run a marathon if he trains properly, but it will take him at least an hour longer than it did at thirty. The best measure of our man's limits is the work rate, which measures how many pounds he can turn with a weighted crank in a minute and still have his heartbeat return to normal after two minutes of rest:

Age 30: 1,110 pounds
Age 40: 1,020 pounds
Age 50: 950 pounds
Age 60: 870 pounds
Age 70: 800 pounds

Skin

A middle-aged man makes his own wrinkles: the lines on his face are drawn from repeated facial expressions, which is why the surly have more furrows on their brows. But an old man's wrinkling happens automatically—the inside of his skin loses water, and nearby molecules bind to one another, making for a stiffer, less elastic skin structure. Meanwhile, the skin itself thins and spreads out, much like a piece of dough that's been stretched. The result is a baggy suit, with the skin too large for the body. This is especially troublesome in places like the jaw, where the bone is shrinking as the skin is expanding.

Age 30: Lines in forehead are present
Age 40: Lines from other facial expressions show up, especially crow's-feet (from squinting) and arcs linking the nostrils to the sides of the mouth (from smiling)
Age 50: Lines are more pronounced; skin begins to loosen and sag in the middle of the cheek
Age 60: Excess skin and fat deposits etch bags under the eyes
Age 70: Face wrinkles everywhere; skin is rougher and has lost its uniform color—he can see a variety of shades in his face

Eyes

The lens of the eye steadily hardens throughout life and begins to cause problems for a man in his early forties. By then the lens is too big for the eye muscles to focus properly on close objects. Eventually this can cause cataracts, but the odds are that our man will die before that happens. The amount of light reaching the retina steadily declines with age (perhaps because the pupil shrinks), which means that our man will have trouble seeing in the dark; he will need especially bright light to read.

Age 30: 20/20 vision; reads without glasses
Age 50: 20/20 for distance vision, but needs glasses to read; a less elastic eye lens makes him more sensitive to glare; his depth perception is beginning to get worse
Age 60: 20/25 vision; a less elastic, yellower lens filters out some shorter wavelengths of light, making it harder for him to distinguish between blues and greens
Age 70: 20/30 vision; peripheral vision is diminished; night vision is worse, and his eyes take longer to adjust to the dark

Flab

With increased weight comes flab—or, to be precise, an increased subscapular skinfold, which is the best index of flab. This skinfold, measured by pinching the skin beneath the shoulder blade and determining the distance the skin can be stretched, is twelve millimeters wide at age twenty, fourteen millimeters at thirty, and remains about sixteen millimeters after forty. Unfortunately the flab also extends below the shoulder—conspicuously to the waist and chest.

	Waist	Chest
Age 20:	33 inches	36 inches
Age 30:	36 inches	39 inches
Age 40:	39 inches	40 inches
Age 50:	40 inches	41 inches
Age 60:	39 inches	41 inches
Age 70:	39 inches	41 inches

Height

A man is able to withstand gravity only so long. As his muscles weaken, his back slumps. And as the disks between the bones of his spine deteriorate, those bones move closer together. The result: The inexorably shrinking man.

Age 30: 5'10"
Age 40: 5'9⅞"
Age 50: 5'9⅝"
Age 60: 5'9¼"
Age 70: 5'8⅞"

Reflexes

His reflexes slow down, for which his brain is probably more guilty than his nerves. The speed at which signals travel along his nerve fibers declines only 2 percent each decade, which is a relatively minor deterioration compared with other changes in the body. The real slowdown happens because the brain takes longer to process information, make decisions, and dispatch signals. If a man looking at numbers flashing on a screen is told to press a button whenever he sees two consecutive even or odd numbers, this is how long it takes him to react:

Age 30: 0.88 seconds
Age 50: 0.90 seconds
Age 60: 0.92 seconds
Age 70: 0.95 seconds

Teeth

Eating slowly files down a tooth, but not enough to make any significant difference to anyone under the age of two hundred. The problem is keeping the tooth, and it is one problem a man can control. Despite the fact that the amount of enamel on the surface will decrease with age and the layer of dentin underneath will become more translucent, most tooth and gum decay is a result of neglect and disease. The average seventy-year-old man today has lost a third of his teeth; because of fluoridated water and better dental care, his descendants should fare better.

Age 30: 2 teeth missing
Age 50: 7 teeth missing
Age 60: 8 teeth missing
Age 70: 10 teeth missing

Hair

Men actually do get hairier with age, but, alas, not where it does them good. Hair grows in the ears, in the nostrils, and sometimes on the back. Eyebrow hairs tend to get longer and more noticeable. As for the top of the head, there are different hormones at work. Balding usually begins at the temples, producing a widow's peak that recedes with age. Next hit is the monk's spot, that circle on the back of the head—it keeps growing until it meets the receding widow's peak, leaving the top of the head bare. Men bald at different rates, of course, and some never bald at all. Still, if our man is going to bald, he will—no amount of scalp massaging will help. Although there are marked differences among men in the rate at which hair falls out or turns gray, there does seem to be a consistent pattern in the way individual hairs thin. A man's hairs are thickest at about twenty; after that each hair shrinks, and by seventy his hairs are as fine as they were when he was a baby. The diameter of a single hair (measured in microns—millionths of a meter) changes like this:

Age 20: 101 microns   **Age 50:** 94 microns
Age 30: 98 microns   **Age 60:** 86 microns
Age 40: 96 microns   **Age 70:** 80 microns

Muscles and Strength

At thirty, about seventy of his 175 pounds are muscle. Over the next four decades he loses ten pounds of that muscle as cells stop reproducing and die. His shoulders narrow an inch. Connective tissue replaces fiber, causing his muscles to become stiffer and to tense, relax, and heal more slowly. The remaining muscle grows weaker as the fiber becomes frayed, jumbled, and riddled with deposits of waste material. His strength peaks at about thirty and then steadily diminishes. The muscles in his hands perform as follows, as measured by the amount of force that can be exerted by the right (if that's his dominant hand) and left grip:

	Right Hand	Left Hand
Age 30:	99 pounds	64 pounds
Age 40:	97 pounds	62 pounds
Age 50:	92 pounds	58 pounds
Age 60:	86 pounds	48 pounds
Age 70:	80 pounds	42 pounds

Head

His features become more distinguished, which is a kind way of saying that they get bigger. Because of the cartilage that begins to accumulate after age thirty, by the time he is seventy his nose has grown a half inch wider and another half inch longer, his earlobes have fattened, and his ears themselves have grown a quarter inch longer. Overall, his head's circumference increases a quarter inch every decade, and not because of his brain, which is shrinking. His head is fatter apparently because, unlike most other bones in the body, the skull seems to thicken with age.

Mouth

He tastes less. When he's thirty, each tiny elevation on his tongue (called a papilla) has 245 taste buds. By the time he's seventy, each has only eighty-eight left. His mouth gets drier as the mucous membrane secretes less. His voice begins to quaver, apparently because he loses some control over his vocal cords. He talks more slowly, and his pitch rises as the cords stiffen and vibrate at a higher frequency: after fifty his speaking voice rises about 25 hertz (cycles per second), from a C to an E-flat (in the octave below middle C).

Now for the Good News...

"No wise man ever wished to be younger," said Jonathan Swift, and some gerontologists today might even agree with him. There's no denying that a seventy-year-old body doesn't work as well as it once did, but it's also true that people's fears of aging are greater than they should be. In the course of chronicling decay, researchers have come up with some reassuring findings:

▷ A man becomes less sensitive to pain after the age of sixty. It takes longer for an old man to notice a disturbing stimulus, thus he can endure greater levels of pain without complaining. This is probably due to the degeneration of his nerve fibers and to the decline in the central nervous system's ability to process sensory information.

▷ A man sweats less with age; his sweat glands gradually begin drying up.

▷ Fat isn't as bad as they say—it may even be good for you. Because thin people have always been thought to outlive the obese, doctors have urged patients to conform to a chart of "desirable weights" 15 percent lighter than the men's average. Yet recent studies show that a man ten to twenty pounds above the desirable weight is likely to outlive the virtuous man who follows the chart. "There clearly is something strange going on," says Dr. Reubin Andres of the National Institute on Aging. It could be that the mildly overweight have more reserve capacity to survive illnesses, but no one knows for sure.

▷ Until the age of sixty-five, a smoker is at least twice as likely as a nonsmoker to suffer a heart attack, but after sixty-five, the odds change. The risks are about even for nonsmokers and for men who smoke less than a pack a day. And a man who smokes more than a pack a day is three times *less* likely than a nonsmoker to have a heart attack. This doesn't mean you should take up smoking in your old age, only that a heavy smoker who survives past sixty-five is a hardy fellow.

▷ A nearsighted youth may be able to put away his glasses when he reaches middle age. The thickening of his eyes' lenses cures nearsightedness.

▷ It may be only a small victory in the battle of the sexes, but a man's skin ages about ten years more slowly than a woman's—his skin has more oil, so it's slower to dry out. Shaving also helps: The mild scraping of a razor strips away dead skin and leaves the face smoother. It's not unlike epidermabrasion, a beauty treatment that skin specialists frequently administer to women with more elaborate instruments.

▷ A man's sexual decline isn't usually traumatic. When Clyde Martin, one of the authors of the Kinsey report, asked old men how they'd react to the discovery of a safe drug that could restore their youthful sexual vigor, most said they wouldn't bother taking it. Martin found that men who were most sexually active in their youth showed the least decline in activity during old age; it was the less active men who dropped off most drastically and brought down the average. The conclusion: Old men can continue with sex if they're interested (most men in their seventies can still produce sperm); it's just that most of them aren't. "They bow out gracefully," reported Martin. "They have other interests." Or, as an aged Sophocles said when he was asked about his love life, "Peace, most gladly have I escaped the thing of which you speak; I feel as if I had escaped from a mad and furious master." ·

▷ If a man reaches seventy, the odds are that he'll live to see eighty. Diseases wreak far more havoc than normal aging; physically, a healthy seventy-year-old has more in common with a healthy thirty-year-old than he does with an ill man of his own age. Seventy is the average life expectancy for a man, but that's only because accidents and disorders kill so many before then. A man who survives until his seventieth birthday, according to actuarial tables, will live eleven more years.

Lungs

As the muscles that operate the lungs weaken and the tissues in the chest cage stiffen, the lungs can't expand the way they used to. A deep breath isn't as deep as it once was. The maximum amount of air he can take into his lungs:

Age 30: 6.0 quarts
Age 40: 5.4 quarts
Age 50: 4.5 quarts
Age 60: 3.6 quarts
Age 70: 3.0 quarts

Brain

His brain shrinks as it loses billions of neurons. The cell loss varies in different parts of the brain—the region that controls head posture, for instance, doesn't seem to lose any, while the region that controls sleep stages is hit especially hard (which helps explain why he sleeps about two hours less at night). If IQ tests are any measure, then his intelligence declines. In order to make the average IQ at every age be 100, the test scores are automatically adjusted according to age. If these adjustments weren't made, the average score would be:

Age 20: 110   **Age 50:** 100
Age 30: 111   **Age 60:** 93
Age 40: 106   **Age 70:** 83

This may only mean that old people are out of practice at taking standardized tests; beyond that, a slight loss of memory is probably the most noticeable change after fifty, though even that is more a matter of faulty retrieval than of lost information. If an old man and a young man each try to memorize a list of words and then are given clues to each of the words, the old man recalls them as well as the young man. But without clues, the old man has a harder time remembering what was on the list.

Age 20: 14 of 24 words recalled
Age 30: 13 words recalled
Age 40: 11 words recalled
Age 50: 10 words recalled
Age 60: 9 words recalled
Age 70: 7 words recalled

Can Youth Spring Eternal?

The more realistic question might be "Can aging be slowed?" and, as you would expect, there are two schools of thought about that. Those scientists who believe that an inner clock automatically shuts down each cell at a predetermined time naturally suggest that it's impossible to lengthen the life-span radically. The less deterministically inclined think that a cell dies because of gradual processes that wear it down and that therefore man has the power to somehow slow the decay. They just haven't figured out how.

All of which means that science offers little help for your aging cells at the moment. But whether or not you can ever extend their little cell lives, you can certainly make their stay in your body more comfortable by following these simple health guidelines:

▷ **EXERCISE:** Studies show that regular exercisers outlive their sedentary peers. But it's a chicken-and-egg problem: Are they healthy because they exercise, or do they exercise because they're healthy to begin with? A recent study found that monkeys reduce their risk of heart disease if they work out on a treadmill regularly. This wasn't absolute proof—monkeys aren't men—but it was probably the most compelling evidence yet for the life-lengthening advantages of jogging. And even if exercise doesn't actually prolong life, it produces other rewards—firmer muscles, less fat, stronger lungs, better circulation—worth aspiring to in their own right.

▷ **SUN:** Unless he's a nudist, a man's youngest-looking skin is on his buttocks. That's because exposure to the sun's ultraviolet rays roughly doubles the havoc normal aging wreaks. Protecting your skin from the sun will help keep it from drying and stiffening, and help you avoid brown "age spots" or "liver spots," which can be signs of overexposed skin.

▷ **DIET:** It's probably a good idea to go easy on fats, but nobody really knows what makes the ideal diet. The fact that life expectancy is almost the same in Japan, France, and the United States suggests that vastly different diets can produce similar results. The old rules probably still apply: Keep your food tray balanced, and Eat your vegetables.

▷ **TOBACCO:** It should be avoided, of course. A cigarette smoker's lung capacity is usually equal to that of a nonsmoker ten to fifteen years older.

▷ **ALCOHOL:** Surprisingly, it's probably better to drink a little than not at all. A recent study found mortality 50 percent higher among both teetotalers and heavy drinkers (three to five drinks a day) than among light drinkers (one or two drinks a day). Apparently, moderate amounts of alcohol increase the blood's supply of high-density lipoprotein, which in turn reduces the risk of heart disease.

▷ **VITAMINS:** As you age your stomach takes longer to digest food, but that doesn't really matter. The body can still extract all the nutrients it needs, and a seventy-year-old man who eats a balanced diet shouldn't require any special vitamin supplements. Some gerontologists think we should take extra vitamin E because it stops "free radicals," which the doctors believe cause aging, from forming. But leading gerontologist Dr. Nathan Shock, among others, doesn't think much of this advice: "Taking vitamin E probably won't hurt you," says Shock. "But the main effect is probably just going to be an increase in the profits of the pharmaceutical companies."

For now, there are few other reliable pieces of advice. When asked for any great secrets to be gleaned from all the studies of the aging corpus, Dr. Jordan Tobin of the National Institute on Aging turns his palms heavenward. "I guess the best general rule is to practice moderation in the way you live," he says. "Well, it's probably a good idea not to let yourself get extremely overweight. Don't drink and drive. And wear seat belts."

Bones and Joints

His bones lose calcium. That's bad for the bones and also for the nearby blood vessels, where the lost calcium can accumulate, clogging up the works. His bones become more brittle and slower to heal. Relatively few men suffer rheumatoid arthritis, but after sixty, chances are good that our man will develop a less serious condition called degenerative arthritis. Years of flexing have worn down and loosened cartilage around the joints; the presence of this stray cartilage, coupled with depleted lubricating fluid in the joints, makes for a slower-moving, stiffer man. Movement is further restricted by ligaments that contract and harden with age. The hardened ligaments are more liable to tear.

Sex

By seventy he has found new activities for the nighttime, and he's all but stopped daydreaming about sex. Just why a man's sex drive declines is unclear—lower levels of sex hormones may be a factor, but psychological changes and the general loss of vitality in the body are probably more important. With age, the testes sag and the penis takes longer to become erect, longer to reach orgasm, longer to recover. The orgasm itself is shorter.

ANGLE OF ERECTION
AGE 20: 10% above horizontal
AGE 30: 20% above horizontal
AGE 40: Slightly above horizontal
AGE 50: Slightly below horizontal
AGE 70: 25% below horizontal

FREQUENCY OF AWAKING WITH ERECTION
AGE 20: 6 mornings per month
AGE 30: 7 mornings per month
AGE 50: 5 mornings per month
AGE 70: 2 mornings per month

FREQUENCY OF ORGASMS
AGE 20: 104 per year (49 solo)
AGE 30: 121 per year (10 solo)
AGE 40: 84 per year (8 solo)
AGE 50: 52 per year (2 solo)
AGE 60: 35 per year (4 solo)
AGE 70: 22 per year (8 solo)

Heart

His resting heartbeat stays about the same all his life, but the beats get weaker as his heart muscles deteriorate. As a result, his aged heart pumps less blood with each beat. The decline in blood flow is more marked during exercise, because his pulse can no longer rise as high as it used to.

BLOOD PUMPED BY THE RESTING HEART	MAXIMUM HEARTBEAT DURING EXERCISE
AGE 30: 3.6 quarts per minute	**AGE 30:** 200 beats per minute
AGE 40: 3.4 quarts per minute	**AGE 40:** 182 beats per minute
AGE 50: 3.2 quarts per minute	**AGE 50:** 171 beats per minute
AGE 60: 2.9 quarts per minute	**AGE 60:** 159 beats per minute
AGE 70: 2.6 quarts per minute	**AGE 70:** 150 beats per minute

Heart disease is the most common cause of death in men over forty years old and is responsible for more than half the deaths of men over sixty. As the level of cholesterol in the blood increases with age, the cholesterol accumulates on the artery walls, which are themselves thickening. The net effect is to clog the arteries, increasing the pressure of the blood against the arterial walls, which in turn forces the heart to work harder to pump blood and makes strokes and heart attacks more likely.

AGE 20: 180 milligrams cholesterol; 122/76 blood pressure
AGE 30: 200; 125/76
AGE 40: 220; 129/81
AGE 50: 230; 134/83
AGE 60: 230; 140/83
AGE 70: 225; 148/81

Kidneys

At seventy his kidney can filter waste out of blood only half as fast as it could when he was thirty. He also has to urinate more frequently because his bladder's capacity declines from two cupfuls at age thirty to one cupful at seventy.

Ears

Over the years, things like a good stereo just don't seem as important anymore—a man can't hear the highest notes no matter how well they're reproduced. A child can hear sounds reaching as high as 20,000 hertz, but in early adulthood the range starts decreasing. This seems to be a direct result of a breakdown of cells in the corti, the organ in the inner ear that transforms the vibrations picked up by the outer ear into nerve impulses, as well as of deteriorating nerve fibers. Fortunately, hearing diminishes least in the range of everyday human speech (below 4,000 hertz)—the average old man can hear conversations fairly well. To the young, an old man often seems deafer than he really is simply because he's not paying attention (perhaps with very good reason).

AGE 30: Has trouble hearing above 15,000 hertz (a cricket's chirp)
AGE 50: Can't hear above 12,000 hertz (a "silent" dog whistle)
AGE 60: Can't hear above 10,000 hertz (upper range of a robin's singing); has trouble distinguishing among tones in range he can hear
AGE 70: Misses some words in normal conversation; can't hear above 6,000 hertz (high notes on a pipe organ)

In Search of Youth

Albert Rosenfeld

Albert Rosenfeld is a frequent contributor to GEO and the author of a book on aging, Pro-Longevity.

In the past, a special brand of pity was reserved for any benighted soul impertinent enough to seek a Fountain of Youth. But look at what's been happening lately in gerontology, the scientific study of the aging process. Listen to the theorists discuss the possibility that there exists within each of us a "clock of aging" that we can hope to locate and adjust to our liking. Observe the experimenters in their laboratories extending the life-spans of cells in tissue culture; keeping skin and blood cells going by transplanting them from older to younger animals; combating the ravages of aging in animals, extending their life-spans and restoring youthful functions that would once have been lost. Observe the explosive advances throughout the biomedical sciences—advances that suggest we have scarcely begun to touch the power we will have to transform our lives.

Sociologists and demographers go on making projections oblivious to these developments, expressing alarm sometimes bordering on panic at the prospect of a population made up of an ever larger percentage of doddering old folks. But all our perceptions may soon be radically revised in light of scientific advances. A significant number of researchers have come to believe that aging as we have always known it may not be our inevitable lot after all. The elderly of the future may well turn out to be healthy, self-sufficient and productive, requiring less medical care. We may even see the nursing home follow the once flourishing TB sanatorium into obsolescence. It is not at all preposterous to imagine that in the not-too-distant future, most Americans will be able to live out their full natural lifespans—say, 110 years—in the best of health.

Many gerontologists here and abroad are focusing on the mechanism of the aging process itself. There are, of course, "early-onset" forms of nearly all major diseases, some of them occurring in earliest childhood. These are increasingly believed to be specifically genetic or familial in origin and quite distinct from later forms of the same disease. Moreover, aging itself is beginning to be thought of as a genetically programmed phenomenon—not merely the accumulated effects of wear and tear on the organism over the years but rather a built-in time clock guaranteeing that life will run down approximately on schedule.

A handful of vigorous gerontologists are trying to track down this genetic clock of aging; many more are content to spend their energies studying the individual ravages of senescence to see what might be done to alleviate its symptoms, to minimize the degenerative changes and retard the loss of function. Both groups have a common goal—to add high-quality years to our lives—and we will need the insights and contributions of both to achieve it. But the news is that the achievement has now become a realistic prospect in our time.

Among those inclined toward the concept of programmed aging, the principal controversy revolves around the question, If there is a clock of aging, where is it? There are two main schools of thought. One says that the clock is in the brain, specifically in the hypothalamus and pituitary regions, which exercise control over the body's hormonal systems. The other holds that the clock is in each individual cell, most probably in the nucleus, where DNA, the genetic material, is in control. Either or both may, of course, be wrong. Either or both may be right.

I happen to think that both schools are right. Each is supported by feasible theoretical arguments as well as by experimental data, and in my view they are in no way incompatible. When space engineers design vehicles for interplanetary missions, they almost always include built-in backup systems to enhance the odds that all will go as scheduled. Why would God and nature possess less wit and foresight than our space-hardware designers?

A hormonal clock of aging would be a naturally attractive idea. We know that hormones regulate nearly all of the body's cellular processes as well as its overall physiological functioning. We know, too, that all of the activities of our hormones and the endocrine glands that secrete them are regulated by the "master gland"—the pea-size pituitary, which sits at the base of the brain. We have also learned that the master has a master of its own, the hypothalamus, located just above the pituitary. Before the pituitary can release a hormone, it must get a green light from the hypothalamus in the form of a chemical messenger, actually a much smaller hormone called a releasing factor, or RF. There seems to be a specific RF for virtually every hormone, and perhaps an inhibitor for each as well, though they are not yet all known to us.

The notion that the aging process is somehow intimately involved with the hypothalamus and the pituitary—perhaps acting at given times in response to feedback signals provided by the levels of hormones circulating in the body—has a number of adherents. In this country, the man who has kept closest track of the relationship between hormones and aging is Caleb Finch of the University of Southern California. He and his associates at USC have studied changes in the reproductive cycles of aging rodents—with fascinating results. In mice, for example, the regular cycle of ovulation stops at the age of about 12 months (the equivalent of about 30 years in human terms). But if the apparently worn-out ovary of an old female mouse is transferred to a young female, the organ begins its cycles again, demonstrating that it wasn't used up after all. On the other hand, if the ovary of a young mouse is implanted in an old mouse, the organ functions as though it were as old as its host—that is, until the scenario is varied a bit. When the ovary of a young mouse is removed, the mouse has no experience of ovulation by the time it ages. If a new ovary is then implanted in that aging mouse, the ovary will begin its cycles. What happens, according to Finch, is that the brain area around the hypothalamus responds to the female hormone estradiol, and when the mouse has gone through its allotted number of cycles, that brain area is programmed to turn off—or it has been damaged or depleted by the wear and tear of all that ovulation activity.

The most daring of the seekers of the hormonal brain clock is endocrinologist W. Donner Denckla of the George Washington University School of Medicine in Washington, D.C. His experiments have convinced him that the pituitary *induces* our bodies to age by means of a mystery substance that has been called the aging or death hormone—but not by Denckla, who prefers the neutral term DECO, an acronym for "decreasing consumption of oxygen." DECO achieves this effect, Denckla believes, primarily by blocking the thyroid hormone—which affects virtually all of the body's major systems, including the immune and the cardiovascular systems.

Does he have the hormone in hand? Not yet. Not in purified form, at least. But even with the impure extract, he has been able to bring on signs of premature aging in rats. And what of the opposite effect—that is, reversing the signs of aging? So far, the only way of withholding DECO that Denckla knows of is to remove the pituitary altogether, a delicate piece of surgery. He has done this with several thousand rats, under varying circumstances, over the years. By excising the pituitary and then providing these handicapped rats with shots of thyroid and other hormones, Denckla has been able to "restore juvenile competence," as he puts it, in a number of important systems ranging from vital lung capacity to fur growth, from immune and cardiovascular functions to the rate at which cells can replace their genetic material.

Denckla's hope is that after purifying and synthesizing DECO, he can find a natural substance that will inhibit its release. Such natural hormone inhibitors do exist in the body; in fact, current birth-control pills work in just that way. If Denckla succeeds in blocking DECO, most if not all of the programmed ravages of aging might be vanquished,

leaving only actual wear and tear to deal with.

Cell biologist Leonard Hayflick, now director of the Center for Gerontological Studies at the University of Florida, is the man who proved that normal human embryo cells in tissue culture will divide about 50 times and then stop (the older the cell, the fewer times it will divide). Now, if cells isolated in laboratory vessels—outside of any living organism and far from the direct influence of the brain or of any hormone—can age and die, apparently on a regularly programmed schedule of their own, then how can it be said that the clock of aging is hormonal and located in the brain? In a series of ingenious experiments in which old nuclei were implanted in young cells and vice versa, Hayflick and other researchers neatly demonstrated that the true "age" of a cell is governed by DNA. Vastly oversimplified, the experiment went as follows: Suppose you take two cells programmed for roughly 50 divisions. Cell A has undergone only 10 doublings, with 40 still to go, while cell B has already divided 40 times and has only 10 divisions left. Transplant A's nucleus into B and vice versa—and suddenly A, now prematurely aged, can only divide 10 more times, while B, rejuvenated, can go on for another 40 doublings!

Any number of scientists have held that genetic material is the key to aging. Biochemist F. Marott Sinex of Boston University is among those who believe that changes, mutations or damage to DNA, or loss of DNA's own repair capacities, could be critical to the process of senescence. It was Dr. Ron Hart of the Food and Drug Administration (formerly of Ohio State University) and Dr. Richard B. Setlow of the Brookhaven National Laboratory who first showed, in the early 1970s, that DNA repair is related to longevity. In a whole spectrum of mammalian species, those that lived longest were those that had the best repair capability. A few years later, zoologist Joan Smith-Sonneborn of the University of Wyoming conducted a startling experiment that underlined the findings of Hart and Setlow. First, she deliberately damaged the DNA of protozoans (single-celled animals) by exposing them to ultraviolet radiation. She then activated their DNA-repair mechanism (a known enzyme) merely by shining black light on them—and discovered that after repeated treatments of damage and repair, these organisms lived a third longer than protozoans that had never been damaged at all. She assumed that increased repair capacity could be used for other kinds of damages—including those associated with aging. It is as if the carburetor in a car had conked out, and the mechanic, while repairing it, had also done a lot of additional tuning and tightening up. The car might now be in better shape and last longer than a similar car in which the carburetor had gone on working and thus never received the mechanic's attention.

Geneticist Philip Lipetz, who worked with Hart at Ohio State and is now collaborating with Smith-Sonneborn, specializes in the very complex ways in which DNA coils itself into tightly wound "superhelixes" that may represent whole clusters of genetic instructions controlling diverse cellular (and therefore bodily) functions. Lipetz believes that these supercoils, as they tighten or loosen or become somewhat disorganized, may interfere with the carrying out of genetic instructions. This would make them responsible for much of the deterioration we recognize as aging.

For a long time, gerontologist Richard Cutler of the National Institute on Aging in Baltimore has argued that because a single, critically placed gene can control whole clusters of other genes, the entire aging process could feasibly be carried out under the influence of a very few genes—perhaps contained in one of those tightly coiled superhelixes. If there does exist a genetic clock of aging, then where might it be? Pathologist Roy Walford of UCLA, one of the most imaginative and productive investigators of aging, believes that evidence increasingly points to a particular supergene on chromosome number 6 (we each have 46 chromosomes) called the major histocompatibility complex, or MHC, which appears to govern nearly all of the body's major immune functions. Walford's name is the one most often associated with the immune theory of aging—the theory that aging is largely due to the running down of the immune defenses that protect us against invading microorganisms and reject foreign grafts. With aging, Walford speculates, the immune cells are somehow damaged so that their recognition capabilities are lost or impaired; hence they might fail to recognize foreign invaders or, perhaps worse still, mistake the body's own cells as foreign and attack them, resulting in autoimmune diseases such as rheumatoid arthritis. Since the MHC is intimately involved in all of these processes, it is Walford's prime suspect for the role of aging supergene—especially since it has now been shown to be related to many other aspects of the cell that affect aging, including DNA repair.

There is no reason why there could not be two (or even more) clocks of aging. There does seem to be a separate "genetic metabolic rate" built into nuclear DNA that is quite apart from the body's overall metabolic rate, and this rate could be controlled by Denckla's DECO through its influence on the thyroid. Such a genetic cellular clock could still play itself out in tissue culture, away from the influence of the brain's hormonal clock—much as a violinist could still play through his part in a symphony even if isolated from orchestra and conductor. Since hormones are known to be able to turn genes on and off, it is even quite possible that DECO could work by influencing the MHC in individual cells—or conversely, that the MHC in the genes of particular brain cells could control the release of DECO. So the two clocks, if they exist, could interact; it would perhaps be surprising if they did not.

The failing immune system may or may not be the major cause of aging and may or may not be the result of genetic programming. But the body's defenses do undeniably decline with age, rendering us more vulnerable to infection and every variety of stress. We may be able to do something about this without waiting for the knowhow required to modify genes or aging clocks. David Harrison of the Jackson Laboratory in Bar Harbor, Maine, has shown that the "stem cells" (precursors of all immune cells) produced by bone marrow can be transplanted and retransplanted from aging animals to younger animals, where they continue to function. Because young marrow that is transplanted to old mice seems to boost faltering immune systems under certain circumstances, Harrison speculates that young stem cells that are transplanted to aging human bodies might well produce similar results.

Boosting the immune system, however, may come about more easily through the administration of chemical immune boosters, such as the hormone called thymosin. The thymus gland, which shrivels early in life, controls the development of whole families of immune cells. As these cells run out late in life, our bodies can no longer make new ones. Biochemist Allan Goldstein of George Washington University School of Medicine, codiscoverer and principal developer of thymosin, is convinced that thymosin will not only be effective against immune-deficiency diseases, cancer and other serious maladies but will also considerably improve the quality of our later years by shoring up the body's defenses against infection and stress.

All of these procedures are directed toward minimizing the effects of wear and tear due to our mere exposure to the world over the years. Much of this wear, if it is the result of genetically programmed aging, will be diminished or abolished once we can do something about the clock of aging. Even then, however, there will be leftover damage to contend with. And meanwhile, we have *all* the wear and tear to manage. A failing immune system is only one aspect of the problem.

As the years go by, for instance, our cells—particularly heart and nerve cells—build up quantities of a fatty pigment called lipofuscin, generally assumed to be undisposed-of waste material. The accumulation of lipofuscin can seriously interfere with cell functions. Among chemicals now being tested are lipofuscin inhibitors that may be able to dissolve it or prevent its accumulation. We also suffer from the effects of "cross-linkage" (the irreversible linking together of large molecules that should be free to do their own work), which causes the stiffening of connective tissue, among other deleterious effects. Chemist Johan Bjorksten, who runs his own research foundation in Madison, Wisconsin, has for many years held that cross-linkage is the principal cause of all aging. He is currently at work testing some cross-link inhibitors that could be beneficial to all of us regardless of what the cause—if there is a single cause—of aging turns out to be.

Cross-linkage—extensive and ubiquitous though it be—may primarily be the result of "free-radical" damage. The free-radical theory of aging has in fact gained ground since it was first put forth in the 1950s by biochemist Denham Harman of the University of Nebraska College of Medicine in Omaha. Harman holds that free radicals, the short-lived but highly destructive by-products of the body's normal oxidation reactions, cause most of the degenerative changes of aging—including not only cross-linkage and lipofuscin buildup but also the decline of immune systems. Again, whether or not free radicals represent the principal mechanism of aging, they surely contribute to it by inflicting various kinds of damage on neighboring molecules. One means of combating the steady assault of free agents is through the use of "antioxidants" that mop them up before they can do much harm, or prevent them from being produced in harmful quantities.

Antioxidants added to the human diet show great promise in being able to slow down the effects of free-radical damage. Pathologist Harry Demopoulos of New York University Medical Center is among those who have done a great deal of high-technology research in this area over the past few years. Demopoulos employs such "micronutrients" as vitamin C, vitamin E, beta-carotene and the mineral selenium in careful dosages and a high purity as yet unobtainable in health-food products. His preliminary results suggest that antioxidant micronutrients will be an important element in our anti-aging arsenal.

There may well be other purely dietary approaches to delaying senescence. It now seems likely, for example, that the slippage of memory that often accompanies aging may be due largely to the shortage of a single brain chemical that can be boosted by eating a diet rich in the natural substance lecithin. It is too early in the experimental work to report any sure results.

The most straightforward technique—for the highly disciplined, at least—may prove to be simply eating less while maintaining adequate nutrition. Most long-lived people seem to eat frugally—and there is a scientific basis for this impression. In a classic series of experiments begun more than 50 years ago at Cornell University, biochemist Clive M. McCay was able to extend the lives of rats considerably by severely restricting their caloric intake—while seeing to it that their limited food contained a proper mix of nutrients. This life-extension technique only worked, however, if the semistarvation began early in the animal's life, well before puberty. The result was a decelerated growth and maturation, as if the development-and-aging process had been run in slow motion. At the University of California at Berkeley, Dr.

Paola Timiras and Paul Segall were able to achieve virtually the same results merely by restricting the intake of a single vital protein ingredient, an amino acid called tryptophan. Only last year, Segall was able to demonstrate the efficacy of this dietary regime when a few of his female rats, long past the age when procreation would normally have been possible, gave birth to healthy offspring.

Since dietary restriction had to begin before puberty and continue over a lifetime in order to extend life, there seemed to be no way of trying it on human subjects. But in the past few years, breakthroughs have occurred. Charles Barrows of the National Institute on Aging and UCLA's Walford have each learned how to extend the life-spans of experimental animals by starting dietary restriction in adulthood. Again, the indefatigable Walford has carried this the furthest, experimenting on himself as well as on his subjects; and he has been gradually putting together what may turn out to be the first workable anti-aging diet for humans.

All this only begins to suggest the riches and diversity of what is going on in aging research today. But it is already feasible to speculate that before too long, we may know for sure whether or not there is a genetic aging program, and if there is, how to control it for our own benefit. Even sooner, we will probably have at our disposal an array of easily available substances—immune boosters, antioxidants, memory improvers, cross-link inhibitors and lipofuscin scavengers, among many others. These—combined with health measures such as getting enough rest and exercise, eating properly and resisting the urge to smoke—should substantially improve the quality of our later years and even abolish many of the symptoms we have come to identify as "old age." If we also learn to cultivate attitudes that enhance the spirit, equipping us to deal successfully with the stresses of a changing world, our chances for healthy longevity are even better.

LIVING LONGER

RICHARD CONNIFF

The subject, a healthy white male, is 29 years old, an age he would like to maintain more or less forever. At the moment, he is sitting in front of a computer terminal in a private office in Corona del Mar, California, about an hour south of Los Angeles. He is about to learn electronically, on the basis of key physical indicators, whether he is still in his prime or if his body is already slipping into the long decline to senescence. Forget what the mind feels, or what the calendar and a searching look into a mirror might suggest; this machine aims to tell how much the body has actually aged—and therefore how long the subject is likely to live.

The test takes 45 minutes. It requires no syringes, blood pressure belts or strapped-on electrodes. In fact, the whole experience is less like a medical examination than a stint at a computerized arcade game. Not quite Space Invaders, but then, the subject doesn't want to be Luke Skywalker. He's just a guy who'd like to live to 120, and never feel older than 29.

In all, there are more than a dozen tests. They measure such indicators as the highest pitch the subject can hear (known to decline significantly with age), the ease with which the eye adjusts its focus between near and far objects (lens and supporting structure become less elastic over the years) and the subject's ability to identify incomplete pictures of common objects (perceptual organization begins to fall off at about age 30).

Then comes a brief whirring of electronic thought and, ladies and gentlemen, the computer's analysis: The subject has the hearing of a 21-year-old, skin as sensitive as a child's and, overall, a body that just barely passes for 32. So much for the sweet bird of youth.

But not so fast. It turns out that there may be loopholes in the standard existential contract of birth, aging and death. Even people now approaching middle age can expect a bonus of perhaps several years of extra living, thanks to continuing medical progress against cancer, heart disease, stroke and other killers.

At the same time, gerontologists—specialists in the science of aging—are piecing together the details of diet, exercise, personality and behavior that make it practical to shoot for 80, or even 114—the longest human life span reliably recorded.

Finding the Fountain of Youth

There is hope even for people who fear diet and exercise almost as much as an early death. At the most minute level, scientists are now deciphering the basic biologic mechanisms of aging and of rejuvenation. Gerontologists are so confident about fulfilling the promise of their discoveries that a healthy young man aiming to live 120 years begins to appear reasonable. Writing in The American Journal of Clinical Pathology, one researcher recently predicted: "The discipline of gerontology is now advancing at such a rapid rate, with so much overflow from other fields . . . that I rather confidently expect a significant advance in maximum

life-span potential to be achieved for the human species during what is left of the present century. . . ." One probable means of life extension is already available, in a tentative form, and it suggests that a 16th-century Italian named Luigi Cornaro was far closer than Ponce de Leon to the fountain of youth. More about him later.

The so-called life-extension revolution couldn't come at a stranger time. American society is already on the brink of startling change. It is growing up. Whether longevity improves by only a few more years, as some expect, or by whole decades, mature people will for the first time predominate. Between 1970 and 2025, the median age in the United States will have risen almost 10 years, from 27.9 to 37.6—as substantial an age difference for a nation as for an individual. The number of people 65 and over will double, from 25 million now to 51 million in 2025, and there will be 85 million people over the age of 55. All without major new increases in longevity. In earlier societies, so few people managed to reach old age that they were deemed special, endowed with magical powers to ward off the demons of aging. In the United States over the coming decades, the elderly will be commonplace, and possibly more: a powerful, organized political and economic force.

Elderly Astronauts

What will it mean to live longer in such a society? One public-relations man, a product of the post-World War II baby boom, finds himself caught up in his generation's frantic competition for good homes and the best jobs. He suffers nightmares of an old age in which winning admission to a nursing home will prove harder than getting into Stanford or Yale. Cemeteries will be standing room only. Others worry that an increase in longevity will merely mean an increase in the time they'll spend bedridden, senile, catheterized.

Not so, say the gerontologists. They argue that even if there is no significant medical breakthrough, today's young and middle-aged can still look forward to a more youthful old age than their parents or grandparents. Instead of applying for early admission to the local nursing home, these future elderly may acknowledge their dotage merely by switching from downhill to cross-country skiing, or from running to jogging. Rather than worrying about death or about overcrowding at Heavenly Rest Cemetery, they may instead be considering the personal implications of a study, recently begun by the National Aeronautics and Space Administration, to determine how well 55- to 65-year-

---

LINUS PAULING
Scientist
Born: 1901

"I think people should try to keep healthy. I'm especially interested in vitamin C. I continue to recommend that everyone get a good supply. I take 10 grams a day."

---

old women withstand the stress of spaceflight. K. Warner Schaie, research director of the Andrus Gerontology Center at the University of Southern California, cites three well-known but rarely noted reasons for optimism about future old age:

● **The control of childhood disease.** Aging is cumulative. Instead of simply healing and going away, the minor assaults suffered by the body from disease, abuse and neglect can have "sleeper" effects. Chicken pox in a child, for example, can lead much later in life to the hideous itching affliction known as shingles. But vaccines and other wonders of modern medicine have largely eliminated such time bombs. Says Schaie, who is 53 and has lived through whooping cough, measles and mumps: "Most people who will become old 30 or 40 years from now will not have had childhood diseases. Most people who are now old have had them all. That's an important difference."

● **Better education.** Where a grade-school background was typical for the older generation, more than half of all

Americans now 30 or 40 years old have completed at least high school, and studies show that people with more education live longer. They get better jobs, suffer less economic stress and tend to be more engaged with life and more receptive to new ideas, which may help explain the third factor.

● **The fitness revolution.** "We really have changed our habits with respect to diet and exercise and self-care," says Schaie. Per capita consumption of tobacco has dropped 26 percent over the past 15 years, and the drop is accelerating, promising a decrease in chronic obstructive pulmonary disease and lung cancer. Life-style changes and improved treatment of hypertension have already produced a dramatic national decrease in cerebrovascular disease, one of the major chronic problems of old age.

Gerontologists say that these same future elderly will also benefit from the increasingly accepted idea that aging is partly a matter of choice. Speaking before a recent meeting of the American Academy of Family Physicians, Dr. Alex Comfort, the author and eminent gerontologist, argued that 75 percent of so-called aging results from a kind of self-fulfilling prophecy. "If we insist that there is a group of people who, on a fixed calendar basis, cease to be people and become unintelligent, asexual, unemployable and crazy," said Comfort, "the people so designated will be under pressure to be unintelligent, asexual, unemployable and crazy." Changing the image of the elderly may change the way the elderly behave.

Just as important as the image itself is the way individuals react to it. Performance declines on average with age, but individuals can practice not to be average. A 75-year-old man whose joints should be stiffening into immobility can run the marathon. An 80-year-old woman whose capacity for work is undiminished can model herself after Sir Robert Mayer, who declared at age 100: "Retire? Never! I intend to die in harness." (Now 101, Mayer is still arranging concerts, and recently remarried).

STROM THURMOND
United States Senator
Born: 1902

"I think the advantage of my age is the wisdom and knowledge that comes with experience. For those looking ahead to a long life, I offer this advice: Read the Constitution and demand that public officials, legislators and judges abide by it."

GEORGE GALLUP
Pollster
Born: 1901

"There's no substitute for experience. As I look back on my life, I wonder how I could have been so stupid.

"Intellectual curiosity is important, too. A lot of people die just from boredom. I have a whole program that will keep me going until age 100, at least. Incidentally, some years ago we did a study of people over the age of 95. We interviewed over 450 individuals; 150 of them were older than 100. What we found was that those who live a long time *want* to live a long time. They are full of curiosity, alert and take life as it comes."

This reliance on choice and something more—spunk, exuberance, a positive mental attitude—may sound romantic, and is, admittedly, an exotic notion in some of its permutations. At the State University College in Geneseo, New York, for example, Lawrence Casler, a psychologist, is convinced that aging is entirely psychosomatic. In 1970, to break through "brainwashing" about life span, he gave "an extremely powerful hypnotic suggestion" to 150 young volunteers that they will live at least to 120. "We're planning a big gala champagne party for the year 2070," says Casler. "I'm looking forward to it." He also gave a hypnotic suggestion for long life to residents of a nursing home who were already 80 or older. Casler says that the suggestion appears to have reduced serious illness and added two years to life span in the experimental group.

But even medical specialists in aging take the role of choice seriously. Dr. James F. Fries of the Stanford University Medical Center writes in The New England Journal of Medicine that "personal choice is important—one can *choose not to age rapidly in certain faculties.* . . ." The italics are added, but Fries himself writes that the biologic limits are "surprisingly broad." With training, experimental subjects have repeatedly reversed the pattern of decline in testing for intelligence, social interaction, health after exercise, and memory—even after age 70. Fries, Schaie and every other gerontologist interviewed for this article reached the same conclusion: To stay younger for longer, you must stay physically and mentally active. As Fries put it, "The body, to an increasing degree, is now felt to rust out rather than to wear out." What you don't use, you lose.

The Gray Revolution

A society dominated by old people will inevitably look different. Without a medical breakthrough, even vigorous old people cannot avoid slowing down. Schaie's interpretation is positive: "Young people . . . make many more errors of commission than omission, but the reverse is true for the elderly." Caution. The wisdom of the aged. To accommodate it, traffic lights, elevators, the bus at the corner will also have to slow down and become more patient.

Housing will be redesigned. But that doesn't necessarily mean handrails in the bathroom, wheelchair lifts on the stairway or any of the other depressing impedimenta of old age. "You're thinking of facilities for the ill elderly," says Schaie. Instead, redesign may mean more one-story garden apartments (stairs waste human energy). Homes will be smaller and require less care. House cleaning, home maintenance, dial-a-meal and dial-a-bus services will proliferate. Condominiums for the elderly will be built not near hospitals—an outdated idea, according to Schaie—but near libraries, colleges and shopping and athletic facilities.

The work place will also change, because more old people will stay on the job. As early as 1990, the baby bust of the past two decades will yield a shortage of young workers. Older workers will gain as a result, and there are few things better for an older person's spunk, exuberance or positive mental attitude than a sense of continuing worth in the marketplace and the paycheck that goes with it. The change is already beginning. The personnel department of one high-technology company, unable to find enough job candidates under 30, recently hired Schaie to convince its own top management that gray-haired engineers are just as able to keep the company on the cutting edge of innovation. Schaie says that it will pay to update and retrain older workers, not just for their expertise, but because they are less prone to accidents and absenteeism than their younger counterparts. In the Information Society, automation and robotics will make youth and strength less significant; the premium will be on knowledge and experience.

Indeed, James E. Birren, who runs the Andrus Gerontology Center in Los Angeles, predicts an era of "the experimental aged." A 75-year-old female lawyer came out of the audience once when he was explaining this idea, took his chalk away and told him in detail, with notes, why he was being too re-strained. At 62, it seems, Birren still suffered the inhibitions of the conservative young. By contrast, he says, the elderly are past child-rearing and mortgage-paying, and they are also often beyond worrying about what the boss or the family thinks. But they have a much better sense of what they themselves think, and it is often surprising. In a 1971 Gallup poll, for example, substantially more older people thought that the Vietnam War was a mistake than did those in the 21- to 29-year-old group. If they did not do much about it, perhaps it was because they accepted the youth culture's image of old people as doddering and ineffective. But given respect, independence, a steady paycheck, the prospect of continued vigor and the knowledge of their own numbers, the old may replace the young, says Birren, as the experimenters, innovators and all-around hell-raisers of the world.

Which brings us to the question of sex and the elderly. Future elderly will enjoy, and perhaps enforce, a more tolerant public attitude toward their romantic activities. Dr. Leslie Libow, medical director at the Jewish Institute for Geriatric Care in New Hyde Park, New York, blames decreasing sexual interest among older men and women at least partly on the traditional popular expectation that interest ought to decrease. But that expectation shows signs of changing. One company not long ago introduced a line of cosmetics specially designed for older women and met with 400 times the response it had predicted. And a New York-area motel offering X-rated movies recently began advertising a senior-citizens discount. Future elderly will also benefit from subtler changes. Bernice L. Neugarten, a psychologist at the University

---

MILLICENT FENWICK
United States Congresswoman
Born: 1910

"Life gets better and better. You know why? You can help someone, and they aren't afraid of you. No one thinks that you're going to seduce them, or breach a promise or be a menace in any way. Here in Washington, your colleagues know that you are not going to interfere with them when they want to run for the Presidency.

"You are free. You aren't a young person, struggling to pay the mortgage and the children's dentist bills, with endless opportunities opening before you. When someone says that youth is the easiest time of life, that person has forgotten the terrible strain of choice."

LATE, GREAT ACHIEVERS

Herein, proof that life begins—or at least continues—after 70.

Konrad Adenauer (1876-1967) 73 when he became the first Chancellor of the Federal Republic of Germany. Resigned 14 years later.
Walter Hoving (b. 1897) Chairman of Tiffany & Company for 25 years; recently left to start his own design-consulting firm at 84.
Pope John XXIII (1881-1963) Chosen Pope at 77; brought the Catholic Church into the 20th century.
Jomo Kenyatta (c. 1894-1978) Elected Kenya's first President at 70. Led the country for 14 years.
Henri Matisse (1869-1954) In his 70's did a series of sprightly paper cutouts that were exhibited at New York's Museum of Modern Art.
Golda Meir (1898-1978) Named Prime Minister of Israel at 71; held the job for five years.
Cathleen Nesbitt (b. 1889) At 92, revived the role she created on Broadway 25 years ago: Professor Higgins's mother in "My Fair Lady."
Pablo Picasso (1881-1973) Complet-ed his portraits of "Sylvette" at 73, married for the second time at 77, then executed three series of drawings between 85 and 90.
Anna Mary Robertson Moses (1860-1961) Was 76 when she took up painting as a hobby; as Grandma Moses won international fame and staged 15 one-woman shows throughout Europe.
Dr. John Rock (b. 1890) At 70 he introduced the Pill; spent the next 20 years as its champion.
Artur Rubinstein (b. 1887) Was 89 when he gave one of his greatest performances at New York's Carnegie Hall.
Sophocles (c. 496-406 B.C.) Wrote "Electra" and "Oedipus at Colonus" after 70, held office in Athens at 83.
Giuseppe Verdi (1813-1901) Was 74 when "Otello" added to his fame; "Falstaff" followed four years later.
Frank Lloyd Wright (1869-1959) Completed New York's Guggenheim Museum at 89; continued teaching until his death.
Adolph Zukor (1873-1976) At 91, chairman of Paramount Pictures.

MAGGIE KUHN
National convener
Gray Panthers
Born: 1905

"There are many stereotypes about growing old. We are not useless, toothless and sexless. In fact, old people have a special place in society. My generation has been part of more changes than any other. We have to share that knowledge. We are the whistle blowers, the social critics. We are the ones who must be advocates for disarmament and safe, renewable sources of energy."

---

of Chicago, suggests that as they put anxiety-producing family and career decisions behind them, men and women are likely to relax more with one another. Sex stereotypes and the arguments they provoke will decline in importance as the years go by. As for male impotence, Libow notes that 20 percent to 40 percent of men continue to have active sex lives well into their 70's even now.

Finally, what about the specter of a long and vigorous life ending wretchedly in a nursing home? The average admission age today is 80, and only 5 percent of the elderly now endure such institutions. Even so, at current rates, the number of nursing-home residents will increase by 57 percent, from 1.3 million now to 2.1 million in 2003. But there are alternatives to terminal "convalescence." Most people now die without what Neugarten calls "a final deterioration that erases individuality." Birren believes that even more people will die "in harness" in the future. Instead of dwindling away, they will remain vigorous longer, then drop away quickly. Temporary "respite care"—an innovation now being imported from Scandinavia—will be available, say, for an octogenarian down with a bad cold. Schaie suggests that old people who are burdened with large homes may also invite friends to come live with them for mutual support. Such communes will give them independence they could never hope for in a nursing home.

Supergenes

So far, all of this assumes that there will be no breakthrough in human longevity, no anti-aging pill or fountain of youth. People will become wrinkled and gray and die at roughly the biblical threescore and ten or fourscore years. But that is no longer a safe assumption.

Dr. Roy Walford is one of the leading gurus of the life-extension move-

ment, and he looks the part. His head is hairless, except for a gray moustache that thickens down past the corners of his mouth. He can seem ferocious on film, but in person he is benign, almost shy. When he tours his complex of laboratories at the School of Medicine of the University of California at Los Angeles, he keeps his elbows close by his sides, and his hands in front of him, tucked like a monk's into the sleeves of his white lab jacket. His colleagues around the country tell you first that he is odd, and second that they respect him more than any other researcher in the field.

Walford believes that he has identified a single supergene that controls much of the aging process. Since 1970, he has been studying a small segment of the sixth chromosome in humans called the major histocompatibility complex. This is the master genetic control center for the body's immune system, and it is a logical suspect in the aging process. The ability to fight off disease peaks in most people during adolescence, and then falls off to as little as 10 percent of its former strength in old age. At the same time, a kind of perversion of the immune system occurs, in which the workhorses of self-defense lose some of their ability to distinguish between friendly and foreign cells. They attack the body's own organs, leading to such characteristic diseases of old age as diabetes and atherosclerosis. The phenomenon is called autoimmunity, and it means that the body is making war on itself.

Walford established the supergene's additional role in aging by comparing 14 strains of mice. The study (conducted by his associate, Kathy Hall) demonstrated significant differences in life span among mice that were genetically identical *except* at key locations in the major histocompatibility complex. Additional study by Walford, Hall and others tied that single genetic variable to two of the most important factors in the aging process as it is now understood. The long-lived mice had improved DNA-repair rates and increased protection against cellular damage from bodily substances known as free radicals. But the most profound idea, first suggested by Richard Cutler of the National Institute for Aging and substantiated by Walford, was simply that genes control longevity. Mice with "good" genes lived longer; the strains with "bad" genes had lives that were nasty, brutish and, above all, short.

Walford points out that there may be other genes controlling longevity. But none has been located so far, and separate studies on the nature of hu-

man evolution suggest that there may be, at most, only a few such supergenes. All of which makes Walford's discovery about the major histocompatability complex more important. What to do about it? Altering the genetic information in the nucleus of every cell of an adult animal is, at least for now, impossible. Instead, scientists are trying to find other supergenes and identify the mechanisms by which they work. If these supergenes have some regulatory mechanism in common, it may then be possible to manipulate the mechanism rather than the gene.

One promising school of thought theorizes that aging results mainly from accumulating errors in the complex, tightly coiled strands of DNA that are each cell's blueprint for accurately reproducing itself. The damage comes from many sources: ultraviolet radiation, viruses, free radicals, toxic chemicals, even the body's own heat. Repair enzymes correct some damage, but some persists. Over the years, tiny breaks and infinitesimal wart-like bulges accumulate, the DNA coils loosen and the cell begins to malfunction.

DR. BENJAMIN SPOCK
Pediatrician
Born: 1903

"Part of living longer has to do with one's genes. I got my longevity genes from my mother. Her side of the family all lived well into their 80's and 90's. The other part depends on optimism.

"It's a platitude in psychology that if you are well fed in infancy, you'll be an optimist no matter what happens later in life. Well, it's very clear that I was taken care of and that my mother loved me. At the age of one, things were marvelous. The photographs show me sitting there, beaming, in a starched coat and sailor hat, all my petticoats and skirts showing. I imagine that my basic optimism comes from that period. I started out assuming that the world is a wonderful place."

The theory suggests that those animals most efficient at DNA repair will live longest and age least. And so it happens in nature. The white lip monkey has a low rate of DNA repair, and lives to be only 12 or so years old. Humans have a very high rate of DNA repair, and live longer than any other primate. Differences in the DNA repair rate appear even among members of the same species, along with corresponding differences in longevity. Walford and Hall's long-lived mice displayed a higher rate of DNA repair than their short-lived counterparts. Walford himself has an unusually high rate of DNA repair. This may be why at 56, he still has pink unwrinkled skin, and looks 45.

What if science could boost other people's DNA-repair rates to the same level as Walford's—or perhaps triple them? The theory is that enhanced repair, probably in tandem with other therapies, would delay the accumulation of errors, slow the aging process and extend human life span. It might even be possible to correct old errors, patching breaks that had become a part of the genetic blueprint, excising bulges, retightening the coils of DNA. In a word, rejuvenation.

MOTHER TERESA
Missionary
Born: 1910

"At the hour of death, when we come face to face with God, we are going to be judged on love—not how much we have done, but how much love we have put into our actions."

Keeping Paramecia Young

Researchers may already have achieved just that in lower animals. Joan Smith-Sonneborn, a professor of zoology and physiology at the University of Wyoming, chose to work with paramecia because the microorganism's single cell in many ways resembles the cells of more complex animals. In an experiment first reported in 1979, she damaged the DNA of paramecia with ultraviolet radiation—the same light waves that cause human skin to tan or burn and, eventually, to age. The damaged animals died sooner than the untreated ones, presumably because they could not repair all the breaks or bumps in their DNA. Damage. Malfunctioning. Old age. Death.

With another group of paramecia, Smith-Sonneborn first induced DNA damage, and immediately stimulated, or "photoreactivated," a repair enzyme known to respond to a particular wavelength of visible light. To her surprise, the photoreactivated paramecia lived not merely as long as untreated counterparts, but substantially longer. They were already at midlife, but somehow achieved a 296 percent increase in their remaining life span, and a 27 percent increase in overall life span. In gerontology, the so-called Hayflick limit represents the maximum life span of each species. It has to do with how many times the animal's cells can divide before they die. There is a Hayflick limit for paramecia and another for humans,

both supposedly inescapable, unmovable. The ultimate deadline. "What we did," says Smith-Sonneborn, "was break through the Hayflick limit for paramecia."

To explain how this happens, Smith-Sonneborn uses the analogy of a sinking ship. When the damage occurs, an S O S goes out. But by the time outside help arrives on the scene, the ship's own crew has plugged the leak and pumped out the bilges. Having no emergency repair to do, the outside help goes to work anyway, overhauling engines and tightening rivets, and may even stay on the scene long afterwards for maintenance. By analogy, the photoreactivated enzymes leave the paramecium more youthful—and youthful for longer—than it was before the damage occurred.

It is, of course, a huge leap from paramecia to human beings. But other scientists have already demonstrated photoreactivation of repair enzymes in human skin. Smith-Sonneborn quickly adds a caveat: No one knows how much ultraviolet damage must be induced in human skin, or with what consequences, before photoreactivation will work as a rejuvenating treatment. So it does not make sense to sit for hours under a light bulb in the hope of unwrinkling or rejuvenating the skin. Then what does any of this matter? The photoreactivation work is important because it demonstrates the possibility of enhancing other DNA-repair mechanisms and other longevity-determining processes elsewhere in the human body. The enhancement may slow aging. And if it is possible to break through the Hayflick limit for paramecia, why not also for people?

MARGARET HICKEY
Public affairs editor
Ladies' Home Journal
Born: 1902

"With age comes serenity, the feeling of being satisfied with what you have done while still looking forward to what you can do. You begin to like yourself."

The Anti-Aging Diet

Another method of enhancement— the only one that is practical now— takes the life-extension story back to the 16th century and to Luigi Cornaro. Cornaro, a Paduan, led such a profligate youth that by the time he was 40, he found his constitution "utterly ruined

by a disorderly way of life and by frequent overindulgence in sensual pleasures." Told to reform, he entered upon the *vita sobria*, a life of moderation in all things. He restricted himself in particular to just 12 ounces of food daily and lived in robust health until he was 98. Since then, scientists have repeatedly demonstrated that undernutrition—as distinguished from malnutrition—extends the lives of experimental animals. But they mistakenly thought that undernutrition had to start at weaning, when it's riskiest. As Walford puts it, "You can't starve babies and you can't have 10 percent mortality rates in order to have a few people live to be 180." When the underfeeding was delayed until midlife, the experimental animals often died prematurely, Luigi Cornaro to the contrary.

I.F. STONE
Author
Born: 1907

"There are great joys in one's later years—as many as there are in one's youth. One of them is learning and studying. The things you study have much more significance; you understand them more fully. I'm studying ancient Greek language and civilization. It's difficult work, but very rewarding.

"My advice is to persist. The mind is like a muscle—you must exercise it."

But by refining the technique of previous researchers, Walford and Richard Weindruch, a co-worker, recently achieved a 30 percent increase in maximum life span for test animals whose diet was restricted after they became adults. The crucial refinement seems to have been moderation. Where other experimenters began adult underfeeding abruptly, Walford and Weindruch gradually reduced the intake of their animals, down to about 60 percent of their normal diet. In humans, Walford says, it would work out to a loss of a quarter to a third of body weight over a six-year period—a big loss, but a slow one.

Walford has not yet developed the optimal human diet for longevity through underfeeding, but says he intends to over the next year or so. For himself, he now fasts two days a week and has shed five or six pounds from his already spare frame. But because undernutrition can easily turn to malnutrition, especially outside a doctor's care, he doesn't recommend that people follow his example. In any case, would such a diet be worth the sacrifice? Walford evidently thinks so. One reason is that experimental underfeeding did not merely delay death, it delayed aging. The lack of extra calories forestalled the development, and hence the decay, of the immune system. Autoimmunity, the body's war on itself, actually decreased. And in other underfeeding experiments, the cancer rate dropped markedly.

As for the sacrifice, it may eventually prove unnecessary. At Temple University Medical School in Philadelphia, Arthur Schwartz is working with an adrenal-gland product called dehydroepiandrosterone, or DHEA. His experiments "suggest that DHEA treatment may duplicate the anti-aging and anti-cancer effects of caloric restriction."

140 and Still Kicking

It is just this piling on of discoveries and developments in all areas of life-extension research that causes Walford, Cutler, Smith-Sonneborn and others to predict a dramatic increase in human longevity. Walford, in fact, believes that it will become possible within this decade to extend maximum human life span to somewhere between 130 or 140 years.

What such a life will be like is anybody's guess. George Bernard Shaw imagined that extraordinarily long-lived people would quickly abandon mating for more mature pursuits, such as higher mathematics. Aldous Huxley wrote of a brave new world in which old men spend their time "safe on the solid ground of daily labor and distraction, scampering from feely to feely, from girl to pneumatic girl."

The possibilities raised by extreme longevity are as numerous as the additional days people will supposedly live. Walford argues that the very vastness of the change is one reason conser-

vative experts on aging prefer to deny the likelihood of significant life extension. "It blows the data base on which they make their projections," he says. A doubling of human life span would, of course, blow anybody's data base. To cite a single example, a young couple starting out with two children, and passing on their belief in zero popula-

---

MICKEY ROONEY
Actor
Born: 1920

"A long time ago I looked around and saw the apathy that the elderly had fallen into. They had nowhere to go, no one to turn to. They were eliminating themselves from the atmosphere of potential. This became a deep concern of mine. So I started a project called Fun Filled Family for people over 45. We have trips, discounts, life insurance policies and gathering places. We have no political or religious ties. We don't use the word age at all, but talk only in terms of experience."

---

tion growth to their offspring, could wind up at the healthy middle age of 90 with 44 direct descendants and descendant-spouses, and at age 150, with six or seven living generations in the family. Alternately, if women were to age much more slowly and reach menopause much later, it might be possible for some future generation to put off parenthood and the whole career-family dilemma until age 50.

Whole new sets of questions arise, and at first they seem to have an absurd Woody Allen quality: If you're going to live to be 150, who's going to pay the rent? But if life extension is as near as

gerontologists suggest, perhaps it is time to begin thinking seriously about seemingly absurd possibilities. Does it make sense, for example, to buy life insurance at 30 if you will be living to 150 and if, barring accidents, medicine makes the time of death ever more predictable? Should you plan now for a second career? (Walford intends to be a researcher in artificial intelligence.) Will longer life encourage a flowering of abilities? Is marriage "till death do us part" practical when there is a good chance that you'll see your 100th anniversary? What if the husband pursues the life-extension therapy and the wife rejects it? What will it mean if marriages and generations become asynchronous? What will happen—in fact, is already happening—to the drilled-in timetables of schooling, mating, child-rearing, income-producing, retirement and death?

To many people, the promise and the possibilities suggested by life extension are truly wonderful. "I see humanity as a fragile organism that has been evolving all along into a more complex, autonomous, intelligent species," says F. M. Esfandiary, an author who lectures at the University of California at Los Angeles, "and I believe that in our time this ascent will rapidly accelerate, propelling us into entirely new dimensions. I also believe that our mortality, the very fragility of life, has for eons drastically impaired the quality of life. It is not just the imminence of one's own death that is so cruel, it is the ever-present fear of losing all the people one loves. In the future, people will not be as programmed to finitude and mortality. Instead, they will see a whole avalanche of new options. . . ."

On the other hand, it may be worth remembering that Moses lived to be 120, and still never entered the promised land.

COPING WITH DEATH IN THE FAMILY

The key to minimizing the impact of death in the family, say experts on the subject, is more honesty on the part of everyone involved. The patient should be told—as much as possible—about the seriousness of the illness. And the rest of the family should openly express their own feelings.

The dramatic news today is that there are experts on death and dying and a large and growing body of knowledge about the subject. Thanks to the work of such people as Chicago psychiatrist-author Dr. Elizabeth Kübler-Ross, the burden of coping with death—from the shock of learning that a spouse or a child is terminally ill, through the death, funeral, and subsequent adjustment period—is being lightened for many families. "There's a healthier, more open attitude today toward death and how to handle it," says Dr. Austin H. Kutscher, who teaches a new course called thanatology (the study of death) at the Columbia University medical school. "People are getting help they couldn't have gotten two or three years ago."

Kübler-Ross, who has written extensively on the subject, is one of many experts who travel widely today lecturing on death at schools, hospitals, and religious institutions around the country. Dr. Mary Cerney, a psychologist at the Menninger Foundation in Topeka, says she has just finished a lecture series on death at a Kansas high school. More and more hospitals and university psychology departments offer seminars on coping with death. The Candlelighters, with 39 chapters around the country, provides counsel to the families of children stricken with cancer, and the National Foundation for Sudden Infant Death tries to help grieving parents.

Orville Kelly was a newspaper editor in Davenport, Iowa, when he was stricken with lymphatic cancer in 1973. He launched Make Today Count for other cancer patients a year later and now counts 54 chapters. "As a cancer patient, I can now share my frustrations and anger with other patients," says 45-year-old Kelly. "We talk, we have speakers, we have hope."

Perhaps the biggest change has come among those who deal with terminal patients in hospitals (where 80% of all Americans die). Dr. Stephen E. Goldston, a psychologist with the National Institute of Mental Health in Rockville, Md., finds hospital personnel increasingly aware that "the dying need to be dealt with honestly, without pretense, and safeguarded against the greatest pain of death, which is terrible loneliness."

Goldston warns the family of someone approaching death that false good cheer only serves to deepen the patient's fear and anxiety. The survivors, in turn, require a period of unrestrained grief in order to adjust to a loved one's death, and that goes for children as well as adults.

"Children," says Goldston, "need to be told the truth and not lied to about a death in the family." Sugarcoating death, say Goldston and others, can cause greater pain—and sometimes serious guilt feelings—among children. "Families have a chance to educate their growing children about death," says Edward K. Leaton, president of a New York City consulting firm, whose two sons died of muscular dystrophy. "This need not be frightening. The death of a pet or a bird gives you a chance to explain and remove fears."

The patient

Step one in coping with death is dealing with the patient, and here the old approach of telling the patient nothing is giving way to a new realism. Patients are being told more today—often to the point of telling a person that he or she is going to die. "Ideally, the patient should be the first to know," advises Dr. Herman Feifel, professor of psychiatry at the University of Southern California medical school. "The only question is how to tell the person. Some must be told gradually."

There are practical reasons for revealing the truth to a terminal patient. The patient, if "protected" by family and friends, suffers through hours of pointless, trivial talk. Another reason for telling the truth is that the patient will then feel less guilty in demanding services or attention or openly crying and expressing grief. Grieving is vital, since it enables the patient to accept the reality of death more easily.

Admitting the likelihood of death to a terminal patient is not a step to be taken lightly. Hope alone can sometimes prolong life; denial of hope can sometimes prod a person to suicide. Obviously, the matter should be discussed thoroughly with the patient's doctor and probably with a clergyman, as well. Several important questions must be answered: Is the doctor absolutely certain that the person is going to die? Does the patient really want to know the truth? "Some people decide to tell the dying person out of a compunction to be honest or a need to absolve their own guilt," says Dr. Kenneth D. Cohen, psychiatrist and clinical director of the Philadelphia Psychiatric Center.

Some people should not be told at all. A strong, relatively independent person can handle the news far better than someone who tends to be weak and dependent. The patient who still hopes for recovery probably should not have those hopes dashed. Rather, the matter should usually be postponed until the patient raises the question of whether he or she is going to die.

"You do not rush the person into a recognition of their condition," says Columbia's Kutscher. "You listen carefully for hints of a desire to discuss the possibility of death." Cohen agrees that "the telling must be approached delicately." A basic point to get across, he feels, is that the patient is not alone and will not be alone.

"Above everything, don't make pretenses," advises a New York City advertising executive whose wife died of cancer. "When you feel that the suffering person wants the truth—tell it. Pretense keeps two people from ever really talking. I regret that before my wife died, we never got to the stage of real frankness. It made her death harder for both of us."

HONESTY IS BEST, WITHIN REASON

Kutscher and others suggest that the wishes of the dying be heeded when it comes to deciding on desperate life-prolonging measures. "Most terminal patients at this point know they will die," says Kutscher. "I suggest that you listen to them. They will probably make their wishes felt about this last-minute fighting to stay alive."

Sometimes, the word of impending death simply can't be concealed from the patient—when there is a will or other legal or business papers to be signed, for instance. Some people are anxious to get their affairs in order, and doing it can help them face death. "But do this gently," Kutscher suggests. "Have the family lawyer present the will. He can be more casual about it than you would be."

Most experts agree on the need to tell children as much as they can handle about a parent's illness. "If a parent has a terminal illness, even a small child should be told what this means—in terms the child can understand," says Dr. Edward Rydman, a Dallas psychologist. "Families tend to shy away from dealing with this," he adds. Says Dr. David A. Switzer, a Southern Methodist University psychologist: "The children need to know that their father or mother is going away, and not just for 15 minutes or overnight."

Most psychologists agree and point out that in explaining the terminal illness of a parent, the child should be told in such a way that he or she can fully comprehend that death is permanent, that every effort was made to save the parent's life, that the loss will be painful, that it is good to cry or get angry to express grief, and that the parent's duties will be taken care of.

"In addition," says Goldston of NIMH, "I would make it clear that the rest of the family will remain together—assuming this is true." He notes that if the terminal patient is a brother or sister, it is important to let the other children know that "any evil wishful thinking they have had about the sick child doesn't really count for anything." This, he explains, can ease often dire guilt feelings among children, who frequently do "wish" bad things on siblings—the wish that a brother or sister would disappear forever, for example.

Don't resort to fairy tales. Telling a child that "your mother went to sleep and will forever rest peacefully" can be frightening, not reassuring. "They will be afraid to go to bed," says Sandi D. Boshak, of Dix Hills, N.Y., whose son died in infancy. Boshak,

who is active in group meetings of the National Foundation for Sudden Infant Death, feels that honesty is vital in explaining death to small children, as well as to teen-agers.

Another common mistake, say both psychologists and parents, is to use a religious explanation of a death in a family that has had no religious background. "Such an explanation will mean little to the child, may create fear, and can cause the child to later react negatively to religion," Goldston explains.

A child's role

Honest explanations to children in cases of a dying parent can also have a positive effect on the parent. Some children secretly fear that they are to blame for their parent's illness. Freed of this anxiety, the child will relate more closely to the ill parent and make the parent feel better. A child should rarely be kept apart from a parent who is dying. "Even though our daughter was only three years old, we kept her in contact with her mother," says a New York businessman whose wife died of cancer several years ago. "She fed her mother cracked ice," he adds. "This made her understand that her mother was very sick, and helped both of them when death came."

When a parent or sibling dies, even children as young as seven or so can and should take part in the mourning ritual observed by the family, say psychologists. "Ask yourself if a young child is capable of participating along with the adults and older children," says Cohen, of the Philadelphia Psychiatric Center. "Most children are capable of this, but some families want to protect and keep the child away from the funeral." This is a mistake, he feels, because the child is denied the outpouring of grief that helps lead to acceptance of the death.

"Equally important," advises Cohen, "is that the remaining parent, or both parents if a sibling has died, be with the child afterward to help the youngster with his or her feelings and talk about the death if the child wants to talk. And there is no need to be a 'stout fellow' about it. It's better to cry."

A number of specialists say today that even a child should be told—very cautiously—about his or her own terminal illness. Says Kübler-Ross: "Children can deal with death sometimes much better than grownups. The worst thing you can do is lie to them."

But the news—if it is told at all—must be greatly softened. David M. Kaplan, director of clinical social work at Stanford University, feels that "you might use such statements as 'you are very sick and we hope the doctor can help.' " But children as young as five or six usually sense that they are seriously ill, he explains, and pretense and lying only loses you their trust and isolates them, making their loneliness more difficult.

"With a child," advises Kutscher, "the task is to be honest—but not frightening. A parent will want to discuss these points with the doctor, clergyman, and possibly other family members, before deciding what to tell a child." But all the warnings about how—and when—to tell a dying patient, apply doubly with a child.

The household routine should be kept as normal as possible when a child is at home with a terminal illness. "That's important to the sick child and the other children," says Spencer Smith, an Atlanta businessman whose four-year-old daughter died after an 18-month fight against cancer.

"We did our best not to change our lifestyle, and treated Margaret as normally as possible," Smith adds. "Cobalt treatment caused her hair to fall out, and we got a wig for her. For 6 of her last 10 months, things were pretty normal and Margaret was a happy child." Smith speaks of his other small children: "We fully explained her illness to the others, ages 5 and 8, telling them about the cancer and that there was a good chance she would not survive. When Margaret died, they understood and were not shocked. They accepted it."

How to handle the five stages of dying*

*Based on the five stages of death outlined in *On Death and Dying* by Dr. Elizabeth Kübler-Ross, psychiatrist and author

PATIENT BEHAVIOR	STAGE	FAMILY RESPONSE
	DENIAL	
In effect, the patient says, "It cannot be true." Patients often search frantically for a favorable diagnosis.		Understand why the patient is grasping at straws. Patience and willingness to talk are important.
	ANGER	
The patient says, "Yes—but why me?" Deep anger follows, and the patient may bitterly envy those who are well and complain incessantly about almost everything.		Consider that the patient is angry over the coming loss of everything: family, friends, home, work, play. Treat patient with understanding and respect, not by returning the anger.
	BARGAINING	
The patient says, "Maybe I can bargain with God and get a time extension." Promises of good behavior are made in return for time and some freedom from physical pain.		If the patient's 'bargain' is revealed, it should be listened to, not brushed off. This stage passes in a short time.
	DEPRESSION	
The patient grieves, and mourns approaching death.		Attempts to cheer up or reassure the patient mean very little. The patient needs to express sorrow fully and without hindrance.
	ACCEPTANCE	
The patient is neither angry nor depressed, only quietly expectant.		News of the outside world means little, and few visitors are required. There will be little talk, and it is time merely for the presence of the close family.

Facing yourself

Your own personal adjustment to a death or terminal illness in the family is made easier to the extent that you can open up to others. "People who share the struggle, who are open rather than secretive, seem to do better," says James Gibbons, director of chaplaincy at University of Chicago hospitals. But "talking it out" may not be easy.

"The well person may have a deep fear of death," notes Menninger Foundation psychologist Cerney. "If a husband has a terminal illness, the wife may freeze and deny the coming death, pretending that it won't happen." The wife might then remain aloof from the husband and cause more pain for both.

Cerney suggests that the spouse of a terminal patient who is concerned about his or her own inability to cope should first try to come to grips with the fear of death.

"The books of Kübler-Ross [such as *On Death and Dying*] offer real help," she advises. "Or phone your local university and ask someone in the psychology department about one-day seminars on thanatology. There are more and more of these—and they aren't morbid."

Hearing a good talk and being a part of a question-and-answer session can help lift some of the unreal fears of death and send a seminar participant home with a clearer idea of how to relate to the terminal patient.

"I dreaded the death seminar idea," confesses a Columbus (Ohio) businessman whose wife had terminal cancer. "But it seemed I was the one pulling us down, while she was the one having the chemotherapy. I went to the sessions at the hospital and came away feeling tolerably better about those difficult talks with my wife."

In Tiburon, Calif., near San Francisco, Nora E. Grove, a lawyer's wife, tells how attending Candlelighters Society meetings helped her family adjust to having a child at home with terminal cancer. "You meet once a month in a church hall for about two hours with 30 to 40 other parents of cancer children," she explains. "You have coffee and then listen to a speaker and have group discussions. Personally, I got some sanity. I felt I would cave under, but meeting with the other parents helped me to know about physically caring for the boy and got me through the sadness."

Most people are psychologically unprepared for their own reaction to the death of a spouse or child, or in some cases, a parent. "The death of a parent usually is manageable," says Goldston, "but losing your wife or child is a different story." And a sudden, unexpected death is the most difficult to face.

There are many psychosomatic side effects from grief, from an inability to concentrate at work to trouble in making even routine decisions. There may be headaches or insomnia, and psychologists note that some people even take on the symptoms of the deceased—stomach pains, where the death was from stomach cancer, or chest pains following a heart attack death.

HOSTILITY IS ALSO A STAGE OF GRIEF

Anger and hostility, a stage of dying, are also a stage of grief and mourning,

PUTTING YOUR HOUSE IN ORDER

There are a number of practical matters that must be dealt with despite the emotional pain and distraction of a loved one dying. A terminally ill person will often feel better knowing that his or her affairs are being put in order. The details can be handled by a spouse, if able to, or by a family lawyer.

DURING ILLNESS

Will: Make necessary changes. Examples: specific financial provision for children's education and provision for personal guardianship of children. This is the time to make any changes in the choice of executor (often spouse or relative) or co-executor (lawyer, bank). A letter apart from the will can cover non-mandatory instructions to the executor—for example, naming children's schools.

Estate tax: Consider buying "flower bonds" to pay any estate taxes. These Treasury issues can be bought at a discount and used to pay estate tax at the full face amount. Discuss with the lawyer a tax-saving trust for the children.

Bank account: Provide funds to carry the family immediately after the death by setting up (or increasing) a savings account in the surviving spouse's name. Bank funds in the patient's name will be frozen upon death. Funds in a joint account are not frozen, but since any jointly owned property becomes part of a decedent's taxable estate, any money withdrawn still would be subject to the estate tax.

Investments: Alter instructions to patient's broker where necessary—"stop orders," for example, that ought to be dropped. It may be wise to sell shares to buy flower bonds or to take the family out of speculative situations.

Gifts: Consider making gifts of the patient's property to family members. If the gift-tax exemption has been used up, there will be a tax. But the taxpayer will be entitled to a credit against estate tax; there may be a net tax saving.

Insurance: Make sure that life insurance beneficiary clauses are up to date. A gift of ownership of the policy itself (right to convert, borrow, and such) will not take benefits out of the patient's taxable estate because of the three-year contemplation-of-death rule.

Power of attorney: Consider a "durable, general" power of attorney, with the power assigned by the patient so the surviving spouse can perform all transactions. This is particularly necessary where a patient becomes incapacitated.

Benefits: Contact the employee benefits department of the patient's company to ensure that desired beneficiaries are named. If an individual is named, noncontributory benefits (mainly pension and profit-sharing) are kept out of the taxable estate.

Funeral: Consider making advance arrangements for the funeral. A funeral director will handle purchase of a cemetery plot and bill you later along with other charges (assuming death is imminent). If you deal directly with a cemetery company, it will want full payment for one grave and will finance the balance if you wish.

AFTER DEATH

Lawyer-executor: Arrange to see the family lawyer and executor or co-executor together, preferably in the lawyer's office, within two or three days after the funeral. Speed is important because the lawyer starts probate of the will.

Papers: Send military discharge papers of deceased to the funeral director so he can file a claim with the Veterans Administration for routine $400 cash death benefit ($800 if a service-connected death). Provide Social Security number for a similar $255 benefit if the deceased was covered.

Miscellaneous: Phone life insurance companies to request claim forms. Notify insurer carrying deceased's homeowner's and auto insurance policies, employee benefits department, banks used by decedent (thus freezing accounts), and stockbrokers (automatically nullifying any brokerage instructions and freezing accounts). Notify credit card companies, and destroy or surrender the cards.

and awareness of this is especially important when a child dies. "Some men suffer more than their wives when a child dies," says Sandi Boshak whose son died in infancy. "From formal meetings with other parents of deceased children, I've seen that the husband has a harder time with his grief. He tends to bottle it up, while his wife cries openly." She explains that feelings of guilt can bog a parent down, particularly following the death of a first child. It is then that meetings of such groups as the National Foundation for Sudden Infant Death, with chapters in 40 cities, can help most.

An excessive grief reaction may justify psychotherapy if daily life has become impaired, at home or the office, and you realize your own conduct is hurting others. But avoid rushing into therapy. "See a therapist only if the level of grief is getting beyond you," says Dr. Harold Visotsky, chief of psychiatry at Northwestern University medical school.

If deep grief lasts more than two months or so, it may be wise to seek help, preferably using a psychologist, psychiatrist, or social worker who has had experience with similar problems. "Just any 'qualified' person won't do," says a Washington (D.C.) psychologist. "You must have somebody who knows thanatology." Most major hospitals will provide such a lead.

Be careful in using drug sedation to cope with excessive grief. "The risk of sedation is that you will lose the impact of the personal loss suffered, and your grief will only be delayed or prolonged," advises Cohen.

Adjusting after a death

Managing a household as a lone surviving parent, and "dating" to start new relationships, is the last phase of adjustment to the death of a spouse.

A formula for handling the children, including teen-agers to age 15, is suggested by an executive who is a widower: "First, if you are a working widow or widower, get a good housekeeper, if possible. She must be kindly and concerned about the kids, but still firm. And she must have the authority she needs to run things. If this is unrealistic, then make contacts with close married friends who have children the same age. Ask for their advice and help. At the least, you'll need some after-school-to-suppertime supervision for the kids."

And there is this cardinal rule: Maintain a spirit of discipline among the children. "The death of a parent should be no excuse for drifting into excessive permissiveness," says the executive.

A structured daily home life should be continued for the children's sake as well as your own. The older children should be given greater responsibilities to help make the household operate smoothly. But it is unwise to treat a teen-ager as a peer. This instant-adult treatment is a common mistake, say the specialists.

Dating again, after a spouse has died, can cause problems. "First of all, don't date to get over your grief," warns USC's Feifel. "Once you start dating," he explains, "it should be a signal that you have worked the mourning through." Catching a new person "on the rebound"—to override your grief—is a common mistake usually leading to new relationships that are shaky, at best.

Conversely, if you experienced a long period of grief before your spouse died and mourning has been fulfilled, then a new successful relationship can be approached fairly soon. "Some people are ready even to remarry after two months," says Kübler-Ross.

The children's reaction to a dating parent, however, poses a difficult problem. Cohen notes that "it is very difficult for the kids to accept another woman or man." Keep family communications open and try to talk matters through with the children.

One point is certain: A parent who waits for the children's approval of a proposed new marriage partner runs a good risk of staying single.

WHO'S WRITING AND WRITTEN ABOUT

INDEX

Credits/Acknowledgments

Cover design by Charles Vitelli

1. Perspectives
Facing overview—WHO photo by Martholor. 11—Professor Thomas Bouchard, Psychology Department, University of Minnesota. 18-19—Farrell Greham. 29—Clemens Kalischer, Image Photos.
2. The Prenatal Period
Facing overviews—WHO/photo. 43—CRM Books, Random House. 46—Joe Baker, The Image Bank. 45-46—Dr. Robert Rugh and Landrum B. Shattlers from *Conception to Birth,* Harper & Row, 1971. 47—From Fitzhugh, Mabel Lum and Newton, Michael; *Posture in Pregnancy,* Am. J. Obster. Gynecol. 85:1091-1095, 1963. 48—Everett Davidson. 51—Diagram by Leonard D. Dank/Medical Illustrations Co.; photographs courtesy of Dr. Robert P.S. Jansen. 52—Diagram courtesy of Dr. A. Lopata.

3. Infancy
Facing overview—United Nations/Photo by John Isaac.
4. Childhood
Facing overview—Unesco photo by Marc Riboud.
5. Child Rearing and Child Development
Facing overview—United Nations/Photo by L. Barns.
6. Adolescence and Early Adulthood
Facing overview—WHO photo by J. Mohr.
7. Middle and Late Adulthood
Facing overview—United Nations/Photo by Gaston Guarda. 239-242—Illustrations by Dean Williams.

WE WANT YOUR ADVICE

ANNUAL EDITIONS: HUMAN DEVELOPMENT 83/84

Article Rating Form

Here is an opportunity for you to have direct input into the next revision of this reader. We would like you to rate each of the 56 articles listed below, using the following scale:

1. **Excellent: should definitely be retained**
2. **Above average: should probably be retained**
3. **Below average: should probably be deleted**
4. **Poor: should definitely be deleted**

Your ratings will play a vital part in the next revision. So please mail this prepaid form to us just as soon as you complete it.
Thanks for your help!

Rating	Article	Rating	Article
	1. Sociobiology: A New View of Human Nature		28. Who's Intelligent?
	2. Twins: Reunited		29. Islands of Genius
	3. Searching for Depression Genes		30. Rites of Passage
	4. Piaget		31. Diet and Schoolchildren
	5. Erik Erikson's Eight Ages of Man		32. The Mismatch Between School and Children's Minds
	6. American Research on the Family and Socialization		33. The Mind of the Puzzler
	7. Heredity, Constitution, and Individual Life		34. Parent and Child Development
	8. Pregnancy: The Closest Human Relationship		35. A New Look at Life with Father
	9. Hi-Tech Babies		36. When Mommy Goes to Work . . .
	10. A Perfect Baby		37. Suffer the Children
	11. Premature Birth: Consequences for the Parent-Infant Relationship		38. The Children of Divorce
	12. Before Their Time		39. What Is TV Doing to America?
	13. The Importance of Mother's Milk		40. How I Stopped Nagging and Started Teaching My Children to Behave
	14. Biology Is One Key to the Bonding of Mothers and Babies		41. Adolescents and Sex
	15. Newborn Knowledge		42. What Do We Know About Teenagers as Mothers?
	16. Ethnic Differences in Babies		43. The Sibling Bond: A Lifelong Love/Hate Dialectic
	17. Your Child's Self-Esteem		44. Too Weary to Go On
	18. Infant Day Care: Toward a More Human Environment		45. The Many Me's of the Self-Monitor
	19. How Children Influence Children: The Role of Peers in the Socialization Process		46. Single Parent Fathers: A New Study
	20. If Your Child Doesn't Get Along with Other Kids		47. Does Personality Really Change After 20?
	21. Moral Education for Young Children		48. The Japanese Brain
	22. The Myth of the Vulnerable Child		49. She & He
	23. Mood and Memory		50. Late Motherhood: Race Against Mother Nature?
	24. The Violent Brain		51. Stress Can Be Good for You
	25. The Instinct to Learn		52. Coping with the Seasons of Life
	26. Learning About Learning		53. The Aging Body
	27. Are Young Children Really Egocentric?		54. In Search of Youth
			55. Living Longer
			56. Coping with Death in the Family

Name _____ Date _____

Address _____

City _____ State _____

Zip _____ Telephone _____

1. What do you think of the Annual Editions concept?

2. Have you read any articles lately that you think should be included in the next edition?

3. Which articles do you feel should be replaced in the next edition? Why?

4. In what other areas would you like to see an Annual Edition? Why?

HUMAN DEVELOPMENT 83/84

BUSINESS REPLY MAIL

First Class   Permit No. 84   Guilford, Ct.

Postage Will Be Paid by Addressee

Attention: Annual Editions Service
The Dushkin Publishing Group, Inc.
Sluice Dock
Guilford, Connecticut 06437-0389